Morrissey

Ten years on this book are dedicated to
Joey Stefano,
Mark Nicholson and
Les Enfants de Novembre
N'oublie pas . . .
La vie sans amis
c'est comme un
jardin sans fleurs

Other books by David Bret and published by Robson Books:

The Piaf Legend
The Mistinguett Legend
Maurice Chevalier
Marlene, My Friend
George Formby
Maria Callas: The Tigress and the Lamb
Piaf: A Passionate Life
Errol Flynn
Gracie Fields
Valentino: A Dream of Desire
Living on the Edge: The Freddie Mercury Story
Tallulah Bankhead
Elvis: The Hollywood Years
Rock Hudson

Scandal & Passion

Morrissey

DAVID BRET

ROBSON

First published in Great Britain in 2004 by
Robson Books
151 Freston Road
London
W10 6TH

An imprint of Anova Books Company Ltd

ISBN 1 86105 968 X

10 9 8 7 6 5 4 3

Printed and bound by Creative Print and Design (Ebbw Vale), Wales

This book can be ordered direct from the publisher
Contact the marketing department, but try your bookshop first

Contents

Acknowledgements

Writing this book would not have been possible had it not been for the help, inspiration, criticisms and love of that very select group of individuals whom I will always look upon as my true family and *autre coeur*. Barbara, Irene Bean, Marlene Dietrich, Roger Normand and Dorothy Squires, *que vous dormez en paix*. René and Lucette Chevalier, Jacqueline Danno, Héléne Delavault, Tony Griffin, Axel Dotti, Betty Paillard and Gérard, Annick Roux, Terry Sanderson, John and Anne Taylor, François and Madeleine Vals, Caroline Clerc and Charley Marouani.

Very, *very* special thanks to the munificent Mark Nicholson. What you don't know about Morrissey and Elvis isn't *worth* knowing! Thanks also to Jeremy Robson, Jennifer Lansbury, Robert Dimery, Melanie Letts and the staff at Robson Books for putting up with me. It never gets any easier!

For their help and contribution to this book I offer *un grand chapeau bas* to Jean-Daniel Beauvallet, Peter Burton, Richard Smith, Murray Chalmers, Adrian Deevoy, Christophe Devos, Ruth Edge, Nicole Garrison, Iestyn George, Dirk Van Gils, Andrew Harrison, Martin Hunt, Kanako Ishikawa, Gianfranco, Danny Kelly, Sandy Lee, Kris Kirk, Stuart Maconie, Gary Day, Nigel Thomas, Boz Boorer, Paul Morley, Tristan, Mark Nevin, Kirsty MacColl, Tony Parsons, Manuel Rios-Sastre, Linder Sterling, Emmanuel Tellier, Pierre Siankowski, Mark Hooper, Jennifer Ivory, Paul Williamson, Robert Mackie, Alain Whyte, Robert Sandall, Michael Bracewell, Johnny Bridgewood, Peter Adams, Spencer Cobrin and Andy David.

Final thanks go to my loyal agent, David Bolt, to my wife Jeanne, who is still the keeper of my soul . . . and to Steven Patrick Morrissey for being so much to so many.

Foreword

He is placed upon a pedestal and worshipped; alternately, he is derided and loathed by detractors. There is rarely room for compromise. The British press call him 'The Pope of Mope', the French 'le coqueluche des mansards-branleurs'. The Americans find it impossible to adequately define him; though currently residing among them, he will never belong on the wrong side of the Atlantic, because he is and always will remain a quintessentially English monument.

He is arguably the *only* English entertainer to have successfully created his own culture, a personal world filled with foibles, likes and dislikes, and above all unsuppressable opinion: the bizarre obsessions with old films, camp icons, obscure entertainers, rough trade, the gay heroes he promoted and emulated, and his hatred of authority, politicians and royalty.

He claims to have loved rarely, his sexuality has been the subject of acres of press coverage for over twenty years, but if his personal life has been intensely private (barring a few press slip-ups), his greatest love affair – with his audiences, who have religiously followed his every pitfall and triumph – has been unashamedly flaunted and reciprocated since the moment he first stepped on to a stage. These are the faithful, many of whom often go to quite extraordinary lengths to flock to his travelling shrine, braving hardship just to attend the extra concert. They hang on to his every word. When he despairs, they despair too; when he hurts, they share his pain.

He is unique, the greatest singer-songwriter of his generation. His is a story of scandal . . . and passion.

He is Morrissey, and this is his story so far.

Introduction

There'll Always Be an England

'I have had nearly everything bad said about me. I can't really be accused of anything else now, except murder, and I'm sure that's bound to come at some stage.'

– Morrissey

Sheffield City Hall, 11 December 1992. This was a whole new world to me. Not so long before we had stood on these same steps, guests of Peggy Lee, the greatest American singer of her generation. Tonight it was Morrissey, perhaps the greatest British singer of *his* generation. Then, it had been suits and cocktail dresses – the show had been filmed for television. Champagne bottles had been cracked open at the bar and the talk had been of how well Ms Lee had looked despite her recent illness. And now . . .

'I never expected it to be like this,' my wife Jeanne observed as we surveyed this devoted crowd of youngsters whose average age could not have been more than eighteen.

We had entered the strange, undeniably exciting, and for someone of my profession potentially dangerous world of Steven Patrick Morrissey. It was raining, yet apart from ours there was not an umbrella to be seen. There was a plump, unsmiling Chinese woman, barely five feet tall, clutching a bunch of daffodils that had seen better days. There was a lanky youth from Amsterdam in a soaked, translucent Arsenal T-shirt and a leather-clad, brash but beautiful gay porn star from Chicago,

Gianfranco, who pronounced without stopping for breath, 'Moz's buddy did a couple of porno movies, you know, but it was such a disappointment meeting him because he wasn't that nice, and straight after the show I'm off to the airport because tomorrow I've got a shoot in Rome, Italy!' Then there was a painfully thin man from Arizona, and a young Spanish teacher complaining about the ad for hamburgers that was printed on the back of his ticket: 'We're vegetarians, for God's sake. *He's* a vegetarian!' – to which the fan from Arizona opined, 'He's also a *god*!'

By the end of the evening I, the eternal sceptic, was inclined to agree with him, for the object of our being there, primarily as part of my research for this book, had joined the ranks of my other singer-songwriter *monstres sacrés* of the recital stage: Barbara, Brel, Brassens, Piaf and Aznavour.

Prior to this revelation I had been compelled to endure the prejudices of the press when, unable to cope with the excruciating support band (The Well-Oiled Sisters), my wife and I had spent thirty minutes at the theatre bar. Here, two very well-known music journalists from the opposing end of my entertainment spectrum had been engaged in a spirited banter over which of them would write the most vitriolic account of the event we were about to witness. 'I saw him last week,' one said. 'He was bloody good, the best concert I've *ever* seen in my life, but the editor still told me to say he was crap.' To which his companion added, 'I don't care *how* good he is. He won't be getting a good review!'

The atmosphere within the auditorium was surprisingly hushed, the air heavy with the scent of flowers – almost like one of the many Dorothy Squires concerts we had attended. There were more males than females, allegedly mostly heterosexual – to a great many people's way of thinking, no one could possibly worship a man like these people did and not fancy him even a little bit. And Morrissey's management had ensured that Jeanne and I would be in full public view too: ours were the so-called 'key seats', those in the balcony that traditionally face the precise centre of the stage. The city's florists, I later learned, had record sales that day, and seemingly thousands upon thousands of these blooms rained down like missiles the moment Morrissey stepped on to the stage – heralded by a dire Klaus Nomi overture, itself quickly drowned by the toneless but stirring chanting of Morrissey's name to the tune of the football chant 'Here We Go'.

He was bigger than I had anticipated, nowhere near as thin as in his early photographs. And he had *talent*, not a word I would use often to describe modern entertainers – the real, heart-stopping brilliance of a hardened trouper who has worked his way through the fleapit ranks to *earn* his success. No male singer since Fritz Wunderlich, or Elvis crooning 'Love Me Tender', had brought such a lump to my throat.

Looking decidedly shy and uncomfortable during his opening song, he overcame this obstacle by transforming the microphone cord into a bullwhip, thrashing the boards and monitors with frenetic abandon during this and several subsequent hard rock numbers. In so doing, he encouraged several crowd surfers to negotiate the steepish drop into the empty orchestra pit, hug their man for a few seconds, then fall prey to the burly, know-all bouncers. Then, having expended enough of his energy on the bullwhip, in a potently Continental soliloquy, Morrissey balanced his hunky frame on one of the monitors, took the spotlight full in the face, and during a tender ballad reached out to brush fingers with the first wave of sweaty, now gently gyrating followers. And, even more impressively, he was wholly unashamed of opening up and displaying his feminine side – of disproving the tenet that big, stiff-upper-lipped Englishmen, excepting the vanquished on the soccer pitch, are not permitted to express emotion by shedding a tear or two.

Most of the songs in Morrissey's set were taken from his innovative new album released that summer – *Your Arsenal*, a pun intended for the irreverent British music press if ever there was one. The album had shot to the upper echelons of the charts, adding lustre to the 'moon-June' lyrical dross more usually found there. Morrissey himself – never backwards at coming forwards when it comes to barbed put-downs – had told Dermott Hayes of *Rage* at the end of the previous year (and subsequently repeated the gist of this time and time again) that 'Most pop personalities are literally so plain and dull, that anyone who appears to have a vaguely working brain comes across as conniving.'

As probably the most intellectually gifted and imaginative lyricist of his generation, Morrissey could always be relied on for a memorable quote or a sharp, witty one-liner. That said, his relationship with the press had rarely been less than problematic. His appearance at Madness's reunion concert at Finsbury Park earlier that year had seen him accused of racism. Music paper *NME*, formerly a fervent champion both of The Smiths and Morrissey the solo artist, had taken to pillorying him for his presumed flirtation with the political Far Right and the lyrics of songs such as 'Bengali In Platforms' and 'Asian Rut'.

In January 1991 he had told Jean-Daniel Beauvallet:

> Newspapers make up stories, hoping to bait me into calling them with *my* version of events. That's how low these people have sunk in order to get an interview. I prefer to leave them to it, hoping the readers will work out for themselves the difference between truth and lies. Even so, I've been terribly, terribly hurt.

Beauvallet explained to me how, prior to meeting him for the first time, he had been forewarned by one British journalist that Morrissey was difficult, very bad-tempered, dangerous and rude. But Beauvallet told me:

> I can honestly say, hand over heart, that he was one of the politest, gentlest men I ever met. The so-called *mauvaise reputation* is solely the invention of the British music press. He's so calm and collected, even when angry. It would be easy to run out of superlatives describing him. England should be proud of him.

The British fans *were* proud of him, but this persistent bile spouting had taken its toll and sowed the seeds of doubt in Morrissey's mind: so far as the British music press were concerned, he could do nothing right. In November 1989 Nick Kent had asked him, 'Don't you feel that England is a doomed country now?', and his response had been that it was 'shambolically doomed'. However, he *had* added optimistically, 'I feel I have to stay. I feel that I have to go down with the ship if that's what must happen. Anything else would be too much like desertion.' Sadly, that 'desertion' was eventually to come to pass, though it would take a good deal more anguish, soul-searching and press butchery to get him to pack his bags and cross the Big Pond, following in the footsteps of P G Wodehouse (whose house he would later live in), Tom Jones, Engelbert Humperdinck and Quentin Crisp.

Shortly after this Herculean upheaval, Morrissey would tell his close pal Michael Bracewell:

> The England that I have loved, and I have sung about, and whose death I have sung about, I felt had finally slipped away. And so I was no longer saying, 'England is dying.' I was beginning to say, 'Well, yes, it has died and here's the carcass' – so why hang around?

It had taken him almost forty years to desert the sinking ship . . .

1

Heir Apparent: Heroes and Villains

'The permutations and contradictions which Morrissey throws in the face of all who seek to analyse him would tax the mightiest machine IBM could produce.'

– George Byrne, *Irish Sunday Independent*

Morrissey was born of Irish stock on 22 May 1959, at Manchester's Davyhulme Park Hospital, the second child (after daughter Jacqueline) of Elizabeth (Dwyer) and Peter Morrissey, who had emigrated from Dublin a few years earlier and married at the city's Moss Side Catholic Church. Ironically, he shares his birthday with cult Russian silent film actress Nazimova – champion of Henrik Ibsen and Oscar Wilde – a *narcissiste* par excellence who became the doyenne of Hollywood's infamous lesbian Sewing Circle after producing and starring in a version of Wilde's *Salome* made by a gay cast and crew.

He was baptised Steven Patrick, the first name after the brooding, famously hirsute and hedonistic American actor Steve Cochran, who had appeared with Mae West in her Broadway revival of *Diamond Lil*. Mrs Morrissey had particularly enthused over Cochran's portrayal of the mobster Nick Prenta, opposite Joan Crawford in *The Damned Don't Cry* (1950). In some shots the physical resemblance between Cochran and the adult Morrissey is uncanny.

Morrissey came into the world when northern England was in the throes of artistic change with the belated introduction of the Expressionist film genre (one such had been the aforementioned Crawford film), which had taken America by storm a decade earlier. Controversial productions such as *Saturday Night And Sunday Morning* and *A Taste Of Honey*, with their gritty plots and dialogue, were riding the crest of their own particular wave, narrowing the chasm in the North/South divide previously exacerbated by the Gracie Fields and George Formby comedy-dramas of the previous generation.

Television soaps were also about to enter a new lease of life. For years, the country had been monopolised by *The Grove Family* – Britain's first authentic soap, set in Hendon – but now Manchester was fighting back with *Coronation Street* (to which the teenage Morrissey would unsuccessfully submit at least one script idea). Soon too there would be a short-lived explosion of Mancunian home-grown musical talent, entertainers who would initially give Liverpool and The Beatles a good run for their money: Freddie and the Dreamers, Wayne Fontana and the Mindbenders and Herman's Hermits.

At the end of 1965, however, while the Morrisseys were ensconced at 17 Harper Street, in the city's Hulme suburb, something happened that imbued Manchester with an infamy it could well have done without: the Moors Murders, about which Morrissey would later conduct a personal crusade.

These particularly abhorrent crimes traumatised a nation. They were perpetrated by Ian Brady – a Glaswegian aficionado of Nazi memorabilia, fascism and the depraved works of the Marquis de Sade – and his lover, Myra Hindley. The couple had tortured, killed and then buried several children on Saddleworth Moor. Morrissey was seven when the evil pair were locked up for good, and though media reports at the time were not as graphic as they are today, these gruesome slayings (one of which was taped) were explored in great depth in Emlyn Williams' book *Beyond Belief: The Story of Ian Brady & Myra Hindley*, published in 1967. One can only assume the effect this had on the 300,000 morbidly curious people who bought it, or on the mind of the impressionable boy who would later use the subject matter of the tragedy to produce a startling and moving reflection on the Moors Murders, a unique achievement in the pop canon – and find himself pilloried for it.

Morrissey recalled the Manchester of the sixties as having been a violent place. On one particular occasion, at a fairground in Stretford, he was hit by a thug simply because he had been standing in the wrong place at the wrong time: 'You accepted it, there didn't have to be a reason.' According to Morrissey, life at St Wilfred's Primary was no bed of roses, but he tolerated whatever crises winged his way and years later used these experiences to sow the seeds for a career that might otherwise have been as bland as those of his less talented contemporaries.

In 1970, as part of an estate clearance operation, the Morrisseys relocated to another council house at 384 King's Road, in Stretford, and Morrissey was enrolled at St Mary's Secondary Modern. His miseries here are said to have been recounted in 'The Headmaster Ritual', a cataloguing of physical abuse that would not be tolerated today, but which in many such establishments (and I speak from personal experience) was par for the course back then: the thwack on the knees, the knee to the groin, the 'good hidings' in the shower block. There were protests from the Greater Manchester Education Authority who declared that none of *its* teachers had ever acted with such brutality and tried – but failed – to get the record banned. When The Smiths put out the song on a single, it was Morrissey's intention to hammer home his point by having a cover-shot of one of his idols, Terence Stamp, in the film *Term of Trial* (1962), hand outstretched, getting six of the best from Laurence Olivier and obviously enjoying the punishment. Both actors objected.

Morrissey tended to disagree with the education authority. 'I can remember being forcibly kicked by a teacher,' he argued. 'I'd taken the ball off him. His response was to ignore the game, ignore the ball, ignore the pupils and just kick me. I stood quite still.' Future Smith Mike Joyce, who attended St Gregory's Grammar School, described his school years as similarly 'barbaric', telling *Select*'s David Cavanagh early in 1993, '*I* had teachers who'd lift you up by the neck and he'd get his knuckles and he'd start knocking on the back of your head as hard as he could, until I was on the floor. Now I mean, was that education?'

The school was run by a rather military headmaster named Vincent Morgan, a stalwart Catholic, who came down hard on anyone, pupils or staff, caught using strong language or discussing sex. 'I was raised with the notion that excitement and exuberance and extremities were something other people did and were not for me,' the singer told *Details* in 1994, recalling a solitary sex education lesson delivered by a 'gung-ho rugby-type' master, who told him, 'You know penis? Well, it's your dick. What more do you want to know?'

According to Morrissey's later admissions, he does not appear to have been particularly happy at home with his warring parents. In August 1987, when Chris of *Les Inrockuptibles* asked him if 'Barbarism Begins At Home' was based on personal experience he replied:

> Yes. I was beaten as a child – with umbrellas or whatever came to hand. Discipline was very strict when I was small, less as I grew older. As a child I had no freedom. For poor children like us, there wasn't enough room to flourish. I just built this wall around myself.

In April 2003 he would more or less repeat this story to Andrew Harrison of *Word*, adding that most of the time he had probably deserved that occasional clip around the head: 'I was a very noisy child. I always stood in front of the television. I wouldn't go to bed, and then I discovered music at the age of six and played it loud, constantly . . . which must have been unbearable. I was surprised they were so tolerant of me, to be honest.'

In the same *Inrockuptibles* interview, Morrissey appears to have attempted to throw a veil over his past by actually denying that he had had a conventional education, adding, 'I didn't go to school very often. I failed all my exams and I *never* attended a secondary school. It was easier educating myself, reading the books I wanted to read, developing my own interests. I couldn't tolerate authority, I was completely undisciplined. *Nobody* could tell me what to do.'

This reinvention of himself and his legend would occur repeatedly over the years: sometimes to throw the press off a particular scent; sometimes, it has been said, so as not to offend members of his family, his mother in particular, who might have frowned upon his youthful activities. As with many great stars who have become *monstres sacrés*, all we know of their youth, mis-spent or otherwise, is largely what they themselves have remembered since achieving fame, and Morrissey appears to be no exception. Few have come forward to speak of knowing him as a child or teenager; the anecdotes of those who have are clouded and influenced by his fame. There have been no interviews with his closest friends or with members of his family. His lovers also have remained dutifully silent. In his early interviews, when he could not possibly imagine what a huge star he would become, he makes no reference to crippling loneliness and celibacy never enters the equation; he is relatively open about matters sexual and does not appear to have an acerbic bone in his body. This does not necessarily mean, of course, that he has anything to hide or be ashamed of, and he may only be admired for keeping up a Garboesque stance and preventing his personal life from being splattered across the tabloids – even more so when one considers how he has treated those he feels have wronged him. What we are sure of regarding his youth was that he was blessed with the redeeming quality of an overactive imagination, and an ability to jot down these vibrant thoughts and ideas. 'Being able to write was *better* probably than having friends,' he told Chris of *Les Inrockuptibles*, adding that he had carried his notebook everywhere, even into the bathroom. Long before his tenth birthday he was drawing inspiration from retro heroes such as Gracie Fields, George Formby, Jimmy Clitheroe and Hylda Baker.

Some of his biggest heroes, however, were the tormented gay or bisexual ones: Billy Fury, James Dean, Oscar Wilde – the ones he could have 'safe' relationships with, as he explained in his *Inrockuptibles* interview:

People who possess *that* much allure, no matter what they produce or do with their lives, are very rare. I *hate* ordinary people. I was a strange child who couldn't function in ordinary society. It's easier to fall in love with images and myths. They don't answer back, they don't deceive you. There's no danger. I've taken precautions choosing them, and I have *such* good taste!

Liverpool-born Billy Fury (né Ronald Wycherley) was an ethereal-looking young man who had always wanted to be a rock star and enjoy the hedonistic lifestyle that went with it. Perhaps terrified of his sexuality becoming public knowledge, he had more or less taken over Johnnie Ray's 'tears on my pillow' mantle, and found fame with heartfelt ballads such as 'Halfway To Paradise' and 'I'd Never Find Another You'. Morrissey included Fury's photograph on the sleeve of The Smiths' 'Last Night I Dreamt Somebody Loved Me' (but wisely refrained from etching 'Eaten By Vince Eager' on the vinyl, a reference to one of Fury's stablemates, when warned of the possible repercussions). He also championed Fury in 'Paint A Vulgar Picture'. Both tracks were recorded in the spring of 1987 for *Strangeways Here We Come*.

'Paint A Vulgar Picture' takes as its theme the 'death = profit' aspect of the recording industry – though to be fair, when a much-loved artiste dies, especially of a heart-attack at just 41 as Fury did, the fans expect this kind of thing, and would be offended if it did not happen. From Morrissey's point of view, however, the 'sycophantic slags' at the board meeting who probably could not stand the singer while he was alive are intent on making a fast buck, and argue among themselves as to which one of them was responsible for putting him on the map. And the song ends with Morrissey expressing the feelings he has suppressed until now, because death has rendered his idol untouchable. 'They cannot hurt you my darling,' he laments. Stirring stuff! 'He's virtually the same as James Dean,' Morrissey told *Sounds* in June 1984, speaking of Fury. 'He too was entirely doomed, which I find quite affectionate.'

James Dean was, of course, *the* archetypal rebel and loner par excellence. When asked if his beyond-the-grave bonding with Jimmy was more than simple admiration, Morrissey told *Sounds*, 'Profoundly more. James Dean was more than the actor in *Rebel Without A Cause*. He was a great symbol. There was nothing that remarkable about his acting in my opinion, but he always seemed in control of every situation. People like that are only too rare. That man's life was so wonderfully perfect.'

If cynics suggested that by making such comments about Dean and Fury, Morrissey was leaving himself open to criticism by exposing his 'feminine' side, nothing could have been closer to the truth. Even the staunchest opponents of Freud and Kinsey cannot deny that all men have a feminine side, just as all women have a masculine side – it's nothing whatsoever to do with sexuality. That said, neither authority would have been capable of pigeon-holing the testosterone-charged, massively talented, equally temperamental, pre-Brat Pack prima donna from Fairmount, Indiana, whose death at 24 had brought about the biggest outpouring of national grief since the death of Rudolph Valentino in 1926.

Morrissey later retraced Jimmy's footsteps – as if, like Atticus Finch in *To Kill A Mockingbird*, he wanted to climb into the actor's skin for a little while. During The Smiths' first ill-fated trip to New York, he insisted upon the group staying at the Iroquois Hotel (next door to the Algonquin, of 'Round Table' fame) where Jimmy had resided for a while with his producer-lover, Rogers Brackett, during *his* first visit to the city – though by the time The Smiths arrived the establishment had gone downhill, and cockroaches were reported in the bedrooms. Two years later, a pre-fame snap of seventeen-year-old Jimmy, taken by a schoolfriend, graced the cover of 'Bigmouth Strikes Again'.

It would be insulting to Oscar Wilde to suggest (as have some of the singer's more fanatical admirers) that Morrissey is his reincarnation – and equally offensive to the Stretford bard to state that he is not a man of similar wit, verbal aptitude, a scribe and raconteur of considerable understanding and insight into the human condition, and above all a man who does not suffer fools gladly. Neither can one deny that he has, albeit in a lesser way than Wilde, been ostracised and pilloried, some-times on account of his own folly, largely on account of misinter-pretation – not always by moralists, but by the barbed quills of the British press. 'As I blundered through my teens,' Morrissey told *Sounds* on one occasion, 'I was quite isolated. In a way he became my companion, and as I get older the adoration increases. I'm never without him. It's almost biblical, like carrying your rosary around with you. He had a life that was really tragic, yet it's curious that he was so witty.'

Wilde nurtured a passion for flowers, notably the white lily, which he adopted as his emblem, for it symbolised purity, beauty and death; his rooms at Oxford were rarely without the flower. Morrissey wanted to follow suit, but settled for the more easily affordable gladiolus or daffodil, depending on the season. He studied Wilde's life intently and became fascinated by the so-called artistic depravity of it all. Wilde and his lover, Lord Alfred Douglas, were fanatical about 'chickens' and 'dollies' – the rent boys who plied their trade around the Earls Court and Piccadilly areas of London; one only has to watch the superb biopic featuring Stephen Fry and Jude Law to see *how* fanatical. So too was Morrissey, though not for the same reasons.

There is a misconception today that these young men were invariably underage, but one has to remember that there *was* no age of consent at the time – all homosexual acts were against the law and, in Wilde's day, an imprisonable offence. The average age of a 'Dilly Boy' was 23, and a great many of these were married and needed the money to support their families. As a mature artist, Morrissey was to champion 'age-gap sex' and 'sex for sale' in numerous songs, with absolutely no suggestion that anyone was underage. He did this sometimes quite brazenly with The Smiths, more subtly as a solo artist, but the one song ('Piccadilly Palare') that commends him by linking Wilde's favourite pastime to modern-day man-to-man sex is maybe more daring than its predecessors, and will be discussed in greater detail later.

There were also the musical heroes and heroines. At six, Morrissey had bought his first 45 rpm vinyl singles: Françoise Hardy's 'Another Place', and Marianne Faithfull's 'Come And Stay With Me'. At some stage, The Smiths are known to have taped two Faithfull songs, their own arrangements of 'The Sha La La Song' and 'Summer Nights'. Morrissey also liked Dusty Springfield, but he was *passionate* about two-hit wonder Twinkle, and barefoot contessa Sandie Shaw. 'I really, really did love these people,' he told *Select*'s Mark Kemp early in 1991, 'I gave them my life, my youth. Beyond the perimeter of pop music there was a drop at the edge of the world.'

Twinkle's 'Terry', like Edith Piaf's 'L'Homme A La Moto' and The Shangri-Las' 'Leader Of The Pack', had attracted fierce criticism in sensitive days because the central character of each had been a maniac motorcyclist who had paid the ultimate price for wreaking terror on the neighbourhood. The song that really impressed Morrissey, however, was 'Golden Lights', Twinkle's 'ode to despondency' which she had written upon the break-up of her romance with Declan Cluskey of The Bachelors. A few years later Morrissey began writing to her, and in 1986 she gave permission for The Smiths to cover the song, one of their most harmonious arrangements, which saw Morrissey duetting beautifully with Kirsty MacColl. 'I think he's wonderful,' Twinkle later told *NME*. 'I've never met him, and I know he has a strange reputation, but he must be very kind underneath because like me he loves animals. I'm very grateful to him for all that he's done.'

Sandie Shaw was one pen pal whom Morrissey would eventually meet. He had been eight when the Dagenham-born chanteuse had won the Eurovision Song Contest with 'Puppet On A String', her third chart-topper; the title of The Smiths' 'Heaven Knows I'm Miserable Now' would be based on her little-known song of 1969, 'Heaven Knows I'm Missing Him Now', and Shaw would respond with a tribute of her own, 'Steven, You Don't Eat Meat'. Early in 1984 she replaced Morrissey to perform a cover of the group's first failed single, 'Hand In Glove', with the three other Smiths. This provided her with her first Top 30 hit in fifteen years. She performed the song with the band on *Top Of The Pops*, the gimmick being that while she wore black and emulated Morrissey's movements by writhing about on the floor, the musicians appeared barefoot. Shaw also covered The Smiths' 'I Don't Owe You Anything', while Morrissey duetted with her on a never-released cover of her 1964 hit 'Girl Don't Come'. There was also a lavishly orchestrated singalong version of 'Please Help The Cause Against Loneliness', though arguably her best work with Morrissey was her duet with him on 'Jeane' – for whereas she unquestionably strains to reach the top notes in 'Hand In Glove' (the 1988 solo rendition is positively dreadful), her delivery in 'Jeane' is breathtakingly simple and emotional to the point that it sends shivers down the spine.

Like Gracie Fields' signature tune 'Sally', 'Jeane' is also a man's song sung to a woman, but without any hint of sexuality. In 1985, Sandie Shaw told *Gay Times'* Kris Kirk that she had once lived with a woman so that they could combine budgets between marriages and better support their children: 'It was a very real closeness. Sex wasn't involved at all but the relationship was really passionate, like that between Morrissey and Johnny Marr. There's no thought of sex in their relationship, just an absolute closeness between them in which they've found they best express themselves.'

Exactly why the alliance between Morrissey and Sandie Shaw ended so abruptly is not known, save that a few years down the line he would be saying, 'I don't hear from her any more. It wasn't exactly a friendship made in heaven . . . let's just put it that way without saying any more.'

As the seventies dawned, Morrissey's musical tastes were developing apace. Already a fan of Roxy Music and Mott The Hoople, he latched on to Nico, the tragic German singer who performed briefly with Lou Reed's Velvet Underground – all but wearing out the grooves of her *Desert Shore* and *Chelsea Girl* albums. 'Yes, the poor Velvets,' he told pen pal Robert Mackie, 'I spent my entire twelfth year locked in my bedroom with *All Tomorrow's Parties*. I was such an incendiary child. Nico's voice paralyses the imagination.' He also became an aficionado of glam rock, with its colourful wardrobe, platform shoes and grossly outspoken, frequently sexually ambiguous frontmen such as David Bowie, with whom he would one day work but not particularly like, and T. Rex's Marc Bolan. Whenever he could, he attended glam concerts at the King's Hall, Belle Vue.

No one, however, had as profound an effect on the teenage Morrissey as perhaps the weirdest outfit of them all: The New York Dolls, one of the most controversial punk acts ever. Morrissey saw them for the first time in 1973, on the BBC's *Old Grey Whistle Test*. 'At my school, you had to be passionate about Bowie or Bolan. It had to be one or the other, never both,' he told journalist Nick Kent in December 1984. 'For me, it was the Dolls because I found traditional rock and rollers stupid, brainless, hyper-machismo soup-sellers. The Dolls were absolutely *male*, not in the least effeminate. They were personalities you didn't treat lightly because *they* were the rock and roll Mafia!'

Three of the Dolls came to tragic early ends. Drummer Billy Murcia drowned in his bathtub after an alcoholic binge in 1972, aged just 21. Guitarist Johnny Thunders (born John Genzale) left the group in 1975 to

front another Morrissey favourite, The Heartbreakers, and embark on a
never-ending series of drink-drugs benders. Thunders' 'speciality' was to
get his friends to play Russian roulette with syringes, not knowing which
one contained water or heroin. It was he who famously got Sid Vicious
hooked on the drug by taunting, 'What are you, man or mouse?' In April
1991, Thunders overdosed on methadone, aged 38, in a New Orleans
hotel. The Dolls' new drummer, Jerry Nolan, died of a stroke nine
months later while undergoing treatment for drugs-induced bacterial
meningitis.

Almost in the same category was the extraordinary German counter-
tenor-rock singer Klaus Nomi, whom Morrissey had also seen on *The Old
Grey Whistle Test*. Born Klaus Sperber (his stage-name was an anagram
of OMNI, the name of his favourite sci-fi magazine), he had relocated to
New York in 1972 and become part of the new-wave performance
scene: in his time he would work as a backing singer for David Bowie and
Madonna, among others. Nomi had had some success in 1981 with his
debut album, a mixture of contemporary rock, sixties pop and opera –
his speciality in this field being Purcell and Saint-Saëns, both of which
opened Morrissey concerts of the nineties. On stage he was impressive:
almost seven feet tall in his platform boots, his hair styled into three
points, wearing the most garish make-up and *Blake's Seven*-style
costumes. Nomi made several albums, all moderately successful, and a
number of promotional videos – the one for Lou Christie's 'Lightnin'
Strikes' has to be seen to be believed. Then, just as he was on the
threshold of major international stardom – not unusual at forty, when
classical singers reach their peak – everything fell apart after he was
diagnosed with Kaposi's sarcoma. In 1983, Nomi became one of the first
show business personalities to die from AIDS, and until 'revived' by
Morrissey had been almost forgotten.

In similar vein was Jobriath (né Jobriath Boone), the inspiration behind
Marc Bolan's 'Cosmic Dancer', who had launched himself on New York's
underground scene at the same time as Nomi. In 1972, claiming to have
signed a $500,000 contract with Elektra, Jobriath commissioned a 41 x
43-foot airbrushed nude poster of himself to be pasted on a Times
Square hoarding. This led to him being discovered by a French

impresario, who compared him with the infamous Texan man-woman Van der Clyde. The latter visited Paris in 1925, met Cocteau and changed his name to Barbette. Appearing in a nude revue at the Folies-Bergère, he had executed a perilous tightrope routine in a blond wig and dress – removing the first to reveal a totally bald head, the second to reveal that he was a man!

Promoting his debut album, Jobriath had opened at the Opéra de Paris in 1973. The curtain rose on him dressed as King Kong, scaling a 50-foot phallic-shaped Empire State Building! Thereafter he had danced out of his monkey suit, and in various states of undress had sung a clutch of off-beat songs, revealing a hunky frame. He finished his act (to rapturous applause each evening) wearing only a spangled posing-pouch. Some believe Morrissey emulated Jobriath with his later displays of narcissism – the diaphanous or shredded shirts, the flaunting of flesh – though unlike his American hero he always kept his trousers on.

Jobriath's star had shone but briefly, and according to his publicist he 'vanished without trace' shortly after releasing his second album, Creatures of the Street, in 1975. In fact, he had not disappeared at all. Failing majestically to become the world's first openly gay superstar – no one would engage him and risk being prosecuted when he threatened to make his lyrics explicitly sexual – Jobriath resigned himself to a life of drugs and debauchery at New York's infamous Chelsea Hotel, famed first for its association with Andy Warhol and thereafter for its celebrity deaths – Nancy Spungen, Sid Vicious and drag queen Christina had all expired there. In 1985, desperately ill and following a bungled suicide attempt, Jobriath was evicted from his tawdry room at the hotel and taken to a local hospital, where shortly afterwards he died of an AIDS-related illness. His last words, from one of his songs, are reputed to have been, 'Please hold that sunrise below, if you don't mind.' In his memory, Morrissey would later adapt and perform 'Cosmic Dancer'.

Because he was a loner, and like many loners spiritually and artistically on a completely different wavelength to his classmates at St Mary's, Morrissey submitted himself wholeheartedly to the worship of these rather oddball heroes. And in an environment that he felt did not understand his world and its foibles, he used his pen as a beacon to make contact with the rest of humanity. To do so he often drew on songs that were an early inspiration to him. 'This Town Ain't Big Enough For Both Of Us', by the American group Sparks, was a big hit in early 1974. It contained the couplet, 'The rain is pouring on the foreign town/The bullets cannot cut you down', which Morrissey would later amend to, 'The rain falls on a humdrum town/This town has dragged you down' for The Smiths' 'William, It Was Really Nothing'. Sparks' keyboard player was Ron Mael, a rake-like individual with staring eyes, slicked back hair and a Hitler moustache. Vocals were provided by Mael's brother Russ, who attacked the song in a piercing falsetto. Fifteen-year-old Morrissey so liked the single, and the group's debut album *Kimono My House* (a pun on the old Rosemary Clooney song 'Come On A My House'), that he wrote a letter to *NME* about them. The editor, at a time when literary merit still counted for something among members of the British music press, was impressed. Not only did he publish the letter, he added a coda of his own:

> Conviction oozes from every sentence like the very ichor of life from the metal life-support systems of the Bronze Giant of Fengorak. The eyes of Mr Morrissey gleam with a missionary zeal that shames into submission the cringing doubts of those yet unconvinced.

Morrissey, the intellectual daydreamer-poet, left St Mary's School during the summer of 1975 with no formal qualifications. He enrolled at Stretford Technical College to read Sociology, English Literature and General Studies, though music was still his be-all and end-all. The following year he latched on to The Sex Pistols, catching their Manchester debut at the Lesser Free Trade Hall (their mentor, Malcolm McLaren, had managed the Dolls for a while). Despite being impressed, the youngster was contemptuous of their attire. In a letter to *NME* he wished them eternal fame, 'So they'll be able to afford some new clothes which don't look like they've been slept in.' His Sex Pistols phase, however, was brief.

It was probably during the summer of 1975 that Morrissey visited the United States for the first time, staying with an aunt in New Jersey. At around the same time, the so-called 'Karen Quinlan Affair' was attracting attention Stateside – a lengthy procedure summoned by the courts to decide the fate of a young woman who had been hooked up to a life-support system for over a year. After much campaigning by religious groups, and with the lawyers battling it out on behalf of the family, the life-support was switched off. Quinlan was moved to a nursing home, where nature was allowed to take its course. Morrissey was later to draw on this for The Smiths' song 'Girlfriend In A Coma'.

The young Morrissey's waspish tongue and his criticism of anyone who did not happen to be on his wavelength was much in evidence not long after his return home from the States, when he became infatuated with the American punk-poet, Patti Smith, whose album *Horses* would remain one of his perennial favourites. Though struggling to keep afloat on unemployment benefit, he managed to travel to Birmingham to see Smith in concert, had a letter published in *Sounds* declaring that the album 'showed more promise than just about any release in recent memory' – then promptly attacked the same publication's reviewer, John Ingham, for his stinging denunciation of The New York Dolls, telling him, 'Stick with The Sex Pistols, whose infantile approach and nondescript music will no doubt match your intelligence.'

Morrissey's bubble would burst during the spring of 1978 when, as a regular contributor to the fanzine, *Kid's Stuff*, he attended a press-conference Patti Smith gave in London. He later told *Sounds*:

She farted four times, and the room was crowded with young, impressionable people. There was one boy at the front who was no more than seventeen. She walked up to him . . . and loudly asked him an extremely vulgar question about how sexually endowed he was . . . The lesson here is that sometimes it's better to cherish your illusions about people you admire than it is to meet them.

When *NME* refused to acknowledge the brilliance of the Mancunian quartet The Buzzcocks, Morrissey penned a withering missive to the editor of the *NME* – almost as if he were gazing into a crystal ball and getting in the first punch:

Buzzcocks differ in only one way from their contemporaries: they possess a spark of originality . . . and their music gives you the impression that they spent longer than the customary ten minutes clutching the quill in preparation to write. Indubitably, Buzzcocks will hardly figure strongly – or even weakly – in the *NME* poll, and in these dark days when Patti Smith, Loudon Wainwright or even The New York Dolls fail to make any impact on Radio 1 DJs, common sense is therefore not so common. But for now they are only the best kick-ass rock band in the country. Go and see them first and then you may have the audacity to contradict me, you stupid sluts.

In this instance, the editor gave as good as he got, though Morrissey was no doubt tickled by his response. After assuring him that a feature on The Buzzcocks *was* on the stocks, he dismissed him with, 'Now go away, you nasty little brat!'

Life in the Morrissey household had not been easy for some time, and finally, on 23 December 1976, when he was seventeen years old, Morrissey's parents separated. Peter Morrissey moved out, and the children stayed at home with their mother. 'Which I actually think is quite natural,' Morrissey told *Details* eighteen years later, adding, 'I love them both very much, but I didn't raise them, and I can't alter the past. Millions upon millions of people come from damaged backgrounds, as they say. Mine wasn't so much damaged as merely *nothing at all*.'

Early the next year, with his parents' divorce very much on the cards, Morrissey began working as a clerk for the Inland Revenue – hardly the sort of employment one would expect a self-confessed anti-Establishment figure to enjoy. The extra money, however, enabled him to widen his musical sphere by attending concerts by Talking Heads, The Ramones and Blondie. Again, as a very vocal anti-royalist, he supported The Sex Pistols' contra-feting of the Queen's Silver Jubilee, which saw Malcolm McLaren and his protégés hosting a hugely irreverent boat party on the Thames opposite the Houses of Parliament, attended by numerous Pistols fans in T-shirts depicting Her Majesty with a safety-pin through her nose. When Morrissey's turn came to insult her some years later, he used the memorable image of 'Her very Lowness with her head in a sling.'

Morrissey is thought to have participated in a local anti-royal demo during the Jubilee year, waving a BAN THE JUBILEE banner and paving the way for some very barbed comments about the Windsors. In *Sounds* in March 1985, he launched an attack on Princess Diana for what he thought was her extreme extravagance:

> To me there's something dramatically ugly about a person who can wear a £6,000 dress when at the same time there are people who can't afford to eat . . . The statement she is making to the nation is, 'I am the fantastically gifted royalty, and you are the snivelling peasants.'

Few people would have agreed with him on this point. It's equally valid to argue that Diana's 'extravagance' was an essential tool of her trade as an ambassadress for the human suffering; that she had to look like a million dollars to raise the vast amounts of money she tirelessly raised for charity; that she remains one of the best-loved Englishwomen in history. That said, Morrissey's anti-royalist stance would be enduring and would later be used to create great art in the form of The Smiths' finest album, *The Queen Is Dead*.

Of course, a wildly imaginative lyricist with strongly held views and a cutting sense of humour is all very well and good, but without a band to provide the music . . .

2

The World Will Listen

'There is more to it than Johnny's guitar sound and Morrissey's lyrics. There was always that naked expression about life and death which was put so eloquently.'

– Geoff Travis, Rough Trade

The eighteen-year-old Morrissey seemed to have already resigned himself to a life of near-loneliness. He had few friends, it would seem, trusting mostly those such as pen pals whom he could keep at a suitable distance. With amazing foresight, a dozen years on from then he would observe, 'I will live my life as I will undoubtedly die – *alone*.' Yet in common with that other great exponent of solitude, Greta Garbo, he seems to have been aesthetically contented with his lot – indeed, to have gleaned great pleasure from it rather than have it fight against him.

An early correspondent was Billy Duffy, a Wythenshawe guitarist whom Morrissey met for the first time in November 1977. Duffy, a huge New York Dolls fan, had just joined the newly re-formed Nosebleeds, who were on the lookout for a vocalist. Morrissey's biting, witty lyrics – particularly those of 'I Think I'm Ready For The Electric Chair' – ensured that he was given the job. The rest of the line-up included Vini Reilly, the gifted guitarist who would later feature on Morrissey's debut solo album. The new Nosebleeds played Manchester Polytechnic on 15 April 1978, and appear to have been well received: among the Morrissey–Duffy collaborations were 'Peppermint Heaven' and 'I Get Nervous'. They played a few weeks later at the Ritz, where Morrissey hit on the novelty idea of tossing sweets into the audience. Also on their set-list was the old Shangri-Las hit, 'Give Him A Great Big

Kiss'. Interestingly, Morrissey did not change the gender in the song, suggesting that he may have been aware and proud of his sexuality, or merely taunting the crowd, or perhaps already singing in character as he would in years to come.

The event earned Morrissey his first mention as a non-scribe in the press: Paul Morley, then writing for *NME*, observed, 'Steven Morrissey has charisma'. Not that this prevented The Nosebleeds from disbanding soon afterwards. Morrissey, who had given up his job with the Inland Revenue, now signed on. His closest friend in those days – as now – was Linder (Linda Mulvey, aka Linder Sterling), born in Liverpool in 1954, and in the late seventies one of the celebrities of Whalley Range, the Manchester suburb known as 'the home of the bedsit' – which Morrissey would evoke in 'Miserable Lie'. Where and how they met is not known: for three decades their friendship has been free from media scrutiny and tabloid sensationalism.

Linder was the vocalist with Ludus, a punk-jazz ensemble who enjoyed moderate success in concert halls and particularly at the Hammersmith Odeon. One of their most popular numbers was the Morrisseyesque, 'I Can't Swim, I Have Nightmares', but his favourite appears to have been 'Breaking The Rules', which he chose as one of the tracks for his *Under The Influence* compilation album in 2003. 'Linder has an *enormously* sexual voice and is also *enormously* underrated,' he told *Word* upon the album's release, adding, 'I find these lyrics remarkable, suggesting that all forms of love are wonderful, whether it's three women together, four men together. Why can it not be so?'

The pair seem to have been on the same spiritual and intellectual planes – foils for each other's search for artistic and poetic inspiration amongst the grimy tangle of Manchester backstreets. A favourite haunt for reflection was the iron-gated South Cemetery, in West Didsbury, the subject of The Smiths' 'Cemetry Gates' – deliberately misspelled as it is spoken, and a work of some charm. For who has *not* ambled amongst the tombstones in some ancient city graveyard, if not in search of karma then in search of deceased celebrities one never would have had the hope of 'seeing' otherwise? Oscar Wilde, Colette, Chopin and Victor Hugo did so in Paris's Père Lachaise, and ultimately chose it as their final resting place. And on Wilde's cumbersome Jacob Epstein tomb, one invariably finds Morrissey quotes daubed in felt-tip pen.

After a brief spell behind the counter of a record shop, Morrissey followed in his father's footsteps and worked (equally briefly) as a hospital porter, only to throw in the towel when asked to collect and clean the surgeon's blood-spattered boots. Once again he returned to the solace of his room, writing letters to the music press (which would later defile him) in praise of Ludus and his other favourites, and penning witty neo-Wildean epistles to a young Scot named Robert Mackie, of whom nothing is known save that one had answered the other's 'Musical Tastes' advertisement in *Sounds*.

Had Morrissey never achieved international fame, these half-dozen letters, clumsily written and with many words deliberately misspelled, would not have seen the light of day. As he did achieve it, however, Mackie subsequently photocopied them into a crude booklet, *Words by Morrissey*, and this provides a fascinating insight into the man's mind back then. It is as if he was *so* self-assured that he would become an icon that he had become The Great Morrissey while still an unknown, for while other Manchester youths were out on the pull, doing pub-crawls and generally letting their hair down after their working week, this particular young man was content to stay in his room, inadvertently or not gleaning information from old Joan Crawford films, Ealing comedies – a host of details from 'the good old days' that would later crop up in his work.

The letters are as irreverent as they are funny, but never vulgar. They are alternatively addressed to Sir Laurence, Paganini, Tugboat Annie (the character in the famous Marie Dressler film of the same name) – and signed Natalie Wood, Oscar Wilde or Ronald Reagan. The first sees Morrissey gently rebuking Mackie for calling him Steve ('It reminds me of the Bionic Man.') – and the last one is signed off Steven, shortly before he dispensed with the moniker for good.

In a letter dated 13 October 1980, Morrissey berates Mackie for not having seen David Bowie, whereas he has seen 'Him' fourteen times between September 1972 and May 1976. He claims to have been born in Odessa and adds, Wilde-like, that he does not work except on his genius. Denouncing Mackie's favourite singer, Kate Bush, he declares that the nicest thing he can say about her is that she is unbearable. He closes with, 'I'm glad you liked me in *Rebel Without A Cause.*' In his missive of 22 October, he enthuses over Lou Reed, but pulls no punches over his hatred of Orchestral Manoevres In The Dark's frontman, Gary Numan, and concludes that to him, all electronic music is a sad accident.

In his next letter, Morrissey callously tells Mackie how sorry he is to hear that Mackie has lost his sister – this is careless, he says, and he wishes he could lose his. In another he laments the death of Mae West – at just 88, it was such a waste! He asks Mackie to send him some pornography, if he has a girlfriend, if he *likes* girls. He says that he has a girlfriend called Annalisa, that they are both bisexual, but that he hates sex! The girl in question was most likely Annalisa Jablonska, who later sang backing vocals on The Smiths' 'Suffer Little Children' and 'Pretty Girls Makes Graves'.

Taking a swipe at 'pretty-boy' music, Morrissey assures Mackie that there are worse groups than Duran Duran, though he is damned if he can think of any. Then he adds, 'Adam Ant bores the shit out of me.' In his letter dated 10 December he combines his sadness over John Lennon's murder with his loathing of Margaret Thatcher, technically his first attack on her before his opinionating got him into hot water. He tells Mackie that he *almost* cried, that he has none of his records and did not care about The Beatles – only to add that he was disturbed that someone who had devoted part of his life to peace could be shot five times for it. Concluding that the wrong people always die he adds, 'Nobody would assassinate our dear prime minister. Is all life sad?'

Robert Mackie was one of the first to be informed, in March 1981 upon Morrissey's return from his holiday in Philadelphia, of the imminent publication of his first biography, *The New York Dolls*. The 24-page booklet, published by Manchester-based Babylon Books, may have been scoffed at by Morrissey's later detractors, but during that summer and despite the limited appeal of its subject matter, it sold over 3,000 copies – a figure not often achieved by mainstream publishers of music books back then. It contained forty photographs of the group, one of Morrissey himself – and the audacious coda added to the Preface, 'Many thanks to Steven Morrissey – watch out for his James Dean book.'

In the meantime, big things were about to happen on the musical front. In one of his last letters to Robert Mackie, Morrissey announced that he was about to form a group, Angels Are Genderless, of which absolutely nothing is known. Why the friendship with Mackie ended is also a mystery. The pair had spoken for the first time on the telephone, and maybe this had put paid to the mystique: on the subject of Mackie's Scots accent Morrissey observes that he would have enjoyed their conversations more, had he been able to understand what Mackie had been talking about. Then, having invited Mackie to Manchester he tells him that there are lots of 'Thoroughly Modern Millies' in the vicinity who look like extras from Fellini's *Satyricon* – therefore if he does not find *him* funny, he can laugh at someone else.

The pair had exchanged photographs – and while Morrissey was undeniably vain and almost ethereally good-looking, his only compliment to Mackie was to observe that he looked as though he had a dead caterpillar on his upper lip. Mackie's own letters to Morrissey have never been seen, but Morrissey's responses to him are suggestive at times, almost like one elderly Noël Coward scene-queen writing to another – as if *daring* a relationship, should they meet, that might transcend the platonic. So far as is known they never did and from now on Morrissey would conduct himself, personally and within his work, with the same degree of guarded titillation – seemingly flaunting his sexuality on the one hand, but always acting defensively when directly questioned about it; feigning lack of experience or celibacy, which many believed was but a cover-up for the fact that he was just another normal young man with normal desires. It is an undisputed fact that just about everyone who meets him, young or old, male or female, enemy or fan, finds him physically irresistible despite his occasionally *un*attractive views.

Morrissey's closest male friend was James Maker, a slightly older Londoner of Mancunian parentage. The singer mentions 'Jimmy' in one of his letters to Robert Mackie, saying that he is going to spend the weekend at Maker's flat in London, adding, 'We often sit on the balcony looking for UFO's. We're such a wild pair (yawn) . . . one so modern as you would find us boring, but most people find us *très* amusing.' James Maker was flagrantly effeminate, possessed of matinee-idol looks, was self-confessedly sex-mad, has admitted to appearing in two gay porn films – *Bike Boys Go Ape* and *Well-Hung Studs* – and in a varied career has fronted several bands. Peter Adams, who ran The Gemini Club in Huddersfield (an ex-local where, amusingly, one had to press a buzzer and be 'vetted' through an upstairs window before being allowed in) was certain that there was something between the two men. He told me:

> We used to run Saturday evening trips to the gay village in Manchester. First we would take in a pub – Dickens, where the trannies hung out, or Stuffed Olives where the drinks were cheaper than anywhere else. When we were feeling especially brave we'd try the Thompsons Arms or the Union, where all the rough stuff congregated – you'd never believe *how* rough! Then we would go on to a club, or maybe the Church in Bolton. In some of those places Jimmy Maker was unmissable: drop-dead gorgeous, showing off on the dance-floor. Morrissey wasn't known in those days. He was your typical shrinking violet, hanging around in the background or sitting at the bar. I never saw either of them cruising. Jimmy could have had the pick of the club. He didn't. He and Morrissey always arrived together, and they always left together, which certainly said something to me.

Much later, Morrissey himself spoke to *Melody Maker*'s Frank Owen about an incident that can only have been an attempted gay-bashing involving himself and James Maker, though by all accounts not the first. Owen had caught up with The Smiths in Cleveland, Ohio, on 8 August 1986, and interviewed the singer shortly before the group were about to go on stage. Morrissey complained bitterly when Owen published his comments in the paper's 27 September issue, yet in all honesty he had seen Owen's tape recorder sitting on the table between them, and should have exercised caution. He did not, and as such had no one to blame but himself, for this certainly *was* a classic case of Bigmouth Strikes Again.

Describing the incident as the worst night of his life, Morrissey explained how he and Maker had been heading for Devilles (a gay club, Owen made a point of stressing), but had begun their evening at the Thompsons Arms. Between the two watering holes, in a car park near the Chorlton Street bus station, they had encountered 'a gang of thirty beer monsters all in their late twenties, all creeping around us'. The pair had taken to their heels, but the mob had caught up with Maker and started kicking him around. He had not been too badly hurt, however, and had managed to get away, and running in different directions in the hope of losing their pursuers they had met up in Piccadilly bus station and jumped on to a bus marked Stretford – only to find it driverless. By now, the thugs had caught up with them again. 'We had all these coins and we just threw them in their faces and flew out of the bus,' Morrissey told Owen, next explaining how he and Maker had rushed across the road, boarded the nearest bus *with* a driver, and encountered more trouble: 'Suddenly the emergency doors swing open and these tattooed arms fly in – it was like *Clockwork Orange*. The bus is packed, nobody gives a damn. So we run upstairs and the bus begins to move and we end up in Lower Broughton. For some reason we get out and we're in the middle of nowhere – just hills.' Morrissey concludes by explaining how he and Maker were compelled to walk back to Manchester, after failing to find a telephone at the nearest house – the door of which had been opened by a 63-year-old Teddy Boy, 'We came back home to my place, finally, at something like 5 am, and listened to *Horses* by Patti Smith and wept on the bed.'

Owen, as if attempting to defend himself, observed how, in Manchester in those days, in order to seek sanctuary from gay-bashers who might pick on the wrong person, one had 'little alternative but to seek refuge in the gay clubs, like Dickens (a sleaze pit where your feet stuck to the floor when you walked in), or the gay pubs, like the Thompsons Arms, the Rembrandt or the Union (the hippest spot of degeneracy in town – full of trannies with plastic legs).' This cannot be right: most heterosexual men would not have been seen dead in this part of town, let alone its clubs and pubs. And Morrissey was very definitely and enthusiastically speaking 'boys-town' from experience when he took Owen on a trip down memory lane:

> The gay scene in Manchester was a little bit heavy for me. I was a delicate bloom. Do you remember the Union? Too heavy for me, as was [the] Dickens. The Rembrandt I could take. It was a bit kind of craggy. There was no place, at that time, in Manchester in the very early stages, that one could be surrounded by fascinating, healthy people – fascinating healthy bikers, for example. It was always like the cross-eyed, club-footed, one-armed, whatever! . . . Do you remember Bernard's Bar, now Stuffed Olives? If one wanted peace and to sit without being called a parade of names then that was the only hope. Bernard's Bar was fine for a while, but what I was really into was the music. That's where punk fitted in . . . I never liked the Ranch. I have a very early memory of it and it was very, very heavy. I never liked Dale Street. There was something about that area of Manchester that was too dangerous.

It probably goes without saying that there must have been *some* attraction between himself and James Maker, added to which was their common bond of wit, high intellect, gross outspokenness and the aforementioned love of danger and recklessness. Morrissey's *New York Dolls* is inscribed, 'This book of mine is dedicated entirely to James Maker, who lives it.' Listening to Maker speak, and reading transcripts of his interviews, he is *so* similar to Morrissey that one may only wonder who influenced whom in their acquiring of carefully nurtured campology mannerisms. Speaking of the young Morrissey, Maker told David Cavanagh of *Q* in January 1984:

> Life had fashioned a Spartan, crushingly monotonous biscuit-coloured pattern for him. His life was hugely unelaborated. He turned to his own contemplations and he sought expression in the ideology and ritual of his own life. He breathed for art . . . depended on nobody but himself. At the age of seventeen he was possessed of great intellect and humour. His presence was entirely unassuming

but he could lay people waste with laughter at a sentence, effortlessly.

Morrissey's final letter to Robert Mackie ended, 'Life is a terrible, terrible thing, Robert. Going Down Slow.' There would soon be another man in his life; however, this relationship would never be considered as anything other than very definitely platonic: Johnny Marr.

The Americans had had Rodgers & Hart, Lerner & Loewe, Simon & Garfunkel, Leiber & Stoller. Britain had had Lennon & McCartney. On the continent there had been Jacques Brel & Mort Shuman. In the wake of these, the very unlikely partnership of Morrissey & Marr would influence *their* generation – failing to attract an international coterie of stars covering their work (unlike these other great collaborators) only because *their* work was so insular and personal to its lyricist. Loosely equating with Barbara – France's biggest ever singer-songwriter, whose songs were similarly intimate – absolutely *no one* can put over a Morrissey lyric other than Morrissey himself. This is why so few artistes have tried, and why when they *have* tried, the results have generally been mediocre at best.

Born on 31 October 1963, Johnny Marr (né John Martin Maher) was, like his future partner, the son of Irish immigrants who had moved to Manchester; since 1973 he had lived in Wythenshawe. He had attended a better school than Morrissey (St Augustine's Grammar), but had not fared as well, and certainly had not acquired the same intellectual standing. Marr's chief interests at school had been football (at one time he'd played for the Manchester Boys and was offered a trial with Manchester City) and music. The first record he had bought had been T. Rex's 'Jeepster'. Not as outspoken as Morrissey, though no shrinking violet and something of a precursor to the Gallagher brothers where expletives were required to make a point, Marr told *NME*'s Danny Kelly in April 1991, when fame was largely behind him, 'I was one of those kids who always got the *plastic* guitar for Christmas. Everybody knew me as "that cunt who walks around with a guitar-case who thinks he's gonna be a big success." I developed a thick skin.'

Marr, a guitar virtuoso at twelve, was also a serious New York Dolls/Patti Smith fan. Cocky and sure of himself, he knocked around with Andy Rourke, a long-haired classmate from Ashton-upon-Mersey who, it later transpired, was already experimenting with soft drugs. The pair, notorious truants, spent much of their time jamming at Rourke's house to recordings of heroes Rory Gallagher, Nils Lofgren, Marc Bolan and Keith Richards – Marr on guitar/harmonica, Rourke on acoustic guitar. By 1977 they were playing semi-professionally with their group, The Paris Valentinos, augmented by two schoolfriends: drummer Bobby Durkin, who spent some time with the Manchester Youth Orchestra, and on vocals/bass, Kevin Williams, who later changed his surname to Kennedy and played Curly Watts in *Coronation Street*. Though their repertoire was excessively tilted towards rock (notably Thin Lizzy and Tom Petty) they performed mostly at church functions before splitting up. Marr later played briefly with Sister Ray, though by the end of 1979 he, Durkin and Rourke had joined White Dice, who *almost* landed a record deal with F-Beat, in London. The failure to do so knocked Marr back sufficiently to warrant him temporarily readjusting his sights and studying for his O Levels at Wythenshawe College – an enterprise he soon abandoned to form another short-lived ensemble, Freaky Party, before taking a job behind the counter at X Clothes, a clothing store in Manchester's Chapel Walks.

By this time, Marr had moved out of his parents' council house and was lodging with Granada Television producer Shelley Rohde, who allowed him use of her sound-proofed attic for rehearsals. Another new pal was Matt Johnson, who later achieved some success as The The, and who came close to persuading the youngster to join *his* group – which, of course, is what eventually did happen in 1989. Then there was Joe Moss, the rag-trade baron who owned the Crazy Face fashion chain and also supplied other outlets (including one where this author worked – we met during the late sixties) with cheap denim jeans. It was Moss who urged Marr to form a group, which he said he would back. Marr therefore set about finding a suitable vocalist and lyricist.

Johnny Marr had apparently already read some of Morrissey's biting lyrics, courtesy of Billy Duffy, but Duffy had fallen out with Morrissey and now refused to have anything to do with arranging an introduction. Some years later, after joining The Cult (then known as the Southern Death Cult), Duffy commented, 'Morrissey hated me because he thought we'd *stolen* some lyrics from him, which we probably had.' Marr therefore acquired Morrissey's address from another source, along with a warning: the Stretford bard could be tetchy and unapproachable. Marr decided to take his chances.

Leiber & Stoller, arguably the greatest American song-writing partnership of the fifties, had written a staggering roll-call of million-sellers for artistes as diverse as Elvis Presley, Peggy Lee, Edith Piaf and The Drifters. According to Mike Stoller (the composer), one morning he had opened his front door to find Jerry Leiber (the lyricist) standing on his doorstep with the announcement, 'Hi! Why don't we start doing songs together?' Poetically romantic, if therefore unoriginal, is the only way of describing the landmark meeting between Morrissey and Marr. The latter, with his foppish X Clothes garb, late sixties hairstyle and charm-the-birds-out-of-the-trees patter, must have been as much of a culture shock to Morrissey as the lanky, soft-spoken, bequiffed and bespectacled Morrissey must have been to Marr. One also gets the impression that the angelic-looking teenager may have been afraid of the older, bigger and tougher Morrissey – or at least apprehensive of having the door slammed in his face. Legend has it that Marr had piped up, 'This is how Leiber and Stoller met. I'm a fabulous guitar player and I'm interested in forming a group. Let me in!' Morrissey's response was a polite, 'What kind of music do you like?' – and the biggest 'musical marriage' since Lennon & McCartney had got off to a promising start, as Morrissey observed with typical Formbyesque fervour to *Sounds* a few years later:

> Johnny came up and pressed his nose against the window . . . it left a terrible stain. I think he'd been eating chocolate. He seemed terribly sure of what he wanted to do, which I liked. He said, 'Let's do it, and do it now!' So we did it! Then!

It is quite possible that neither account is accurate. Naturally, no witnesses were present at the time and, besides, both were speaking after their particular bubble had burst – romanticising the facts may have helped cushion the blow of their split. This is immaterial: all that matters is that they *did* meet.

The pair's working methods mirrored Leiber's & Stoller's, in that they rarely sat down together to produce a song. Morrissey, the trouper, maintains that his happiest moments have been spent in front of audiences, where reaction to his work is instantaneous. Johnny Marr, however, has always preferred the close confines of the studio, and from the outset of their professional relationship had the unenviable task of slaving away with the other members of the group for hours on end, day or night – to dutifully present the patron with arrangements for him to set his lyrics to, or so that he might pen new ones. This may explain why, in some of their songs, Morrissey sounds desperate to fit so many words into the shortest bar – Freddie Mercury-like – or grossly extend others, a system he uses to this day and which gives his work a unique extra dimension.

The day after their historic encounter – Morrissey's 23rd birthday – and allegedly surveyed by the James Dean poster in his bedroom depicting the actor's 'crucifixion' pose from *Giant*, the pair produced their first two songs. These were 'Suffer Little Children', and 'The Hand That Rocks The Cradle', the latter title possibly inspired by a 1917 US birth-control short of the same name. Its message ties in well with the theme of Hindley and Brady in 'Suffer Little Children'. The voice of a typical sixties parent promises the child protection from the horrors of a recurring nightmare, but probably makes matters worse by reminding him what these contain: the bogey man, the meat cleaver, the terrifying shapes of the darkened furniture. And Morrissey's *pièce de résistance* is the clever weaving of Al Jolson's 'Sonny Boy' into the closing stanza – an innocuous action that would later bring undue criticism from the tabloids.

The two songs were put on to demo tapes at Manchester's Decibel Studios, with the engineer, Dale Hibbert, playing bass and Freaky Party's Simon Wolstencroft on drums. From this point, things moved quickly. While Morrissey was jotting down lyrics on every conceivable subject, Johnny Marr set about arranging the group's first engagement – though effectively there *was* no group at this point. He secured a spot at the Manchester Ritz, supporting the ten-piece ensemble Blue Rondo A La Turk whose most recent album, *Chewing The Fat*, had been part-produced by Clive Langer; some years later, he would work with Morrissey, the solo artiste. Marr also accepted responsibility for finding the combo backing from a reputable record company, travelling down to London and sleeping on the floor of Matt Johnson's flat to save on hotel bills. For his part, Morrissey chose the name for his group, eschewing the latest fad for fancy names by picking a nomenclature that identified with his Northern roots and basic ordinariness: The Smiths. 'This is real music played by real people,' he would soon be telling journalists, 'There's no façade. We're simply here to be seen as real people.'

He also took the important step of dispensing with his Christian names – declaring that, as history had so often proved, poets worthy of their salt were only ever remembered by their surnames. This was taking a grandiose, indeed a blatantly arrogant stance that, had he fallen flat on his face with his adventure, would have made him a laughing stock. Fortunately, it was as if he had seen his guardian angel standing over his shoulder.

As a frontman, Morrissey would prove a determined, if not ruthless taskmaster. Because *he* had lived a straightforward, reasonably sanitised life, he was anxious that anyone who worked with him should follow his example. The New York Dolls and The Rolling Stones had lost members through drugs and debauchery. Jimi Hendrix, Janis Joplin and Jim Morrison had all self-destructed before thirty. Manchester's 'golden boys', Joy Division, had recently been devastated by the death of their singer, Ian Curtis: that good-looking, sad young man had made a spectacular exit by *carving* a smile on his face with a Stanley knife before hanging himself. Morrissey, unenthusiastic about the group, upset more than a few New Order fans by commenting, 'I saw them just before "the death" and I was astonishingly unmoved, as were the audience.' The Smiths would therefore be solidly anti-drugs, anti-violence and free from vice – albeit that Morrissey himself was *the* champion of thuggery in his lyrics and, cynics might say, not as sexually inexperienced as his self-proclaimed press liked to make out. Like him, the other members of the group would have to be pro-Northern, intelligent to a degree, and supportive of *his* views on issues such as politics and vegetarianism. Had he known of the drug habits of one of his future band mates, of course, The Smiths' line-up may have been entirely different: not only would he have rejected Andy Rourke, but also quite possibly the man who recommended him – Johnny Marr.

The drummer, Mike Joyce, was the first to be recruited. A few months older than Johnny Marr, this slightly frowning Fallowfield youth had played with punk band The Hoax before leaving school. More recently he had joined Victim. His audition for The Smiths took place at Spirit Studios, where Morrissey and Marr were so amazed by his 'balls-out' playing to their new song, 'What Difference Does It Make?' that they hired him on the spot, thereby signalling Victim's demise. What they did not know was that Joyce's frenetic performance was allegedly on account of his having just eaten magic mushrooms.

The Smiths – comprising Morrissey, Marr and Joyce, with Dale Hibbert on bass – made their public debut at the Ritz on 4 October 1982. Morrissey engaged James Maker as MC/go-go dancer: wearing a sixties-style suit and women's high-heels, he introduced the group in French! They performed three of their own songs ('The Hand That Rocks The Cradle', 'Suffer Little Children' and 'Handsome Devil') – and The Cookies' 'I Want A Boyfriend For My Birthday' without raising any eyebrows. Mike Joyce got carried away and burst a drumskin, and there was a problem with the microphone, which would not detach from a stand set far too low for the six-foot Morrissey, who spent the whole time on stage with his shoulders uncomfortably hunched. Even so, the group were well-received by the 300-strong, mostly gay audience, while James Maker pranced back and forth, alternating between the tambourine, the maracas, and flinging handfuls of confetti into the crowd.

'Handsome Devil' would bring condemnation from so-called moralists, but widespread approval from the gay community, who would quickly adopt Morrissey as an icon for almost a decade demanding, 'Is he or isn't he?' – until an ill-timed remark to a journalist from *The Face* appeared to give them their answer. His fascination with the subjects of rent boys, age-gap sex, car backseat dalliances, and even the fact that The Smiths' record label was actually *called* Rough Trade cannot be ignored, though this of course did not necessarily imply that Morrissey practised what he preached or extended his interests beyond the lyrical – tough-guy actors leave their characters behind on the film lot before heading home to their families, after all. It is an indisputable fact, however, that over the coming years The Smiths would immerse themselves in more gay and camp imagery than any other show business act. On the other hand, in these formative years, it should also be remembered that Morrissey was first and foremost an 'interpreter of situations', as near as damn it to France's Georges Brassens, who always performed his neo-pornographic vignettes in character.

The lyrics to 'Handsome Devil' pull no punches, but they are literary rather than vulgar, and would set Morrissey apart from out-to-shock contemporaries such as Frankie Goes To Hollywood. A teenager stops an older person (maybe a policeman – 'I say, I say, I say!') in the street to ask the time, but the elder character knows what the teenager *really* wants and declares, 'Let me get my hands on your mammary glands.' Then, having obviously 'scored', the older person offers to lend a hand to help see the teenager through examinations, adding, 'And when we're in your scholarly room, who will swallow whom?' Delectably poetic, but hardly subtle!

'Handsome Devil' was one of two songs recorded on to demo tapes at Chorlton's Drone Studios a few weeks later: the other was the only slightly less suggestive 'Miserable Lie', which contained the choice locker-room line, 'I look at yours, you laugh at mine.' By this time, Andy Rourke had replaced Dale Hibbert on bass. The Smiths, however, still lacked a recording contract. There were rumours that a deal *might* have been forthcoming from Factory Records. The company had been founded in 1979 by Tony Wilson, the former Cambridge graduate turned television presenter (*Granada Reports*) who also owned the Factory Club in Hulme, and the Beach Club. Wilson had booked all the big Manchester groups, including Joy Division and Ludus. He saw The Smiths at Manhattan Sound in January 1983, but possibly on account of the high-camp nature of their act, he merely offered them a thirty-minute spot at his newest acquisition – the Hacienda, on Whitworth Street West, which had opened the previous May. This catered largely for gay audiences, and was famed for its notorious 'Gay Traitor Cocktail Bar' cruising area. The group performed eight songs at the Hacienda including the newly composed 'Jeane', 'These Things Take Time' and 'Hand In Glove'. The latter boasted the phrase, 'The sun shines out of our behinds', informing would-be competitors, the audience (many of them high on poppers) and Tony Wilson especially, that they were *not* witnessing the latest five-minute sensation who would end up as last year's news.

The Hacienda's auditorium was gloomy, to say the least, which is why the group turned up with armloads of flowers to add a little colour. 'Flowers are virtually as important as the sound system,' Morrissey once said in a radio interview that was preceded by Dorothy Squires' 'Say It With Flowers'. Tony Wilson appears to have been suitably impressed by The Smiths' music that night, but a few years after the event he fell victim to the sharp end of Morrissey's tongue. Claiming that he had once seen a one-act play written by Morrissey, he compared him with lesbian scribe Jeanette Winterson, adding, 'He's a woman in a man's body – she's a woman in a man's body.' This was hardly a compliment and Morrissey hit back below the belt, with, 'He's a *pig* trapped inside a man's body. The day somebody shoves Wilson into the boot of a car and drives his body out to Saddleworth Moor, that's the day Manchester music will be revived.' When the critics took him to task over this, he compromised an apology, declaring that the first part of his statement had been misquoted – that he had actually said, 'Wilson's a *man* trapped inside a *pig's* body!' He also strenuously denied the claim made by Wilson's business partner, Richard Boon, that he had heard a pre-Smiths tape of Morrissey, unaccompanied, performing 'The Hand That Rocks The Cradle' with a different melody to the more familiar one, and (if such a tape does exist, with uncanny synchronicity bearing in mind that this was two years *before* he met Johnny Marr) Bessie Smith's blues classic, 'Wake Up, Johnny'.

With or without Wilson's help, The Smiths had crashed on to the Manchester scene and now began acquiring a cult following – or rather

Morrissey did, with his songwriting partner running a close second. For just as the likes of Queen were nothing without the flamboyance of Freddie Mercury, so The Smiths would have been 'just another group' without their flower-waving leader. The Smiths would prove themselves the most innovative British group since The Beatles and The Rolling Stones; in Morrissey they had a peerless lyricist. Despite their later gimmicks and overt campness they were never gender benders like Adam and the Ants and Culture Club. On the continent, *réaliste* singers were nothing new: death and unrequited love were as much a part of life as the daily diet. For the first time since the fifties, British audiences were to be treated to articulate, meaningful and inspirational lyrics set to stylish musical arrangements. The quartet *were* attractive to look at, of course, but attractiveness was not the key component of their being – as happens with today's grossly inferior boy bands. The Smiths always offered considerably more than glamour.

Such traits, so far as the more insular British were concerned, did have certain drawbacks, largely because as far as blinkered critics were concerned, intellect and commercialism did not always mix. Most of The Smiths' early eighties peers, particularly Duran Duran and Adam and the Ants, made up for a lack of lyrical know-how by making the most of the promotional video. Adam and the Ants' video of 'Prince Charming', with its superb characterisations and the bonus of an appearance by Morrissey favourite Diana Dors, becomes just another bland, repetitive ditty when heard on the humble turntable. For this reason The Smiths vowed that they would never make videos – and with few exceptions, never did.

An unwelcome guest at their early shows appears to have been Morrissey's father. Writing in March 1988, the editor of *Rock Sound Français* repeated a story that Morrissey had told him:

There was this man of a certain age who, behind his whiskers and alcohol-ravaged pallor, looked incredibly like Morrissey. He would jump on to the stage and try to dance with the group. This was Morrissey's father. He used to hang around a lot backstage, trying to pick up girls. He became such a terrible embarrassment for the singer, who ended up barring him from all The Smiths' future concerts.

Morrissey, meanwhile, was faced with a quandary when Babylon Books published his second biography, *James Dean Is Not Dead*, commissioning an initial print-run of 5,000 copies and effecting an option contract for a follow-up, to be provisionally entitled *Exit Smiling*. This was to have been a compendium of lesser-known (in Morrissey's opinion, though not that of the Hollywood box office) kitsch icons such as Sandra Dee, Agnes Moorehead, Thelma Ritter, William Reynolds and Sal Mineo – and rounding off the fifty-plus-page tome, 'Slush Be My Destiny', an essay on the deliciously outrageous Tallulah Bankhead. This was placed on the backburner, then abandoned completely in favour of The Smiths' debut single, 'Hand In Glove'/'Handsome Devil' – recorded during the Hacienda show and, financed by Joe Moss, mixed at the Strawberry 2 Studio.

On 23 March 1983, The Smiths made their London debut at the Rock Garden, in Covent Garden. Here, they were actually billed 'A Mancunian Five-Piece'. Both Joe Moss and Johnny Marr had urged Morrissey to dispense with James Maker: his 'exotic' dancing was acceptable in the Manchester gay clubs, but Moss in particular felt that his on-stage antics were distracting and he was afraid of inciting trouble from the anti-gay element that flocked to the Rock Garden on Wednesday nights. The songs, of course, were still the same, and not for the last time Morrissey, in his Evans Outsize Shops blouse, attracted wolf-whistles from some of the establishment's precursors to lager-louts. Even so, the evening was a success, and, clearly en route towards national recognition, The Smiths supported the notorious Sisters of Mercy on 6 May at the University of London. A little later, they supported Altered Images at the Hammersmith Palais. They *should* have appeared at the Leeds Futurama Festival, but Morrissey allegedly threw a tantrum and cancelled upon learning that the proposed headliner, former Buzzcock Howard Devoto (at one time Linder's boyfriend), had been replaced by The Bay City Rollers, whom, critics say, he could not stand.

The Smiths' very first interview for *NME* appeared on 14 May, headed CRISP SONGS AND SALTED LYRICS (an allusion to the famous Smiths potato snacks) and conducted by Cath Carroll, who had seen them at the Hacienda. She aptly observed, 'Smithville could be anywhere, a timeless zone where high-school and low-life collide. They're the young generation and they've got something to say.' Though the Wildean quips and Marr expletives were not in evidence that day, Morrissey and his partner were very sure of themselves, with the other two members of the group barely getting a word in. 'Songwriting just isn't there any more and that's why we're important,' Morrissey expostulated. And when questioned about the 'meaningfulness' of 'Handsome Devil', without wishing for the conversation to get around to sexuality, Morrissey chimed in, not for the first time hoping to avoid being asked *that* question, 'The lyrics I write are specifically genderless. I don't want to leave anybody out. Handsome is a word that people think is applied to males . . . but I know lots of handsome women. After all, there *is* such a thing as a pretty male.'

'Hand In Glove'/'Handsome Devil' was released that same month as part of an anticipated temporary contract with Rough Trade, whose headliners in those days were the now largely forgotten Aztec Camera, until something better came along. In March 1994, the company's director, Geoff Travis, recalled his very different meetings with Morrissey and Marr to Brian Boyd of the *Irish Times*: 'There was something about Johnny Marr. He didn't look or act like all the other hapless musicians with demo tapes in their hands.' And of Morrissey he said, 'He had a very striking presence and he seemed to bear down on me. He said, "I want to know everything that is going through your head. The first Smiths single is being recorded. This is a very important day in my life."'

Later, when it was all over, Travis changed his opinion of the 'nice Manchester boy', telling the same interviewer, 'I've seen Morrissey in a lot of different states over the years, both good and bad. As an artist I have nothing but the highest respect for him – as a human being I think he has some way to go in certain areas.'

The single did well in the independent charts, got nowhere in the national, but has since more than made up for this. Most importantly, it got The Smiths noticed. The sleeve, setting an important camp-classic precedent, caused even more of a stir than the lyrics: it depicted a nude, rear-view shot of gay porn star Leo Ford, one-time lover of the outrageous diva Divine, who appeared at the Hacienda around the same time as The Smiths. In the shot, Ford is leaning against the locker-room wall on the set of one of his films. The Huddersfield Gemini Club's Peter Adams, who witnessed the group's Hacienda show, recalled, 'Leo Ford wasn't restricted to films. He did jerk-off shows all over the world, including one in Manchester which The Smiths were invited to. I very much doubt their manager even gave them the message. Still, it was a nice sentiment seeing as they'd used his arse to their advantage, so to speak.'

Morrissey stirred the pot of dissension in July 1983 by telling *HIM* magazine's Catherine Miles:

> I adore the picture. It evokes both sorrow and passion. It could be taken as a blunt statement against sexism, yet in using that picture I am being sexist. It's *time* the male body was exploited. Men need a better sense of their own bodies. Naked males should be splashed around the Co-op. I'm sure this would go a long way towards alleviating many problems, even that of rape.

'Hand In Glove' and 'Handsome Devil' are songs about unconventional love, possibly gay love. Certainly, as The Smiths made the transition from clubs to mainstream venues, Morrissey's flirtation with gay culture escalated. Yet the more famous Morrissey became and the more he flaunted such frequently beautiful, plaintive stanzas, the more reticent he would be when expected to discuss the rumours he had nurtured.

In later years, as a solo artiste with an indisputably 'laddish' air to him, Morrissey would not have discussed the merits of gay nudity with anyone, let alone *HIM* magazine – which, in the early eighties, was the biggest-selling such publication in the country. During this first balmy summer of Smithdom, however, when fame and fortune were just beckoning, he spoke freely with the gay press. When Catherine Miles remarked that even openly gay rock stars would never take the risks he was taking with his lyrics, Morrissey responded, 'Obviously people don't want to insert cyanide in chocolate because it won't sell. Pop *is* tame.' When asked if, in view of The Smiths having been engaged for Manchester's *September In The Pink* celebrations, he would like to play more specifically gay venues, he replied, 'To me, it's just people with ears. We're a group that doesn't recognise any boundaries. I don't want to get up on a soapbox. I detest sexual segregation. One of the things that separates The Smiths from other bands is the concern with words.'

It was the group's 'concern with words', in the days before Morrissey's interviews were peppered with such words as 'loneliness' and 'celibacy' – or at least it was the three other Smiths' willingness to follow, seemingly without question, the path their frontman had marked out for them – that had endeared them to the gay community in the first place. Before The Smiths, known gay or bisexual stars such as Johnnie Ray, Michael Holiday and Billy Fury had *always* addressed their love songs to women, though more often than not they were singing them with men in mind. But what did Morrissey actually think of the gay scene at the time – and did he still go clubbing? His response would endear him to thousands more gay men:

> I had a brief spasm some time ago. Hmph. I was never terribly popular. The gay scene seems so full of hate in all directions. Then there's the heterosexist behaviour of a lot of gay men. Before clonism, the scene was extreme in being so totally *female*. Now some of the men are undistinguishable from Tetley Bittermen. Obviously gays shouldn't be frightened of *rock*, but again it comes down to wanting as many people as possible to hear our music. I want to be pinned on everybody's wall – or pinned *against* everybody's wall. Could you possibly make me a sex symbol?

Morrissey certainly liked exploiting his own body, regularly whipping open his shirt to expose his finely tuned torso as often as not inscribed with some potent message, or occasionally he would shrug the garment back over his shoulders to titillate, while always staying well within the bounds of Catholic decency. In his definitive biography of James Dean,

The Mutant King (Plexus, 1974), David Dalton writes of his subject's androgyny and the fact that he obviously fancied himself – and might just as well have been describing Morrissey. All one has to do is swap their names around and substitute 'singer' for 'actor':

> Androgyny is the traditional sexuality of the classic performer. Jimmy's interest in his own body has the autoerotic quality of all great actors. The relationship of an actor with his audience takes place in a zone of sexually-charged reciprocal currents, and the androgynous character of Jimmy's roles is a fusion of both male and female elements. It was the material out of which he created, composed his polymorphous body. All vices have claws and can be traced through the unerasable hieroglyphics of the features and gestures . . .

It was during The Smiths' show at the University of London that they were 'spotted' by John Walters, the producer of Radio One's *John Peel Show*, who invited them to record four songs for the programme's 31 May edition – which remains one of the series' most memorable and most-repeated by public demand, though much of the fuss centred around the airing of one of Morrissey's most controversial lyrics, the stunning 'Reel Around The Fountain'.

Again, when discussing the song, one has to consider that Morrissey may be singing in character. Fifty years earlier, Gracie Fields sang, 'Marry me, Sally, you're more than the whole world to me', while Al Jolson once crooned, 'I'm just wild about Harry . . . the heavenly blisses of his kisses fill me with ecstasy.' No questions had been asked, no stones cast. Though it's doubtful, when one considers his knowledge of Polari slang, Morrissey may not have known that the title of his song was also a gay porndom term for oral sex (running the point of the tongue around the tip of the penis until ejaculation occurs), though 'Shove me on the patio, I'll take it slowly' coming straight after: 'It's time the tale were told of how you took a child and made him old,' should be self-explanatory. What also must be taken into consideration, bearing the widespread but erroneous theory that the song is about paedophilia, is that it is the younger of the two who is taking the initiative to importune/seduce the older one, and not the other way around. Also the line, 'You can pin and mount me like a butterfly' is purloined from the film *The Collector* (1965), the line delivered by lepidopterist Terence Stamp to Samantha Eggar, at a time when the word 'mount' had a different connotation than today. Years later, when asked for his idea of perfect happiness, Morrissey would respond, 'Being Terence Stamp!'

Following their runaway success on the *John Peel Show*, The Smiths were given a spot on the similarly high-rating *David Jensen Show*, also on Radio One – but with one proviso: they were not permitted to perform 'Reel Around The Fountain'. Someone connected with the programme who knew *exactly* what the term meant contacted the *Sun*, resulting in a badly researched feature appearing on 25 August headed, CHILD-SEX SONG PUTS BEEB IN A SPIN. Its author, who obviously cannot have listened to the song, observed, 'it contains clear references to picking up kids for sexual tricks' – and worse still added, 'As part of their live act, they also do a version of "Climb Upon My Knee, Sonny Boy", about picking up a seven-year-old in a park.' Not only was all of this wrong, the latter statement was blatantly slanderous. The other tabloids followed suit, accusing The Smiths of condoning paedophilia, again seemingly without listening to the song. Plans to issue the track as a single were aborted, and Morrissey hit back with a press statement of his own, saying that the author 'has misinterpreted the facts. Quite obviously we don't condone child molesting or anything that vaguely resembles it. What more can be said?'

Morrissey's only support came from Alex McKenna, *HIM*'s news editor, who had watched the singer fend off hundreds of admirers with a massive bunch of gladioli at London's Venue on 15 September. In the magazine's November 1983 issue (appearing too late, on account of the monthlies' lengthy printing set-up, by which time much of the fuss had died down), McKenna observed, 'Out-gay Morrissey wrote the lyrics of "Handsome Devil", which cloth-eared journalists on the *Sun* and *Sounds* magazine, enlisting the help of Tory MP Geoffrey Dickens, have tried to allege is about child-molesting. Buy [the record] and see why The Smiths' office told *HIM*, "It's such a ridiculous thing to say that none of us even bothered to read the articles."'

For once, silence might have been the better policy, for though the lyrics of the song definitely do not suggest child molestation, the sexually active narrator leaves us with no doubt that he *does* want to have sex with the older person (not necessarily a man) he has long been fascinated with – adding to the equation that, in cases like this, it is frequently the younger party, regarded as the 'victim' by the unknowing, who does the chasing.

Because Morrissey did not argue with the BBC themselves over the banned song, The Smiths were invited back on the *John Peel Show*. Of their new songs, aired during their brief recent summer tour, 'This Charming Man' was considered the best of a good clutch, and was chosen as their next single. Produced by John Porter and coupled with 'Jeane' (produced by former Teardrop Explodes guitarist Troy Tate), it was released in November 1983 in a cover that, though less controversial than its predecessor, was no less striking.

Morrissey had requested a still from Jean Cocteau's avant-garde film, *Orphée* (1949), featuring Cocteau's lover, Jean Marais, face and hands pressed against a mirror as if embracing his own image. Regarded by cinema-goers at the time as The Most Beautiful Man In France, Marais granted permission to use the still, originally used to promote the film on playbills, but strongly disapproved of what Morrissey did with it – turning it on its side and 'adding' sand, so that the actor looked like he was lying down at the edge of a pool. 'Cocteau would have turned in his grave,' Marais told me in 1990. 'By changing the photograph he completely misinterpreted and *ruined* the message of the scene. I wish I had never given permission for it to be used.'

The song, preceded by a stirring introduction by Johnny Marr, is yet another tale of age-gap sex – the story of the 'jumped up pantry boy' (a later Victorian term for a rent boy) who, after his bicycle gets a flat tyre, finds himself being picked up by the nice man whose car has smooth leather seats, but who ultimately cannot understand why someone so handsome should *care* about him.

The Smiths made their *Top Of The Pops* debut with the song on 24 November 1983, shortly before their return visit to Manchester's Hacienda. It brought them instant national recognition, and reached number 25 in the charts. Sting, The Police's frontman, thought he was doing the group a favour by asking them to support The Police on their forthcoming tour. Johnny Marr's response to this was a sharp, 'We're a hundred times more important than The Police will ever be.' The group's success also saw them parting company with Joe Moss, who wanted to spend more time with his family. As for Morrissey, when asked to explain The Smiths' cult following, he rattled a few more cages by responding, 'People are dedicated to us because we deserve it. It's all quite natural because I really think we merit a great deal of attention.'

Unable to find a major record company, despite their success, Morrissey and Marr had re-negotiated a clever fifty-fifty deal with Rough Trade – not dissimilar to the ones some of the major American movie stars had signed upon the collapse of the studio system – which also offered them a share of the profits. The money they subsequently earned for the company is more than the company ever thought possible. The hurricane speed with which The Smiths moved, and the idolatry bestowed upon their singer, was alarming. Their 7 December performance at Derby's Assembly Rooms – exciting to watch, but with Morrissey persistently half a tone off-key throughout – was filmed, and two days later broadcast on BBC2's *The Old Grey Whistle Test*. For the first time, it would appear, the proceedings had been brought to an early conclusion when dozens of mostly male fans invaded the stage to *hug* Morrissey – their actions were initially (and in later concerts, often purposely) misinterpreted by security staff, whose rough handling of the situation resulted in several injuries. Whether any of these pasty-faced apostles actually understood the message of 'Reel Around The Fountain', which astonishingly did not end up on the cutting-room floor, is not known. The programme led to a doubling of the group's fanbase.

In December 1983, reluctantly it would appear, The Smiths made their first trip to America: a dance mix of 'This Charming Man', along with several remixes, had been released against their wishes by New York producer Francois Kervorkian – and on the strength of this they had been booked at the city's Danceteria on New Year's Eve. Professionally and personally, the occasion was a disaster. Mike Joyce caught chickenpox; Morrissey tripped during the performance and fell off the stage. The group were offered a brief tour of the East Coast, but turned this down and flew back to England – Johnny Marr to his flat in Earls Court and Morrissey to his new Kensington home. The only good thing to have emerged from their American misadventure, they later said, was 'Heaven Knows I'm Miserable Now', written in their dingy room at the Iroquois Hotel. Released in May 1984, the single would reach number 10 in the charts.

Also in December 1983, The Smiths were given the official seal of approval by the gay press when the legendary Kris Kirk of *Gay Times* included them in his annual *New Year Gay Alphabet* round-up, describing Morrissey as gay:

What a gay chart we have at the close of the year with Marilyn, Georgie, Frankie Goes to Hollywood, Tom Robinson, Elton John, and the sensational Smiths plus a large number of closet cases crowding out the single scene. *S* stands for Sexy and The Smiths which, in my book, are synonymous. Gay lead singer Morrissey has one of those voices which makes you feel horny and want to burst into tears at the same time . . . Mark my word, they'll be HUGE in '84.

Meanwhile, The Smiths' next single, 'What Difference Does It Make?'/'Back To The Old House' (according to one *Les Inrockuptibles* interview, the former was the one Smiths song Morrissey truly *loathed*), was released in January 1984, and reached number 12 in the charts. Continuing his fascination with the 1965 film *The Collector*, Morrissey commissioned a still from the film of Terence Stamp, holding a lepidopterist's chloroform pad. Stamp objected, and a hasty cover-switch was effected with Morrissey himself emulating a near-exact pose – quiffless, and holding a glass of milk!

Voted Best New Act in the *NME* poll, at the end of the month The Smiths began their first international tour: by the summer they would have played over fifty dates in England, France, Belgium, Holland, Germany and Scandinavia. Part of their show at the Amsterdam Meerward was released on a bootleg album, and an edited version of their longest show so far (25 songs) at Hamburg's Markthalle was

filmed and broadcast on the hugely popular *Rockpalast* magazine. On
9 May, Morrissey donned a gold-lamé jacket and eschewed his quiff
for a Brylcreemed Teddy Boy hairstyle when The Smiths took to the
stage at L'Eldorado, on Paris' Boulevard de Strasbourg. Beforehand,
there had been considerable outrage when the director of this, one of
the city's most hallowed music halls, had been accused of 'cashing in
on mediocrity' by hiring a little-known foreign pop group to follow in
the footsteps of immortals such as Piaf, Mistinguett and Chevalier.
The performance itself, part of which was screened on the French
showcase *Les Enfants Du Rock*, was dire on the whole, though there
was a fleeting special moment when Morrissey, en-profile in the
legendary silver spotlight, inadvertently raised his eyes towards the
rafters. It was a magical instant. As an audience member myself that
night, it reminded me of the dated but still potent images that survive
on old newsreel footage of the period fondly remembered by the
French as *Les Années Folles* – and made up for the mediocrity of
everything else that had transpired that evening. I remember telling a
journalist friend at the time, 'The group probably won't survive the
decade, but their singer certainly will!' Several years later, as a solo
artiste with a string of hits tucked under his belt, Morrissey would
prove me right by triumphing at another bastion of Parisian working-
class culture, L'Elysée Montmartre, receiving a ten-minute standing
ovation for what many French fans saw as his signature song, 'Will
Never Marry'.

   In those early days, it is extremely doubtful that Continental fans with
an astute knowledge of the English language grasped the *full* meaning
of most of Morrissey's lyrics until these began appearing on record
inserts. Once this happened, one song that had a particular impact,
especially in France, was 'Pretty Girls Make Graves', with its theme of an
older, voracious woman attempting to 'straighten out' the timid man,
using the 'quick and easy way', despite his plea, 'I'm not the man you
think I am!' Later on in the song, when she has almost succeeded in
dragging him to the end of the pier, he confesses his impotence – 'He
will not rise for *anyone*!' – and she latches on to another stud who may
satisfy her needs.

The Smiths only performed twice on French soil. They always refused to play the out-of-town arenas favoured by their Gallic contemporaries because, they declared, these were impersonal. Yet the Olympia, the Palais de Congrés, and the Théatre de Chatelet would have nothing to do with them because of the brouhaha caused by their engagement at L'Eldorado. My friend Fernando Lumbroso, who ran the Mogador, said, 'I *almost* booked them, but I valued my beautiful red velvet seats. And their manager was one of the *rudest* men I ever spoke to!'

Foreign audiences, accustomed to the more conventional *chansonniers*, were bemused to witness Morrissey gyrating about the stage with a bunch of flowers sticking out of the back pocket of his usually baggy denims. The fans loved the gimmick, while serious rock fans used to the more stylised performances of Johnny Hallyday and Eddie Mitchell scoffed because these movements usually detracted from Morrissey's lyrical voice and frequently made him sing flat. In Britain, the flowers were once eschewed for a miniature bush, and in one *Top Of The Pops* appearance the 'gormless Lancashire lad' effect was completed with a pair of NHS spectacles. Morrissey claimed that this was his way of displaying that the entire British music scene was way over the top, and added with deliberate George Formby double-entendre, 'I don't mind if people remember me for my bush, so long as it's for artistic reasons.'

As had happened in New York, The Smiths felt uneasy performing away from home, much of this being down to the strictly vegetarian Morrissey and Marr trying to cope with over-rich foreign food. Even so, they might have thought about that before undertaking the tour, and they earned themselves few favours when, after flying back to London for a *Top Of The Pops* appearance with Sandie Shaw, they cancelled their remaining dates in Germany, Switzerland and Austria.

3

Oscillating Wildly:
A Band of Brothers

'He's childlike, very extreme in his emotional reactions to people. I feel
he's been indoctrinated against trusting people at some stage in his life.'

– Jo Slee

The Smiths had arrived back in England to tremendous acclaim: their
debut album, simply bearing their name, had been released on 20
February. The group had originally put down ten tracks in a Wapping
basement studio, run by Troy Tate, during the summer of 1982 *before*
their first stage appearance. These had subsequently been scrapped, and
the whole concept re-recorded with additional material in new sessions
produced by John Porter at Manchester's Pluto Studios. Three of the
songs taped by Tate – 'These Things Take Time', 'Handsome Devil' and
'Accept Yourself' – were replaced by 'Suffer Little Children', 'Pretty Girls
Make Graves' and 'Still Ill'. In the latter, Morrissey champions the dole
queue, cockily declaring, on behalf of those who know the system and
are getting enough cash from the state to make working for a living
unnecessary, 'England is mine and it owes me a living.'

The album, which reached number 2 in the charts, arguably contained more gay themes and references than straight ones, and its cover
was graced with a doctored photograph of Andy Warhol's in-house 'wet
dream-hustler-stud' Joe Dallesandro, taken from the 1968 underground
movie *Flesh*. Nicknamed 'Little Joe' on account of his phenomenal
endowment (inasmuch as Little John had been so named because he

had been very tall), Dallesandro had started out posing for beefcake pictures for the Athletic Model Guild before being discovered by Warhol producer Paul Morrissey, and put into a series of semi-pornographic films, best described by the title of the one he made in 1970 – *Trash*. In *Flesh*, Dallesandro plays a rent boy whose customers, unappealing as they are, are still far better-looking than him. The still acquired for The Smiths' album depicts him bare-chested, six-pack rippling and head down, perched on the edge of the bed next to a young client (Louis Waldon), who is licking his lips in anticipation of what is on offer.

Much of the imagery and Morrissey's lyrics appear to have been rather alien to the other members of the group. Mike Joyce and Andy Rourke were so thrilled to be part of a high-profile pop unit that they took potential sleeve photographs and demo-tapes home to impress their families, who apparently *did* understand some of what was going on. Joyce recalled to David Cavanagh of *Select* early in 1993, 'Johnny said to me, Uh, I've got the cover of the new album. And it's a picture of a bloke going down on another bloke. So I'm like, GREAT! FAN-TAS-TIC! Hey, Mam, look what *I've* been doing for the last eight months!'

There was no way, of course, that The Smiths would have got away with using the whole shot: Dallesandro's image was therefore blurred slightly and Waldron removed completely. Even so, it caused a stir – largely because the tabloids informed a generally unknowing public *where* it had come from.

The 'gay issue' was alluded to on 7 June when *Rolling Stone* published a feature on The Smiths. That evening the group were giving a concert at the Hammersmith Palais, and a somewhat weary-through-rehearsing Morrissey spoke of his literary interests and dashed off a perfunctory attack against Margaret Thatcher: 'She's only one person and she can be destroyed. I just pray there is a Sirhan Sirhan somewhere. It's the only remedy for this country at the moment.' Morrissey's sexuality, however, was foremost on journalist James Henke's agenda. He began his piece, 'He goes by a single name . . . He calls himself "a prophet for the fourth gender", admits he's gay, but adds he's also celibate.' Given his propensity for privacy, one cannot imagine Morrissey making so direct a statement, and he laughed off the situation later by saying that the 'gay' tag had been wishful thinking on the journalist's part.

More press attacks came in May 1984 when, promoting 'Heaven Knows I'm Miserable Now', Morrissey appeared on *Top Of The Pops* wearing his usual baggy shirt, denims, NHS spectacles and beads – and dangling an unconnected hearing-aid. The tabloids accused him of mocking the afflicted; more knowledgeable viewers may have imagined he was emulating another idol, fifties 'Nabob of Sob' Johnnie Ray. Morrissey said that the gesture was his tribute to a deaf fan who had written to him, professing the miseries brought about by such a handicap. He added, 'I did it to show the fan that deafness shouldn't be some sort of stigma that you try to hide.' Even so, many die-hard fans copied him.

On the flipside of 'Heaven Knows I'm Miserable Now', The Smiths placed 'Suffer Little Children', a work of astonishing sadness and conviction by Morrissey, simply but effectively orchestrated by Johnny Marr – quite possibly the first truly great British *réaliste* song. The piece denounces Hindley as the more evil of the two murderers – because she supplied Brady with his victims, luring them to him – and the dialogue alternates between the spirits of the children who plead, 'Over the moors, take me to the moors – dig a shallow grave and I'll lay me down' and the censurer (Morrissey himself), who reminds Hindley that her crimes will haunt her until the day she dies, then darkly concludes, 'Manchester, so much to answer for . . . but fresh lilaced moorland fields cannot hide the stolid stench of death.'

The title for the song came from a feature about Hindley that had appeared in the *Sunday Times*. Under the heading THE WOMAN WHO CANNOT FACE THE TRUTH, the editorial claimed that the murderess was unable to leave her prison cell without the other inmates chanting from the Bible, 'Suffer the little children to come unto me!' 'Suffer Little Children' was also the title of Chapter 20 in Emlyn Williams' book *Beyond Belief: The Story of Ian Brady & Myra Hindley*; Chapter 13 was headed, 'Hindley Wakes', also quoted in the song, as is the line, 'Wherever he has gone, I have gone . . . whatever he has done, I have done,' spoken by Hindley at her trial when asked about her involvement with Brady.

The song got Morrissey into hot water with the media. It refers to the children by name – paying especial attention to the 'pretty white beads' worn by Lesley-Anne Downey at the time of her death. When relatives of another victim, John Kilbride, heard the record on a pub jukebox, they contacted the *Manchester Evening News*, which led to a very much overblown attack on Morrissey being syndicated to the national press. The *Sun*'s Jim Oldfield quoted the dead boy's surviving brother as saying 'Whoever wrote the song must be as sick as the killers. It's just blood money', while Lesley-Anne Downey's mother, Anne West, accused The Smiths of bringing back the horrors of the worst incident in the city's history. Neither they, nor the *Sun* journalist, can have listened to the song.

Morrissey was personally denounced as 'grossly insensitive' for including a photograph of Myra Hindley on the record sleeve. In fact, had any of these people taken the time to read the caption on the reverse they would have realised that the photograph, taken around the same time as the Moors Murders, of the hard-featured young woman with the badly peroxided hair, standing in front of a row of grimy terraced houses, was actually 'Spend! Spend! Spend!' pools winner Viv Nicholson, returning to her home town of Castleford after her husband's death in a car crash. Nicholson's picture had been substituted at the last minute when Morrissey's original choice, Albert Finney, had refused to be depicted with the slogan, 'Heaven Knows I'm Miserable Now', at a time when he was at the peak of his career. However, and again without listening to the lyrics to see what all the fuss was about, several major outlets removed the record from their shelves.

Not for the first time, Morrissey found himself the victim of a smear campaign, very much in the vein of the spate of celebrity rape or child abuse allegations that would clutter the tabloids twenty years down the line: often groundless accusations, bandied about indiscriminately, resulting in the limitless prejudice against the 'accused', who suddenly becomes the victim while the accuser is permitted to remain anonymous, even if the allegations are dismissed. Morrissey's press office released a statement that explained what should have been obvious in the first place:

The song was written out of a profound emotion by Morrissey, a Mancunian who feels that the particularly horrendous crime it describes must be borne by the conscience of Manchester . . . It is a memorial to the children and all like them who have suffered such a fate.

Morrissey made it blatantly clear that the song was a tribute to the children, that the photograph on the record sleeve was *not* the loathsome Hindley. He also contacted Anne West and John Kilbride's family – the former for two decades the unofficial spokeswoman and campaigner for the families of other murdered children. Morrissey and Mrs West met and became friends after she realised how truly sincere he was. She also realised that he was just as keen as she was that Hindley should rot in jail, despite the relentless efforts of campaigners such as Lord Longford who believed that if she was released, rehabilitation and counselling would put her back on the straight and narrow. Mrs West died before Hindley, still desperately worried that this monstrous woman might be granted her freedom.

As for Viv Nicholson, Morrissey was very much taken with the rags-to-riches-to-rags story of the coarsely spoken West Yorkshire housewife who had scooped over £150,000 on the football pools – an enormous amount in those days – blown the lot on a series of spending sprees and then, after her husband's death, become a Jehovah's Witness. Her ghost-written autobiography *Spend! Spend! Spend!* had been turned into a television drama, and would later be transferred to the legitimate stage. Nicholson's photograph appeared also on the cover of The Smiths' 'Barbarism Begins At Home' that was originally issued as a 12-inch promo in the UK – she looks very unladylike in a home-crocheted 'fanny-belt' mini-skirt, and is depicted standing in front of a Castleford pit. Morrissey actually met her: the pair were photographed strolling along Blackpool's promenade; he borrowed the line, 'Under the bridge we kissed [and] I ended up with sore lips,' from her book and included it in another song, 'Still Ill'.

Viv Nicholson also sang Morrissey's praises in *The South Bank Show*'s Smiths documentary, filmed at around the time their friendship ended quite abruptly. Having already expressed her delight at appearing on two of the group's sleeves, Rough Trade assumed that she would be pleased to make the hat-trick when Morrissey commissioned the cover for a Dutch CD of 'The Headmaster Ritual' in 1987. In the picture she is seen painting at an easel. According to Rough Trade (see Jo Slee's *Peepholism*, 1994), however, Nicholson objected when the CD was released in Britain – as a Jehovah's Witness she 'was embarrassed by the expression "spineless bastard" on the track 'Headmaster Ritual''. Many who knew Nicholson were surprised by this: on the two occasions that I encountered her, her own language was colourful to say the least.

The inimitable Morrissey wit was harnessed for a rare non-singing television appearance at around this time when he guested on the arts programme *Eight Days A Week*, alongside Wham!'s George Michael and DJ Tony Blackburn. *They* may have been enthusiastic about *Breakdance: The Movie*, but Morrissey put on his best Sitwellian voice to denounce it with a deliciously snappy, 'I find it almost *impossible* to care!'

The Smiths' next single, released in August 1984 – at a time when singles were not taken from albums commercially milked for all they were worth – was a new song, 'William, It Was Really Nothing'. It reached number 17 in the charts and caused another controversy with its cover: a homoerotic 'morning-after-the-night-before' shot of a nearly naked young man sitting forlornly on the edge of his bed. The photograph was tasteful, inoffensive. Even so, Rough Trade was instructed to change it, and subsequent pressings of the record were housed in a sleeve featuring a no less exploitative still of Billie Whitelaw from the 1967 film *Charlie Bubbles*. As for the subject of the song, the more gullible believe that it was Billy Fisher, the central character played by Tom Courtenay in *Billy Liar* (1963) – the story of a young man who evades a dull life by daydreaming that he is treading the gold-paved streets of London, in the days when such a myth existed. A more likely theory is that the subject is Billy Mackenzie, the bisexual singer from The Associates. Morrissey had met him earlier in the year, describing him as 'a whirlwind', whereas Mackenzie apparently told friends how much he *fancied* The Smiths' frontman. If so, Morrissey was arguably flying the gay flag when, as the narrator, he urges the eponymous hero to ditch his 'fat girl' and marry him instead. Simon Goddard observed in the June 2003 issue of *Record Collector*, 'Legend has it that [Mackenzie] paid a visit to the singer's flat only to abscond with a *James Dean* book and one of his shirts. "It wasn't my favourite," Morrissey lamented, "but these things are sacrosanct."' The devilishly attractive Mackenzie would respond with a song of his own: 'Steven, It Was Really Something'. Suffering from depression following the death of his much-loved mother, paranoid about his rapid hair loss and addicted to cottaging (picking up men for sex in public toilets), Mackenzie was found dead of a Paracetamol overdose in January 1997.

Meanwhile, in the wake of an Irish tour blighted by seasickness, dietary problems and flu (Johnny Marr became so ill that he was hospitalised), and with their second album, *Meat Is Murder*, nicely underway, Rough Trade put out *Hatful Of Hollow*. This was a comfortably assembled mid-price compilation album, a mixture of rarities and songs from the Peel/Jensen sessions, the whole packaged within an attractive gatefold sleeve depicting a pre-war Cocteau model reproduced in a French magazine from 1966. Inside the package was a photograph of The Smiths, snapped in their dressing room at Glastonbury: Morrissey bespectacled and wearing his controversial hearing aid, and Mike Joyce, himself looking Ortonesque in his under-shorts. 'For all their sexual ambivalence and lyrical unorthodoxy,' *NME* observed in those Morrissey-friendly days, 'Morrissey's songs are universal in the vulnerabilities and desires they seek to express.'

Morrissey's outspokenness and much-discussed *causes célebres*, which had alienated him from some sections of society but endeared him to many more, were challenged at around this time by the emergence of three very different gay-orientated ensembles: Bronski Beat, Culture Club and Frankie Goes To Hollywood. Boy George, as effeminate as they came, made headlines by professing that instead of sex, 'I'd rather have a cup of tea!' Bronski Beat's Jimmy Somerville discussed in the greatest anatomical detail the physical aspects of gay sex. Frankie Goes To Hollywood said everything in their lyrics – the BBC's ban of 'Relax', which championed fellatio, only sent it zooming to the top of the charts.

Of course, record companies, including Rough Trade, were interested in this 'pink explosion' not because it applauded specific issues, positive or otherwise, but because these groups were bringing in *money*. Peter Burton observed in the August 1984 issue of *Gay Times*, at a time when the charts were dominated by Hi-NRG records and hits by bands with a gay orientation:

Is the high-visibility of gay men in the pop charts going to bring about a change in attitudes? Will queerbashers drop their weapons because they happen to like [Bronski Beat's] 'Smalltown Boy', 'Relax', or any of the string of The Smiths hits? Somehow it doesn't seem very likely. Will struggling gay bands suddenly find themselves snapped up by greedy record companies? Maybe – but it will simply be bandwagon jumping rather than enterprise. And – after all – the music *has* to be good to make an impression and sell.

The Smiths saw no point in trying to compete with these outfits, whose chief selling points were (certainly in Frankie Goes To Hollywood's case) vulgar lyrics and raunchy, no-holds-barred videos. When questioned by Martin Aston of Dutch magazine *Oor* in November 1986 about the elements of camp and camp humour in his songs, in comparison with the songs of these rivals, Morrissey would reflect, 'I worship camp humour and the several levels of it, but there's the very frivolous "You old queen" level that I never indulge in. Alastair Sim and Margaret Rutherford – *that's* the campness I idolise.' The Smiths declared themselves a smut-free zone, and believed that they possessed sufficient originality to outlast any rival, which of course is ultimately what happened, long after their demise, with the record-buying public.

Morrissey, for whom commercialism had never been the be-all and end-all, was also astute enough to think carefully before speaking to journalists, now that his group was the biggest in the country. In January 1985, leading reporters from several music publications joined forces with *Gay News'* Neil Bartlett for a feature on the latest gay attack on the charts, and *NME*'s Neil Spencer singled out Morrissey – who after eighteen months of being labelled gay had neither categorically admitted nor denied the fact, but given some less-than-subtle hints to the affirmative – as his role model. 'The only way we cover gay issues more is with people being willing to talk about their sexuality,' Spencer observed. 'Morrissey put it well in our Christmas issue. He said, "I'm not heterosexual, homosexual, bisexual, asexual – just sexual."' His change of 'tactic', however, displeased the same magazine's Janice Jaye, who scathingly awarded The Arthur Rimbaud Misunderstood Genius Award, 'To Morrissey of The Smiths, who would like us all to think he is, without having to prove it.' Jaye concluded by predicting that by the end of the following year the group would have 'faded gently into obscurity . . . The only thing left that will make him a legend now is suicide.'

That same month, Rough Trade put out another ode to loneliness which, though it only reached number 24 in the charts, remains just as memorable as anything these other groups released – *and* which has since caught up with their chart-toppers, sales-wise.

'How Soon Is Now?', of which *Melody Maker* remarked, 'Rarely has catharsis been tinged with so much regret – and shared with such purity,' was housed in a sleeve featuring an obscure actor named Sean Barrett, and which is controversial only in that he is cupping his crotch in both hands (actually, *praying* in Leslie Norman's compelling war film of 1958, *Dunkirk*). For this reason – ignorance *not* being bliss once more – the sleeve was banned in America and replaced by the *Hatful Of Hollow* insert from Glastonbury, minus of course the 'athletic' shot of Mike Joyce. The lyrics to the song were not as hard-hitting or suggestive as Morrissey's previous forays into same-sex attraction, and were a refreshing anodyne to some of the smut in the charts. The narrator knows of a club where one can find love, if this is what one wants, though so far *he* has been unsuccessful and feels that he always will be. And for the detractors there was the message, 'You shut your mouth . . . I am human and I need to be loved!' Lovely!

The Smiths' next two singles, 'Shakespeare's Sister' and 'That Joke Isn't Funny Anymore', offered the group something of a commercial lull, charting at 26 and 49 respectively. The former, an invitation to clifftop suicide, had as its inspiration an essay by Virginia Woolf: in Morrissey's case, the narrator is urged by the rocks to throw his skinny body down so that he and the singer he once loved may be reunited in death. The singer is believed to have been Tim Buckley, the manic-depressive singer-songwriter who had died of a heroin overdose in 1975, aged 28. Buckley's equally famous singer son, Jeff, thought so: he reportedly carried a torch for Morrissey for years, and was so inspired by the tribute that he recorded the most exquisite cover version of a Smiths song, 'I Know It's Over'. This was played in June 1997 over newsreel footage of the police recovering Buckley's body from the Mississippi, near Memphis, after he had tragically drowned.

'That Joke Isn't Funny Anymore', marginally less grim but equally fascinating, dealt with death inspired by solitude. The song appeared on The Smiths' next album, *Meat Is Murder*, which more than made up for the commercial lameness of the previous few months by rocketing to the top of the charts, 'dethroning' Bruce Springsteen. For seemingly no reason at all, Morrissey now hit out at the 'Born In The USA' rocker, declaring, 'Springsteen calls out to the philistines of America, and naturally there is a huge response.' The album's February 1985 release coincided with certain problems within the group, largely because Morrissey was now becoming belatedly aware of Andy Rourke's heroin addiction. 'Things are bloody horrendous at the moment,' Johnny Marr told *The Face*'s Nick Kent, 'Morrissey's just found out about Andy and he's going frantic demanding he leave the group. And I'm in the middle, trying to hold everything together.' Perhaps not surprisingly, given Morrissey's wizardry for keeping personal matters personal, the matter was kept out of the press. His main concern right now was getting over the new album's message. From his point of view, there were no ethical differences between child abuse, death in military action, and the killing of animals for human consumption. 'I don't *hate* meat-eaters,' he told *Sounds*, 'But I've found that if I say to certain journalists that I'm a vegetarian, they immediately assume that I detest to the point of death anybody that eats meat.'

The album cover, almost as important to The Smiths as the goods it contained, depicted a doctored still of a US soldier from Emile de

Antonio's anti-Vietnam film of 1969, *In The Year Of The Pig*. The caption on his helmet that had read MAKE LOVE NOT WAR (amended in some prints to MAKE WAR NOT PEACE) now read MEAT IS MURDER. Morrissey drove the point home by launching an attack on animal rights organisations for being too peaceable, his point being that they would only truly get their point across by giving the meat industry magnates a taste of their own medicine. Though he later threatened Norfolk turkey baron Bernard Matthews with legal action for using a Smiths poster in a television campaign, for the time being he only 'attacked' Matthews' contemporaries by declaring that if he ever met Kentucky Fried Chicken's Colonel Sanders in heaven, he would effect a swift knee to the groin – hardly 'tough tactics' by Morrissey standards!

Morrissey remained fervently anti-Establishment, and his disdain for the Royal Family remained as intense as ever – witness this no-nonsense stanza from *Meat Is Murder*'s 'Nowhere Fast': 'I'd like to drop my trousers to the Queen/ Every sensible child will know what this means/ The poor and the needy/ Are selfish and greedy on her terms'. That same year, he caused outrage among royalists after watching a television news bulletin of the vast crowd outside Clarence House eagerly awaiting the walkabout celebrating the Queen Mother's 85th birthday on 4 August. 'If the woman had died, there would have been less,' he quipped to *NME* in September. 'And I would've been hammering the nails in her coffin to make sure she stayed there!' Shortly after repeating this particular comment in my book *Morrissey: Landscapes Of The Mind* I received a letter from the world's best-loved grandmother – the threat of a lawsuit, I told myself, as I slit it open with trembling fingers. But no, it was a request from the Queen Mother, asking me to keep her informed of the biography I was writing of her favourite (and, ironically, one of Morrissey's) entertainer, Gracie Fields. Even so, I would have been perfectly willing to publicly condemn him for what he had said, much as I admired him.

Of the album's other songs there was the wailing vignette of 'I Want The One I Can't Have', in which the narrator – Morrissey himself – bemoans the traditional working-class behaviour expected of men like him because this is how things have always been. He is actually in love with the thug who, when he was just thirteen, murdered a policeman – and further suggests that if the young man needs 'self-validation', then he should meet him in the alley by the railway station. 'My most personal songs,' he told *Les Inrockuptibles*' Mishka Assaya during the summer of 1986, 'These are "Stretch Out And Wait" and "I Want The One I Can't Have". They just about sum me up.' There is more sexually linked thuggery with 'What She Said', the story of the literate woman who is sexually dead, smoking herself into an early grave, until her eyes are opened by a tattooed boy from Birkenhead.

The key statement on *Meat Is Murder*, of course, is the title-track itself, strategically placed at the end of the album so that by the time one reaches it, bearing in mind Morrissey's intention for the listener to experience the ten songs chronologically, one has received an education in just about every emotion in the book. Even so, it is a far from morbid excursion. The album's crowning glory, 'Meat Is Murder' is said to have genuinely terrified many Smiths fans out of eating meat – those who, so obsessed with their singer and willing to follow his every word to the letter, were not abstaining already. And while Andy Rourke later confessed to not eating meat only when Morrissey and Marr were around, Mike Joyce also turned vegetarian 'by fear'. It is a tremendously disturbing *chanson-grise*, whether one supports its sentiments or not: the buzzing of electric saws, the sharpening of knives, the authentic sounds of baying beasts as they are being led to the slaughter while Morrissey opines, 'Heifer whines could be human cries . . .'

Neither was Morrissey's powerful protest transitory. Seven years later, when asked by American reporter David Keeps, of *Details*, to define evil, he would pull no punches:

> I do see McDonald's as the core of modern evil because it is the death industry. I just feel rage that they will promote themselves from every possible angle, but they will not show the process by which the hamburger is made. They will not show the cows' throats being slit, the bull trying to commit suicide by banging its head against the stone floor.

Not all Smiths fans, however, were enthusiastic. Hugh Miller of *Gay Times* loved the album, but found the title-track 'patronising', adding, 'While people should be able to express their preferences, lyrics as loaded as this come across as empty as a policeman's speech. With clichés such as "the unholy stench of MURDER" the song makes a sharp contrast to "Nowhere Fast" and makes the listener wonder if these two songs were written by the same person.'

The Smiths' *Meat Is Murder* tour opened in Cheltenham three weeks after the album's release. The group frequently appeared in I DON'T EAT MY FRIENDS T-shirts, while Morrissey attempted to prick the consciences of the uninitiated by being photographed holding a kitten on a plate – the fake hearing-aid deflecting the seriousness of it all. There were 23 dates, all sell-outs, and each night – setting a precedent for extravagantly effective Continental-style entrances – the group were played on to the stage by Prokofiev's 'March Of The Capulets' from *Romeo And Juliet*. Memorable moments – aside from the nightly stage invasions always directed at Morrissey and never the other three (and one occasion when someone flung a string of sausages at him!) – included Morrissey's impromptu duetting of 'Barbarism Begins At Home' with Pete Burns, the Liverpool-born singer from Dead Or Alive. Morrissey courted controversy by telling *Sounds* of the event, which took place on 6 April, at the Royal Albert Hall, 'I felt a great affinity with that situation. He's one of the holier saints that ever walked the earth.' He also joked over their recent exchange of birthday 'gifts', though many believed that with these two anything might have been possible. 'He sent me twenty-six roses. I sent him forty-eight naked sailors.'

The diminutive Burns had caused something of a commotion in March 1984 when he had told *HIM*'s Kris Kirk, 'The pop chart is full of faggots, myself included to a degree,' adding, 'I'd prefer to see my face staring out of *HIM* than *Record Mirror* and know that I'm appealing to people who've got more in common with me than ten-year-old girls with wet panties.' On top of this, in just about every interview he gave, Burns was unabashed at confessing that he shared his bed most nights with his wife and a live-in lover named Steve.

Morrissey's close friendship with Pete Burns did not go unnoticed by the gutter press, and more than a few less knowledgeable journalists jumped to the wrong conclusion that Burns' love, Steve, and Morrissey could only have been one and the same – particularly Antonella Black, who interviewed Morrissey for *Sounds*' 20 April 1985 issue, though she was sensible enough not to refer to Burns by name.

One only has to read the introduction to Black's feature to see what Morrissey was up against, though he of course would not have known this at the time:

Nobody told me that, in the flesh, Steven Patrick Morrissey looks like Judy Garland's understudy. Nobody informed me that Steven Patrick can't quite wrap his pretty tongue around the letter 'S'. Nobody unbridled the fact that my arse was to be booted out of Steven Patrick's boudoir once the interview reached a sticky consistency. Steven is celibate, yet Steven has a double bed. Steven isn't paranoid, yet now all his interviews are doubly recorded. Steven shrills long and loud about castrated cows and lambasted lambs, yet he confesses to finding leather seats highly erotic. Steven is a funny little kettle of fish.

Black wanted to know if Morrissey was a 'professional paranoid' and 'mega misery guts', and when he denounced the word 'mega' as 'very provincial', levelled at him, 'One more crack like that and I'll put you across my knee and wallop you!' He played straight into her hands by responding, 'At last! Prayers answered, prayers answered!' From here the tension increased, as mutual silliness allowed the interview to spin out of control. Black asked Morrissey what was preventing him from being happy – hardly giving him the chance to answer before doing so for him, immediately raising his hackles and bringing the outburst: 'Give me the chance to answer the question! Good heavens, that's the first time I've shouted since 1976! Now I've forgotten the question!' Morrissey calmed down at once, but as the banter took a turn for the juvenile, the situation grew increasingly more volatile.

MORRISSEY: I've been in every conceivable situation in human existence.

BLACK: You've had group sex on a rubber mat with a bowl of custard?

MORRISSEY: Daily. It's a terrible yawn.

BLACK: You have swung from chandeliers with black grapes in your teeth?

MORRISSEY: I do it every February.

BLACK: Don't you think that your frailty has become redundant?

MORRISSEY: Well, it always seems that way as soon as something becomes big business. How can it become redundant?

BLACK: In the same way as somebody like Prince has become nauseating in his fixation with fucking and rubber jockstraps.

MORRISSEY: It's not the same thing. I've never sung about a jockstrap.

BLACK: Do you think that *Meat Is Murder* is self-conscious self-flagellation for practising or latent homosexuality? Did you have a bad experience as a child?

MORRISSEY: (allegedly blushing) What – with meat?

BLACK: What do you find highly erotic at the grand old age of twenty-five?

MORRISSEY: As a child in the Sixties, when the seats of cars were made of leather, to me there was something highly erotic about actually being in a car. I have always found cars highly erotic. Not the driver's seat. There was just something about the old leather seats. The things I find erotic are certain situations. They don't ever have to be particularly sexual. I don't have to tell you! The erotic feelings I have are very conventional, I'm afraid . . .

BLACK: But if you have erotic feelings, why don't you sleep with anyone? Why don't you make it happen?

MORRISSEY: (getting anxious) I don't want to any more, I don't want to. I don't! No, I'm not going to instigate things any more . . .

BLACK: So you're telling me that if some dark man came up behind you in the hall, pulled your Marks & Spencers down, and . . .

Black got no further. The interview was over, and she was promptly propelled towards the door.

Morrissey's championing of strong women was akin to Alan Bennett's affection for the same demonstrated in *Talking Heads* and the American gay community's fondness for stars such as Crawford, Bette Davis and Judy Garland in the fifties – but in Morrissey's case the stars frequently had a rough edge to them. In May 1985 *Blitz* magazine unusually (for a pop publication) secured an interview with 61-year-old Pat Phoenix, for years the brassy tart-with-a-heart barmaid Elsie Tanner in Granada Television's *Coronation Street* – but with one condition: she should be allowed to choose her own interviewer. She chose Morrissey, whom she had never met, though she had been impressed by some of the nice things he had said about her, not only of her work in *Coronation Street*, but also in *The L-Shaped Room*, one of his favourite films. Later she would say, 'He's an astute, gentle young man, good-looking, intelligent, sincere. Mark my word, he'll go a long way in life.' Phoenix was so bowled over by the singer's 'deep-set charm' that she insisted on his photograph going on the cover of the magazine instead of one of them together.

Morrissey could have been referring to someone close from his own life when he wrote of her character, 'Elsie was the screen's first angry young woman, a wised-up, tongue-lashing cylindrical tempest sewn into cheap and overstuffed dresses, harnessed by severe poverty, staunchly defending her fatherless children, devouring a blizzard of temporary husbands in dour Salford council dwellings.' Later he observed, 'She was an absolute blizzard of professionalism – you simply wanted to rush towards her bosom and remain there for ever.'

At the end of that same month, when asked to select his own interviewer for a Smiths profile on Channel 4's controversial late-night magazine *The Word*, he plumped for Liverpool actress-siren and self-styled sexologist Margi Clarke, whom he had raved about as the sluttish heroine of the film *Letter To Brezhnev*, then on general release.

The interview/sketch, according to Morrissey, took place 'some-where in the Scottish Highlands, near some ruins', and turned out to be a hoot with both stars 'taking the piss'. Morrissey announced Clarke as 'a luminary, a Venus who rises from the waves', and persistently called her 'Margox' (the name under which she had presented a 'what's on' Granada TV show in the late seventies). He confided that it had always been his ambition to act (a 'career' that had begun and ended with four lines in Phil Redmond's *Brookside* spin-off, *South*), and this of course was arranged with a re-enactment of a scene from *Letter To Brezhnev*. Clarke and a girlfriend are sharing a toilet cubicle in a nightclub, when Morrissey strolls in by mistake. 'He's frigging gorgeous, like that bloke from *Doctor Zhivago*!' she exclaims, after watching him re-arrange his quiff in front of the mirror. She then loans him her lip-salve – it is 'Choosy Cherry' – after which the action jumps to The Smiths' concert at the Glasgow Barrowlands.

In the middle of May 1985, The Smiths flew to Rome for a concert at the Tendetrisce. They should have made several television appearances, but owing to the nature of *Meat Is Murder*'s subject matter, these were cancelled at the last minute. The promoters, Virgin Italia, were less concerned with Morrissey's 'meat is murder' proclamations than they were with the age-gap/thug-sex content of some of The Smiths' other songs. In San Sebastian, Spain, the group themselves cancelled a show within an hour of curtain-up when the public-address system broke down with no guarantee that it would be repaired on time. For the first time, a riot erupted between agitated fans, theatre security and the police. All went well in Madrid: the 5 May concert, which formed part of the Paseo de Camoens Festival, was recorded and released on an excellent bootleg album that contains quite possibly the definitive version of 'Meat Is Murder'.

The Camoens Festival was by all accounts one of the few happy moments of The Smiths' European trip. Also in Madrid there was a row between the group and their then manager, Rough Trade's Scott Piering, which led to a parting of the ways. Not for the first time, Morrissey would be condemned for his searing perfectionism and demands that everything should be exactly right. Piering later told *Select*, 'On a professional level, he's a total nightmare. I don't think if he came to me on bended knees I would ever want to work with him again.' For his part, Morrissey would defend this regular to-and-fro of personnel, accusing managers of taking too much for granted by trying to inject creative ideas into the group, instead of staying behind the scenes and doing the job they were being paid to do. 'They can't resist meddling,' he told *Les Inrockuptibles* in 1991, 'thinking that they too are making the album, designing the cover. The Smiths was an absolutely closed society!'

Piering was replaced by Matthew Sztumpf, Madness' former manager, and it was he who finalised The Smiths' tour of America, which opened at Chicago's Aragon Ballroom on 7 June 1985. It was Morrissey's idea to hire a drag queen to open the proceedings by miming – badly – to a playback tape. A few minutes into his patter, the audience began pelting him with beer cans, and when this happened again in Detroit and Washington, he was unceremoniously dropped.

In San Francisco, on 20 June, Johnny Marr married his long-time sweetheart, Angela Brown. There was virtually no time for a honeymoon: The Smiths headed for Philadelphia, the city that was already preparing for what was predicted would be 'the biggest concert in its history' – Bob Geldof's Live Aid would be simultaneously relayed with the extravaganza he had organised to take place in London on 13 July. Bearing in mind what Morrissey had said about its predecessor, Band Aid, The Smiths were never even considered for the event, though this time it was Johnny Marr who had his 'five-penn'orth' about some of the artistes on the bill. Marr attacked Rolling Stone Keith Richards, declaring that he could no longer play the guitar, and accused Bryan Ferry of attempting to resurrect his flagging career by using the event to promote his new single. Then, leaving the US press to make what they wanted of this, the group played dates in Canada before flying home to more controversy. They had been booked for a guest-slot on the 19 July edition of *Wogan*, Terry Wogan's thrice-weekly television chat-show – an institution in the days when, by and large, stars were stars and questions were rarely vetted. Marr, Rourke and Joyce were at the studio and about to go into make-up when a call was put through from Morrissey: he had decided to give the show a miss. And yet only days later he complained in *Record Mirror* about the lack of airplay The Smiths were getting, adding, 'I'm tired of being broke!'

Also at this time, the Church was up in arms over the cover of the latest *NME* – Morrissey, complete with halo, and holding up one hand to reveal blood dripping from a stigmata wound. The banner headline read, FEAST OF STEVEN: MORRISSEY, FALLEN ANGEL OR DEMI-GOD. Within was another 'martyrdom' shot captioned, 'Tour of Deity: Moz Crucified By The Press, In Glorious Colour, Every Wednesday'. Interviewed by Danny Kelly at Manchester's Britannia Hotel, where for refreshment the singer ordered a samovar of hot chocolate, the talk had got around to Morrissey's inspirations: Oscar Wilde, James Dean, the heroes from his favourite old British films. 'I'm very interested in what emerges from the ashes of poverty or the bruises of torture, to see what people are capable of in extremes,' he told Kelly, in light of recent press attacks; ironically, seven years hence Kelly would be helping to launch the most vituperative attack of them all. 'People who achieve things artistically after persistent public floggings, after being roasted alive by the critics, interest me when they come out on top, smiling, in control, impregnable.'

In September 1985, The Smiths released another exploration of loneliness and unrequited love, quite possibly Morrissey's best example of this so far, and also the first to be promoted with a video. 'The Boy With A Thorn In His Side' had a cover depicting Smithsonian Institute alumnus-author Truman Capote, perhaps best known for writing *Breakfast At Tiffany's*. Capote had famously once said of his sexuality on a live American chat show, 'I was a beautiful little boy and everyone had me – men, women, dogs and fire hydrants!' – which ultimately led to Morrissey himself being photographed by Jurgen Teller, clutching the hydrant that still stands at the junction of Tench Street and Reardon Street in Wapping! The Capote picture, dating from 1949, was by the equally renowned Cecil Beaton – but only The Smiths' French fans would have picked up on the pun, intended or not, that *capote* is the old-fashioned French word for condom.

The record reached number 23 in the charts. Almost as exquisite was the flipside, 'Asleep', in which Morrissey was again accused of romanticising suicide. One is reminded of the death of Marilyn Monroe – who graced the cover of a Smiths bootleg album at around this time, *A Nice Bit Of Meat* – particularly the line 'Deep in the cell of my heart I will feel so glad to go', variations of which Monroe pronounced many times during her final months – though Morrissey was probably thinking of no one in particular when he wrote this. He told *Sounds* in August, 'There are many people who expect that I will be found dangling from some banisters, or swinging from the rafters of some darkened church.' Speaking of these 'sometimes quite agonising mood-swings', Kirsty MacColl told me in 1994, 'It's always been at the back of our minds that he might do something like that – that if he ever did, it would have to be something suitably Wildean or gothic. God forbid that he ever will!'

Morrissey's depressions and anxieties were rumoured to be at an all-time high during this autumn of 1985 when The Smiths embarked on a seven-date Scottish tour. Their next album, *The Queen Is Dead*, had been scheduled for a December release, but in-house problems resulted in this date being moved forward by six months. The group attempted to find another record company, but this only made matters much worse when Rough Trade served them with an interlocutory injunction – hardly the sort of thing to make them wish to stay with the company, though for the time being they were stuck with Rough Trade whether they liked it or not. By the end of the year, personal problems were exacerbated by a recurrence of Andy Rourke's heroin addiction. The bassist was now taking methadone substitute, and this had begun to affect his playing. In Dublin, after a poor performance, Morrissey told George Byrne of the *Sunday Correspondent*, 'I find heroin absolutely detestable, though a great many people who take it do so willingly. The more the authoritarian finger is wagged at these people, the more they are inclined to please themselves.' Those close to The Smiths – not least of all the fans – knew exactly who he was referring to. Then he went off at a tangent by actually attacking the Conservative government's anti-heroin campaign, adding, 'I found it very absurd that the British government could care about people on heroin, when they could scarcely care about people who are killing themselves because of unemployment.' And this coming from the man who, not so long before, had in one of his songs encouraged unemployed people not to bother looking for work!

Even so, desperate measures needed to be taken. Morrissey and Marr, who to all intents and purposes *were* The Smiths, ordered

Rourke to leave the group until he could convince them that he had kicked his habit. 'We told him to sling his hook,' Marr told *The Face*'s Nick Kent. He was replaced by Craig Gannon, a former guitarist with Aztec Camera and The Bluebells who was recommended by Marr's pal, Simon Wolstencroft.

Mere days after his dismissal, Andy Rourke was arrested for possession of drugs. Despite his comments to George Byrne, Morrissey was the first to rush to his aid, and soon afterwards a clean Rourke was taken back into the fold. For the time being, Craig Gannon was retained, and when The Smiths appeared on television in May 1986 to promote their new single, 'Bigmouth Strikes Again', as in the days of James Maker there were five of them.

There were also problems at around this time from 'stalker' fans, one in particular from northern England who spent a lot of time loitering around Morrissey's home – collecting such ridiculous 'memorabilia' as plants and leaves from his garden, pestering his mother, persistently ringing the doorbell and trying to take photographs through the windows. He is even thought to have secured the singer's telephone number. Morrissey was informed of his and several other fanatics' details, and dreaded bumping into them after concerts. However, because they did no actual damage to the property, he was unable to take action other than to inform the police. 'They're emotionally unbalanced,' he told *Les Inrockuptibles*' Mishka Assaya, 'I find it very hard dealing with them, wondering what to say or what not to say. These people think they know me. They say very personal things, and I can't respond to somebody I don't know. I just wish they would leave me alone.'

Even The Smiths' harshest critics would have to agree that *The Queen Is Dead* remains their finest album. Released in June 1986, it proved once and for all – if proof were needed – that Morrissey was the most articulate songwriter of his generation. And of course, because of the very nature of its title, it brought more media attacks than anything they had done since 'Suffer Little Children'. Johnny Marr told *NME*'s Dave Haslam in the spring of 1989, 'When we listened back to it, it made the hairs on the back of our necks stand up. It's what I'm most proud of with The Smiths and being involved with Morrissey, that juxtaposition of rock from a housing estate.'

The cover picture – French heartthrob Alain Delon, unrecognisable in a shot from the 1964 film *L'Insoumis* – caused no problems, but the gatefold's inside photograph of The Smiths posing outside the Salford Lads Club made up for this. The club's committee threatened Rough Trade with legal action unless the company made it patently clear that the group were in no way connected with the club itself, which the committee described as 'a Boy Scout Association type'. The fact that The Smiths had dealt with the subjects of unconventional sexual practices in their songs were the chief causes for concern, as were the contents of the album that the photograph was seen to be promoting: notably the title track, and 'Vicar In A Tutu' (with its guitar riffs reminiscent of Nancy Whiskey's 1957 hit, 'Freight Train') which tells the tale of a youth who, while filching the lead from a church roof, espies the priest prancing around in drag.

One might almost commend the Salford Lads Club committee for actually sitting down and listening to the record before voicing their disdain, which is not what happened elsewhere. Morrissey's ill-timed confession to the press that the group had been terrorised by ten-year-old girls while posing for the picture, and his comment, 'Everybody in the street had a club foot and a vicious dog', was brought to the attention of old enemy MP Geoffrey Dickens, who tried but failed to get the record taken off the shelves. It missed topping the charts by a hair's breadth. Support for The Smiths came from the unlikeliest source – Princess Diana, who had married into the very family Morrissey was lampooning, went public by declaring that they were one of her favourite groups. (Some years later, when the world had been made aware of her problems with 'the Establishment', a sketch on television's *Spitting Image* featured her puppet-caricature, introduced by Jimmy Savile, singing 'Heaven Knows I'm Miserable Now'.) Doubtless the princess was unaware of Morrissey's put-down, the previous year in *Sounds*: 'The writers and designers of *Spitting Image* should be unmercifully sued for making the Royal Family more attractive and intelligent than they actually are.'

Morrissey's supreme attack on the Royal Family, one that in retrospect overshadows The Sex Pistols' 'God Save The Queen', was 'The Queen Is Dead'. 'We don't believe in leprechauns,' Morrissey said at the time, 'so why should we believe in the Queen?'

In this instance, one did not have to be on his side to see his point. The song was witty, acerbic and above all intelligently structured. In the days of Oscar Wilde, Britain had been a mighty empire, thought of as invincible, but an empire built all the same on bloodshed, greed and racial prejudice – and times had changed. To many of its subjects, the present-day Royal Family were little more than figure-heads, albeit still much respected, and – in 1985 – pillars of the community that most people still looked up to. One shudders to even think of what 'The Queen Is Dead' would be like if Morrissey wrote it today, in the wake of the divorces and sex scandals.

Indeed, the Windsors were fortunate in that the song was just an attack on the Queen and Prince Charles. Morrissey launches his salvo with unfettered brilliance – reminding us of how life used to be in 'the days of yore' by using a snatch of 'Take Me Back To Dear Old Blighty' to prologue the piece before Johnny Marr's noisy chunk of feedback. The song was a World War I music-hall ditty, revived by Cicely Courtneidge (who sings it here); the version is taken from the soundtrack of *The L-Shaped Room*, one of Morrissey's favourite films, which had also starred Pat Phoenix. 'The Queen Is Dead' is a *chanson-grise* wherein the narrator, this time unquestionably Morrissey himself, bids 'Farewell to this land's cheerless marshes hemmed in like a boar between arches'. The latter is thought to be a reference, long before the 1992 *NME*-fuelled nationalism debacle, to the House of York's King Richard III (whose emblem was the White Boar) – one royal much revered by Northerners, who was based in the North and was wholly unafraid of doing things his way. Like Richard, who usurped the throne of his brother Edward IV and was succeeded by Henry Tudor, thereby changing the line of succession for ever, Morrissey stakes equal claim as the pale descendant 'of some old queen or other' – though the term queen is more suggestive here of its homosexual connotation than of anything monarchic. Morrissey then goes on to criticise Prince Charles for being so boring, asking whether he never feels the urge to do something spontaneous or outrageous, such as appearing on the *Daily Mail*'s front page dressed in his mother's bridal veil! He envisages himself emulating Michael Fagin, the man who had a few years previously broken into Buckingham Palace and chatted amicably to the Queen, sitting on the edge of her bed while awaiting arrest – save that in true *Carry On* tradition, in the song the narrator gains access to the royal bedchamber by means of a sponge and a rusty spanner. And finally, having touched on castration, poverty and the Church, he heads off to inform his gang, 'The Queen is dead, boys!' before rounding off the proceedings with the Garboesque quip, 'Life is very long, when you're lonely!' Superb!

Taken as a whole, the album represented a quite unprecedented diversity of emotions and mood swings. 'Frankly Mr Shankly' evokes the rich Northern humour of George Formby and Jake Thackray. It is allegedly based on the poetry-writing undertaker Mr Shadrack in *Billy Liar*, though one of the teachers at Morrissey's school – 'a flatulent pain in the arse' – had also apparently been called Shankly. Again, it deals with the 'I-want-what-I-can't-have' young man who returns home to his mother, sad and disillusioned after the break-up of a love affair that ended almost as soon as it began. Yet from his mother there is little sympathy – she reminds him that despite, or maybe because of, his wit, intelligence, fame and physical beauty he is still alone, sleeping in an empty bed while the lover who spurned him now languishes in someone else's arms. The conclusion, however, is that while it is easy to laugh and hate, it takes guts to be gentle and kind.

'Never Had No One Ever', a bad-English quip that often cropped up in the 1960s *Bootsie And Snudge* television series, explains in one elongated six-line stanza that he has not loved at all – and makes cryptic reference to a time (twenty years, seven months and 27 days) at which a particularly bad dream ended, though we are given no clues to its significance. 'Bigmouth Strikes Again', on the other hand, was an exercise in satire: Morrissey's way of getting one over on his critics by reminding them that he was not incapable of slapping himself down every now and again. More fun comes with 'Some Girls

Are Bigger Than Others', in which Morrissey borrows from *Antony and Cleopatra* – not the Shakespearean version but from *Carry On Cleo*, with Antony (Sidney James) quoting the song's title to Amanda Barrie as he opens a crate of ale. And the piece ends with the singer cheekily crooning a snatch of Johnny Tillotson's 1962 hit, 'Send Me The Pillow You Dream On'.

The song on *The Queen Is Dead*, so far as most of the fans and this author are concerned, is the penultimate track, the sublime 'There Is A Light That Never Goes Out'. The sentiment of actually dying for love was nothing new, of course. In 1949, after the death in an air crash of French boxing champion Marcel Cerdan, Edith Piaf composed and sang 'Hymne A L'Amour', proclaiming, 'If you die, I don't mind so long as I may die too.' The recording of this has sold over twenty million copies world-wide, and there is even a link of sorts with The Smiths: Jeff Buckley, who also sang it in French, declared that it was the only song better than 'I Know It's Over'. In Morrissey's case here, borrowing Judy Garland's utterance from the end of her 1961 Carnegie Hall comeback perfor-mance – 'I never, never want to go home!' – he is so in love for once that he wants to preserve the emotion by perishing with his grand amour after a last night on the town. How this happens is immaterial, and he very nearly asks his love to make it happen: 'To die by your side, such a heavenly way to die!' What makes the song even more poignant is that Morrissey claimed in one interview (for Dutch magazine *Oor*) that it was autobiographical. He told Martin Aston:

> There are three lines in that song I can't bear to listen to because I find them too personal: 'In the darkened underpass/ I thought, Oh God, my chance has come at last/ But a strange fear gripped me and I just couldn't ask.' I can't listen to those lines . . . I have to sit down. It's like someone hitting me with a hammer.

Aston went on to ask Morrissey about this realist's fascination with the darker aspects of life and suicide, and his response was in retrospect somewhat alarming, bearing in mind that in the not too distant future some Smiths fans would pick up on it and follow his credo to the letter.

Declaring that the ending of one's own life was not taking the coward's way out, he went on:

> It's the strongest decision an individual can possibly make, as it's so obviously very frightening. I dislike the term 'commit suicide' – it sounds like robbery, or something rude or bad. I admire people who take their own lives. I don't find fighting wars quite so very brave, or being in the army. To me, that's incredibly stupid.

One only has to see film footage of The Smiths' later concerts (and those of the solo Morrissey, some twenty years on) to witness how much 'There Is A Light That Never Goes Out' means to the fans: hundreds of young men, mostly, tears streaming down their cheeks as they join in with the refrain. One of these, the famous porn star who introduced himself to me in Sheffield, told me quite seriously, 'It's just like ancient Rome, when the emperor walks through the streets, points to someone and says, "Citizen, fall on thy sword!" Most of those apostles out there were so crazy with admiration for Morrissey, he could ask them to do anything.'

With the new album riding high in the charts, in July 1986 The Smiths embarked on their second major tour of the United States and Canada: 24 dates in concert halls, ballrooms and open-air theatres. The tour was a sell-out despite a severe lack of publicity: virtually nothing about the group appeared in the press; radio stations pronounced their records 'too depressing' for airplay save late at night, when there were fewer listeners. Some of the local independent radio stations showed interest, but only after hearing what had happened at a previous concert, and even then they only wanted to interview 'the tall guy with the flowers', as one put it.

On 29 July, Morrissey was interviewed by CHRW Radio, in Ontario – but only after the presenter had been 'briefed' as to who he was. For ten minutes, he struggled, responding only to the bland questions on the presenter's screen. After playing a track from *The Queen Is Dead* – the first time this presenter had heard Morrissey sing – he quipped, 'Your voice seems like a bit of a throwback to the era of crooners', bringing the weary, unappreciated response, 'Yes, I listen to lots of people who fall into that bucket. I even like Doris Day, so what hope is there for me?'

The tour ended prematurely when the last four shows were cancelled: the problem was Johnny Marr, who had suddenly begun hitting the bottle – at the time, he cited the pressure of work as the reason for his lapse. Little did The Smiths know that after their 10 September concert in Tampa, Florida, they would never visit America again as an ensemble.

The Chernobyl disaster of 26 April 1986, when the near-meltdown of a nuclear reactor fogged the atmosphere with radioactive material, brought widespread storms of protest from around the world. In the United States, Barbra Streisand attacked the Reagan administration, which she said was at least partly responsible for 'the proliferation of nuclear plants and warheads' across the planet – and gave a concert that raised $2 million to elect as many Democrats as possible to oust the Republican government. In England, on a much lesser scale of attack, and partly in response to Radio One disc jockey Steve Wright's ill-timed playing of Wham!'s 'I'm Your Man' straight after the newsflash announcing the Chernobyl disaster (many listeners inferred that Wright may have been dismissing the event as 'just another overseas mishap') Morrissey wrote 'Panic'.

The song was given more publicity clout by the fact that the promotional video (itself a rare outing for The Smiths) was directed by the hugely controversial Derek Jarman, of *Sebastiane* fame. Jarman did The Smiths proud, incorporating not just 'Panic' but 'The Queen is Dead' (the video's title) and 'There Is A Light That Never Goes Out' into a fifteen-minute short, positively glowing with the violent imagery and blatant homoeroticism for which the director was famed – two pretty youths kissing, another blowing smoke into a skull, and the image that would cause much less trouble for the director then than it would for Morrissey six years on: a semi-naked woman flying the Union Jack.

Inasmuch as Streisand pulled no punches in denouncing Reagan, so Morrissey went for Steve Wright's jugular, ending the song with the line 'Hang the DJ,' chanted by children in Jarman's film. The gist of the song was twofold: the singer predicting how he imagined much of the populace would react, should there be the equivalent of a Chernobyl disaster in Britain – and an attack on the uninspiring music they were churning out day after day on Radio One. The attack would reach its climax with Morrissey striding on to the stage at Carlisle's Sands Centre on 13 October, wearing a Steve Wright T-shirt and swinging a noose!

Meanwhile, in August 1986, *Melody Maker*'s Frank Owen caught up with The Smiths in Cleveland, Ohio, while they were in the middle of their American tour. Owen's interview with Morrissey was published at the end of September, by which time it had been spiced up with some very personal comments.

Referring to the chasm that he said now existed between indie pop and 'black' pop – proof of which supposedly came from the number of complaints the music press received from the former each time a black face appeared on a front page – Owen accused Morrissey (not The Smiths) of widening this gap by releasing 'Panic', even though Morrissey said that the song was not about racism. Morrissey's original, full response to Frank Owen's question, 'Is The Smiths' music racist?' should therefore be studied in its entirety, and not bit by bit and way out of context, as picked up on by the tabloids:

Reggae, for example, is to me the most racist music in the entire world. It's an absolute total glorification of black supremacy. There is a line when defence of one's own race becomes an attack on another race and, because of black history and oppression, we realise quite clearly that there has to be a very strong defence. But, ultimately, I don't have very cast iron opinions on black music other than black modern music, which I detest. I detest Stevie Wonder. I think Diana Ross is awful. I hate all those records in the Top 40 – Janet Jackson, Whitney Houston. I think they're vile in the extreme. In essence this music doesn't say anything whatsoever. I don't think there's any time any more to be subtle about anything. You have to get straight to the point. Obviously, to get on *Top Of The Pops* these days one has to be, by law, black. I think something political has occurred among Michael Hurll [the show's producer] and his friends, and there has been a hefty pushing of all this discofied nonsense into the Top 40. I think, as a result, that very aware younger groups that speak for now are being gagged . . . If you compare the exposure that records by the likes of Janet Jackson and streams of other anonymous Jacksons get to the daily level of airplay that The Smiths receive – The Smiths have had at least ten consecutive chart hits and we still can't get on Radio One's A-list. Is that not a conspiracy? The last LP ended up at number 2, and we are still told by radio that nobody wanted to listen to The Smiths in the daytime. Is that not a conspiracy? I do get the scent of a conspiracy.

Morrissey *was* criticising black music, but only that of the eighties, which he felt in no way compared with the Motown boom of the sixties, quite simply because it was not as good. What Frank Owen and Morrissey's other detractors failed to mention was that Morrissey had also criticised Madonna ('Closer to organised prostitution than anything I've seen!'), George Michael ('I'm not impressed!'), Bucks Fizz ('One would hear more vocal passion from an ape under anaesthetic!'), Frankie Goes To Hollywood ('An entire career orchestrated by unseen faces!') – and many, many others had much less eloquently criticised him – but to blinkered detractors, the fact that he disliked certain artistes and types of music only pointed to the fact that it was on account of the colour of their skin.

In June 2003, when asked to select fifteen of his all-time favourite songs for the compilation album, *Morrissey: Under The Influence*, one of his choices was 'Swan Lake', by the bluebeat band The Cats. He told *Word*'s Andrew Harrison, 'I once said "Reggae is vile," did I? Well, several tongue-in-cheek things were said in those days which, when placed in cold print, lost their humorous quality. This track, along with "Double Barrel" and "Young, Gifted And Black" were staple teenage necessities to me.'

Morrissey, who like everyone else in The Smiths' camp was glowing with the tidings that *Spin* magazine had voted *The Queen Is Dead* Best Album of All Time, had returned home from the US tour to encounter more tabloid trouble with the publication of the *Melody Maker* interview, which Frank Owen had embellished with a few very personal comments of his own. Morrissey was alternately referred to as 'the

Queen' and 'the missing link between Norman Wisdom and Joe Dallesandro'. 'Morrissey doesn't need to have sex in private because he does it all on stage,' Owen wrote, adding that his British fans were 'grubby' and 'self-righteous'. He then opined, 'Morrissey's genital continence might be a strategy to rise above the debased form of rock 'n' roll sexuality we know today with its obsessive phallic focus . . . It wouldn't surprise me to find, in a couple of years time, Morrissey eulogising the joys of fist-fucking and water sports.'

Of Morrissey's reference in his interview to the 'dangerous' Manchester gay scene and his confessed love of punk, Owen levelled, 'You big jessy, you big girl's blouse, Morrissey. But he's right. It was dangerous and, with the increased media visibility of punk, the violence got worse. You see, punks were not only faggots, they were uppity faggots as well.'

What caused Morrissey the most humiliation was Owen's reference to cottaging – a subject which, to be fair to the journalist, Morrissey had brought up in the first place. 'I was born in Central Library – in the crime section,' he had observed. Then, after recalling all the happy hours spent here, the lunchtimes when he had hung around with 'the older bohemian set in the basement café', he had added, 'The toilets were guarded by uniformed gorillas. It was like guerrilla warfare going on in there – an awful, frightening place.' 'And what about Whitworth Street toilets?' Owen had asked, referring to the infamous cottage, to which Morrissey had responded, 'Aah, yes, Whitworth Street toilets. I never knew Bert Tilsley. But let's steer away from public toilets.'

Morrissey had been referring to the *Coronation Street* actor, Peter Dudley, who had been arrested at the aforementioned toilets and charged with importuning – and soon afterwards died of a stroke. These points, however, along with Morrissey's opinionated but valid comments about the glut of black music in the charts at the time, were picked up by the tabloids, who as per usual quoted chunks of the interview grossly out of context, thereby giving Morrissey's words an entirely different slant. Johnny Marr, slight and not known for being pugnacious, allegedly vowed that if ever he met up with Frank Owen, he would give him a 'good thumping'!

Gay Times, on the other hand, were interested only in satirising Morrissey in their November 1986 issue. The feature 'Who Do You Do?', in the wake of the popular television series, listed the personalities most likely to go down a storm at that year's seasonal fancy dress parties: Morrissey, Quentin Crisp, Tina Turner, Mother Theresa, Rock Hudson, Cilla Black and Japanese hara-kiri hero novelist Yukio Mishima! That Morrissey was included in such a line-up was a tribute in itself, and one gets the impression that he would have found the whole thing amusing. Emulators were advised to reel into the party emitting loud groaning noises, while clutching their forehead with one hand, then slump over the ice-box and sing 'Heaven Knows I'm Miserable Now'. Other points to remember were CLOTHES AND APPEARANCE: a baggy, unironed shirt covered in busy little paisley patterns, on no account tucked into one's appliquéd jeans. Also, one should cut random chunks out of one's hair with an electric knife. Then there were the ACCESSORIES: a biography of Oscar Wilde or James Dean, a 'frightfully conspicuous' NHS hearing-aid and a chastity belt. For a party piece, one was advised, 'Sit on the stairs crying. Refuse to join the end of the conga line or do the hokey-cokey. If there's any threat whatsoever that you might end up enjoying yourself, leave immediately – preferably unobserved.' In closing, participants were advised not to do this impersonation at a wedding reception!

It appears to have been Morrissey's decision, around this time, to sever The Smiths' association with Rough Trade. The group signed a lucrative contract with EMI, which brought with it much criticism – they were accused of using a small company to turn themselves into the biggest group of the decade, only to dump them. In fact, Rough Trade was only supposed to have been a stop-gap in the first place, and in any case, no one had *made* The Smiths: they had been created and nurtured by Morrissey and Marr. For now, however, contractual obligations prevented them from actually recording with EMI, and in October 1986 Rough Trade released 'Ask', coupled with 'Cemetry Gates' and housed in a cover featuring *George And Mildred* star Yootha Joyce, snapped in 1965 soon after she had appeared in *Fanatic* with Morrissey favourite

Tallulah Bankhead. Some thought that by using Joyce, who virtually no one knew had been alcoholic until after her death from cirrhosis of the liver, Morrissey was offering a veiled warning to Johnny Marr to curb his own drinking. The song, which reached number 14 in the charts, brings to mind Morrissey's pen-pal days: the narrator, too shy to venture out, spends 'warm summer days indoors, writing frightening verse to a buck-toothed girl in Luxembourg', but though he may be shy, if she wants to 'do' anything, he tells her, all she has to do is ask. There is, however, the typical Morrissey coda – for if love fails to bring the two of them together, the bomb will!

Morrissey formed another 'postal' friendship with Kirsty MacColl, the talented singer-songwriter daughter of Ewan MacColl, who had provided the backing vocals on 'Ask' and 'Golden Lights' (the Twinkle song appeared on the 'Ask' 12-inch). She told me of their first meeting:

> I was working in New York at the time. My manager called and said he's found the latest letter from Morrissey on the mat. All it said in that funny writing of his was, 'SING WITH ME!' I didn't know what to make of it. When I came home I found out which studio he was working at, and went down there and met Johnny Marr and his wife. Johnny said, 'Moz is in there. Go and sing with him!' I was terrified, but I did it. Morrissey greeted me as if he'd known me for years. I suggested that maybe he ought to hand the tapes over to my then husband [Steve Lillywhite] for mixing, which he did, though I'm not so sure the others liked that! He's one of the nicest, kindest men I've ever met.

The Smiths' autumn 1986 tour was infiltrated by a few royalists who had taken exception to *The Queen Is Dead*, and numerous incidents added to the general sense of ill-feeling within the group. Hecklers made their way to the front of the stage to hurl abuse and spit: one of these, pretending to be a fan, reached up to shake Morrissey's hand at Newport on 19 October, but instead pulled him off the stage; the singer hit his head on the floor and was taken to hospital with suspected

concussion. A week later, at the Preston Guildhall, he was hit in the face
by a coin. Taking no chances, he abandoned the concert and a fracas
erupted in the auditorium, resulting in the police making fourteen
arrests. There was also a massive row with Craig Gannon, who left The
Smiths under a dark cloud at the end of the tour.

On 14 November, The Smiths should have topped the bill in the
Artists Against Apartheid gala at London's Royal Albert Hall. They were
forced to pull out when Johnny Marr wrote off his car in an accident in
the rain near his Bowden home. Marr suffered whiplash injuries, and
hurt his hands whilst stumbling away from the scene of the crash in a
dazed state, so playing the guitar was wholly out of the question. Forced
to wear a neckbrace, he was back on form for The Smiths' concert on
12 December at the Brixton Academy – where Morrissey delivered a
severe, spine-tingling 'There Is A Light That Never Goes Out' and glared
at his partner throughout. What the fans did not know was that they
were watching their idols' very last UK performance. The combination of
the pressure that had come to bear on Marr's too-slender shoulders
and the burden of Morrissey's perfectionism – not to mention his
mercurial temperament – had pushed their partnership beyond the point
of no return.

More relaxed with foreign journalists who published his comments
verbatim and, unlike many of their British counterparts, never twisted
them to suit their own prejudiced agenda, Morrissey had already given
the indication of changes afoot in an exclusive interview to *Les
Inrockuptibles*' Mishka Assaya in July 1986:

> I'm afraid the day is coming when I'll have to bid farewell to the past,
> when I'm going to want to be somebody else. It hasn't come yet, but
> it will. It must. It seems inevitable that we'll split up one day because
> there's only so much in each of us to give. When it becomes hard for
> me to concentrate on writing songs, when I no longer feel I'm doing
> the right thing, then I'll stop.

Astonishingly, the contents of the French interview were not picked
up on by the British music press. Neither did his comments reach The

Smiths' entourage, or their inner circle, where it was business as usual. In January 1987, Rough Trade released a new single, the quaintly titled 'Shoplifters Of The World Unite', which reached number 12 in the charts. The cover featured a very young Elvis, snapped on the set of *The Ed Sullivan Show* exactly thirty years earlier. Needless to say, the song was denounced by the tabloids: not content with championing criminals, animal rights and underage sex, they complained, Morrissey was now encouraging his fans to steal!

Lyrically, the flipside was much more interesting. 'Half A Person' tells of a fan's six-year attempt to meet his idol, to be afforded only a few seconds of his valuable time. It calls to mind a group of Morrissey fans I encountered in 1994: having spent most of their money on the air fare from America, there had been little left for food, so they had spent a whole day trekking the streets of London in the pouring rain in search of ad-hoc work so that they would be able to follow the rest of the tour! In this particular song, which may be Morrissey recalling his earlier excursion to see Patti Smith, a young man books himself into the YWCA (note that 'W'!) and timidly asks, 'Do you have a vacancy for a back-scrubber?' – an essentially Northern term used in backstreet seduction.

These two songs were included in a mid-price compilation album, *The World Won't Listen*, released in March 1987 – something of a misnomer, for where The Smiths were concerned, one had no option *but* to listen. The cover photographs, obtained at considerable expense, were from the Jürgen Vollmer Collection – the Hamburg-based artist who, having given The Beatles their famous haircuts, had gone on to photograph just about every European superstar, then turned towards street youth, as here with this group of fans at a 1962 Johnny Hallyday concert. A bonus for Smiths admirers was the previously unreleased 'You Just Haven't Earned It Yet, Baby', reminiscent of Marianne Faithfull's 1967 hit, 'Is This What I Get For Loving You?' The album reached number 2 in the charts, and coincided with the group's American record company, Sire, issuing their own compilation, *Louder Than Bombs*, with a cover-shot of the playwright Shelagh Delaney, of *A Taste Of Honey* fame. This contained 24 songs, but when fans complained that the imported album was too expensive, Rough Trade released a cheaper edition. This was a mistake:

coming out so soon after *The World Won't Listen*, it barely scraped into the Top 40.

On 7 February 1987, with Morrissey observing that this was what would have been the eve of James Dean's birthday, The Smiths participated in the San Remo Festival, sharing top billing with The Pet Shop Boys and Spandau Ballet; Martin and Gary Kemp of the latter would delight Morrissey with their portrayals of the Krays on the big screen. There was a new, short-lived manager: Ken Friedman, a 29-year-old American with big ideas who all too soon fell foul of Morrissey by daring to question his penchant for audience intimacy and suggesting that the group play in the stadiums where there was more money to be made. Johnny Marr told *Sounds*, 'Stadiums are fine for the likes of Dire Straits – boring people worshipped by even more boring people.' With Friedman hoping to turn The Smiths into another Queen, it was evident that his days would be numbered.

Rumours were now circulating of discord within Smithdom, and Rough Trade were intent on squeezing as much mileage out of them as they could – and out of the fans' already overstretched budgets. In April 1987 they released the single, 'Sheila Take A Bow', which reached number 10 in the charts. Exactly who the Sheila of the title is, is a matter for conjecture. Many think it was written in honour of Shelagh Delaney, though there is no direct reference to her. There was also a French singer called Sheila (pronounced 'Shay-lah'), a contemporary of Françoise Hardy, whose big hit had been 'L'Ecole Est Finie' (School's Out), which would tie in with the line, 'Throw your homework into the fire.' It is a very kitsch song. One might imagine any one of the *Carry On* stars saying, 'Sheila, take a bow – boot the grime of this world in the crotch, dear!' The song also provides the only example of gender-bending in a Morrissey song – 'You're a girl and I'm a boy . . . I'm a girl and you're a boy' – and featured Candy Darling (né James Slattery) on the cover. The transsexual Darling was one of Andy Warhol's in-house stars, though it is doubtful many Smiths fans had heard of her until now. She had appeared in *Flesh*, but the picture is from the 1971 film *Women In Revolt*. Unlike most of the Warhol discoveries, Darling died of natural causes (cancer), and she held a very special place in The Morrissey Camp

Hall of Fame. 'To be able to inflict Candy Darling on the record-buying public was a perfect example of my very dangerous sense of humour,' he told *NME*. It is also interesting to note that, with the release of the record, there was a sudden rush by Smiths fans to acquire the video of *Women In Revolt*, just as they had acquired *Flesh* and all the other films Morrissey liked, whether they liked or understood them or not. This was what made the complete apostle.

The song was coupled with 'Is It Really So Strange?', the story of a boy who relocates from the North to the South, experiences threats, prejudice and confusion, but only gets more of the same when he heads back to his roots. Better perhaps is 'Sweet And Tender Hooligan', Morrissey's hard-hitting but honest appraisal of a violent youth who swears that he will never get into trouble again – at least, not until the next time. He tries to convince us that the bludgeoning of an old man with an electric fire was an accident; that the woman he strangled was old and would have died anyhow. The narrator begs the jury to look into the boy's 'mother-me' eyes before reaching its verdict – after all, he only turned to crime because he was in debt!

The Smiths' final studio album, *Strangeways Here We Come*, was recorded at the Wool Hall, Bath, during the spring of 1987 – reputedly in a friendly atmosphere, though dissension appears to have set in as soon as the ten tracks had been canned. *The Face*'s Nick Kent dropped in on the group, allegedly to 'snoop' and see for himself if the in-studio picture was as rosy as it was being painted. The Smiths were sensibly playing their cards close to their chests, though Kent still headed his lengthy feature THE BAND WITH THE THORN IN ITS SIDE, summarised the personal problems of the last two years, referred to 'Mad Mozzer' as being 'Manchester's very own Whacko Jacko' (the mis-spelt 'whacko' amusing Morrissey, for this had been the title of Jimmy Edwards' hugely successful sixties television series) and concluded,

> Smithdom in many respects is his version of Ambrosia, the fantasy land
> Billy Liar inhabited. It has given him a place to live out his adolescence;
> given him the fame he so craved yet which hasn't made him contented.

Faced by the pressure of success, he has often buckled and vacillated endlessly in matters of life as it is lived.

It was at this point that Johnny Marr, protesting that Morrissey was still his closest friend, informed him all the same that he wanted to end their partnership. What Andy Rourke and Mike Joyce had to say about this was immaterial, and it was Morrissey who made a last-bid attempt to keep the four of them together. They had fulfilled their contractual obligations with Rough Trade, and were now free to record for EMI in a reputed £1 million deal – and they were about to begin filming a retrospective of their career for *The South Bank Show*.

The split was postponed for the time being. In August, Rough Trade put out 'Girlfriend In A Coma', which peaked at number 13 in the charts. As mentioned earlier, the song had been inspired by the case of Karen Quinlan, a young American who had survived on a life-support machine in a comatose state for a year, during which the moral dilemma of whether or not to remove her from the machine provoked national debate in the USA. It is an immensely catchy but moving piece, which some journalists denounced as 'sick' for romanticising a deathbed scene. Morrissey caught the nuances of the scene beautifully: the familiar chit-chat of how the girl had been a handful at times ('There were times when I could have "murdered" her',) but that her parents would put all of that behind them just to see her come to – which, of course, is not going to happen. The song was very much in keeping with the songs by Juliette Gréco and Barbara (such as 'Vieillir' and 'Si D'Amour A Mort') dealing with harrowing subjects such as lung cancer and AIDS, that were storming the European charts at the time in countries where it was perfectly normal to sing about all aspects of life, even the worst kind, without being thought of as abnormal.

On the B-side was an old Cilla Black song, 'Work Is A Four-Letter Word', from the 1967 film of the same name that Black had made with David Warner; it was recorded at Streatham, along with Morrissey's 'I Keep Mine Hidden', which appeared on the 12-inch single. There was also a cover version of Elvis Presley's 'A Fool Such As I' – assigned to the Rough Trade vault because an engineer accidentally erased the introduction, though it has been restored, sounds good, and may resurface one day.

A few days after this session, Johnny Marr flew to Los Angeles, ostensibly for a break, where he bumped into Rolling Stones guitarist Keith Richards. The latter had obviously forgiven Marr's earlier press attack on him and was ready to offer some sound advice once the younger man had opened his heart about his woes with Morrissey: 'The music business isn't worth knocking yourself out for. It's not worth killing yourself or stepping on other people.' This was a rather strange statement coming from a man who would have been nothing without the music business, but Marr apparently heeded him, and over the coming weeks the British music press was awash with conflicting reports of The Smiths' demise. The then all-powerful *NME* ran the headline, SMITHS TO SPLIT, on 30 July 1987, though much of the editorial appeared to be supposition:

> Morrissey, when approached through his press office for a comment, said, 'Whoever says The Smiths have split shall be severely spanked by me with a wet plimsoll.' While *NME* newshounds await the arrival of young Steven armed with soggy footwear, sources in both London and Manchester continue to feed us with snippets . . . Marr has reportedly told friends in Manchester that he and Morrissey are no longer pals, and he is sick of the singer acting the self-centred star . . . Morrissey is not pleased with the company Marr is keeping, acting the guitar hero and playing on albums by Keith Richards, Bobby Womack and Bryan Ferry. The final straw was allegedly Marr interrupting Smiths recording sessions to fly to the States to record with Talking Heads, and using Rough Trade money to pay for the trip. Insiders say Morrissey blew his top and declared it was the end of The Smiths, and he never wanted to work with Marr again.

Blitz more or less reported the same story, published a photograph of Morrissey and Marr that featured a dotted line and a pair of scissors down the middle so that Marr could be removed – suggesting, as had the statement, that he was now seen more as a dispensable guitarist than as co-founder of The Smiths. Whether Marr had ever used Rough Trade money is not known.

Morrissey and Marr each took it in turns to virulently deny they had leaked the story to the press, and it would take years for everyone to stop blaming everyone else. In 1992, one of *NME*'s contributors, Iestin George, told me, 'We did have one or two leads which came from neither Morrissey nor Marr, but by and large we were just spot on with our guesswork.' One of George's colleagues, who asked not to be named, claimed that it went much deeper than this:

> There have been four Jimmys in Morrissey's life – five if you count James Dean. Work the others out for yourself. There was a freelancer called Jimmy. In The Smiths' early days he was hanging around all of the time. He had this enormous crush on Morrissey . . . Then, as happens with everyone who gets close to Morrissey, Jimmy found himself dumped. Morrissey sent him a postcard with some silly quote in that daft handwriting of his. One of Jimmy's pals decided to get even on his behalf by leaking the news to us about The Smiths' split.

In April 1989, Johnny Marr told *NME*'s Dave Haslam:

> It was a hideous private explosion, but it was also a hideous public explosion . . . like a fantasy, turned into a soap-opera by the news-papers. Nothing that was said was true. People around us, both on my side and on Morrissey's, handled the whole thing so badly that it became their whole trip . . . the whole story. It had nothing to do with how I feel about Morrissey and how he feels about me, and that's true up till today. And that's really silly. I despise the way we became public property.

Marr should of course have realised that The Smiths *were* public property: made by the public, nurtured and made wealthy and famous by the public. 'Somebody should have grabbed hold of Morrissey and Marr and banged their silly heads together,' a *NME* spokesman told me.

'Then they should have banged Johnny Marr's head against the nearest brick wall for being so ungrateful!' Neither did Marr appear to have any sympathy for The Smiths' fans when he told Haslam:

> People seemed to think that the most important thing in the world was for their favourite group to stay together. They didn't know anything about the way things were. They'd have preferred me to have died, rather than split the group up. That was their sense of what mattered. But that wasn't what mattered to me.

The irreverence would intensify over time, with Marr achieving relatively moderate success in most of his subsequent musical projects, and with Morrissey going on to become an even more massive British institution on his own. 'He now refers to his former soul mate as "Dorissey",' Danny Kelly reported in the *NME* of 20 April 1991, 'and he has re-christened the limpid lad's [then] 45 ("Our Frank") as "Alf Wank".'

In the same issue of *NME*, Marr stressed almost defensively that The Smiths' more controversial songs had nothing to do with his or the other group members' beliefs: 'We were making music that said very different things about sex, politics and social stuff. The lyrics were unique to Morrissey, to his life, but the audience really picked up on them. It was brilliant. We were creating rock music with art in it.'

Effectively, Marr was shooting himself in the foot: what he was really saying was that Morrissey alone had been the artistic inspiration behind The Smiths. When Kelly confronted him with his drink problem ('seeing off a bottle-and-a-half of Remy Martin a day') and Andy Rourke's drugs dilemma – and asked what effect this had had on the group's collapse – Marr was similarly defensive:

> It was more complicated than that . . . I just stopped liking the other members of the group, and I stopped liking myself . . . We all wanted to be a success, make some money and have a good life. But that became all we lived for and that's the path to becoming completely self-obsessed, shallow and lonely. I thought we were all up our own

arse! We had completely inflated senses of our own importance. Ultimately, I was giving every single moment of my life to somebody else. I started to feel very unnatural and abnormal.

When asked if he was specifically referring to Morrissey, Marr's response was, 'Of course.' However, Kelly seems to have touched a sore point later in the interview when he prompted, 'You're very offhand about this: the last time I interviewed you, you said that you "loved" Morrissey.' Marr's response was a snappy, 'Did I? I must have been talking about my bottle of Remy Martin.'

In 1994, when the former partners were reputedly back on speaking terms, Stuart Maconie asked Morrissey on behalf of Q, 'Do you love Johnny Marr?' The response was, 'Yes . . . that's not a hard one. I loved and love Johnny Marr,' though he added, referring skittishly to the other members of The Smiths, 'but I feel tremendous indifference to Bruce and Rick.'

Danny Kelly meanwhile drew his own conclusions, particularly when taking into account Morrissey's attack on Marr's work with Electronic – and Marr's partner, Barney Sumner, of whom Morrissey had quipped, 'No talent whatsoever!' 'There is the unmistakable smack of thwarted love about these pronouncements,' Kelly opined, 'a sort of "If-I-Can't-Have-Him-Then-Nobody-Can" pathos, like the "best friend" mind games kids weave in playgrounds.' Marr's reply, pointing to the fact that he was clearly envious of Morrissey having made more of his Smiths afterlife than himself, was a sharp, 'I know it's an old phrase, now, but in Morrissey's case he should really get a life.'

Ten years later, on the eve of Morrissey's return to glory, Johnny Marr was interrogated in Manchester's Night And Day café by Andrew Harrison of Word. Discussing the numerous accounts that had circulated about The Smiths' split, he concluded:

There is, however, another version of the story which I've heard enough times over the years to make me think it is more than rumour. That the breakdown was personal . . . That essentially, Morrissey was in love with Johnny Marr. That he told Marr, in those typical hand-written notes left at his house, that Marr must choose between

Morrissey and his wife Angie . . . When I put this to Johnny Marr, he doesn't sigh or give any sign of surprise.

Denying that Morrissey was in love with him and that he had ever offered such an ultimatum, Marr's response was calm, but candid:

All the way through that time with Morrissey, I felt like the luckiest guy in the world . . . playing great guitar in a great band with people I love, a partner I love and the girl I love – and it's all working. Morrissey and I had a super-intense, close relationship, as close as it can get without being physical. He sent me correspondence all the time . . . but for him to have crossed a line would have been a serious misjudgement. For it to be suspected that I would have left my own band for a reason like that would be a complete insult to me and the work I put in.

*

In Britain, several distraught Smiths male fans, now bereft of their group, attempted suicide – though these had little effect on Morrissey, who believed that these people could only have been unbalanced before The Smiths came along. A group of enthusiasts in Arizona hired a coffin, filled it full of Smiths records and memorabilia, and held a wake. In Denver, Colorado, a fanatic entered a local radio station and held a disc jockey at gunpoint while forcing him to play the group's records for several hours. Handcuffed and led away by police officers, he sobbed to reporters, 'It was worth it for every minute I'm gonna spend in jail!' Unfortunately, the young man was sectioned and sent to an institution.

Meanwhile, on 28 September 1987, Rough Trade released the 'posthumous' *Strangeways Here We Come*. For some reason, Morrissey had wanted a sleeve photograph of Harvey Keitel from the 1968 film, *Who's That Knocking At My Door?* Although the studio owned the rights to the still, Keitel's permission was sought, and his alleged response – 'Who the fuck are The Smiths?' – at a time when he was location shooting in Scotland and their picture was in all the news-papers, did not go down too well with Morrissey, who immediately approached Richard Davalos, the blond actor who had played James

Dean's brother in *East Of Eden*. Davalos was happy to oblige, and supplied a picture of himself and Jimmy, taken on location while making the film, though by the time Morrissey and Jo Slee had finished with it – curiously 'de-homoeroticising' it by removing Jimmy, and using just part of Davalos' face – it looked little better than a blurred mugshot. When asked why he had chosen the title for the album, Morrissey replied tongue-in-cheek, obviously knowing something the press did not yet know, 'Because the way things are going, I wouldn't be surprised if I wasn't in prison twelve months from now. I don't have any particular crimes in mind, but it's so easy to be a criminal these days, I wouldn't have to look far!'

The album was superb, the perfect curtain-call for the greatest British pop group of their generation. The opening song, 'A Rush And A Push And The Land Is Ours' – the surrealist story of 'Troubled Joe', whose young life had ended on the gallows – refers to Morrissey's Irish ancestry and is based on the writings of Lady Jane Francesca Wilde, Oscar's hostess-poet-Nationalist mother who from 1845 wrote under the pseudonym 'Speranza'.

In 'I Started Something I Couldn't Finish', Morrissey becomes Wilde himself. In 1895, when his lover Lord Alfred 'Bosie' Douglas's father had accused Wilde of being a 'sodomite', Wilde had unwisely sued for libel, and had himself been prosecuted and imprisoned for homosexuality. 'I grabbed you by the gilded beams,' Morrissey pronounces, though Bosie is known to have been a very willing participant. And one cannot possibly imagine Wilde saying of his jail sentence, 'Eighteen months hard labour seems . . . fair enough.' The song became The Smiths' pen-ultimate single in October 1987, with a cover-shot of actress Avril Angers from *The Family Way* (1966), and might almost be regarded as the first Morrissey solo single: only he appeared in the rare promotional video, bespectacled and cycling around a chilly Manchester with a group of lookalikes. This song, and the plaintive 'Last Night I Dreamt That Somebody Loved Me', had introductions consisting of crowd noise from the 1984 miners' strike. Both records reached the Top 30, but the latter is by far the more poignant of the two. Morrissey's voice has never sounded more haunting and tortured, particularly when the piece reaches its crescendo. It is also perhaps fitting that the last Smiths release during their lifetime should feature a cover shot of Billy Fury, the object of Morrissey's apparent desire in 'Paint A Vulgar Picture', also on the album. What is surprising is that this truly astonishing pastiche never became a standard, as had happened with George Harrison's 'Something'. Both Shirley Bassey and Tony Bennett are thought to have been interested in doing cover versions, but their managements never got past that of The Smiths.

Murray Head, who had also appeared in *The Family Way*, was on the cover of 'Stop Me If You've Heard This One Before' (for which the aforementioned cycling video is used in the compilation *The Smiths: The Complete Picture*). Rough Trade planned to bring it out as a single and it was released as such in Germany and Holland, but cancelled after the BBC complained over the lines (after the drunken narrator has had an accident with his bicycle), 'And the pain was enough to make a shy, bald Buddhist reflect and plan a mass murder.' A witty observation when one seriously thinks about it. Not so long before, however, a man named Michael Ryan had gone berserk and shot seventeen people dead in Hungerford before turning the gun on himself; the sensitive Beeb felt, therefore, that the song might be considered in poor taste. Of course, that tragic incident had nothing to do with Morrissey or the song, which he had written some time before the event, and deservedly gave rise to a waspish comment by *NME*'s Len Brown in February 1988, 'They said people would instantly link it to Hungerford and it would have caused thousands of shoppers to go out and buy machine-guns and murder their grandparents.' Of the other songs on the album, 'Girlfriend In A Coma' has already been mentioned; of almost equal emotion are the veiled bitterness of 'Unhappy Birthday' and the abject indifference of 'Death Of A Disco Dancer' – the very real fact that when such tragedies become so commonplace, one more makes little difference.

The reviews for the album, mingling with the eulogies for the now-defunct group, were exceptional. *Smash Hits* observed, 'If you fail to be moved by songs like "Last Night I Dreamt That Somebody Loved Me", then you're missing out on a beautiful experience.' Giving the album 10 out of 10, *Record Mirror*'s Sylvia Patterson also singled out this song as its best, lamenting, 'And so for the last time, Morrissey brays his mournful billowings a-top the most skilled 'n' jingling guitar froths on this hapless globe.'

The South Bank Show aired on 17 October 1987. The group's split, on the cards when Tony Knox made the film but not made known to him, had necessitated a last-minute script rewrite. Many fans claimed that the documentary merely skimmed the surface in trying to get the Morrissey–Marr message across. It opens with George Formby performing 'Why Don't Women Like Me?' – not a subtle choice from the producer's point of view, for this ran straight into Morrissey gyrating in camp regalia to 'This Charming Man'. He, never one for personal interviews, seems lost. Journalist Nick Kent (whose feature in *The Face* was yet to be published), looking very emaciated, describes The Smiths as 'the first original English pop group', and predicts that by the end of the decade they will be held in the same esteem as The Beatles. Sandie Shaw, seen performing 'Hand In Glove' – and in a stylised shot with Morrissey at her feet, clutching a rosary – declares, 'He hides behind other people's experiences.' And Morrissey closes the proceedings by stressing that there will be no going back:

> I think this is more or less the end of the story. Ultimately, popular music will end. The ashes are already about us, if we could but notice them . . .

The Smiths' passing was lamented not just by their legion of fans, but by stalwarts of their own profession, though of the many 'obituaries', only that of Marc Almond made any sense and accurately forecast the future: 'Splitting The Smiths at their peak will ensure that their aura stays intact. Without doubt, Morrissey will go on to greater heights.' And in *NME*, an anonymous scribe borrowed a leaf from the Morrissey Book of Camp:

> Turned out finally that Morrissey and Marr weren't the soul brothers, the creative peas in a pod we'd imagined, but more like Dennis

The Menace and Walter, with Dennis fed up with wearing the tutu and bunking out, freelance, with various hoary old rock institutions.

Compared with what he achieved with The Smiths, Johnny Marr's subsequent career has been no great shakes. He worked with Quando Quango, Electronic, Everything But The Girl, Impossible Dreamers, Billy Bragg, Bryan Ferry and others – but he never did and never will find another Morrissey.

The absolute truth concerning the group's demise will probably never be known. There were so many contrasting stories. Morrissey blamed the split on immaturity – the fact that he had been five years older than the other Smiths. He also blamed bad management and their treatment by the press – citing one publication in particular. In February 1991, still annoyed, he told Jean-Daniel Beauvallet of *Les Inrockuptibles*,

> Nothing would have happened if the *NME* hadn't listened to certain rumours concerning Johnny's intentions. That paper is largely responsible for The Smiths' split. I was furious with them. They brought out the coffin long before the corpse was cold. Their attitude traumatised me. They printed so many lies about us – so much so that rumour became reality. If everyone had kept their mouths shut, our problems would have been resolved in private.

In November 1989, Nick Kent of *The Face* asked Morrissey what he would do if Johnny Marr called and asked him to work with him again. Without hesitation he responded, 'It's no secret that I would be on the next bus to his house. I don't feel, by saying that, that I have no confidence in my present standing as a solo artist. But he wrote great music and the union was absolutely perfect.'

In March 1991, when much of the heat had died down, Morrissey again brought up the age gap between himself and his fellow Smiths. 'When I first met them, they were teenagers and I was twenty-two going on twenty-three,' he told Mark Kemp of *Select*. 'It's a vast difference. I think The Smiths just snapped due to that kind of pressure, that boring old rock 'n' roll pressure.'

There would be a swansong, *Rank*, a live album of thirteen songs (whittled down from seventeen) and a Johnny Marr instrumental ('The Draize Train') recorded at the Kilburn National Ballroom on 23 October 1986. Housed in a stunning sleeve featuring *The Champions* star Alexandra Bastedo, its original title should have been *The Smiths In Heat*, which Rough Trade had considered too risqué. It was only on the publication of Jo Slee's *Peepholism* that the company found out that Morrissey had taken them for a ride with the new title. Slee includes a photostat of a handwritten note forwarded to her by the singer: 'Call me morbid, Call me pale, but I'm just not happy with the live LP TITLE and, trusting it causes little commotion, I newly nominate: 'RANK' as in j. Arthur.' In other words – 'wank'. Released in September 1988 and worth buying for one track alone – the definitive version of 'Rusholme Ruffians', which starts off as Elvis Presley's '(Marie's The Name) His Latest Flame' – the album peaked at number 2 in the charts.

The Smiths' rupture had been acrimonious and over the years the fighting would not merely continue, but would be augmented by a book that brought out the very worst in Morrissey's vituperative tongue. *Morrissey & Marr: The Severed Alliance*, subtitled *The Definitive Story Of The Smiths*, was published in the summer of 1992, and became an instant best-seller. Its author, Johnny Rogan, had previously published biographies of The Byrds, Roxy Music and The Kinks among others. The Smiths had provided him with his biggest challenge, however.

In his foreword, Rogan declared that it had taken him three years to research his book, that he had conducted over a hundred interviews, including several with Morrissey's relatives – and one with Johnny Marr which, according to Morrissey, his former partner had 'regretted enormously'. Many people were suspicious of Rogan and his more eccentric traits, particularly the pair's lawyers: the fact that he allegedly changed his address every ten weeks, that he had once written in total isolation for a whole year 'without speaking to another human being', or that he possessed neither refrigerator nor television, for example.

Morrissey might have ignored the book were it not for Rogan's claim to the press that he had once spoken to him, and that his book was therefore a 'true and unsanitised story of The Smiths'. Morrissey hit back with spectacular virulence, issuing the first in a trilogy of 'fatwahs' that simply resulted in Rogan receiving more publicity than ordinarily might have happened: 'Personally, I hope Johnny Rogan ends his days very soon in an M3 pile-up!' When Rogan responded that this was unlikely because he did not drive, Morrissey amended his death-wish: 'Okay, I hope he dies in a hotel fire!'

There had been a previous biography: *The Smiths*, by Mancunian journalist Mick Middles, in 1985. Middles had observed in his text, 'When I first approached The Smiths in regard to this book, although treated with sympathy by their manager, I was waved aside without so much as an acknowledgement.' It had originally featured a cover shot of Morrissey by Joelle Dépont: with his fingers threaded through his hair and his eyes starting out of their sockets, he had resembled a tormented Zachary Scott in an American Expressionist movie. Morrissey had said nothing about the book then, other than that he had disliked it, and had left Johnny Marr to launch the attack. In April 1989, Marr dismissed the book in *NME* as 'Hacienda cocktail bar hearsay'.

Morrissey liked everyone to believe that he had not read *The Severed Alliance*, but he confessed to Adrian Deevoy of *Q* that he had 'squinted at a friend's copy from across the room just to see who'd blabbed'. He did read the book eventually, however, and told Deevoy in July 1992,

Of course, the only definitive story is my story. Johnny Rogan has interviewed anybody who bears a grudge against me. Any of the people who've been close to me over the past decade he has not got near. Basically it's 75 per cent blatant lies. I made a statement when the book was published which said, 'Anybody who buys this book wants their head tested.' According to sales figures, a lot of people need their heads tested. A lot of people have bought it, and a lot of people will believe it.

The press gave the book mixed reviews. It covered the lives and careers of two men whose average age was only thirty, at three hundred pages extant of a well-researched discography, and was somewhat long-winded. 'After having waded through the book's first half,' observed Richard Smith of *Gay Times*, 'You feel ready to sit O-Levels in modern Irish History and the Stretford secondary system.' Tony Parsons, writing in the *Sunday Telegraph*, called it, 'A beautiful monster . . . a page-turner of the first degree.' Many criticised the poor editing and Rogan's frequently insensitive juxtaposing of events in Morrissey's life with the pop headlines of the day. Did we really need to know that he had come into the world on the very day that Elvis Presley had topped the charts with 'A Fool Such As I'?

Rogan claimed that Morrissey's 'fatwahs' had left him unperturbed, and that hundreds of people had written in thanking him for writing the book – including Mike Joyce, Andy Rourke and Morrissey's own father. None of these letters, however, were shown to the press.

In May 1993, in the wake of Johnny Rogan 'having the audacity' to interview Johnny Marr for Morrissey's own favourite publication, *Les Inrockuptibles*, Morrissey told the magazine's Christian Fevret:

> If God exists, then Johnny The Rat will be gobbled up by his German Shepherds. I was furious. I haven't lost my sense of humour. I thought very seriously of what I was saying about him [when I made those announcements] . . . that his underhand enquiries prove him to be a dangerous person, one who writes only lies. I could discuss this with him, but why should I? I'm not afraid of confronting anyone, but not just any imbecile. I insist upon at least a minimum of intelligence!

Christian's colleague, Jean-Daniel Beauvallet, told me that *Les Inrockuptibles* had probably been wrong to publish the Rogan/Marr interview, but that the editor-in-chief had been hoping that Rogan might have made 'some sort of apology for what he had done to our favourite singer'. In effect, because this was a much-respected, Morrissey-friendly publication, the text had been cleaned up somewhat – Marr's expletives were removed – and the whole feature, aside from the singer being referred to as 'L'Ayatolla Morrissey', was generally laudatory. 'Let's get one thing clear,' Marr told Rogan, 'Morrissey and I *were* The Smiths. Mike and Andy could leave the studio when they'd finished. We couldn't.'

He went on to speak of their career highs and lows:

Only Morrissey could do justice to my music. I'll never forget his voice on 'I Know It's Over'. One of the most outstanding moments of my life, so moving. Also, he and I shared the same sense of humour, very dry, ironic. That last year was different. Everything was dead serious. Then our final session together for the B-sides of 'Girlfriend In A Coma'. I'd written 'I Keep Mine Hidden', and we'd done 'Work Is A Four-Letter Word', which I loathed. That's the drop of water which overflowed the vase. I hadn't founded a group to do Cilla Black songs! That and 'Golden Lights' were definitely our worst moments.

'Out of respect for Morrissey,' Jean-Daniel Beauvallet told me, 'we included just one photograph of The Smiths, the one which had appeared on their [bootleg] *Eldorado* album. There was no photograph of Johnny Rogan because he was terrified of anyone seeing what he looked like.'

Rogan hit out at Morrissey's latest 'fatwah' in a radio interview in July 1993, when *The Severed Alliance* was published in paperback: 'Morrissey's made a Freudian slip. I don't have German Shepherds – but Johnny Marr does!' Rogan's book (and my own too) were criticised by some sections of the press for not delving into Morrissey's sexuality, and though Rogan did not specifically 'out' him now, the hints were there in the revised edition – bringing the observation from *Gay Times*' Richard Smith that, 'La Mozz has already wished that Rogan dies in a hotel fire. When he reads this he'll probably run out and buy the matches. Excellent!'

The following year, Rogan brought out *The Smiths: The Visual Documentary*, promoted in *Select* with a photograph of Morrissey, in pre-quiff days, with shaggy long hair. Fans might have welcomed such images and the day-to-day account of his life before fame beckoned – the family trees, concert set-lists, the useful and extensive bootleg-ography – but one imagines Morrissey must have been livid at this public airing of so much dirty linen. 'No wonder La Mozz hates Johnny Rogan,' Richard Smith wrote of this one, 'If someone knew this much about me, I'd want to kill them too.'

Morrissey has always run the risk of certain aspects of his personal life being made public knowledge by the other Smiths and their respective families and associates, particularly in view of some of the incredibly mean things he has said about them since the split. That his was at least a partly self-fabricated persona goes without saying. In the spring of 1987 he had told Mishka Assaya of *Les Inrockuptibles*, 'If I don't work at being Morrissey for so many hours each day – if I stop at say, five in the afternoon, to do something else – then I don't think everything would be as significant, as strong as it is. I have to work at being who I am.'

The singer was morally supported by long-time companion James Maker. Adopting the stance of unofficial character witness, Maker very grandly told *Q*'s David Cavanagh at the end of the year: 'Despite the popular portrayal of Morrissey as an inhibited, retiring character, I know him as a young man who was capable of great resolve and purpose . . . He could be benignly considerate and gracious to those whom he deemed disagreeable. He is the most self-actualised person I know.'

At the time, Maker was fronting the band RPLA, who had recently released a single, 'The Absolute Queen Of Pop', dedicated to Morrissey. The outfit had taken out a full-page advertisement in the November 1993 issue of *Gay Times*, depicting a posturing, black-clad, high-heeled James Maker lounging across the top of a television set. Earlier, Morrissey had turned up for the group's performance on *The Big E* and heard Maker tell the audience, 'He's a very good friend of mine. I love him. So, I dedicated a song to him, yeah!'

Morrissey's and Maker's friendship has reputedly weathered its fair share of ups and downs over the years, yet Maker and the other Smiths have thus far proved astonishingly loyal towards respecting Morrissey's privacy – barring a courtroom outburst in December 1996 during the infamous royalties battle which, had the judge not imposed a partial press embargo, might have made for some unsavoury tabloid headlines. More of which anon . . .

4

All This and Heaven Too

'I don't take to praise and fawning because I feel that if you accept that, you have to accept it when someone calls you a pile of shit, which I also don't accept. The moment is the performance, and when it's over the communication is over as well.'

– Morrissey

Several months before The Smiths' split, convinced that he and Johnny Marr would never iron out their differences – or at least feeling that a break might enable tempers to cool and allow for a recharging of batteries – Morrissey had engaged Stephen Street (who among other things had produced *Strangeways Here We Come*) as his personal producer and new songwriting partner.

Morrissey had doubtless entered the most apprehensive phase of his career so far. Having professionally only worked with Johnny Marr, whom he had not heard from since the previous May, Marr's company, support and above all his guiding hand must have been sorely missed. Even so, by the middle of September 1987, work on his first solo album was well underway at the Wool Hall Studios, near Bath. Augmenting the project was Vini Reilly, the guitarist with Durutti Column who had been worshipping Morrissey from afar for some time. Reilly knew Andrew Berry, a friend of Johnny Marr's from his X Clothes days and a former glam rock enthusiast turned celebrity hairdresser whom Marr had brought along to The Smiths' first Hacienda performance to act as DJ. It was Berry, also a friend of Stephen Street, who introduced Reilly to Morrissey.

At the time, Reilly was too gushing with admiration to be objective about working with an artiste renowned for being difficult, but he genuinely appears to have encountered few problems, and the glow was still there in March 1994, long after it was all over and he participated in a debate on Morrissey commissioned by the *Manchester Evening News*. Confessing that like everyone else he had been frightened of Morrissey on account of the reputation that preceded him, he recalled for Rosemary Barratt the pleasant surprise that had awaited him:

> I think he appreciated that someone actually spoke to him about real things. Too many people just try to be nice and please him. We talked about everything – sex, love, girls, music, politics. I found him to be one of the nicest, most genuine people I've ever worked with. I was more of a prima donna during these sessions than he ever was. Most musicians are pompous and self-important. He's quite the opposite, a very humble person . . . When I saw Morrissey on stage, I couldn't take my eyes off him. People describe it as a sort of psychiatric transference. It's like being in love, and real stars reflect it back at you. Whether you like him or not, he's a star.

For Reilly, the most trying aspect of his venture was getting used to Morrissey's unorthodox working methods – the fact that he rarely visited the studio during the early stages of putting a song together, more often than not constructing his songs around a set piece of music from the wealth of lyrics and ideas scribbled into the notebook he carried around with him. Technically, of course, neither Reilly nor Stephen Street were in the Johnny Marr league, but where they did succeed was in composing generally gentler music which, combined with Reilly's playing, brought out the melody in Morrissey's voice – the kind of approach that had made lower-range numbers such as 'Last Night I Dreamt That Somebody Loved Me' so memorable. Marr's often aggressive riffs had frequently forced Morrissey to overreach his limited vocal range – or when this was not possible, to remain flat, as had happened during The Smiths' concert at the Paris Eldorado. As for drama – this was intensified by his new drummer, Andrew Paresi, who was probably more effective than Mike Joyce had been because he too never went over the top, thereby allowing Morrissey to avoid straining his voice.

One of the first songs to emerge from the Wool Hall sessions was 'Suedehead', coupled with 'I Know Very Well How I Got My Name', which EMI released as a single in February 1988. And if there were scoffs from detractors that Morrissey would never make it on his own, this first solo release silenced them: the record peaked at number 5 in the charts, higher than any Smiths single. In fact, the situation was exactly the same as it had always been – there was no transition from frontman to solo artiste. Morrissey had simply found himself a new set of musicians.

'Suedehead' owes its title to one of the novels in the Richard Allen trilogy (*Skinhead*, *Suedehead*, *Suedehead Escapes* – 1971, 1972 and 1973 respectively), which follows the unpleasant adventures of anti-hero Joe Hawkins and his group of racist, anti-gay cronies – harrowing reading and absolutely nothing to do with the song, though Kris Kirk once suggested that this was Morrissey poking fun at Billy Mackenzie, who was just starting to lose his hair at the time. The lyric calls to mind Mackenzie's alleged visit to Morrissey's flat; it certainly refers to an intrusion of privacy along with the unwanted telephone calls and 'silly notes'. Morrissey confessed that the song was about someone, but would not elaborate – and with a shrug of the shoulder ends the piece by declaring, 'Still, it was a good lay,' suggesting that though the intrusion might have been unwelcome, the outcome had certainly proved worthwhile.

'I would like to go to Indiana and mess with James Dean's soil,' Morrissey once told *Sounds*, 'But so many others have done it. They have taken away the monument and the grass. What's left for me?' He would achieve his ambition in February 1988 when filming the 'travelogue' video for 'Suedehead'. Brilliantly directed by Tim Broad, the iconography packed into this little gem (none of which has anything to do with the song's lyrics) is more potent than that of any other Morrissey video. It begins at the singer's home, where he is reclining in his bath, dreamlike, surveyed by a huge but unflattering picture of the bespectacled Dean. Next to the typewriter on the table spanning the bath are: a volume of Byron (also the actor's middle name); a handwritten sheet containing Dean's thoughts and signed 'Jim Brando Clift Dean'; and a copy of the *Fairmount News* announcing his death. The bathmat, a gift from an American fan, is inscribed THERE IS A LIGHT THAT NEVER GOES OUT; the title of The Smiths' song itself comes from a Hoosier work by Indiana poet laureate James Whitcomb Riley, whose book Morrissey is espied reading in the film. Next we see a photograph of Richard Davalos, the actor who played Jimmy's brother in *East Of Eden*, before Morrissey's nephew shows up with a parcel – containing Antoine de Saint-Exupery's allegorical fable, *Le Petit Prince*, said to have been Jimmy's favourite read. Morrissey is next seen poring over this in the streets of Fairmount – Tim Broad had anticipated him kicking through the puddles and emulating Jimmy in Gottfried Helnwein's famous study *Boulevard Of Broken Dreams*, but on 7 February 1988, the eve of what would have been Jimmy's 57th birthday, the town was snowbound.

All the familiar sights are taken in, less commercial than Graceland and as such affecting an air of genuine, heartfelt sadness: the café where Jimmy hung out as a boy, the drugstore, the high school where he first trod the boards, the Winslow farm, the handprint and initials in the cement. Morrissey poses on Jimmy's motor-scooter, plays his bongos in the paddock, and is even permitted to drive the old red tractor, aided by a little off-screen instruction. In the icy barn, Broad borrows from Valentino's *The Four Horsemen Of The Apocalypse* by having Morrissey snort steam down his nostrils like a stud stallion on a frosty morning. Then he heads for the cemetery where there are two graves – that of the fictitious Cal Dean (Cal Trask was Jimmy's character in *East of Eden*) and the real grave, where Morrissey reverently kneels amongst the snow-capped floral tributes. And again Tim Broad borrows from the Valentino film (a scene also used to close Elvis Presley's *Love Me Tender*) when, as the picture fades, James Dean's image materialises, ghost-like, to take over the screen, one sad young man surveying another in what has been a four-minute masterpiece of cinematography.

Astonishingly, the 'Suedehead' film – which was approved by James Dean's surviving relatives, Marcus and Ortense Winslow – attracted severe criticism from the tabloids. The 'exclusive' in the *Daily Mirror* read, WEIRD: MORRISSEY SITS ON JAMES DEAN'S GRAVE! –

which, of course, he had not done. The reporter, Gill Pringle, added that the singer had 'wept at the graveside', which was true, though Tim Broad had respectfully not captured this on camera. Broad himself only exacerbated the detractors' scoffs by boasting, 'Morrissey is a genius and a poet. In some ways I think James Dean is his spiritual guide.' Morrissey hit back below the belt by accusing Gill Pringle of lying.

The classic camp cover stars had died out with The Smiths. Now, it was Morrissey's turn! He was, and always had been, immensely photogenic. There was no such thing as a bad angle for him, and the photograph of the bare-chested singer that adorned the sleeve of this single release – snapped by a fan the previous year at the London Palladium – set a precedent for some very beautiful, almost always homoerotic images. Some fans were known to have bought two of each release so that one could be framed! An unnamed *NME* journalist, recalling the Leo Ford picture on the first Smiths single, asked Morrissey if he would like to pose naked for one of his covers – bringing the response, 'Well, it might detract from record sales. I don't want to enter the charts at number 92.' Such a record, of course, would doubtless have proved a smash hit.

The photograph gracing the cover of Morrissey's debut album, *Viva Hate* – a shadowy profile by Anton Corbijn – was even better, eliciting the comment from *The Face*'s Nick Kent, 'His solo career will see him becoming the Montgomery Clift of the Nineties.' A few years previously, when asked what his life would be like, should The Smiths ever disband, Morrissey had said, 'Misery, despair. I'll probably end up in a room somewhere, bearded and with a beer-belly, surrounded by books and a cat.' Upon reading the comment, Johnny Marr had responded, 'Sometimes I think he's in need of a good humping.' On the back of the album was a shot of clouds – which made little sense until the full photograph from which this segment had been taken appeared in the press: it was a shot of the tomb of George Formby Sr, in Warrington Cemetery.

Viva Hate was released in a blaze of publicity and zoomed straight to the top of the charts. Accompanying it were several self-deprecating philosophies that could just as easily have been penned by Oscar Wilde himself:

'I don't blame anyone for bringing me into the world, but I do feel that life is excessively over-rated.'

'I find hate omnipresent and love very difficult to find. Hate makes the world go around.'

'I often pass a mirror, and when I glance into it slightly I don't recognise myself at all. You look into a mirror and wonder, "Where have I seen that person before?" Then you remember. It was at a neighbour's funeral, and it was the corpse.'

The album was stunning, each of the dozen songs firmly, faithfully adhering to the *réaliste* tradition, and just as good as anything Morrissey had produced with Johnny Marr, who kept his opinions about his erstwhile partner's solo releases to himself until the spring of 1991. Then, speaking to *NME*'s Danny Kelly, the sour taste was clearly still in his mouth when he said, sarcastically, 'I thought *Viva Hate* was very good. I listened to it in its entirety, and I haven't heard it since.'

Stephen Street audaciously told *NME* at the time of the album's release, having confessed that he had not been overly fond of The Smiths, 'It's only since I've heard this new material that I've realised how major a talent he is. Where it's sad and emotional, it's really heart-breaking stuff.' Writing for the same publication on 19 March, Alan Jackson also hailed Morrissey's Johnny Marr-less success:

Viva Hate finds Narcissus poking a stick into the murky waters of his private pond, disturbing and distorting his reflection and seeming not to care if he detracts from his appearance. It's a brave record, and sometimes beautiful – honest, angry and vulnerable, mercifully free of commercial restraints.

The American magazine *The Advocate* devoted an entire page of its 10 May 1988 issue to singing Morrissey's praises. Sire Records had despatched the album with a topless promo shot of the singer, one arm raised suggestively. Under the heading, MORRISSEY'S REVENGE: Homo Hymns For Misfits & Outcasts, reviewer Adam Block enthused:

> *Well*, we have a *shaved* armpit, Mr Morrissey. Isn't that special? I wonder: when did we last do drag? *Viva Hate* is the vinyl equivalent of that shaved armpit flashed at the pop public: nervy, outrageous, and wickedly blasé . . . 'Pity Me Because I Am Too Sensitive For This World, And Everyone Is Wrong Except Me.' When Morrissey penned that chapter title for his brief fan bio *James Dean Is Not Dead* – published before the heyday of The Smiths – he could have been reciting his own mantra. Morrissey's dry extravagance, devotion to misfits and outcasts, homo lyricism and vicious wit are all deliciously queer and shimmer against lush, ragged and playful melodies on *Viva Hate* . . . This LP by Morrissey, the self-professed gay, celibate, militant vegetarian and British pop's most beguiling brat – is a masterpiece. The Smiths are dead. Viva Morrissey!

The album kicks off with a roisterous 'Alsatian Cousin', whose title (nothing to do with the song) comes from *Forty Years On*, the 1968 play by Alan Bennett, who later became a friend. The song deals with the old chestnut of age-gap sex, to which is added a touch of voyeurism. The narrator has watched a pair of lovers in the forecourt, then later at a campsite where the tent-flap is deliberately left wide open. But there is a problem: the fact that, al fresco, sex is unsatisfactory because the older lover with the leather elbow patches has always been accustomed to doing it on his desk.

'Little Man, What Now?' is a slant on the old Judy Garland song, 'I'm Just An In-Between' – here, the 'too old for toys, too young for boys' theme is transcribed as 'too old to be a child-star, too young to play leads', though the title comes from a 1932 novel of German social problems (*Kleiner Man, Was Nun?*) by Hans Fallada. There have been numerous suggestions as to the identity of the song's subject, a nervous juvenile axed from a television soap because of his lamentable acting – the most likely candidate being Roger Tonge, who played the wheelchair-bound Sandy Richardson in the original *Crossroads*.

Without any doubt, the most accomplished song on the album is 'Everyday Is Like Sunday', backed with a luscious, six-piece string section headed by virtuoso violinist Fenella Barton. One is instinctively reminded of the similarly self-deprecating poet laureate John Betjeman, a great social observer and loather of modernity – notably in the bleakness of 'Death In Leamington', or the inspiration here, the condemnation of modern architecture: 'Come, friendly bombs, and fall on Slough/It isn't fit for humans now.' In Morrissey's case, the attack is against 'the seaside town . . . they forgot to bomb', and one instinctively thinks of the grotesque ugliness of Blackpool with its overblown, addictive commercialism. Who has not experienced the misery of such a place, out of season, where there is nothing to do but play bingo and slot-machines, quaff 'greased tea' and generally wish one were some place else? The song, released as a single in June 1988, reached number 9 in the charts. There have been a number of cover versions since, none worthy of mention.

The video for 'Everyday Is Like Sunday' was filmed by Tim Broad at the much more pleasantly located Southend-on-Sea, and was supposedly based on the film *Jacques Brel Is Alive And Well And Living In Paris*, in which Brel makes cameo appearances between performances of his songs by others – in Morrissey's case as a cyclist, a café patron, shop assistant, etc. However, following a row with yet another short-lived manager, Gail Colson, he failed to turn up for the shoot, and Broad carried on without him. Image-wise, it is almost as important as the video for 'Suedehead'. A trio of women (Billie Whitelaw, ex-*Coronation Street* actress Cheryl Murray and Lucette Henderson in an I DON'T EAT MY FRIENDS T-shirt and inscribing 'Meat Is Murder/Cruelty Without Beauty' on postcards) are out shopping. Morrissey is everywhere. In the record store, surrounded by posters of him, everybody has the 12-inch version of the single being promoted tucked under their arm; on the television he is seen at home, sitting in his bath; he appears half-naked on hoardings. He is seen in the 'flesh' just once (filmed in London and added to the video later) when the ladies return home to spy on him through a telescope. And on the television in the lounge is *Carry On Camping*, Charles Hawtrey's last film – save that here, his 'Morning everybody!' has been overdubbed by Tallulah Bankhead.

Of the other songs on *Viva Hate*, 'Bengali In Platforms' is mentioned elsewhere. The subjects of 'The Ordinary Boys' are so institutionalised by their mundane, backstreet lives that they never want to change. 'Dial-A-Cliché', one of the weaker songs, links this theme with the 'do-as-I-do' tactics of Northern parenthood, and asks whether one should follow in the footsteps of one's elders with one's own offspring. 'Angel, Angel, Down We Go Together' has the singer offering his strength and support to dissuade a friend, who has fallen in with the wrong crowd, from suicide. 'Late Night, Maudlin Street', a very long, morose pastiche but brilliant nonetheless, recalls the tough Manchester suburb Morrissey grew up in, juxtaposing this with the name of the problem-hit school in *Carry On Teacher*. From personal experience, one has sensed the feeling of immense relief to be finally saying goodbye to the source of one's unhappiness, the place where generations have forcibly lived in misery and hardship – 'Where the world's ugliest boy became . . . the world's ugliest man' – afraid of breaking away from drudgery and tradition because this is how life has always been. The narrator recalls the dramas in his youth: the picture he kept at the side of the bed of the lover he never meant to hurt; the time he drove the lover home after the last bus had gone; the first time they saw each other naked – 'Me – without clothes? Well a nation turns its back and gags.' In similar vein, though much more optimistic, is 'Break Up The Family', with its reference to 'There Is A Light That Never Goes Out' – the fact that the young man, tough and gung-ho, is so happy to be getting out of a rut for the first time that he will not mind if the brakes fail on his lover's car. And again the lover is a man. Then, almost in the next breath, Morrissey declares, 'I Don't Mind If You Forget Me' – words spoken to a lover whose hope of a possible reunion is dashed by the stark put-down, 'Rejection is one thing, but rejection from a fool is cruel.'

Originally intended for the album *The Queen Is Dead*, but subsequently shelved, 'Margaret On The Guillotine' resurfaced on *Viva*

Hate. Adam Block of *The Advocate* aptly applauded the piece as, 'A chilling dollop of Ortonesque deadpan that makes The Sex Pistols' "God Save The Queen" sound like an infantile temper tantrum.' For a number of years, Morrissey's hatred of prime minister Margaret Thatcher appeared to be bordering on the pathological. On 12 October 1984 – the very day The Smiths had begun a tour of Northern Ireland – an IRA bomb exploded at Brighton's Grand Hotel, killing three people and badly injuring some twenty more, including the wife of Norman Tebbit, the then Secretary of State for Trade and Industry. Morrissey was quick to comment: 'The only sorrow of the Brighton bombing is that Thatcher escaped unscathed'. It was an opinion shared by others who were, like himself, not supporters of terrorism but were weary of Conservative rule. The tabloids were full of such remarks; jokes about the tragedy were cracked on radio and television programmes. A working-men's club in South Yorkshire seriously considered a whip-round 'to pay for the bomber to have another go'.

The tabloids, some of whose members shared Morrissey's sentiments but who, of course, would never have dared make this public, singled him out by re-publishing some of the earlier attacks he had made on the Tories and the royals – not that this dissuaded him in the least. When asked by one reporter, tongue-in-cheek, what he would do if one of his fans shot Mrs Thatcher, Morrissey replied seriously, 'Well, I'd obviously marry that person!' In 'Margaret On The Guillotine', he politely requests of the Iron Lady, 'Please die . . . make the dream real'! The song was revered by his massive gay following, virulently opposed to the Tories' notorious Clause 28, the law that banned councils and schools in England and Wales from intentionally promoting homosexuality. In March 1988, Morrissey told Shaun Phillips of *Sounds*,

I find the Thatcher syndrome very stressful and evil. The most perfect example is Clause 28. I think that embodies Thatcher's very nature and her quite natural hatred. I think that's been the story throughout her reign, so I don't see the point of wandering about Marble Arch in a pink T-shirt carrying books by Andrea Dworkin.

In France, Morrissey's near-contemporary, Renaud, was impressed enough by Morrissey's song to compose 'Miss Maggie', lyrically a better piece, which caused a storm when he introduced it on stage at the pantheon of French entertainment, the Paris Olympia. Slipping filthy epithets into the propagandist stanzas, he ended the piece by doing something Morrissey would never have done: turning his back on the audience, he feigned urination against a portrait of Mrs Thatcher. The song topped the French charts for two months, but although it was poetically better constructed than Morrissey's offering, the latter's was the more romantic of the two – for even the swish of the guillotine at the end sounds erotic. José Artur, the French broadcaster who played both songs on his cult evening show on French Inter-radio, said of Morrissey, 'He has fashioned the most dramatic ending to a song since the shattered glass of Edith Piaf's "Les Amants D'un Jour".'

Morrissey had hit the headlines in 1984 with what was ultimately a perfectly logical condemnation of Band Aid, Bob Geldof's brainchild, which raised millions for the victims of the Ethiopian famine – and which, like the celebrity reality programmes of today, also revived the flagging careers of many artists involved, who might otherwise not have bothered participating without pay. Morrissey's theory, by no means a racist view, was that England should first of all put its own house in order, particularly when the Ethiopian problem almost solely lay with Ethiopia itself – due to ignorance of birth control and too much of its resources being spent on weapons and warfare. His subsequent press statement – 'People like Thatcher and the royals could solve the Ethiopian situation within ten seconds, but Band Aid was almost directly aimed at unemployed people' – went down like the proverbial lead balloon, particularly when added to his earlier anti-Conservative comment, 'One can have a great concern for the people of Ethiopia, but it's another thing to inflict daily torture on the people of England.'

Morrissey's attacks on Margaret Thatcher only intensified with the passing of time, and repeated attempts to gag him always failed – such as on the occasion of The Smiths' first visit to Dublin early in 1986, when the *Sunday Correspondent*'s George Byrne asked him if he really had meant all the 'mean things' he had said about Mrs Thatcher. 'Every word,' he replied. 'When people who are intelligent come along, they want to get rid of them or gag them . . . It's not because I'm a vile person, but because I have views.' He was however treading on thin ice when, having referred to his family background, Byrne asked him for his views on the Anglo-Irish agreement:

> You can turn on the news and hear that six innocent people have been shot dead in Belfast, and it doesn't warrant comment, which I say with massive regret because death and murder are part of a situation which is obviously unbridgeable. I certainly don't think that in England there's any desire, politically, to make life any easier in Belfast. Distance gives great comfort to the politicians who have to deal with it.

It would take almost another decade for Morrissey to address the Anglo-Irish problem in song. 'This Is Not Your Country', written with Alain Whyte, was on the B-side of 'Satan Rejected My Soul', released in 1997, and commemorated the thirtieth anniversary of the Northern Ireland Civil Rights Association. This long, obscure but stirring piece tells of the Irishman who feels he is no longer welcome in the country of his birth when all he sees are road-blocks and barbed wire. He cannot go out without being questioned and harassed: 'British soldier pointing a gun, and I'm only trying to post a letter!' He does not know why his son was shot – he has just laid him in a three-foot box, and no one cares. 'Home Sweet Fortress,' he says sarcastically to the soldier, 'We hate your kind' – only to be told, 'Zip up your mouth!'

In the same interview, Morrissey took another swipe at Band Aid, and again, 'distance' was the operative word – 'It confronted a problem that wasn't actually in our land. Distance made it remotely glamorous. I wonder, if Bob Geldof had been concerned with certain domestic problems, would the idea have been so warmly embraced by the music industry?'

In the wake of his attacks on Margaret Thatcher, the *Star* had run the headline, MAD MORRISSEY IN 'KILL MAGGIE' FURY, and this ultimately led to one of several brushes with Geoffrey Dickens, the Conservative MP for Littleborough & Saddleworth who had been out to get Morrissey for some time – not just on account of his political views, but because of what Dickens referred to as his involvement with 'witchcraft' ('Ouija Board, Ouija Board') and 'the child sex issue' (The Smiths' 'Reel Around The Fountain', for example). As a founder member of the Conservative Family Campaign, Dickens had petitioned for the recriminalisation of homosexuality, and advocated the obligatory tagging of 'well-known' gay men and lesbians 'to keep AIDS under control'. Despite the gravity of the matter, Morrissey must have howled along with thousands of others to hear Dickens announce, in a speech during the Clause 28 debate, 'The homosexual fraternity are only likely to get support from us if they stop flaunting their homosexuality and thrusting it down our throats.'

Dickens now accused Morrissey of being actively involved with a terrorist network! As a matter of course, officers from Special Branch were therefore ordered to search his Manchester home. Nothing untoward was found, and whether he was actually cautioned or had his fingerprints and a mugshot taken is not known – but it's extremely unlikely, as the visit is known to have ended with police officers asking Morrissey for his autograph. As for Geoffrey Dickens, it seemed that he did not practise what he was fond of preaching where family values were concerned – he was to hit the headlines himself when it emerged that he had left his wife for a woman he had met at a tea-dance. When he died, Terry Sanderson of *Gay Times* observed, 'Perhaps his gravestone should be etched with the epitaph, "Here lies a man who talked bollocks" – and let's hope that the witches he so feared don't have the urge to dig him up again.'

Whether Morrissey really wanted to see Margaret Thatcher assassinated is a matter for conjecture; certainly there were many like him who would have shed no tears over her demise from natural causes. Even so, he did not submit lightly to being taken to task by a hypocrite MP in what was supposed to be a democratic society, though it should be said that, as a public figure whose every last word was adhered to by many impressionable young people, Morrissey should surely have kept some comments to himself. No one can deny that, as with any great artiste, his fanbase contained a tiny element who might have done anything to please him.

There was a coda of sorts a few years later with 'He Knows I'd Love To See Him', from the *Bona Drag* album. The 'He' of the title is widely regarded as Morrissey's semi-estranged father, and the song ponders what Peter Morrissey might have had to say about his son's being accused by the police as 'Just another fool with radical views' – hence the line, 'My name still conjures up deadly deeds and a bad taste in the mouth', suggesting that even as a child he had been opinionated. In interviews, Morrissey has always spoken of his mother with great affection, often regretting being unable to spend as much time with her and his sister, Jacqueline, as he would like. About his father, he appears indifferent. In April 2003, when Andrew Harrison of *Word* asked Morrissey what his father did, the response was a sharpish, 'He does . . . certain things. Let's leave it at that.'

Margaret Thatcher resigned as prime minister in November 1990 and her successor, John Major, received no sympathy from Morrissey. Speaking in the spring of 1994 to Stuart Maconie for *Q*, he proclaimed, 'John Major is no one's idea of a Prime Minister, and is a terrible human mistake . . . If we focused on Clare Short or even Harriet Harman, here are people with some personality . . . John Smith [then Labour leader, who died soon afterwards] . . . would be better suited to selling bread and no-one would buy it. It makes one long for Communism.'

In the same interview, Maconie brought up the topic of assailant David Kang firing blank shots at Prince Charles during his recent visit to Australia, and asked if Morrissey wished the bullets had been real. 'I think it would have really shaken British politics up . . . I think it would have made the world a more interesting place,' he replied. 'But one of them is bound to get it soon . . . Could be me!' Observers might have posed the question: was Morrissey referring to himself as the proposed victim, aka 'the 18th pale descendant of some old queen or other' – or as the would-be assassin?

Morrissey did not have a great deal to say about the first Gulf War, other than that he was not interested. He was vocal about its successor, however. 'Who do you hate?' Andrew Harrison asked him:

In the wider world, George W and Tony Bland are insufferable, egotistical insane despots. It is unforgivable of them to send people to Iraq, and certain death. In this country [by this time Morrissey was a resident of Los Angeles] American error is unthinkable . . . I was here on September 11 and you could see clearly that it has given America another opportunity to bully people . . . In this country the police have absolute power – they can shoot you in the street and the courts will always side with them. So it is a very fascist country.

The singer's sly reference to Tony Blair as 'Tony Bland' was no slip of the tongue – as anarchic as ever, he was linking the British prime minister to the young coma victim from Derbyshire who in the nineties had been at the centre of a very heated public debate, as had Karen Quinlan before him, over whether he should be allowed to remain on a life-support machine when doctors at a Sheffield hospital had pronounced him clinically dead.

The irreverence continued in June 2003 when, in an interview with Manchester's *City Life* magazine, Morrissey made comparisons between Blair and one of Britain's best-loved camp comedians:

More dangerously [than the Americans being unable to find Saddam Hussein – at the time of the interview – and Osama bin Laden] has anyone noticed the facial and physical similarity between Tony Blair and Larry Grayson? And is it not a coincidence that Larry Grayson 'died' as soon as Blair became Prime Minister? Am I the only one who suspects that this country is being run by Larry Grayson?

Most of Morrissey's fans and detractors had read these comments in print and, probably like myself, imagined some sort of dictatorial figure standing upon a soapbox, waving his arms about in a foul-tempered frenzy. No so! In *The Importance Of Being Morrissey*, billed as his first television interview in sixteen years (in fact, it was his first major screen interview, period) and broadcast on Channel 4 during the late spring of 2003, it is astonishing to witness just how laid-back he is while delivering these withering attacks. His sore points, aside from the omnipresent barbs against the British music press, were still meat-eaters, the royals and politicians. Linking the first two he said, 'It's all just abuse and it's human evil, which is why I think the Royal Family is evil because they enjoy fox-hunting. These are despicable people – and Charles above all has no intelligence whatsoever.' Alluding to his own declining interest in English football, he added, 'If it was a politician they were kicking around, if it was Tony Blair instead of a round object, I'd be captivated!'

To tie in with *Viva Hate*'s release, Morrissey granted interviews to three very different journalists: Paul Morley, one-time marketing executive of Frankie Goes To Hollywood; Shaun Phillips of *Sounds*; and *NME*'s Len Brown. A fourth interview, with *Gay Times*' Kris Kirk, was allegedly turned down: Morrissey had gone a long way since his interview with Catherine Miles, Kris said, and would not have relished 'being backed into a corner by one of his own'.

Of the three, Morley's was the most literate, his questions bordering between the witty and the downright audacious, though Morrissey started this particular ball rolling by greeting his fellow Mancunian with, 'The last time we met, we romped naked together at playschool.' What ensued was a high-camp Louella Parsons-versus-Hedda Hopper debate, with Morley asking his subject, 'How did you move from being the village idiot to being the gangleader?' A little more such bantering, and it was down to the more serious stuff. Morrissey spoke of his shyness, of how he still had to go into another room when the window-cleaner called. He let slip a couple of one-liners: 'Being selfish is the first step towards maturity' and, 'If I hadn't found my social position when I was a teenager so amusing, I would have strangled myself.' He spoke of his horror of flying: 'I always feel that I have to be racked by physical fear, and if I am I'll arrive safe. I feel if I relax, drink a whisky, converse, the plane will crash. I have to be in total turmoil, or the plane won't make it.'

Sex, of course, was an obligatory topic, but when asked if there was any sex in Morrissey, he replied philosophically, 'None whatsoever, which in itself is quite sexy. In a particular sense, I'm a virgin . . . I've always felt above sex and love because all the emotions I need to impress come from within myself.' This was a far cry from the interview given at around the same time to Kris Kirk by his former soulmate, James Maker, who claimed his own most recent enterprise had been feature roles in two gay porno-flicks, *Bike Boys Go Ape* and *Well-Hung Studs*. Speaking of his fondness for the casting-couch, Maker told Kris, 'Begin with your managers and screw your way up the hierarchy.' Another friend, Pete Burns, had told the story of how he preferred sharing hotel rooms with his wife and one of his male musicians. 'That way,' he added, 'I can give it or take it, depending on the mood I'm in. It was always my ambition to form a homo band.' Kris was unmoved by such boasts and observed, 'In a world where stars are too often pigeon-holed, my candidate for sainthood is Morrissey, who artistically and morally is streets ahead of these people. He sets out to be a decent man, and he succeeds because this is what he is.'

Shaun Phillips' interview took place at London's Hyde Park Corner, and did not get off to a brilliant start when, observing Morrissey's inflamed eye – he was breaking in new contact lenses – Phillips suggested a 'corrective visit' to a nearby public toilet renowned for importuning, hardly a welcome comment after the Frank Owen piece in *Melody Maker*, which still rankled, though the singer reacted only by arching an eyebrow. It also seems portentously ironic that the subject of George Michael cropped up several times during the ensuing conversation, with Morrissey stating categorically, 'I don't feel institutionalised. I don't feel faintly akin to George Michael or his world, for that matter. If he had to live my life for five minutes, he'd strangle himself with the nearest piece of cord.'

Another sore point was Morrissey's recent Peel session for Radio One. This had been recorded but not broadcast – he claimed that he had not given of his best because the Maida Vale technicians had been rude, insensitive and disrespectful. 'It was really awful, horrible,' he told Phillips. 'They're quite accustomed to treat everyone like they were some insignificant, unsigned group from Poole. That's how I felt . . . as though I'd never seen a record, let alone made one.'

Locationally perhaps, Morrissey's most important interview – albeit that the printed result was no great shakes – took place at Chelsea's

Cadogan Hotel, in the very room where Oscar Wilde had been arrested in April 1895. Morrissey appears to have been in a doleful mood, largely because various refurbishments over the years had left no trace of his hero. 'I thought the aura of the room would create some interesting physical vibrations,' he told *NME*'s Len Brown in February 1988, 'but they seem to have painted over even the energy.' Aside from 'Suedehead', there was no mention in Brown's piece of any Morrissey work extant of The Smiths, whose demise he now reflected upon with genuine sadness: 'The Smiths were almost like a painting. Every month you'd add a little bit here and a little bit there . . . but it wasn't quite complete and it was whipped away.'

Morrissey's first two solo singles had zoomed into the Top Ten with virtually no airplay and little publicity. His first solo concert, however, was a frenzy of emotion and reminiscent of Dorothy Squires' December 1970 comeback at the London Palladium when, unable to find backing despite one of her records ('My Way') staying in the charts for fifty weeks, she had hired the place herself. For his comeback on 22 December 1988 – though like Squires he had never truthfully been away – Morrissey hired the unlikeliest of venues: the Civic Hall in Wolverhampton. Then he filled some fans with dread by announcing, 'This is me saying goodbye', while others, upon hearing that he would be accompanied by Andy Rourke, Mike Joyce and Craig Gannon, believed that what he was effectively saying was that he was abandoning his solo career and re-forming The Smiths, but without Johnny Marr.

This rumour was the topic of conversation among the long line of apostles gathered outside the theatre, ones who had made the pilgrimage from all over the country. Some of these had lived and slept rough for several days and nights – in the backs of trucks, in bus shelters and shop doorways, heedless of the cold and police harassment. Nothing had been too much trouble for what might have been their last glimpse of the man they loved.

The reason for the concert was twofold: the crowd scenes before and after the event, as well as part of the show itself, were to be filmed for inclusion in a showcase video, directed and edited by Tim Broad:

Hulmerist, which would also contain the promotional videos for six Morrissey singles, including 'The Last Of The Famous International Playboys', scheduled for release in February 1989.

NME's James Brown would observe the following week, 'The excitement and atmosphere inside the hall was like nothing I have ever experienced at any public event. Sensible and intelligent fans were transformed into screaming Mozettes (male and female) at the return of their beloved rebel boy.' The fervour, however, had begun long before Morrissey stepped on to the stage. Because the show was to be filmed, the organisers were not allowed to charge for tickets. Under normal circumstances, this would have meant dispensing complimentary tickets to local advertisers and businesses, civic dignitaries and such who were rarely interested in who was on the bill so long as they were getting a free night out – and with the residue being offered to the public on a first-come-first-served basis. Morrissey was having none of this, and because it was his baby, so to speak, he had decided that tickets would only be allotted to fans who turned up wearing Smiths or Morrissey T-shirts. Wolverhampton town centre had to be cordoned off when 5,000 fans besieged the box office for the 1,700 tickets on offer – smashing down barriers and trying to get into the theatre via side doors and windows. When some of these were broken, the police brought in dogs, though there was no trouble to speak of.

The scenario was reminiscent of one of the *Carry Ons*. Adjacent to the Civic Hall there stood a blood transfusion van, and a compound housing several pit donkeys – said to have been Morrissey's belated tribute to the 1984 strike. The spirit of Christmas was evoked by strategically placed ghetto-blasters playing seasonal songs by Bing Crosby and Ruby Murray – and adding to the general bonhomie of the atmosphere were jugglers, Morrissey lookalikes, and one young man who entertained the crowd by eating the bunch of daffodils he had brought! Morrissey himself arrived in a 1950s cream-and-green Vista school bus that had been used in one of the *St Trinian's* films. 'The bus was the wrong choice because it broke down twice,' he told James Brown, 'I had a driver, he also broke down twice. It was very typical of Old England to let me down.'

The thunderous applause that greeted Morrissey when he strode on to the stage lasted almost ten minutes – to the artiste, an eternity. He was wearing a black diaphanous shirt, through which was revealed a markedly hunkier torso than hitherto: since his last appearance he had obviously worked out, though he has always denied doing such things. (In January 1994 The Smiths' PR man/chauffeur, Dave Harper, told *Q*'s David Cavanagh that though Morrissey had never appeared to eat anything but cake while with the group, he had been immensely strong. Recalling the day he helped Morrissey to move out of his Kensington flat, Harper admitted he had been unable to lift his iron dumbbells off the floor, while Morrissey had effortlessly picked them up with one hand!)

Watching from the gallery, the *Observer*'s Simon Reynolds had described the singer as, 'A paradigm of a certain ethereal, inhibited masculinity which would rather live in dreams than risk being disappointed by reality.' Effectively, though, this was a dream come true. The concert was fairly short, just seven songs beginning with The Smiths' 'Stop Me If You've Heard This One Before', but each one represented a histrionic event. A precedent was set too in that Morrissey performed in front of a massive canvas stage backdrop – this one featuring the uncredited Italian child actor from a sixties Anna Magnani film, the same image that had appeared on the sleeve of 'That Joke Isn't Funny Anymore'.

The live song that ended up on the *Hulmerist* video was 'Sister I'm A Poet', for which there was the obligatory exposing of pectorals – though it could also be said that Morrissey was offering them his heart. 'Sweet And Tender Hooligan' was an invitation to scores of stage invaders: the security men who had rough-frisked youngsters on their way into the theatre had been instructed to go easy on these once the performance began, and this show of affection is endlessly touching. Not surprisingly there was hardly a dry eye in the house, and at times Morrissey too was on the verge of tears. It must also have been an emotional time for Stephen Street, witnessing for the first time the overwhelming response to his compositions – though his stay within the Morrissey court would be brief and prove far from satisfactory. As for Morrissey, he was so carried away by it all that at times he seemed oblivious to his surroundings. Vocally, he was not at his best on account of the non-stop hugging and kissing. But who cared? 'It would have been nice to complete a song without interruption,' he said afterwards, 'but for some reason it just didn't matter. The night went for me beyond performing. It was something else.' After 'Interesting Drug', he wallowed in Strangeways nostalgia with 'Death At One's Elbow', and closed with 'Disappointed' – which ended portentously with the line, 'This is the last song I will ever sing' . . . then raised an almighty cheer by adding another, 'No, I've changed my mind!'

NME's James Brown, obviously as enthralled by and attracted to the spectacle as everyone else at Wolverhampton, summed him up as, 'The sweet and tender, untouchable topless Adonis, always ready to reveal his inner thoughts and passions, yet just as eager to veil them in lyrical and sexual ambiguity.'

In retrospect, it seems an entirely logical progression after this otherwise softly spoken man's exploration of teenage thuggery and murder, after his championing of shoplifting and violent death and suicide, that Morrissey should turn to gang rivalry. He even went so far as to form a 'gang' of his own (albeit one comprising only his rockabilly musicians), paying a kind of homage to the two most notorious such outfits in recent memory – the Kray and Richardson gangs who, by the time he began to adopt an interest in gangster iconography, had already passed into East End legend and the realms of hero worship.

Just as there are regular Smiths sightseeing trips around the band's native Manchester, so one of the essential stopping-off points of 'Morrissey's London' is the area associated with its most famous villains. Twins Ronnie and Reggie Kray, born in 1933, had resided at 179 Vallance Road in Bethnal Green – though the house they grew up in has long since been demolished. Throughout the sixties they had led a regal existence almost rivalling Hollywood's elite, making a fortune from illegal drinking-gambling clubs, and extortion and collection rackets, simultaneously gaining both fear and respect among the community. Boxing enthusiasts (like Morrissey himself), they sparred at Repton Boys Club, and held 'Firm' meetings at several local pubs including the Lion, the Carpenters Arms and – more notoriously – the Blind Beggar, where in February 1966 Ronnie Kray shot dead George Cornell, a member of the rival Charlie Richardson gang – one of the few who had not been rounded up by the police and put away. Arrested, both Krays were sentenced to a minimum of thirty years in prison, and never saw freedom again. Ronnie died in 1995, Reggie five years later. Morrissey is known to have sent flowers to Reggie Kray's funeral.

'The Last Of The Famous International Playboys', Morrissey's magnificent anthem to hero-worship of the corrupt, revolves around the Krays. Not that he necessarily condoned their actions, as he explained on New York's WDRE Radio in November 1991:

> I think a lot of people, in order to be seen, in order to be famous and in order to be acknowledged, do something destructive or commit murder. In America, the perfect example is serial killers who quite obviously don't mind being caught and don't mind being known as mass-murderers. They want their element of fame, and they get it always.

In January 1989, speaking to *NME*'s James Brown and confessing that he was interested in the infamy attached to grisly crimes that perversely created celebrities out of murderers, Morrissey had accused tabloid journalists of 'furthering the male hetero-sexist fantasy' by the way they had reported some of these crimes. In particular he denounced them for 'glamorising' a serial-attacker of female students in Manchester by labelling him 'The Fox'. 'It's always done in relation to men who attack women,' he told Brown. 'When men attack men they're never ever given glamorous names.'

A gay theme persists throughout Tim Broad's stunning video for 'The Last Of The Famous International Playboys', which opens with a nipple-flashing singer, Craig Gannon, Stephen Street, Andy Rourke and Mike Joyce playing against an unlucky green background, and it is this which alternates with the vignette of the terrified youth, perceived as the 'dear hero imprisoned' – not in jail, but in his bedroom whose walls are plastered with macho Elvis/Jack Nicholson/George Best posters. The hunky actor is Jason Rush, a blond bombshell who had appeared in the hard-hitting gay acceptance TV drama *The Two Of Us*, a role he later extended to the character he played in *EastEnders*. Indeed, in Broad's film he is wearing an *EastEnders* T-shirt. We see him sparring and punching the air, psyching himself up for an excursion into the dark, dangerous streets of Bermondsey that sees him sprinting as if pursued past a Prince's Trust hoarding – depicting a skinhead and the slogan, HELP US TO ENCOURAGE HIM TO CREATE WEALTH, NOT AGGRO. Then, having achieved nothing and seen no one, we see the youth back in his room, where he feels safe once more.

Surprisingly, the song brought no media condemnation for eulogising the Krays twice, but instead unexpected quibbles over the North/South divide. In February 1989 a journalist from *Record Mirror* sarcastically asked Morrissey why he, a Northerner, should be singing about 'an obviously Southern hero'. Never short of a cutting response, Morrissey replied, 'They are known in the North . . . we do have televisions now, though there's a slight shadow on the commercials.'

For thousands of fans, wishful thinking took over. There was only one playboy and Morrissey played straight into their hands – and hormones – by telling James Brown of *NME*, 'The Last of the Famous International Playboys are Bowie, Bolan, Devoto and me!' Many would have argued that he was better-looking, and certainly more charismatic if not more tongue-in-cheek arrogant, than the other three added together. But there was more. In 1923, *Variety* had asked Rudolph Valentino who, male or female, had been in his opinion the most beautiful person in Hollywood and he had responded, quite seriously, 'Myself.' Morrissey had also witnessed mass adulation close at hand, and one can imagine the fans applauding – and the detractors cringing – upon reading what he told James Brown next, confirming that of all the heroes and villains he worshipped, one stood out from the rest:

> I think I must be, absolutely, a total sex object in every sense of the word. A lot of men and a lot of women find me unmistakably attractive. It amuses me. I sit down and wonder why, and then someone writes me a beautiful letter and tells me why . . . And a lot

of the male followers who are as far as the eye can see natural specimens have very anguished rabid desires in my direction. I find that quite histrionic. Even though an equal proportion of female followers do too, perhaps that's less remarkable than having a vast army of male followers. They're not multi-sexual beings or urban Warholian creatures, they're just your very, very natural living breathing boys.

'The Last Of The Famous International Playboys' entered the charts with such gusto that the music press were sure it would give Morrissey his first number 1. It stalled at number 6, not that this prevented it from becoming an immediate standard, a set piece of his shows, and a song that may only rightfully be performed by him without attracting severe criticism.

The song was coupled with 'Lucky Lisp', a pun on 'Lucky Lips', a big hit for American singer Gale Storm (who recorded it the week of Morrissey's birth) and subsequently revived by Cliff Richard. When Morrissey pronounces, 'When your talent becomes apparent, I will roar from the stalls . . . The Saints smile shyly down on you . . . Jesus made this all for you, love,' one is hard put to determine (as Cliff does have a slight lisp, and considering his religious stance) whether he is praising or mocking him.

No sooner had '. . . Playboys' dropped out of the charts than EMI released its successor, 'Interesting Drug', which reached number 9 in the charts. This bouncy piece had backing vocals by Kirsty MacColl. On the flipside was 'Such A Little Thing Makes A Big Difference', a hopeless plea to the bicycle-chain-wielding thug to shape up and be nicer, and which contains the classic Morrissey observation, 'Most people keep their brains between their legs.' The 12-inch included 'Sweet And Tender Hooligan' from the Wolverhampton concert, and there was a supplementary 12-inch etched with the words, 'MotorCycle Au Pair Boy' (thought by some to be a sly reference to James Maker and his porn-star practices), and featuring a portrait, drawn by Morrissey himself, of Oscar Wilde clutching a sunflower.

Tim Broad's film vignette for 'Interesting Drug', also included on *Hulmerist*, caused a stir with its juxtaposition of anti-Conservative propaganda and *Carry On* humour. The fictitious Hawtrey High School For Boys becomes a base not just for Animal Rights activists, but for the then unemployment crisis and Norman Tebbit's controversial statement to state benefits dependants, 'Get on your bike and find yourself a job!' The busty actress Diane Alton is seen chaining her bicycle to the school railings, as the camera zooms in on the manufacturer's logo: CHOPPER. Her badge is inscribed, 'I've Never Had A Job Because I've Never Wanted One' – a line from The Smiths' 'You've Got Everything Now'.

Within the school, the hunkier-than-usual sixth formers (average age twenty) lounge around reading *NME*, cover courtesy of Diana Dors. Some wear women's high-heels and chalk slogans on toilet walls. A shot of the graffiti, THERE ARE SOME BAD PEOPLE ON THE RISE, precedes the pupils rushing out into the playground where Morrissey is handing out Animal Rights leaflets. Led by Diane Alton, weary of campaigning and now dressed as a bunny girl, the pupils raid the laboratory and set the animals free. A much more disturbing message follows with scenes of seal-clubbing and anti-fur posters.

These final images, coupled with the wording of the graffiti, brought about a national outcry, which led to the film being banned by the BBC. For once, *NME*'s Danny Kelly supported Morrissey, albeit in a lampooning way, urging fans, 'Whip out your STREET IS MURDER promotional quill now, dash off a series of letters to EMI and all the TV companies and demand to see it TODAY!' The film was eventually shown on *Top Of The Pops*, but only after the word 'rise' had been changed to 'right', which made little sense to the press until Morrissey enlightened them ('The bad people on the rise are the willing students of Tebbit') and the seal-culling scene removed.

For the time being, Morrissey's massive success in Britain meant that he did not seek to try his chances overseas, despite the flood of offers. The almighty dollar, he declared, was of secondary importance to patriotism. And once more he hit out at the de-Anglification of the country of his birth, telling James Brown of *NME* in March 1989:

> The generations of people who made England such a fascinating, interesting and artistically gentle place are slipping away. That

generation is almost all but gone. We're almost at a stage when there won't be anyone living who can remember the Second World War . . . Even the English language, I find, has been hopelessly mucked about with and everything is American or Australian. It's not that I dislike America. America is fine on the other side of the Atlantic. It works quite well and it's interesting. If Margaret Thatcher was a strong person, which she isn't, she wouldn't allow this Americanisation to happen.

With his apparent dislike of travelling, neither did Morrissey seem in any particular hurry to visit Europe again. 'I'm not going to pop up in some greasy Greek festival or at some waterlogged field in Belgium,' he told James Brown, 'I'm not going to be photographed in the Greek Amphitheatre with Yoko Ono and Art Garfunkel.' This innocuous comment brought complaints from aggrieved Greek and Belgian fans. Morrissey found an irate letter from one of the latter, Christophe Devos, sufficiently amusing to warrant a reply, which concluded, in large letters, 'BELGIUM IS SO FAR AWAY!' Devos told me, 'It did not make my day – but it made my whole life!'

Neither did Morrissey appear to have any plans for performing on home territory. Much of the first half of 1989 was spent writing songs. No longer keen on working with Stephen Street, he had a new production team: Clive Langer and Alan Winstanley, who had previously worked with Blue Rondo A La Turk, Madness and Elvis Costello. The pair owned the Hook End Manor Studios near Reading, in Berkshire, which had formerly been a Tudor monastery: importantly for Morrissey, it was within easy driving distance of the jail where his hero Oscar Wilde had been incarcerated. Even so, due to unforeseen problems, there would be more leftover songs produced or co-written on the new, as yet untitled album, than anything else. One was 'Ouija Board, Ouija Board', released as a single in November 1989. On the B-side was 'Yes, I Am Blind' with music by Andy Rourke and the 12-inch featured a very neat cover of the old Herman's Hermits hit, 'East West', far superior to the original.

The record reached number 18 in the charts, and like its predecessor was condemned by the tabloids, who should by now have learned how to recognise Morrissey's fate-orientated cynicism: the narrator lamenting the death of a friend who has left 'the unhappy planet with all the carnivores and destructors on it' – but whose attempts to reach her on the other side backfire when the board spells out his name and tells him, 'P-U-S-H O-Double F!'

Morrissey engaged comedienne Joan Sims for his 'Ouija Board, Ouija Board' video of 1989. Shot in the garden of his then home in the Manchester suburb of Bowden, it featured Sims as a deranged medium. At the shoot for the video, the two got along like a house on fire: 'He treated me like a princess all day,' Sims recalled, 'he had such a ripe sense of humour. And if ever you want a CV of my *Carry Ons*, he knows them better than I do. He's a very brainy chap. I hate to call him a pop star because it's such a horrible word. He's a very nice gentleman.' Of Sims, Morrissey observed, 'Standing next to her was my greatest moment of the year. She was so enormously gifted. And here was I, a silly sausage from somewhere near Manchester.'

Astonishingly, the song was attacked by the Church who, without listening to the lyrics and supported by tabloid hacks, accused Morrissey of inciting fans to become involved with the occult. His biting response, when asked to comment on the rag that had branded him 'devil worshipper', was, 'The only contact I ever made with the dead was when I spoke to a journalist from the *Sun*.' In November 1991, the subject would be brought up in an interview with New York's WDRE Radio. When asked if he believed in the afterlife, he said that he did and enlightened listeners as to the practice known as 'Twelve O'Clock Handle':

> If you stare into a mirror at midnight in a completely darkened room with a candle below your face, your face supposedly changes into the face of somebody who has died and who wants to reach you, or somebody who has died and doesn't want to reach you. I find that incredibly effective. Have you tried it? It's extremely frightening because most people's faces do change automatically . . . It's a very, very private thing, and I think it depends on how open or sensitive you are. If you're closed, nothing comes to you.

Nick Kent, mistrusted by Morrissey, but handy to have on side because he was still one of the most widely read journalists on the music scene, had been invited to Hook End Manor in November 1989. As had happened during the recording of *Strangeways Here We Come*, Morrissey also taped the interview, though with his propensity towards evading personal questions one might also have expected him to choose his responses more carefully. Kent confessed to liking 'Ouija Board, Ouija Board', though by the time the feature finally appeared in *The Face* in March 1990, he had demoted it to 'numbingly bad'. Neither did Kent do himself any favours by revealing that Clive Langer had referred to Morrissey as, 'Someone who comes up with the best song titles in the world, only somewhere along the line he seems to forget the song', before adding, 'It looks as if Langer is about to join Stephen Street in Morrissey's out-tray.' Hardly surprising, one might feel, if Langer had really said this.

The interview had begun badly, with Kent addressing him as 'Mozz' – bringing a snappy, 'It makes me sound like a racehorse.' One also gets the impression that Kent was deliberately trying to wind him up – or catch him off his guard, particularly when he proceeded with, 'Don't you feel you have to come out in some way to face the Nineties?' Again, the response was a grandiose, 'I believe my position in this coming decade is perhaps one of the most challenging and interesting things that's ever happened in British pop-music.' His interrogator, however, was insistent:

KENT: You write a lot about the homosexual experience . . .

MORRISSEY: Well . . . not a lot.

KENT: Okay, you write a lot about homosexual longing.

MORRISSEY: I've always said that I leave things very open and that I sing about people. Without limitation. And I don't think that automatically makes me a homosexual.

KENT: What about . . . sexual relationships?

MORRISSEY: I don't have relationships at all. It's out of the question.

KENT: Why?

MORRISSEY: Partly because I was always attracted to men or women who were never attracted to me. And I was never attracted to women or men who were attracted to me. So that's the problem. I've never met the right person.

It seemed that Kent, the music world and the fans had their answer: by his own admission, it appeared that Morrissey was currently – for want of a better description – a non-practising bisexual. The 'news' delighted *Gay Times'* Kris Kirk. 'Did you see the photograph in *The Face*?' he asked me, 'Morrissey's wearing a wedding ring . . . I mean, who could do something like [1990 single] 'November Spawned A Monster' – all that prick-teasing and exposing of flesh, and *not* be a Friend of Dorothy?'

Kris Kirk had attended The Smiths' very first performance in London, and in his stunning joint-feature ('Morrissey: Saint Or Sinner') with Richard Smith for *Gay Times* in August 1990, in the wake of Nick Kent's *Face* interview, Kris coined the gay Smithdom quip of the year, 'Here was a young shaver whose oxters I'd dearly love to sniff close up!' Even so, he was not sycophantic toward his idol, criticising Morrissey for his comments about Margaret Thatcher, for what he considered had been careless remarks about black music, and for his romanticising of suicide. Moreover, he took him to task for his extreme arrogance.

The second part of the *Gay Times* feature, Richard Smith's 'The God That Failed', picked up on Morrissey's obsession, in his early Smiths songs, with males, and explained why he thought this had in recent times been changed to more of a sexual ambiguity. His conclusion was spot-on, and hardly surprising:

He never believed he'd be anywhere near as successful as he went on to become. Once it became clear that The Smiths were destined not for the originally intended Indie cultdom, but for stardom, a large lyrical retreat and rethink was swiftly undertaken. None-the-less, whilst his songs then became non-gender specific to a man, they still only stood up to a homosexual reading.

Linking his analysis with the long line of Smiths 'Camp Hall Of Fame' covers, Smith concluded, 'Like anyone reasonably well-raised in gay culture, I could pick up the references, allusions and signs . . . The message couldn't have been any clearer if he'd put Jeff Stryker or Judy Garland on them.'

In September 2003, in the issue of *Gay Times* feting what would have been The Smiths' twentieth anniversary, Richard Smith could safely observe, 'Looking at the man, jumping to the conclusion that Morrissey was gay as a goose was as easy as sliding off a butter mountain.' Now, he pleaded, 'If you are gay then please, please, please wake up [to] the fact that it's the Nineties and some sort of stand is expected.'

The feature brought in a flood of letters from irate fans who claimed they had 'proof' of Morrissey's sexuality: some from heterosexual women (sent to a gay magazine!) claiming he could not possibly be gay because they had shared intimate moments with him, others from gay men declaring the opposite. 'The tone of every letter was that of wishful thinking,' Kris said. The next issue of *Gay Times* published a 'defence', penned by a fan named David Semple, part of which read:

It's a good story. Cultish singer writes songs with a clear gay message, then when he becomes successful he hushes down that message, disregarding all the gay people who put him where he was. The problem is, it isn't true. Morrissey's lyrics have never been more explicitly homosexual than on his most recent album, *Viva Hate* . . . but like Julian Clary [he] prefers double-entendres to direct statements. Morrissey couldn't sing 'Glad To Be Gay' or 'There's More To Love Than Boy Meets Girl' because he writes in the persona of a shy, unloved loner, closeted not so much about his sexuality as about his whole being. Tabloid readers would love to believe that homosexuals are an alien tribe appearing on earth from elsewhere, not their children or their brothers and sisters, but Morrissey rejects such a simplistic and repressive view and writes about a world of uncertain, awakening sexuality.

For the time being, if not for ever, Morrissey was keeping quiet: he had said too much already to Nick Kent, and would never speak to him again. As for Richard Smith, he would never stop singing Morrissey's praises in his highly individual no-nonsense way, and in August 1993 he wrote a feature for *Gay Times* entitled 'Cock Rock', which detailed 23 of 'the most noted penii in pop'. Morrissey appeared in eleventh position, behind Bowie and Lennon but ahead of Prince and Elvis Presley. Morrissey's photograph was captioned, 'Included here as one of only two pop stars who claim not to use their naughty bits for anything naughty. The other is, of course, Cliff Richard. You can draw your own conclusions.'

Meanwhile, on 9 February 1990, Morrissey flew to Los Angeles for a brief visit that began with an appearance at KROQ, the city's most important 'alternative' radio station. There had been little publicity, yet he was still greeted by over a thousand screaming fans, and at one stage of the proceedings was photographed with tears in his eyes. The interview itself was unrevealing. The American public in general knew little or nothing about him as yet, other than that he seemed to cause a big fuss wherever he went, and the questions were centred around a potted biography and a list of his likes and dislikes made available to the DJ. Only one caused him hassle: when he was asked if, in the world of pop music, there was any place for Madonna or Janet Jackson. Morrissey had revised his opinion of the Material Girl, who had been elevated from 'the nearest thing to organised prostitution' to 'quite an independent individual person'. Of the other singer he stated, 'Janet Jackson, as far as I'm concerned, has no talent at all.' This brought in dozens of complaints – though many others would argue he was simply speaking the truth.

Even so, the officials at KROQ knew that they were on to a good thing, and adopted Morrissey as a 'foundation artiste' – an honour almost equating to one being given Freedom of the City, promoting subsequent record releases with receptions, posters, car-stickers, calendars and other memorabilia. The move also led to a Smiths boom – bearing in mind that to the Americans, as to everyone else, Morrissey and The Smiths were one and the same. Over the next few months, six of their albums would go gold, selling in excess of 500,000 copies each.

And, while the British music press were still busy insulting him, an anonymous journalist observed in a syndicated column, 'When words aren't enough to describe the way someone else's words set to music make you feel, you know you are dealing with a genius.'

Morrissey returned to England, where for the first time ever he was forced to consider taking legal action against a fan. In March 1990 a feature entitled 'Morrissey's Manchester' appeared in the *Independent*, in which Jim White escorted readers on an exhaustive tour of the city – the usual Smiths spots, along with Boddington's Brewery, Strangeways Prison and some of the seedier sides of Hulme. For his piece White had been assisted by a fan named Robert Graham, who in 1989 had written a play about The Smiths (Morrissey had ignored his invitation to attend the premiere at the Contact Theatre) and Eliot Marks, another fan who had been organising Smiths conventions since the band's demise. The first, in August 1988, had attracted 1,200 visitors from around the world, and there had since been successful conventions in Tokyo, Los Angeles and latterly at Le Locomotif, a gay club in Paris's Pigalle-Blanche district.

Morrissey was indifferent towards these events, but he saw red when he learned of Marks' proclamation, read out in Paris, 'All monies raised by conventions past and present will go to the charity of Morrissey's choice.' Morrissey's press office threatened Marks with prosecution, and in turn was sent a petition, part of which read, 'Discos around the country laugh when we request your music, so we need somewhere where we can all come together away from the music that's destroying our country. Please give us your blessing to hold further events. Life is not worth living without the music to cling to.' The response was that such profiteering under someone else's name would not be tolerated, and Morrissey's blessing was denied.

Robert Graham would exact a revenge of sorts, later telling the *Independent* that in his opinion, Morrissey was a conman, adding, 'He encourages longing in his fans that he knows is empty and destructive. He was a fan himself, he should know better.'

Morrissey, meanwhile, returned to Hook End Manor where work resumed on the new album, now titled *Bona Drag*. Several new songs were cut: 'He Knows I'd Love To See Him', 'Striptease With A

Difference' (which tells of manipulating a game of strip poker so that one loses) and 'Get Off The Stage'. The latter was Morrissey's comment on the so-called 'geriatric content' of the *Billboard* charts, which had appalled him during his last visit to America: The Grateful Dead, Bob Dylan, The Rolling Stones and Eric Clapton were all considered by him to be way beyond their sell-by date. 'Oh, you silly old man, you're making a fool of yourself,' he expostulates, declaring that all the songs sound the same. Then the piece delightfully almost turns into an old-time French-Canadian reel as the musicians join in with the chorus and he concludes, 'When we get our money back, I'd like to see your back in plaster!' Very nice, but because of 'difficulties' that were never made public, it soon emerged that the album would never see the light of day as Morrissey had intended: instead, it became a collection of singles, B-sides and oddments.

Morrissey was besieged by journalists wanting interviews, but was in no mood for pleasantries. He was also still seething about Nick Kent's feature in *The Face*. 'He's more obsessed with me than he is with his own mother,' he told Jean-Daniel Beauvallet, 'but I take that as a compliment.' 'I could tell you things about Nick Kent that would take the frizz out of your Afro,' he told Len Brown, writing a profile for the November issue of *Vox*, to coincide with the album's belated release – though truthfully he only had himself to blame for speaking about his sexuality in the first place.

Only six songs were salvaged from the proposed album. 'November Spawned A Monster' was a tremendously bold, beautiful, moving pastiche that wrenched every last fibre of emotion from the Morrissey frame. Coupled with 'He Knows I'd Love To See Him' and 'The Girl Least Likely To', it reached number 12 in the charts. For backing vocals, Morrissey had hired Canadian singer Mary Margaret O'Hara, who had recently toured Britain and released an album, *Miss America*. 'I haven't in a decade heard someone singing because of a deep-set personal neurosis, absolute need and desperation,' he said of her at the time. 'You'd think she might fall apart at any second and become a pile of rags and bones on stage.' O'Hara's singing is certainly an acquired taste, though in this particular song it works astonishingly well.

The song (though otherwise unconnected with its title) does fit into the category known by the French as 'Les enfants de novembre' – collectively, the oppressed peoples of the world, whether this be by way of creed, colour, sexuality, war, or in this instance disability. As so often in his work, Morrissey helps us to comprehend her plight by climbing inside the skin of the 'poor twisted' child who must suffer life not just a 'frame of twisted limbs', but the object of everyone's pity, which is the last thing she wants. It rails against the limitations imposed upon a wheelchair-bound young woman whose only ambition in life is to walk down the street, wearing the clothes she has bought for herself. As usual, the critics donned their blinkers to attack the song, particularly the line, 'If the lights were out, could you even bear to kiss her on the mouth?' – to their way of thinking, this was Morrissey mocking the afflicted.

The promotional video for the song, filmed by Tim Broad at Mushroom Rock, in the remote, sun-scorched Death Valley, remains the finest piece of Morrissey's work ever captured on celluloid. Wearing a black, diaphanous top, neither shirt nor blouse, he is the epitome of narcissism, homoeroticism, pain, anguish, and muscular male beauty – yet despite his writhing and preening never seems to go over the top. On the Continent, favourable comparisons were made between this vignette of vignettes and the death throes of the young Resistance fighter in the famous Wajda film of 1958, *Ashes And Diamonds* – no little wonder, for its star Zbigniev Cybulsky was regarded as 'The Polish James Dean'. Indeed, when the Morrissey film was premiered on Warsaw television in the autumn of 1990, he was introduced as 'The English Cybulsky'.

According to Morrissey's record company, there was no promotional video for his next single – 'Piccadilly Palare', released in November 1990 and peaking at number 18 in the charts – because they considered it 'insufficiently commercial', which begs the question: why release it in the first place? The statement was, of course, untrue: though Morrissey's videos usually have little if anything to do with the subject of the song, EMI were worried that there would always be a first time, and felt that the topic of rent boys would prove too much for mainstream television. The song was backed with 'Get Off The Stage', and Stephen

Street's 'At Amber' which, because the critics were too busy deciphering and attacking the A-side, got off more lightly than it otherwise might have done. In this one the narrator, staying at a seedy hotel where 'the clime and the grime gel' and compel him to sleep in his clothes, calls his disabled friend to say how much he envies him for not being able to walk so that he doesn't have to put up with what the narrator is having to endure.

Modern rent boys – the ones who were legally underage, as opposed to those of Wilde's day – had been brought to the attention of the uninitiated general public during the late sixties, courtesy of television drama-documentaries such as *Johnny Go Home*. Watching this enables one to appreciate Morrissey's song all the more. The 'rails' he refers to are the black iron railings separating the terraced buildings from the pavements – from here, or from 'The Rack' (the notorious Meat Rack amusement arcade, which turned up again in the television's *The Vice* in 2003) the Dilly Boys plied their trade, calling out to well-heeled gentlemen (the 'belted coats') who, of course, ignored or insulted them if they were not interested in paying for their 'easy meat'.

Polari – derived from *palavrear*, Portuguese mariners' argot for 'to chatter to locals' – was a popular form of communication among the gay community of late 19th-century London, a nonsensical-sounding collection of phrases and buzzwords that enabled one to size up a potential client without attracting attention from bystanders. Of course, if the man under scrutiny was not interested in having sex, he would have had no idea what was being said. The parlance came back in a big way during the sixties, courtesy of the Light Programme's (a predecessor of Radio 2) Sunday afternoon cult comedy radio show, *Round The Horne*. This featured Julian and Sandy, the first openly gay characters to appear on British national radio, portrayed by Kenneth Williams and Hugh Paddick. The Polari term for homosexual, *omme poloni* ('man-woman'), frequently appears in biographies of Oscar Wilde. My good friend Peter Burton, for over thirty years the peerless keystone of gay journalism, explained the gist of Polari in his fascinating personal memoir, *Parallel Lives*:

As *freely ommes* (young men) . . . we would *zhoosh* (style) our *riah* (hair), powder our *eeks* (faces), climb into our *bona* (fabulous) new *drag* (clothes) don our *batts* (shoes) and *troll* off to some bona *bijou* (little) bar. In the bar we would stand around with our *sisters*, *varda* (look at) the bona *cartes* (genitals) on the butch omme *ajax* (nearby) who, if we fluttered our *ogle riahs* (eyelashes) at him sweetly, might just troll over to offer a light for the unlit *vogue* (cigarette) clenched between our teeth.

Other choice Polari phrases included *dolly basket, naff lucoddi* (nice crotch, shame about the body), but in the recorded version of his song (several verses had to be deleted to keep it to an acceptable length) Morrissey sticks to just a few of the regular words. Also, by the time he wrote it, some of these had taken on new meanings, as has happened in other areas of the English language – examples being *bona* (hard-on) and *troll* (cruise). One also has to remember that the majority of men who spoke Polari were adults heading towards middle age. The critics, therefore, were both ignorant and wrong to accuse Morrissey of encouraging underage sex in the song.

Surprisingly, it was the gay press leading the attack this time. In his excellent combined feature with Kris Kirk for *Gay Times*, 'Morrissey: Saint Or Sinner', Richard Smith took exception to 'Piccadilly Palare' and demanded, 'If you're not gay, then get your hands off our history. You can't steal the very words from our lips just so you can embellish your songs with (pardon the pun) a bit of rough.'

The publicity that 'Piccadilly Palare' attracted resurrected once again the question of Morrissey's sexuality. He had intimated at a non-practising AC/DC status to Nick Kent, though few people genuinely believed that no one had ever found one of the handsomest men in British show business attractive, no matter how picky he might have been. In fact, he could have made the situation a whole lot easier on himself by telling journalists to mind their own business. As things stood, with his appetite for certain elements of gay culture, he had allowed himself to be forced into an awkward corner. And *Gay Times*' Richard Smith had a valid point: if he was gay, the gay press wanted him to come out properly and offer strength and support to all those fans who had shut themselves up in bedrooms – seeking solace in his music to help them come to terms with being gay. And if he was not totally gay, then they wanted him to say so, leave off their culture and stop flaunting it in their faces. 'Being gay isn't for making money out of unless you're a fully paid-up member of the company,' Kris Kirk admonished. 'Otherwise you get out of the theatre and find yourself another job.'

While interviewing Morrissey for *Vox*, Len Brown wisely steered clear of the issue of sexuality, and focused instead on the recent insurgence of Mancunian groups: The Happy Mondays, 808 State (who, according to one unfounded story, Morrissey had thought of joining), The Stone Roses and Northside, to name but a few. Then there were the 'old guard': New Order, James and the like. Morrissey was unimpressed. 'If I was herded in with those groups,' he told Brown, 'believe me, I'd emigrate to Norway. I'm not the enemy of those groups, but I still have a boring, old-fashioned notion of talent.'

The gist of the interview was that, despite being an established artiste with one of the biggest labels in the UK, and with millions of record sales behind him, he was now actually selling less records than some of these acts. For Morrissey, though, it was quality that counted, not quantity. 'I never believed that sitting on top of the pop arena was a nice place to be,' he told Brown, before confessing one of the secrets of his success, 'I think there's always a danger in trying to give an audience what it wants. I think it's more interesting to give an audience something it might not want.' The audience certainly wanted the rehashed *Bona Drag*: it went to number 9 in the charts.

The album's release coincided with yet another reshuffling of the Morrissey cabinet, in preparation for the recording of his next album. Again, this displayed the difficulties he so frequently encountered when working with others, but at least it was a process that kept everyone on their toes and ensured the freshness of his work. The latest manager was Fachtna O'Ceallaigh, who had worked with The Boomtown Rats and Sinead O'Connor. Tom Verlaine, the American guitarist formerly with Television, was approached to work with Morrissey as a songwriter, but declined, throwing away a potential fortune, declaring that Morrissey's working methods – adding lyrics to taped, prepared tunes – were unacceptable. The problem was solved when Clive Langer brought in Bristol-born songwriter-musician Mark Nevin, a glam-rock enthusiast who had formed Fairground Attraction with Eddi Reader and topped the charts with 'Perfect'. He told me:

Fachtna O'Ceallaigh promised me that Morrissey would call me at home, but that never happened. I just sent him some tapes through the post, and waited for his response, which seemed to take for ever. Then suddenly I received a postcard. It was the first of hundreds, and he'd scrawled across it just one word – 'PERFECT!' I was thrilled. Our first song together was 'Tony The Pony', though I doubt anyone remembers it now.

The line-up was completed by Andrew Paresi (the drummer who had worked on *Viva Hate*), keyboard players Seamus Behan and Steve Hart and Madness' bass player Mark Bedford, raga-violinist Ali Khan adding a touch of the exotic. The new album, recorded at Hook End Manor, was given the title *Kill Uncle*, and as a taster in February 1991 EMI released the single 'Our Frank' (coupled with 'Journalists Who Lie'/'Tony The Pony'), a cynical ballad not quite up to Morrissey's usual standards and which barely scraped into the Top 30. Neither did the song impart any particular obvious message, though the line 'Give me a cigarette' was taken literally by some fans – in future concert performances, cigarettes would be flung on to the stage along with the customary flowers, mindless of the fact that Morrissey had never smoked!

Kill Uncle was released in March 1991, and reached number 8 in the charts. Despite much adverse criticism it is a good album, not as intense as its successors would be, but enjoyable all the same – its only fault being that, including only ten songs and running to just 33 minutes, it is too short. And because of its lack of drama, it is one of those 'mood' albums best listened to late at night when the lights are low.

The album opens with 'Our Frank', while 'Asian Rut' is discussed in the next chapter. The third song on the album, 'Sing Your Life', was released as a single in April and reached a disappointing number 33 in the charts – hardly surprising, for despite its catchy tune it received virtually no airplay. It was coupled with 'The Loop' (which certainly ought to have been on the album) and Paul Weller's 'That's Entertainment', of which more later. To whom, in the song, Morrissey is urging, 'Just walk up to the microphone and sing . . . now's your chance to shine' is not known.

There were two collaborations with Clive Langer. 'Mute Witness' tackles once more the topic of disability: the story of the deaf and dumb thalidomide victim who is hopelessly trying to describe an event that has distressed her – and to complicate matters, Morrissey has allowed this to happen in the notorious gay cruising area of Clapham Common. The second Langer contribution was 'Found, Found, Found', an ode to Morrissey's friendship with Michael Stipe, the gifted, frail-looking singer from REM, who was slightly younger than himself.

As with many of his early friendships, this too had started off on a pen-pal basis, with Stipe writing to Morrissey first; recently the pair had met, 'to walk in huge circles through Hyde Park'. Stipe, in those days, was as famed for his intense privacy as for his searingly lachrymose vocal technique. Since then, the singer has emerged from the closet and lost few if any of his fans, chiefly because they had always suspected him of being gay in the first place. Looking back, one therefore re-examines the question of why he would have been platonically drawn to Morrissey: both were eccentrics, admirers of off-beats such as Patti Smith and The New York Dolls; both were vegetarian; both were loners infatuated with realism, homoeroticism and death; both claimed when tongues inevitably started wagging that their lyrics were specifically genderless – though while Morrissey was hedging to explain the boast, 'Still, it was a good lay', Stipe was cutting to the chase by pronouncing, 'I'm in your possession/Nothing's free, so fuck me kitten.'

In 'Found, Found, Found', Morrissey steps into the shoes of the *réaliste*, or torch singer, to emphasise, 'The more you offer trust, the more you chase, the more you cry, the more you're bound to lose.' He told *Select*'s Mark Kemp in March 1991,

Michael is a very kind, generous person. The whole joy of the friendship is that music doesn't come into it. We don't ever talk about REM or whatever it is I do. There are other things to discuss . . . and who knows, we may even get a cover on *Hello!*

Morrissey was referring to the time-honoured superstition that couples snapped for the famous glossy celebrity weekly rarely stay together once they have appeared in it. What Stipe had to say about such an albeit tongue-in-cheek statement, or whether their friendship progressed beyond the platonic, is not known. That Morrissey was the more forceful partner in the friendship was suggested when Kemp asked him if he would like to work professionally with Stipe: 'It isn't decided yet what we'll do, but it would be nice to do something unusual, some Righteous Brothers type thing. I'd like to lead the way. It would be one of those funny, historic bits of television that's so rare these days, especially in England.' One finds it hard even envisaging such a project between the immaculately turned out Stretford bard and the rather more raggedy REM frontman. 'It'd be like teaming Donny Osmond with Albert Steptoe,' Kris Kirk observed.

The lyrics of *Bona Drag*'s 'The Harsh Truth Of The Camera Lie' could almost be autobiographical, were it not for the fact that the friendly photographer who is the narrator shares the humiliation of his subject's compulsion to put on an act in public life – coupled with his/her aversion towards facing unfriendly photographers who seek out tell-all blemishes. It was almost an allegory of how, in the not too distant future, some sections of the media would be applying the 'warts-and-all' technique to Morrissey himself – particularly the closing stanza, 'I don't want to be judged any more . . . I would sooner be just blindly loved.' And with 'The Last Of The Family Line', the 'I-will-never-marry' theme resurfaces when Morrissey dons the proverbial hairshirt to avow that, after fifteen generations of 'honouring nature', this last family survivor is at least 'spared the pain of ever saying goodbye'.

Two of the weaker songs on the album (weaker by Morrissey's standards, anyway) are 'Driving Your Girlfriend Home', with Linder on backing vocals, and 'King Leer'. In the former, Morrissey assumes the mantle of the kindly agony uncle who explains to a friend's boyfriend the despondency in the relationship she is trying hard to avoid. He tells him, 'She's laughing to stop crying.' In 'King Leer', the plight of the long-suffering girlfriend resurfaces, when rescue from the money-grabbing boyfriend is attempted by the temptation of bribery: 'vodka and Tizer', 'a homeless Chihuahua', and finally the narrator's body – though as usual with the self-deprecating Morrissey, nothing much happens in this department, and in any case his caring efforts are not appreciated by the ungrateful, spoilt little rich girl.

Few songs better sum up Morrissey's life than the closing track of the album, 'There's A Place In Hell For Me And My Friends', later adapted into French by this author for Barbara, who sadly did not live long enough to record it:

> Nous espèrons qu'autour du fourneau
> La peau et l'sang et les os
> Ne nous empêch'rons de pleurer
> Pleurer comme quand on était vivant

The truly dazzling, unadorned studio version of this song, enriched by Mark Nevin's solitary piano accompaniment (far more poignant than the arrangements for the subsequent concert and KROQ versions) becomes a graceful, tender hymn to malignity, an early epitaph – the fact that death, in common with nakedness, removes social boundaries and enables all mankind to become equal. Not surprisingly, it became his most requested song in France, and when *Les Inrockuptibles'* Jean-Daniel Beauvallet asked him in February 1991 if he merited such a place, he replied seriously, 'There's no other alternative. Some of us have to end up in hell and I'm ready to suffer the flames. In any case, there won't be enough room for all of us in heaven!'

At least one of the *Kill Uncle* songs is thought to have been pencilled in for the soundtrack of the gay road-movie *The Living End*, directed by Greg Araki and released in 1993. This tells the story of two HIV-positive lovers who, while not knowing when the end will come, blaze a trail of destruction across America. Why permission to use the song(s) was denied is not known – Kris Kirk believed that it might have had something to do with video director Tim Broad's recently discovered HIV status – but the actor Craig Gilmore was allowed to wear a Morrissey T-shirt in one scene, a shot from which was used for the playbills, and the film became a big favourite with gay Morrissey fans.

Meanwhile, wary of the difficulties posed by an ever-changing line-up, and also aware that his fans had been starved of live performances for far too long, Morrissey had begun his search for a reliable backing group long before the release of *Kill Uncle*. He wanted Mark Nevin, but Nevin had contractual obligations elsewhere that prevented him from going on the road. First up was Boz (Martin) Boorer, a 27-year-old guitarist who had worked with Sinead O'Connor, the offbeat Irish singer Morrissey had always admired. Morrissey was entering his rockabilly phase; in 1978 Boorer had joined The Polecats, average age fifteen, hailed as a 'genuine rockabilly band'. Morrissey had admired their 'Rockabilly Rebel'/'Chicken Shack' single, released on the Nervous label. The Polecats had successfully played New York and toured Europe, disbanding around the end of 1990 – coinciding with Boorer's meeting with Morrissey in a Holland Park restaurant. Another short-lived rockabilly outfit that Morrissey liked was The Memphis Sinners, comprising Alain Whyte and Spencer Cobrin – respectively lead guitar/backing vocals and drummer – and a multi-tattooed bassist named Gary Day. All were in their mid-to-late twenties. Their first 'assignment' with Morrissey had been backing him in the 'Sing Your Life' video, an audition of sorts filmed at the Camden Workers Social Club (with cameos from Mark Nevin and Chrissie Hynde), which they had passed with flying colours.

Neither Whyte nor Cobrin had been big Smiths fans, which Whyte figured would work in his favour. 'That's why we've always got on so well,' he told me in 1995, 'Moz had rid himself of all that excess baggage before we came along. He likes the way we've always taken him at face value. He's a good bloke to work for.' Spencer Cobrin was more direct: 'I was raised on Jimi Hendrix and The Who. Whenever The Smiths came on the radio, I'd switch the bloody thing off!' By far the smallest of the ensemble, but solidly built, Cobrin made up for any lack of stature with his ferocious playing, rivalling Mike Joyce at his best and even purloining one of his statements – 'Balls-out is my only speed!'

In amassing his quartet of rebels, Morrissey was saying goodbye to The Smiths for ever. Indeed, rather than being left behind in a sparkling blaze of regret, his best years were in many ways still to come.

5

Hail, Hail, the Gang's All Here!

He is a living link between Victorian literary ideals and modern-day bedsit drama . . . the uncrowned, undisputed champion of some of the more complex aspects of the human condition, and as such quite possibly the most influential entertainer of his generation.

David Bret

The gathering of The Morrissey Gang coincided with his 'black phase' with the British music press, when seemingly everyone was out for the jugular, attacking his every move and utterance. Even the simple question on one edition of the BBC's *University Challenge*, 'Who was the singer with The Smiths?' brought scornful remarks. Mark Nevin told me,

I remember asking myself, why did these people have to be ugly? It just shows how wicked some people can be when you give them a pen and an opportunity to write something in a newspaper. That's why I feel Morrissey enjoys touring so much. Because of the way the press has turned against him, he likes to be where he's more appreciated, like in America where they're more positive about him. The British press live in this journalists' Never-Never World where people do all these weird things that only make sense in a newspaper.

Even Tony Parsons, the respected scribe who subsequently defended the singer against his fiercest critics, was unable to resist taking a dig in the *Independent*, though he did confess to liking some of the songs:

> Morrissey documents the hot passions that stir the hearts of old English boys; he is the embodiment of pimply angst that seethes behind polite lace curtains. He is a music-hall Hamlet, a stand-up depressive, the revenge of the nerds . . . but, three solo albums down the line, the patron saint of miserable little buggers is still waiting for solo greatness to come along . . . Let's hope he hasn't lost Johnny Marr's number.

This latter comment was but one of many waspish remarks that Morrissey was starting to find irksome, but the *Kill Uncle* tour must have restored his faith in humanity. When, in November 1989, Nick Kent had asked him about touring, and particularly about touring America, he had replied – very assuredly, as if gazing into a crystal ball – 'The way I feel about America now is, if I had a strong body of people and went to America, I would be an absolutely suffocatingly enormous figure. But until I find that body of people, I'm not going to do it.' Now, he seemingly had found the right people, certainly the right musicians, but he was still not interested in visiting America – or England, for that matter. It was *NME* who announced that he would be playing Dublin, Paris, Deinze in Belgium, Utrecht in Holland, Cologne, Berlin and Hamburg – and that hopefully he would be playing a few Scottish dates, and maybe some English ones at the end of the year. The fans, particularly those who had flocked to the pilgrimage at Wolverhampton, were far from pleased.

Next, there was the question of who would be supporting him; more importantly, bearing in mind that 90 per cent of Morrissey concert-goers are interested only in him, there was the stage backdrop. For the former, several Morrissey-friendly acts are thought to have been proposed, some of whom had supported The Smiths: James, Easterhouse, The Woodentops, Lloyd Cole. Morrissey told *Les Inrockuptibles*' Jean-Daniel Beauvallet, 'I wanted to give them a helping hand, but not one of them offered me any gratitude – and Lloyd Cole was a very good friend until he started saying nasty things about me behind my back.' He therefore chose Phranc, an American folk singer who billed herself 'The first all-out Jewish lesbian poet'. As for the backdrop, Morrissey announced that the *Kill Uncle* tour mascot would be Edith Sitwell, the Scarborough-born poet-eccentric extraordinaire who had once publicly declared that her immense wisdom had been born of a long, unrequited love affair with the Russian painter, Pavel Tchelitchew – unrequited on account of his homosexuality.

The Sitwells – Edith and her younger brother, Osbert and Sacheverell – were almost the Warhols of their day, publishing between them a mountain of essays and poems covering every aspect of the arts. Like Morrissey, they championed many 'human interest' causes; like him they were revered without question, or loathed like pariahs. James Agate, the most influential American critic of his day, called them 'artists pretending to be asses'. Edith Sitwell's shock-tactic poem 'Façade', set to music by William Walton, had outraged 1920s London society; in the poem 'Gold Coast Customs', she had expressed her 'horror of all civilisation'. Her poems had become even more daring after World War II, and had been set to jazz and dance rhythms. Like Morrissey, Sitwell also had a knack of putting her foot in it, pontificating at one of her world famous Bayswater tea-parties, 'I have been brought up on Rhythm as other children are brought up on Glaxo!' – and at another, when a coach load of noisy children were arriving, 'It almost makes one wish for another King Herod!'

Also like Morrissey, Edith Sitwell nurtured a fondness for hats: turbans, pompadours, hideous creations with plumes and stuffed birds, but in her case these had rarely suited her bony, heavy-lidded features. She also favoured dressing in black, telling journalists in her resonant contralto tones, 'I'm in mourning for the world!' In the en profile by Cecil Beaton – which, as well as the on-stage backdrop, appeared on *Kill Uncle* posters, passes and laminates – Sitwell wears white, looks birdlike in her high toque, and clasps her lizardous, multi-ringed hands to her breast. Printed on to a massive sheet of canvas and illuminated by a spotlight, the image looks awesome.

Even so, due to a technicians' hitch, Edith Sitwell did not make her debut at Dublin's National Stadium on 27 April 1991 – Morrissey's first full-length concert as a solo performer. The 2,000-plus tickets had sold within an hour of the shutters going up. As at Wolverhampton, hundreds of fans had camped out overnight (albeit in better weather conditions than for Wolverhampton), to be assured of access to the standing area in front of the stage. Word soon got around that upon Morrissey's instruction there would be no protection barrier: he needed those hugs just as much as the flowers the fans had brought. Phranc managed to get through her whole 40-minute support slot without being heckled. Then the house-lights dipped as the speakers shook to the aria 'Death', by Klaus Nomi . . .

The fact that the venue was actually a boxing stadium (in retrospect, perhaps an indication that Morrissey had shrugged off his 'angst' years and was heading towards a tougher image) informed the turn of phrase in the review of the evening by *NME*'s Stuart Maconie: 'Rabbit-punched by his former friends, declared out for the count by a score of Harry Carpenters, the old champ is coaxed out of retirement for another shot at the crown.' Maconie also observed that the audience was much younger than the crowd of former Smiths fans he had anticipated: 'The only way they could have bought *Meat Is Murder* is by being wheeled into the store in a pram.'

Morrissey's entrance was stupendous, like that of a national hero returning from the front, save that this hero had eschewed his trenchcoat for tight-fitting Levi's and a baggy gold lurex chemise. He had made a statement that had appeared in syndicated columns earlier that week: 'If I were knocked down by a passing train tomorrow, I would be considered the most important artist ever in the history of English pop music. I'm a one-off. Every word I speak is cherished. It's a terrible curse, and sometimes I wish I could just blend in and go to the pub.' The boast rang true when for two whole minutes he stood, cruciform, in the spotlight as the flashlights popped and the screams and yells of the fans seriously threatened the foundations. The Garda, having watched footage of Wolverhampton and fearful of a riot, had placed supple-mentary chairs in the pit – these were now passed, hand-to-hand, to the back of the auditorium. Only then were the fans permitted to surge forwards and pelt Morrissey with thousands of flowers.

His opening number, 'Interesting Drug', was virtually inaudible on account of the fans' excitement. One of these grabbed the microphone from him to yell, 'I love you, Steven!'; Morrissey grabbed it back and growled, 'Thank you, but I don't know who Steven is!' By the time he had worked through a tremulous 'Mute Witness', the stage invasions, with fans skidding on the carpet of mushy flowers, were getting risky. 'This is all very touching,' he announced, 'but if you stay off the stage, we'll be able to play better!' This of course was like inviting a child into a sweetshop and expecting him to keep his hands in his pockets. During the 'birthing' section of 'November Spawned A Monster', Morrissey doubled up as if in agony – causing the Garda to think he had been genuinely injured – until he just as suddenly sprang to his feet. He certainly was not expecting the rugger tackle that brought him down halfway through 'Our Frank' – he hit the deck with a heavy thud, but decided against breaking off the song – and, like an astute thespian, at exactly the right moment spat out the appropriate line, 'Give it a rest, won't you?' The audience went wild!

Two songs were premiered in Dublin: 'Pregnant For The Last Time', and the delectable 'I've Changed My Plea To Guilty' (this author's second-favourite Morrissey song), one of the most emotive numbers he ever performed and which later would be criminally relegated to a B-side. The fact that this song was being delivered in a country devoured for decades by political strife – and was this *really* about the tragically heroic Bobby Sands, as some suggested? – only made the song doubly moving. Bravo, Morrissey!

By this time, not wishing to ruin his beautiful top, Morrissey had changed into an already-shredded shirt, which would not survive the rest of the evening. The New York Dolls' 'Trash', a quickly rehearsed late addition to the programme, was introduced as a tribute to Johnny Thunders who had died earlier that week. For many, though, one of the evening's highlights was Morrissey's and Alain Whyte's mind-blowing adaptation of Paul Weller's *revenchard* anthem, 'That's Entertainment', which one eye-witness described as 'orgasmic'. The piece was a modern, acerbic response to the Irving Berlin standard of the same title, belted out in the 1950s by Judy Garland and Ethel Merman – save that in the Weller version of events the 'entertainment' culminates with 'lights going out and a kick in the balls'.

The reviews were ecstatic. Friend Michael Bracewell paraphrased Oscar Wilde, writing in the *Guardian* that, 'He has nothing to declare but his genius.' *Melody Maker*'s Everett True, having seemingly witnessed a different performance to everyone else, customarily attacked Morrissey in a lengthy feature, but came right in the end by cryptically pronouncing him, 'The most charismatic performer this side of an Oliver Stone movie.' A perspiring, still bare-chested Morrissey afforded Cathy Dillon of *Hot Press* a few minutes of his time in the wings. 'He's an interviewer's dream – Woody Allen's mind in Montgomery Clift's body,' she enthused. To prove this latter point, as if proof were needed, the photograph accompanying Dillon's lament for Smithdom was airbrushed from the waist down, giving every impression that Morrissey had posed naked, which he had not.

Two evenings after Dublin, Morrissey played L'Elysée Montmartre in Paris – like the earlier Eldorado a prejudiced establishment frequently out of bounds to pop stars, though in the eyes of the French he had ascended the *chansonnier* ladder since then; he would never reach the very top, but he was held in much higher esteem than any of his contemporaries. The concert was taped by Bernard Lemoin, and relayed later in the week by France Inter on José Artur's *Pop-Club*. Subsequently it appeared on a bootleg CD, *Posing In Paris*. Although Morrissey never spoke a word of French – not even a *merci* between songs – the people had taken him to their hearts. *France-Dimanche* reported how, when he had announced, 'I *still* cannot speak French,' a dozen Japanese girls standing next to the stage had begun sobbing hysterically. The newspaper feature compared him not with any French male singer but with Barbara – the greatest of all the modern *chanteuses* since Piaf and a close friend of this author's. The comparison was neither condescending nor bizarre. Barbara was an intensely private woman who conducted an equally private love affair with her public for close on forty years: concert seasons, chart-topping albums (her last, in 1996, sold two million copies in a week), divided by lengthy, crippling periods of solitude at her country retreat. And, as with Morrissey, her lyrics focused on subjects frowned upon by the 'brush-it-under-the-carpet' Anglo-Saxon world: AIDS, the drugs-related death of a teenager, the death and roadside burial of her errant father in 'Nantes', her first million-selling single. Like Morrissey, Barbara placed the love of her public before that of any partner. Like him too, her best work was in front of an audience. Unlike him, on the other hand, she never risked sabotaging her career by persistent deliberation or attacking others.

Such qualities were not overlooked by Jean-Daniel Beauvallet, who for the April 1991 issue of *Les Inrockuptibles* asked Morrissey the same question he would subsequently put to Barbara. Was he afraid of the prospect of growing old alone? To a British journalist, the response might have been flippant. To a trusted, sensible foreigner it was rather sad:

> Whatever happens to me, my situation couldn't be worse than when I was seventeen. Do you remember a poem 'At Seventeen' by Janis Ian? [Sings a verse of this] What more can I add? Age doesn't frighten me. I could say that having money makes life easier the older I get . . . The truth is, as I get older, I'm better able to understand myself, to tame my terrible depressions. I can't eliminate them completely, but I have learned how to confront them head-on. When you've endured such an atrocious childhood, you have to make the best of what's left. The only certain companion for me is myself . . . The only way of escaping my own particular world would be by letting someone else into it, to *drag* me out of it. Otherwise I find it best to make do with waiting, with dreaming.

After sell-out concerts in Deinze and Utrecht, The Morrissey Gang moved on to Germany, by which time their number had been augmented by Wigan-born journalist Stuart Maconie, commissioned to write a piece for *NME*. Morrissey was made aware of Maconie's alleged abhorrence of the prejudiced treatment the singer was getting from his music press colleagues and, warming to his Lancashire twang, he invited

Maconie to tag along with himself and the musicians for a night on the town. Describing him as, 'An enormous, capricious talent who's come through a hail of slings and arrows of outrageous fortune with the stoic optimism of a Captain Mainwaring', Maconie told me:

> Morrissey was in his element in Berlin, laughing all the time and cracking jokes. He's a very witty man. Somebody wanted him to pose for a photograph so he lay down in the middle of the road and got hit by a bicycle. He just stood up and said, 'I don't know whether to throw the bike into the Rhine, or whatever the river's called here, or act like a perfect gentleman, which is something I'm good at!' Later on, myself, Morrissey, the lads from the band and a few others had a couple of drinks in the hotel bar, and I suggested going walkabout. That surprised him a bit, being treated like a mate. So we set off around Berlin looking for things to do. We went into a couple of clubs, but none of them were brilliant, so we all talked. He told me that he was frighteningly happy, and he seemed to enjoy being treated like a normal person, which is what he is. Morrissey's at his most relaxed when he's with other Northerners. I'm also very proud that one of the best interviews he ever did was with me. Us Northerners have to stick together!

Maconie's interview with Morrissey, the last time he afforded *NME* the time of day, was inspiring – due to the absolute absence of misinterpretation, the fact that Maconie published his comments verbatim ('On the grounds that you'd prefer to listen to him than me!') without attempting to draw attention to himself, as too often happens with the music press. At a time when the tabloids were into their 'outing' phase, the headline itself was an attack on the system: MORRISSEY COMES OUT! (FOR A DRINK). And as was to be expected, Morrissey's observations were rich with gritty, razor-sharp humour. First and foremost, he was fed up of talking about his old group, and felt that a rational man such as Maconie might help him convince everyone else of this:

How they met: 'Johnny came up and pressed his nose against the window.'
Morrissey and Marr, England's finest songwriting partnership, pictured in 1985.

The Smiths in 1987, shortly before their split.

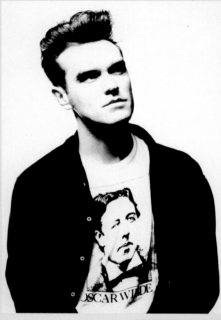

Speaking of Oscar Wilde in 1989, Morrissey said, 'In a way he became my companion, and as I get older the adoration increases.'

Pictured after Belfort, France, 1992 — by now Europe had awarded him the prestigious *chansonnier* tag.

In Minneapolis, USA, 1992.

At JFK airport in 1992,
Morrissey said of America,
'It seems that people like me
here more than anywhere
else in the world.'

'I think there's always a danger in trying to give an audience what it wants. I think it's more interesting to give an audience something it might not want.'

Above and below: During the *Your Arsenal* tour, 1992. Mark Nicholson/Annette Wikander

'I'm in a dialogue with my audience and that's something I need.'

Above and right: The warrior and his battle scars during the Boxers tour, 1995.

Manuel Rios

Above: Morrissey tells his audience: 'We're fully grown adults. If you want to stay in your seats that's okay with me — but you don't have to!'

Manuel Rios

Right: 'I am human and I want to be loved.' Taking a moment to bathe in his fans' adulation, the Boxers tour, 1995.

Manuel Rios

Morrissey, on the eve of his mighty comeback, promoting *You Are The Quarry* in (*above*) Las Vegas and (*left*) New York, April/May 2004.

At the moment I look on The Smiths as a dead cat that must be buried in a shoebox at the bottom of the garden. And that is not to spit upon anyone who might walk in here wearing a Smiths T-shirt. I would never do that. But my past is almost denying me a future. So as for The Smiths, I have my tin hat on, and I'm bringing down the blackout.

On the subject of idolatry, he commented, 'It's drastically simple. At the risk of sounding more pompous than I am, I was always more loved than adored. Eric Clapton is admired. But who could love him – his own mother, perhaps?' And on the subject of solo success and his new band of brothers:

What amazes me is the number of people who say my solo records aren't as good as The Smiths'. It's a logic that they don't apply to any other ex-Smith. So what they're in effect saying is, 'Morrissey, we consider you to have *been* The Smiths.' I've been pinching myself so much that my legs are brown. Everything I've worked for these past twenty-four months has come right, and the core of that is the four individuals I'm working with. They are central to everything I do. They are the best musicians I've had the joy of working with. I do hope people will not constantly want to write about The Smiths and the Good Old Days, the days when we got bad reviews and we didn't play so well sometimes. These musicians are *better*. I don't want people to wait until I'm hit by a milk-float to realise what a great group this is.

And, of his despondency with the music scene, Morrissey pronounced, 'Given the competition, it's easy to shine, or at least to shine in a reasonably buffed manner. The rock press is currently having to create personalities out of a dull herd of new groups. You're kidding if you think The Manic Street Preachers mean anything to anybody. Watching *Top Of The Pops* and, I shudder to say it, MTV, is like watching a road accident.'

Maconie wanted to know if Morrissey was still contemptuous of journalists, and of British journalists in particular. He replied that he was not, adding, 'This will seem an unreadably bloated remark but, as time goes by, my individuality is affirmed by those writers who can't stand my guts. They are constantly handing me back-handed compliments . . . I must mean more to them than their own mothers.' And finally, referring to Morrissey's stalwart patriotism, would come a remark that his music press enemies would recall in years to come, made after Maconie indicated the purple varnish on his thumbnails, and asked what this stood for: 'Skinheads in nail-varnish represent the Britain I love. The skinhead was an entirely British invention. If ever I was asked for an autograph by someone wearing some of those awful Cure baseball boots, I'd take it as a sign from hell that the curtain was coming down!'

Tim Broad took advantage of the sojourn in Berlin, using it as a backdrop for the promotional video for Morrissey's next single, 'Pregnant For The Last Time'. He and the musicians were seen on stage in the spartan-looking Metropole Theatre with the obligatory flaunting of flesh to reveal messages scrawled across Morrissey's chest: first the word SINGER in capital letters, then VOICE – pretty tame compared with the invitation INITIATE ME, a photograph of which had graced the front page of *NME* and which now appeared on bootleg posters on sale outside the theatre. The bequiffed quintet were also seen out in the city streets – playing Frisbee and visiting the Brandenburg Gate. There was an impromptu appearance by Eva Busch, the veteran actress-singer who had been Marlene Dietrich's rival at the time of the Weimar Republic – and the late Jobriath, who featured courtesy of an album cover brandished by the singer. What the German fans made of the new, argot-laden song, even those fluent in English, is anybody's guess – particularly the phrase, 'corned-beef legs', a term coined during World War II to describe the blotches pregnant women suffered through sitting too close to the coal-fire for too long. It was a fine, bouncy companion-piece to the earlier 'End Of The Family Line', dealing as it does with traditional expectations of ordinary working-class folk who are too stuck in their ways to ever do anything different than ordinary. Released in July, the record only reached number 25 in the charts. On the B-side was 'Skin Storm', while the 12-inch featured 'Disappointed' and Marc Bolan's 'Cosmic Dancer', both recorded on stage in Utrecht.

The brief European tour ended a few days later in Copenhagen, leaving a week's gap before Morrissey's three Scottish dates. These did not go so well as anticipated. In Aberdeen on 14 May he complained of feeling unwell, and by the next morning had developed a severe throat infection and high temperature. He managed to get halfway through that evening's concert at Dundee's Caird Hall, but the next one at Glasgow's impressive Concert Hall had to be cancelled. Some fans reacted badly, causing pandemonium outside the venue until informed by an EMI spokesman that Morrissey would make amends by returning to Glasgow immediately after his American tour, scheduled to open at San Diego's Sports Arena on 30 May.

On the eve of his biggest venture, the British music tabloids announced that Morrissey and support act Phranc would soon be entering the studio to record a cover version of the 1975 Elton John–Kiki Dee hit, 'Don't Go Breaking My Heart'. This was supported by a statement, supposedly from Morrissey, 'Our song will help break the ice at discos and stop the boys huddling in corners and make them ask the girls to go for a twirl around the tiles.' According to EMI, no duet had ever been planned and there was no statement – Morrissey's enemies were attempting to discredit him again, by the fact that if yet another promised project never got underway, he would be seen to be letting the fans down once more. That such an undertaking had never even been discussed should have been evident from Morrissey's outburst to *Select*'s Mark Kemp earlier in the year, 'I could never ever begin to explain the utter loathing I feel for dance music. That two people can sit in their bedroom in Detroit with a little bit of machinery and come out with this huge wall of sound is sterility at its utmost. I want to see real people on stage, playing real instruments.' And in any case, Phranc had to drop out of the tour owing to the death of her brother.

In his interview, Kemp had asked Morrissey what he would do if it all ended suddenly. He had replied almost with abject indifference,

I would absolutely mind my own business. I'd live in a crumbling cottage somewhere in Somerset, out of the way. I would not try to re-invent a pop persona. I'm too saddled with dignity to do such a thing. I'm persecuted by a sense of pride and dogged by cunning foresight.

If American ticket sales were anything to go by, this rural retreat was a long way off. British bands such as EMF and Jesus Jones who had done well in the US charts had recently been criticised for their inability to fill 3,000-seater venues. Morrissey, who had enjoyed no chart success at all in America since turning solo, staggered everyone by selling the 18,000 tickets for the Los Angeles Forum concert of 2 June in just fifteen minutes, and the 20,000 tickets for his opening concert in San Diego in less than an hour – faster than any predecessor, including Michael Jackson and Madonna, though why the press should have made an issue of this (and demoted the Forum's capacity to 14,000 in print) when he was just as big in his field as they were is baffling.

Fans at the Forum were given a surprise when, toward the end of the concert, David Bowie walked on to the stage and joined Morrissey in a somewhat tremulous duet of 'Cosmic Dancer'. Kristine McKenna of the *Los Angeles Times*, astonished to have seen so many young men clambering on to the stage to kiss Morrissey, was just as surprised when he confessed to having a feminine side – and when he drew comparisons between himself and the biggest gay icon of them all:

> Take women singers. They're allowed to say intimate things and be fragile, whereas men aren't. Singers like Judy Garland had enormous strength, yet they were on the edge and you know that they simply couldn't end the song and walk away. The song went with them. They carried that burden throughout their lives. Singers attract fans who have aspects of their own personality. I think people think I'm very passionate and obsessive, and they know this isn't a profession for me – it's a vocation.

The remaining 25 venues also sold out in record time: only the Sacramento Exposition Center failed him, with a third of its tickets remaining unsold due to poor advertising. Television newsreels even broadcast footage of tearful, disappointed fans at freeway exits –

waving Edith Sitwell posters and flagging down similarly recognisable fans with $100 bills.

As in England, there were the detractors, albeit on a smaller scale. Warlock Pinchers, a Colorado-based group, had recorded their attack on the singer, 'Morrissey Rides A Cock Horse', two years previously and this had gone virtually unnoticed. Now, hoping to ride as such on the immense publicity surrounding the tour, Tupelo Records re-released it in a cover adorned by a very attractive photograph of Morrissey. Many of his fans bought it just for this, only to be horrified when they took out the record itself, the inner label of which depicted a drawing of Morrissey, chanting 'Ouija Board, Ouija Board', whilst simulating anal sex with a skeleton over James Dean's grave. And if this was not enough, the lyrics included the line, 'Crybaby son-of-bitch no-talent motherfucker.'

Morrissey was understandably furious, but took no action against the group or their record company, declaring rightly that this would only bolster their publicity. Suffice to say, they very quickly faded into obscurity. He also rejected innumerable requests for 'in-depth' interviews, though he did allow media admittance to a soundcheck at the Orange County Amphitheater on 1 June where, in Edith Sitwell T-shirt, shades and a large hat, he was filmed rehearsing 'Sing Your Life'. There should have been an appearance on a local television show, *Request Video*, hosted by Gia Desantis, but Morrissey backed out at the last minute, which was perhaps just as well. Permitted to interview his musicians but specifically instructed not to ask personal questions about Morrissey, Desantis giggled her way through the proceedings, and asked such silly questions as, 'What's the funniest thing Morrissey's done whilst he's been here?' The replies were mostly monosyllabic; Spencer Cobrin, bored by it all, fell asleep.

The American fans differed from their British counterparts. Robert Sandall of *Q* observed, 'There is no typical American Mozzaphile: androgynous teenagers, Latino gangsters, booted skinheads, suited thirtysomethings, a few stray gays and a handful of senior citizens have all been sighted.' Jo Slee, Morrissey's long-time personal assistant-factotum-temporary manager, told the press, 'He attracts this gentle adoration from everybody, but you'd need a degree in sociology to work him out.'

At some venues, audiences were restrained from 'stepping out of line' and from throwing 'missiles' – in other words, stage invasions and flowers were forbidden. Considering the fact that these were key components of a Morrissey recital, most of his performances were muted and lacking in spontaneity. KROQ Radio had scheduled a return visit, but rather than risk the ballyhoo of having him show up at the station, his three songs were recorded live at the Capital Studios. Later, they were released on a CD: the version of 'There Is A Place In Hell For Me And My Friends' is in a class of its own.

At Berkeley's Greek Theater on 8 June, one official, thinking he was acting in everyone's interest, placed large cardboard boxes outside the venue labelled GIFTS FOR MORRISSEY. These were quickly filled with all manner of paraphernalia: volumes of Oscar Wilde, greetings cards, red ('Our Frank') pullovers, flowers, nude snaps of fans – along with dozens of packets of pork scratchings, underwear to which were attached the donors' names and addresses in the hope that Morrissey would wear the items and send them back – and condoms, presumably with the same thought in mind!

In Phoenix on 11 June, Tim Broad shot the promotional video for 'My Love Life', though as yet this had only been pencilled in for Morrissey's next single. In it, he is seen driving the gang through the streets of the city in a hired 1970s Rolls-Royce Corniche, the top down and the breeze blowing through his hair – welcome relief in the 104-degree temperatures. The combination of dreamy music and monochrome imagery gives the piece a relaxed David Lynch-like effect. The single was released in the UK the following October, but only just edged into the Top 30. The song was coupled with the superb 'I've Changed My Plea To Guilty' – almost certainly the record would have done better with this on the A-side – and the KROQ live version of 'There's A Place In Hell For Me And My Friends'. And in Britain, for the first time, a Morrissey sleeve was given the thumbs-down by many allegedly 'copycat celibate' fans because it contained a sunbathing shot by Linder Sterling of the singer's shapely lower half encased in tight-fitting boxer shorts bearing the logo,

'Campus Oscar Wilde'. Obviously, the thought of their hero having a little fun every once in a while was too much for some.

Morrissey, meanwhile, irked by the enforced lack of contact with his fans this side of the Atlantic, according to the promoter 'threw a wobbly' and demanded that security should be relaxed for his concert at the Dallas Starplex on 11 June: this was to be filmed by Tim Broad, and 'put into storage' for future release as a commercial video. It was released the following year on 26 July, the date Oscar Wilde had visited Dallas during his trip to the USA.

Live In Dallas brought an unexpected attack in *Select* from Stuart Maconie, the reporter Morrissey had got along with so well in Berlin, and who would interview him again a few years hence – suggestive that Morrissey cannot have seen what Maconie wrote in *Select*, otherwise he might have given him a wide berth. Referring to him as 'an emotional cripple with a cruel streak', and 'an old tart', Maconie criticised the singer for spending so much of his time on stage with his shirt off, and added of Morrissey's 'dead cat buried at the bottom of the garden', 'If The Smiths had never existed it would be possible to watch videos like this without rocking back and forth and sobbing quietly.'

Why Morrissey had his video filmed at a venue where the acoustics were below average is not known; it may well be that this was the only venue prepared to submit to his relaxed security demands and give the fans free rein to their emotions. To most of these American establishments he was an unknown quantity, and as with some of the older Parisian theatres, their proprietors did not want the places wrecked. They were yet to find out that Morrissey fans were not hooligans. Even so, the stage invasions became increasingly difficult for the staff at the Starplex to tolerate, and the final straw came after a stupid, unwarranted guitar-smashing sequence following 'That's Entertainment'. 'There were so many kids milling around the stage, looking like they were in a trance but that they might explode any minute,' an official said later. 'The fans had had their money's worth, but if anybody was to blame for the fiasco it was the idiot on the guitar.'

News of the guitar-smashing episode spread like wildfire. In Detroit, DO NOT CROSS signs were posted in front of the barrier: three fans, invited on to the stage by Morrissey to join in with the chorus of 'Sing Your Life', were dragged off by bouncers, handed over to armed police, and subsequently fined for 'civil violation'. There was a similar incident at Chicago's World Theater, capacity 30,000. Afterwards, accusing his American record company, Sire, of attempting to spice up his shows by feeding the media with false rumours of his 'prima donna tactics, mood-swings and tantrums' unless he was given all of his own way, Morrissey told the *Chicago Tribune*'s Greg Kot:

> It's all lies. It's disheartening, but I would never, to coin that delightful American expression, kiss ass. I don't *want* to become a commodity, a dishrag, and [regarding the future] I'm completely fatalistic in that I believe whatever happens is meant to happen for the eventual good, if not the immediate good. Though I can go through moments that are quite depressing, I secretly know that I'll profit from them. I just have to wait and see why things happen.

Philadelphia was something of a family affair, with Morrissey's mother, sister and his two nephews turning up for the show. The whole glamorous shebang – or at least the first leg of it – ended on 13 July with a triumphant recital at New York's Madison Square Garden, after which he was felicitated by Michael Stipe, Matt Dillon, and Lloyd Cole, the latter obviously forgiven for what he is supposed to have said. 'That was Morrissey through and through,' Kirsty MacColl told me. 'He would be all over a person one minute, then kick them out of his life the next, often never explaining why. I was one of the lucky ones . . . I'm really surprised that his love-life didn't make the tabloids, especially the way he treated some people whose only crime had been to care about him unconditionally one way or the other.'

One week later, Morrissey played his first London date in five years, at the Wembley Arena – an event that was preceded by chaos when trains to the venue were terminated several miles from their destination. Unaware of this, Morrissey inadvertently made matters worse when he brought the starting time of the show forward by half an hour. Phranc had returned to the fold for the British leg of the tour, but on account of the mad dash the fans missed not just her, but some of Morrissey's performance too. The Sitwell backdrop had been replaced by a less effective one of Harvey Keitel – the 'Bigmouth Strikes Again' pose from the 1968 film *Who's That Knocking At My Door*, which Morrissey had been after for years. There was further drama when the microphone failed during his opening song, 'Interesting Drug'. Even so, everything else he did was exemplary, as determined by the quality of the bootleg CD that appeared soon afterwards.

The reviews in the British music press were mostly vacuous, vulgar and lacking wholly in professional integrity. *NME* managed a little decorum for once by publishing a sensational picture spread by Kevin Cummins. One, of the singer draped upside down over a monitor – captioned 'The Arched Back-Deacon of Wembley' – remains definitive. Their reporter David Quantick observed, 'This is so impressive that Mozzer's other stage actions – tearing his clothes up, baring a breast to the audience, and good old waving his arms about – seem mundane and workaday.' Another photograph, with Morrissey looking slightly menacing, later graced the cover of this author's *Morrissey: Landscapes Of The Mind*. The reviews in the broadsheets were generally better penned and more respectful. David Sinclair of *The Times* called it 'one of the most gripping spectacles likely to be seen this year'. *Select* drew attention to Morrissey's delivery of 'Mute Witness' – on his back, feet pointing to the rafters and executing 'a mating ritual originally meant for some species of parrot.' Various publications reported the moment when a bear-hug from a burly fan went wrong – Morrissey grabbed him, effortlessly raised him inches from the floor, and swung him around in such fashion that those nearest the stage found themselves ducking in case he let go! 'So many people underestimate him,' Linder Sterling told me. 'They don't even begin to realise how phenomenally strong he is.'

After Wembley it was the Brixton Academy, the scene of The Smiths' very last British concert in December 1986. Many fans expected him to mark the occasion with at least one Smiths song, but he did not. From London he moved on to Brighton, Liverpool, Doncaster, Blackpool and Glasgow's Concert Hall – where admirers were still miffed about the May cancellation. Here, the bouncers were worse than they had been in

America. Three youngsters were hospitalised after falling foul of their over-zealous security.

The Japanese have always been wildly receptive of drama queens, *chanteuses-réalistes*, and generally over-the-top performers: Barbara, Freddie Mercury, the great French *tragedienne* Damia who specialised in songs about death, Jacqueline Danno (this author's godmother) – Japanese fans could never get enough of them. Morrissey was already well known here. Smiths and Morrissey memorabilia could be found in shop windows in the Ginza, Tokyo's liveliest thoroughfare, almost a Japanese Soho or Pigalle: geisha boys in the classy *kage-me-jaya* ('tea-houses amongst the shadows') sported Morrissey quiffs. The country's most famous female impersonator, Miwa (Akihiro Maruyama) – 55 but still very glamorous and known as 'The Japanese Piaf' – was not averse to adding the odd Morrissey song to his impressive repertoire.

The announcement of Morrissey's impending visit was of sufficient importance to warrant a feature on the front page of the anti-show-business *Nihon Keizai Shinbun*, Japan's equivalent of the *Financial Times*, on 23 August 1991. The tabloids followed this up with resumés of his career, though there were no bare-chested photographs in a country that frowned upon such things. His fan base was strongest among the gay community, where he had joined the ranks of *gaijin*, as welcome foreigners are called – because Western men are frequently bigger, better endowed and more hirsute than their Oriental counterparts – and comparisons were made with Freddie Mercury, a massive star in Japan, by the ones who heeded the rumours (very wrong!) that Morrissey enjoyed a similar lifestyle. Obviously, they would be in for a big surprise: unlike Mercury, Morrissey would not be painting the town red each night after the show; neither would he be taking to the stage at the (albeit highly respectable) Miwa Club, a gay Lido-style nightspot much favoured by tourists, which had nevertheless added his portrait to its famous Stars Gallery.

The first concert took place on 27 August at the recently built Fukuoka Sun Palace, a smallish venue where the security, like every-where else on the tour, was atrocious. Because the Japanese authorities had never heard of Morrissey, and because of the comparisons with

Freddie Mercury, they expected a Queen-sized throng to turn up for the 1,500 tickets on sale. Subsequently the building was surrounded by police with batons, and the starting time of the concert (again, as everywhere else) – at 6.30 p.m. already early by European standards – was brought forward by two hours! This was only the beginning. Fans were searched on their way into the auditorium: all flowers were confiscated, checked for hidden devices and drugs, labelled with the sender's name, and taken backstage to be given to Morrissey after the show – defeating the objective, of course. Additionally, the tannoys blasted out police warnings: anyone trying to get on to the stage would be arrested. Morrissey accused the authorities of meanness, encouraged fans to make a move on him, and was delighted when one over-enthusiastic handshake led to him being relieved of a shirtsleeve. The spoils were squabbled over by a group of completely hysterical girls, one of whom appeared to go into a fit. The repercussions would be severe, however.

Preferring not to spend the night in Fukuoka, seeing as the show had finished two hours earlier than expected, Morrissey and his entourage boarded the bullet train to Osaka – followed by two dozen admirers 'chaperoned' by a charming young lady named Kanako Ishikawa who, through her sheer politeness, very soon earned Morrissey's respect and later founded the *Lucky Lisp* fanzine. During the journey he actually made the effort to visit their carriage, where he chatted, posed for photographs and signed autographs. These youngsters were certainly more fortunate than their peers, for Morrissey had flatly refused to give any press interviews, and neither would there be any radio/television appearances. Against his wishes, EMI-Toshiba had released a Japan-only six-track CD that the authorities had banned from the airwaves because, they declared, one of the songs (Paul Weller's 'That's Entertainment') had been responsible for 'inciting eruptions' between bouncers and fans.

Such problems, aggravated by an acute lack of communication, brought out the riot police in Osaka long before fans began arriving at the 8,000-seater County Hall. These ordered barriers to be erected not just in front of the stage, but in the aisles. Because of the impeccable acoustics, plans had been made to record the performance in its entirety for commercial release, but these were shelved because of Morrissey's refusal to meet the Toshiba executives. The result was an otherwise excellent bootleg CD, *Nothing To Declare But My Jeans.*

The security staff continued their hounding of the fans at Nagoya's Century Hall on 1 September – for the innocuous throwing of cigarettes on to the stage during 'Our Frank'. Matters came to a head the next day at the 10,000-seater Budokan, Tokyo's most prestigious concert hall. Here, each block of seats had been fenced in, as Kanako Ishikawa explained:

> Morrissey spent part of the morning walking around the animal market. That evening, we were the ones in cages. Fans who committed the crime of standing up in their seats were grabbed by bouncers and dragged, by their clothes or hair, and thrown into the street. The flowers which we had taken for him were on the stage, still in their wrappings like in a florist's shop. He threw these back through the bars after his first encore, then took off his shirt and threw this. One fan did manage to get past the security, and when he hugged Morrissey, Morrissey was terrified of letting him go. It was such a cold, horrible atmosphere.

During his walkabout, trailed by some of the most timid fans he had ever seen, Morrissey felt wholly at ease, not in the least threatened. Kevin Cummins had tagged along to photograph him for *NME*, though there would be no interview: headed ANNOYING NAGOYA, there would be just a clutch of exceptional pictures, captioned by Morrissey himself under the pseudonym Alf Button. A group of very ecstatic concert-goers were labelled, 'a good lay, a-ha!'; one of him about to board the bullet-train was inscribed, 'It's Hiroshima That We're Nearing'. Above a stage-shot in front of the backdrop he had written, 'On A Clear Day You Can See Edith Sitwell.' More controversially, a snap of him holding up a T-shirt depicting a snarling skinhead was captioned, 'Bury My Heart At Broadwater Farm' – a reference to the site of the murder of PC Keith Blakelock. Other gems included an adaptation of a line from Noël

Coward's *Private Lives* – 'Excuse me, but have you seen a biscuit tin by Moonlight?' – penned by Tallulah Bankhead in her famous send-up when she had toured with the play for several years back in the forties amidst scenes of gay hysteria. And finally there was a photograph of Morrissey posed next to the slogan, PENIS [sic] MIGHTIER THAN THE SWORD, and captioned, 'Bring Me Home And Stab Me.' More reverently, he visited the Hie Ginja Shinto shrine at Akasaka. Many shoppers and tourists paused to watch this posturing and to take photographs themselves, aware that someone important was in town, but far too polite to ask who he was. Aware of this, he began handing out scraps of paper upon which he had scrawled not his autograph, but MISTAKEN FOR JOBRIATH YET AGAIN! The Jobriath quip referred to the Japanese CD, the cover of which featured a photograph of Alain Whyte and Gary Day poring over Jobriath's first album, and it later emerged that attempts to track down the singer for a support slot in a future tour had failed. Astonishingly, no one appears to have found out that he had been dead for seven years. Meanwhile, that evening and the next, 'Will Never Marry' was dropped from Morrissey's set and replaced with 'Cosmic Dancer'.

Morrissey's final concert in Japan, on 3 September, was at the huge 15,000-seater Yokohama Arena. Here, he growled at the bullying bouncers and actually smashed his microphone against one of the barriers in protest. Early the next morning, he took the train to Narita airport, no doubt relieved that it was all over. 'A few of us accompanied him,' Kanako said. 'He looked sad to be leaving, and I know that part of his sadness was over the way we had been treated. I half expected him to announce that he would never come here again. That wouldn't have surprised me at all. But he just waved, and left.'

It would take him a long time to set foot in Japan again.

In 1992, Shinko, a Japanese publishing house, encouraged by folksinger-journalist Goroh Nakagawa, attempted to right the wrongs of the recent past – and of course made a great deal of money in the process – by issuing what was promoted as a 'tribute anthology': a 335-page tome containing translations of all 112 Smiths songs, and around 90 per cent of Morrissey's output – 'Piccadilly Palare' and the other vernacular numbers were given up as a bad job. Some of the translations were by Yuji Sakamoto, who would have acted as interpreter should Morrissey have given any interviews to the Japanese press. Given some of the interpretations in this book, one may only express relief that their paths never crossed: the relative innocence of 'This Charming Man' is transformed into an ode to male prostitution, with the observation, 'The charming man is seized and captured . . . and a man says, "To stay beautiful, you need money!"' Dreadful or not, the fans still rushed out to buy the book in their thousands.

Though he looked fit and well, the long hours travelling and the stressful concerts in Japan had taken their toll, and when Morrissey arrived in New Zealand for the start of what should have been a ten-date Australasian tour, the press reported that he was suffering from 'excessive fatigue'. The concert at Auckland's Campbell Centre on 7 September went well. There were no problems with security, and he seemed relaxed in his backstage interview with the *New Zealand Herald*'s Jill Graham, one of the country's most respected journalists. Morrissey used Graham as a sounding-board for an attack on the British music press, not that this would have much effect thousands of miles away from the root of the problem. 'The only good pop-writer now is someone creased with cynicism, who despises everything,' he said. 'I've been scarred too often. Nowadays I only speak to people who like and understand me. I feel I don't have to curtsy to anyone.' Graham also wanted to know why he did not converse with the audience between songs, though she should have known that with any *chansonnier*, dialogue only robs the performance of emotion and continuity.

In Wellington, Morrissey was in fine form, but three days later when he walked on to the stage in Brisbane, he looked gaunt and found himself making a Herculean effort to get through his set. A doctor was summoned to his dressing room; the singer had a temperature of 102 degrees and was diagnosed with viral flu aggravated by acute sinusitis – the worst malady that can befall a singer, particularly in hot countries. There was no question of the tour continuing, and he flew home at once – leaving disappointed Australian fans with only a brief spot on a chat show in which he performed 'King Leer' to savour.

On 29 September, back to full health, Morrissey embarked on a brief British tour: seven dates, beginning with the Dublin Point, and with Phranc supporting once more. By now, the music press had sunk to an all-time low in their treatment of him. The hacks were no longer content with attacking his performances, which were better than they had ever been – they started a lynching campaign against the man himself. One criticism *was* justified, the fact that at the Brixton Academy there was yet another senseless, premeditated smashing of guitars. 'To see someone who at one time purported to be a "sensitive person" actively involved in it is absolutely incredible and appalling,' one fan complained to *NME*'s letters column. In fact, it was all a cleverly arranged publicity stunt thought up by EMI – to get Morrissey into the newspapers and hopefully push his new single, 'Pregnant For The Last Time', further up the charts than its predecessors. There was, however, no excuse for journalists to pass extremely vitriolic remarks about his persona. Barbara Ellen's comments in *Melody Maker*, following Morrissey's Hanley concert, were more of a personal attack than a musical review and it is no small wonder he did not sue her, as Cliff Richard once had.

Morrissey's 4 October performance at London's Hammersmith Odeon was filmed by Fuji of Japan, for transmission on their WOWOW satellite channel (more dreadful subtitles, Kanako said!), but not released commercially as originally planned – a shame, for the quality is better than that of *Live In Dallas*. It did end up on the bootleg market, though, and is well worth searching for. What fans do not see here is the unpleasant incident halfway through when, during 'Driving Your Girlfriend Home', Morrissey invited a young man on to the stage – only to have him set upon by four burly bouncers who drag him off the stage and into the aisle. Morrissey ordered the band to stop playing, begged the audience to excuse him while he sorted out 'this sham of security' – and disappeared for fifteen minutes. The offending bouncer was himself removed from the theatre after a very heated argument in the wings, and the recital allowed to continue.

The second and final leg of Morrissey's seventeen-date North American tour opened in Vancouver on 28 October. With Phranc now having left the 'company' for good, he was supported by The Planet Rockers, a not-so-good rockabilly outfit from Nashville. The backdrop was a still of a weeping Diana Dors, as the condemned murderess in *Yield To The Night* (1956, US title: *Blonde Sinner*). As before, tickets for every venue had sold out in record time, with very little advertising. At San Francisco's Shoreline Amphitheater, on Halloween, many fans turned up wearing fancy dress – there was a coach load of Teenage Mutant Ninja Turtles, another of vampires. Even guitarist Boz Boorer entered into the fun of it all, dressing up as a 'tart' in a spangled dress!

There were severe security problems at Westwood's Pauley Pavilion, on the UCLA campus. The venue, a hockey stadium, was staging its first major concert since 1981 when The Pretenders had taken it by storm, and the authorities – having been told of Morrissey's 'difference of opinion' with the bouncer in the wings at the Hammersmith Odeon – anticipated trouble when 11,500 tickets moved in just sixteen minutes. The shutters were brought down, leaving several hundred tickets unsold: instructions had been given that the pit should remain empty, and that everyone should stay seated throughout the performance. Morrissey must have been reminded of his Japanese concerts, when there had frequently been a thirty-foot void between himself and the front row, and to an artist for whom personal contact was vital, this was tantamount to damming his life-blood. He tossed his tambourine into the crowd during his fourth song, 'The Loop', hoping to coax them into moving forwards. When this failed to work he announced, 'We're fully grown adults. If you want to stay in your seats, that's okay with me – but you don't have to!'

What Morrissey did not know was that the first ten rows of seats were unsecured folding chairs. During 'Sister I'm A Poet', the 'invasion' song from Wolverhampton, pandemonium ensued when the upturned chairs acted as caltrops, entangling hundreds of pairs of legs and sending fans careering in all directions. Many of the more sensible fans helped some two hundred security staff to aid the injured, whilst the lunatic fringe took advantage of those on the floor, using them as bridges to get to the stage, while Morrissey yelled down the microphone, 'Please don't tread on anybody's toes!' Then his 'phenomenal strength' referred to by

Linder Sterling was put to the test when a hefty fan, tripping over a cable and grabbing hold of Morrissey's thigh, found himself being dragged from one end of the stage to the other – with Morrissey still singing and not once going off key!

Clearly, the situation had got out of control, and could not be allowed to continue: halfway through his ninth song, 'We Hate It When Our Friends Become Successful', two huge bouncers stormtrooped the stage and escorted him into the wings for his own safety. The musicians followed, and while the debris was being cleared from the pit, Morrissey chatted to the casualties in the makeshift first-aid room – fifty or so, none of them badly hurt. He was all for resuming the concert, but this was considered too risky, and when the ones out front heard the announcement over the tannoy that the building would have to be evacuated, there was a frantic smashing of seats and setting off of fire alarms. A merchandising stall was ransacked and its till looted. To top it all, the whole sorry saga – including the arrival of the riot police, who were seen beating fans, willy-nilly, with batons – was filmed by a television news crew who happened to be in the neighbourhood. Damage was estimated at around $2,000. Morrissey did offer to pick up the tab, and may even have done so. 'He looked so very, very sad,' observed a Reuters columnist, 'but he behaved like the perfect English gentleman right until the very end. It was our own people, notably the cops, whose behaviour was objectionable.'

A warning was issued prior to Morrissey's show at San Diego's Starlight Bowl that anyone leaving their seats, for any reason, would be ejected from the stadium. A hundred people were allowed into the pit – winners of a local radio competition – which only slightly took the chill off the atmosphere. In Santa Monica on 4 November, a television crew was actually on standby to film a hoped-for riot. The best they got, according to Jo Slee, was 'footage of a bunch of sweaty teenagers fainting'. From a personal stance the evening was perhaps the most important in Morrissey's current calendar: amongst those ushered into the dressing room after the show were The New York Dolls' guitarist Sylvain Sylvain, and their bassist, Arthur Kane. He must have been very flattered to be told that they considered his version of 'Trash' better than their own.

When Morrissey arrived in Minneapolis on 7 November the city was under three feet of snow and recovering from days of sub-zero blizzards. It was equally cold in Chicago the next day, and adding to the dilemma was the last-minute change of venue. Many tickets for the UIC Pavilion had been snapped up by scalpers, and resold for several times their value. These were deemed acceptable by the Aragon Ballroom like any others, but only after they had been exchanged for general admission tickets. As many fans liked to hang on to their ticket stubs (and often frame them, along with the receipts, so that they could boast how much they had paid to get in!) this caused a great deal of dissension amongst a small group of fans. These publicly accused Morrissey of ripping them off, when it had been their fault in the first place for paying over the odds. Before long, this small but vitriolic band of dissidents would be thirsting for revenge.

On 11 November, shortly before his concert at the Nassau Coliseum, Long Island, Morrissey was interviewed by New York's WDRE Radio. He sounded weary, and as had happened in Australia was reported to be under the weather: the dramatic changes in temperature between indoor and outdoor arenas, the merciless American winter, the non-stop stream of personal appearances, the long hours on the road – all these had taken their toll. Even so, he admitted that he loved touring, and that surprisingly he was not homesick. Referring to the mindless violence of the security staff at the Pauley Stadium, he defended the fans – and himself:

> It only becomes disturbing when security *assumes* that it's violence and not passion. It's *always* passion, never *ever* violence, and the people who get to the stage and on to the stage are very gentle people, but unfortunately they're dragged off by their hair and in some cases get beaten up. It's a shame. I don't imagine that some-body would go through all the trouble of scrambling towards the stage and getting past security, climbing up. They wouldn't go through that trouble for anybody, so they must mean it.

After the show, Morrissey was driven away from the venue in a state of near exhaustion: later that night he collapsed in his hotel room. As in Australia, a doctor was summoned who advised him not to continue with the tour. Therefore the remaining eleven dates on the circuit were cancelled. Most of the fans were sympathetic, despite being distressed over not being able to see him, and many of these would have been seeing him for the first time. As for the so-called 'Chicago-turncoats', who had seen Morrissey dozens of times and often prevented the former from getting tickets by way of their sheer greed, these lodged an 'official' complaint with an influential fanzine: Morrissey was now accused of having such an ego in allowing this to interfere with his professional integrity – unable to fill large venues, they claimed, and unwilling to be relegated to smaller ones – that he had taken the coward's way out and abandoned his tour. Such fans, of course, he did not need. Even those who professed to being his most fervent admirers – the ones producing the *Sing Your Life* fanzine, its pages filled mostly with vacuous, long-winded 'The Time I Met Morrissey' stories – went out of their way to discredit him, though these had long since been demoted by him to the ranks of the nuisance fans.

Such accusations, entirely false and aimed at a performer for whom there had hardly ever been such a thing as emotional or physical compromise – who had put on 68 highly charged concerts in six months, putting up with all manner of discomfort and despite an almost paranoid fear of flying – were nothing short of spiteful. Again, he did not need to be associated with such selfish, grasping individuals – for this was the man who, not so long before, had told an American reporter, with the utmost sincerity, 'It seems that people like me here more than anywhere else in the world.'

'I always maintain that I'm very rarely interviewed, but persistently cross-examined,' Morrissey told *Rage*'s Dermott Hayes towards the close of this most extraordinary year. 'Most pop personalities are literally so plain and dull, that anyone who appears to have a vaguely working brain comes across as conniving. Therefore I'm drilled.'

He was becoming increasingly reticent about speaking to the British music press, though by and large the troublesome element was with the weeklies – the magazines were generally less vituperative. Even reporters alternating between one discipline and another changed tactics to suit the editor's agenda, but so far as the weeklies were concerned, Morrissey's face simply did not fit – save on their front covers to boost flagging circulation figures. *Rage* seemed to fit into neither category and in his piece, 'Mistletoe And Whine', Hayes made a point of professing his surprise that the 'nutty recluse' was still around, and even went as far as asking him why he was – bringing the caustic response, 'I can't think of being a postman.' Robert Sandall, writing for *Q*, audaciously adorned the subtitle of his account of Morrissey's American tour with the pun, 'He's The Biggest Cult That Ever Was'. Little wonder then, that the singer began turning his back on these people.

A formidable component of the American adventure had been 'We Hate It When Our Friends Become Successful', one of Morrissey's first collaborations with Alain Whyte, though one doubts many of his admirers Stateside grasping its theme of the North/South divide. In England, it was performed for the first time at the 30th Amnesty International show, televised on 28 December 1991, and bringing to a close Morrissey's most successful year so far as a solo artiste.

Oscar Wilde had famously opined, 'Your friends will sympathise with everything but your success.' Few British songs have so significantly linked their authors with a topic: the fact that a Northern upbringing does not equate to coalmines, ferrets, pigeon fanciers and hotpot. 'I've never worn a flat cap, and I don't smoke Senior Service,' Morrissey made a point of saying. And, like every other Morrissey song, this one tells a story: the fact that he was starting to find life in a Manchester suburb, albeit an opulent one, increasingly intolerable now that he was famous, with pestering fans hammering on his door day and night, with the locals envious of his success and persistently looking down their noses at him. He told Adrian Deevoy of *Q*, 'There's the most vicious sense of competition in Manchester – so many jealous, vile creatures. That's what "We Hate It When Our Friends Become Successful" is all about. In Manchester you're accepted so long as you're scrambling and on your knees. If you have any success, they hate your guts.'

The single was released in April 1992, coupled with three of the songs from the Hammersmith Odeon, and reached a modest number 17 in the charts. There was a promotional video, filmed in a disused mid-19th-century schoolhouse and its incumbent wasteland, off Wapping High Street. The clean, smart clothes of the Morrissey gang (he wears blue satin, they Lonsdale T-shirts in different colours) contrast sharply and shockingly with the ramshackle buildings. Looking at them, one finds it hard to discern if they are out in search of trouble, or kicks. Gary Day toys with his flick-knife (the scene was cut when the video was televised) while Spencer Cobrin sizes up Morrissey as one might approach a sex-for-sale stud – he leans against him suggestively, but all he wants is to offer Morrissey a lick of his ice-cream cone, which gives him a fit of the giggles. The video ends with them all wandering off, and a close-up of the graffiti-daubed REARDON STREET sign, featuring slogans such as 'I Never Wanted To Kill, I'm Not Naturally Evil' and 'I Will Live My Life As I Will Undoubtedly Die, Alone'.

The song, and the subsequent *Your Arsenal* album, was the brain-child of Hull-born Mick Ronson, possibly the best producer Morrissey worked with, the man who helped him reach unsurpassed heights in his career. Theirs was also an extremely cordial working relationship, attributed by both of them to their geographical connection. 'It affects the way you look at the world, the way you deal with people. It affects everything,' Ronson told Tony Parsons of his Northern upbringing.

Ronson had been a pioneer of British glam rock, playing in a local group, The Rats, before a momentous meeting with David Bowie in 1970 that had transformed The Rats into The Spiders From Mars and resulted in five million-selling albums: *The Man Who Sold The World*, *Hunky Dory*, *Ziggy Stardust*, *Aladdin Sane* and *Pin-Ups*. Ronson had also very successfully worked with Mott The Hoople and Lou Reed (arranging the controversial 'Walk On The Wild Side'). What particularly enabled Morrissey to place Ronson on a pedestal was that he had worked with ex-New York Doll, David Johansen. In the summer of 1992, Morrissey told Jean-Daniel Beauvallet of *Les Inrockuptibles*, 'Mick was responsible for Bowie's best work, of that there's no doubt. He's a very underestimated talent who combines showmanship with great humility. Working with him on my new album has been the greatest privilege of my life.' Sadly, *Your Arsenal* would also prove Ronson's swansong: he had recently been diagnosed terminally ill with cancer.

The album was released in July 1992, and reached number 4 in the charts. It was universally acclaimed as Morrissey's best since *Viva Hate*, and equalled anything he had ever done with The Smiths. The sleeve bore two thought-provoking photographs by Linder Sterling, snapped on stage at the Nassau Coliseum, of the singer suggestively brandishing his microphone at crotch height. Morrissey's 'stomach scar' (his navel), we were reminded, appeared courtesy of Davyhulme Hospital! There was no lyric sheet with this one – just an inner shot of the Krays' rival, Charlie Richardson, taken during a trip to the seaside with his toddler daughter circa 1960. The reason for the missing lyrics, Morrissey declared, was because this time he wanted the fans to listen to the album for its overall value, with equal emphasis on his musicians and the melodies as opposed to just the words – which in the past many fans were said to have studied for days before actually putting the album into the machine. Detractors from the music press would argue that Morrissey had purposely omitted the lyrics because some of them were so contentious that, had the fans read them first, they would have given the album a wide berth. Not, one would imagine, very likely.

Leading the plaudits was *The Times'* David Sinclair, who called the album 'concise, dramatic and artful' and praised the musicians' ability to 'weld the motor of Morrissey's erratic inspiration to the golden chassis'. An anonymous reviewer in *Q*, still in mourning for The Smiths, called it 'a kind of "Kenneth-Williams-Meets-Laurence-Olivier-Down-On-The-Rainy-Pier-For-Pie-And-Mash" that captured our hearts way back when.' And whereas the usually offensive remarks made by the tabloids are not worthy of repetition, *Select* published a lengthy feature headed THE FEAST OF STEVEN – within which the album was in turn reviewed and reviled by '15 top pop celebrities' who by and large did not have a clue what they were talking about, and many of whom are forgotten today. A couple of exceptions were Siobhan Fahey of Shakespears Sister – who spoke for the fans when she said, 'He's my complete idol, like a cosy blanket you pull over you when you're feeling down' – and Linder Sterling, who observed:

Your Arsenal has Morrissey riding bare-backed on rich, feisty guitars, glistening as he rises with the audacity to still believe in the enduring embrace of a simple song. In his quieter moments he dives deep into our ventricles, wistfully celebrating his search for the domain of the heart.

Your Arsenal was Morrissey's all-embracing, symbolic lament for the decline of the British culture he had been passionate about all his life. No song better represented his feelings about this than 'Glamorous Glue'. 'We won't vote Conservative because we never have,' he opines, a phrase pronounced by many obstinate Northerners when election day comes around: no matter who the Labour candidate is, they will always vote for him or her because this is a matter of identity. Then he reminds us of what we already know: 'We look to Los Angeles for the language we use . . . London is dead!' When asked by Jean-Daniel Beauvallet what, in his opinion, was dead in the England of today, he replied, 'England itself. Everything is influenced by American culture – everyone under fifty speaks American, and that's sad. We once had a strong identity and now it's gone completely.'

In the same vein as 'Glamorous Glue', but perhaps more controversial, was 'We'll Let You Know', Morrissey's take on the depiction of an unwanted member of our society: the football hooligan. It is a sad state of affairs that the archetypal Briton in the eyes of many Europeans is the thug who attends football matches solely in order to make life a misery for genuine fans. The song, a lilting ballad embellished with the creaking of turnstiles and muted stadium screams, is a direct contrast to the raucous chanting one hears at these events – Morrissey is mocking the hooligans much as he ridicules the National Front for attending a disco. And likewise it was misrepresented by the media, for the narrators are the hooligans themselves, the otherwise self-confessed 'nice boys' who offer the paltry excuse that it is the *turnstiles* that make them hostile, before finally boasting, 'We are the last truly British people you will ever know.'

'Glamorous Glue' should have been released as a single in America, for the purpose of which a video was shot in a Chicago blues club where there is only one customer – black musician Al Lewis, here to listen to a group of English lads lamenting, 'England is dead!' 'Tomorrow', the replacement release, had a video shot in and around Nice (by Zach Snyder). This is almost a monochrome re-enactment of the scenario of 'We Hate It When Our Friends Become Successful' – The Morrissey Gang, looking like they are on the prowl again, acting laddishly as they wander through alleyways of crumbling brickwork towards the Old Town, and its unsuspecting al fresco diners. The single, like the earlier 'My Love Life', was housed in a sleeve that some fans found outré: Morrissey, in tight-fitting swimtrunks, reclining next to Gary Day on a sunlounger! The song, which topped the University charts, tells the familiar tale of the prevarication experienced during the quest for lasting love – the fact that the narrator, Morrissey, begs the object of his desire to put their arms around him and reassure him that he really is loved, only to dampen the proceedings by declaring, before this happens, 'I know you don't mean it!'

The song that was to prove Morrissey's most controversial, 'The National Front Disco' is an outsider's observation of recruitment techniques once employed by the National Front – the movement had at one time blatantly distributed leaflets outside schools. In this song he steps not just into the shoes of the oppressor, but into those of his bewildered parents who lament, 'Where is our boy? We've lost our boy!' – bringing the response from the well-raised, led-astray young man, 'England for the English!'

The song was to attract criticism from the usual quarters, but what most detractors failed to see was that Morrissey was poking fun at the National Front by suggesting that its supposedly hard-bitten recruits would attend something so 'wimpish' as a disco. 'The *phenomenon* of the National Front interests me,' he told Robert Chalmers of the *Observer Magazine*. 'It interests me like it interests everyone, just as all manner of sexuality interests everyone. But that doesn't mean that you necessarily want to take part.' Morrissey himself had said more or less the same thing to *Q* magazine's Adrian Deevoy, linking 'The National Front Disco' with the earlier 'November Spawned A Monster':

> Whether you choose to write about wheelchair-bound people or the subject of racism, the context of the song is often overlooked. People look at the title and shudder and say whatever is in that song shouldn't exist because the subject, to millions of people, is so awful.

In other words, Morrissey was saying that in criticising him, these people were only revealing their own prejudices.

Of the remaining songs the opening number, 'You're Gonna Need Someone On Your Side', is a perfect example of Morrissey's promise that this was going to be a 'physical' album: a mass of unfettered glam-rock guitars, crowd noises, ticking clocks, snatches of radio/television dialogue. The lyrics are so fresh and innovative that one might assume Morrissey has assigned himself to total seclusion and soul-searching to come up with them. In fact, he and Alain Whyte had worked on some of them during the maelstrom of pressure that had constituted the previous American tour. Indeed, the line, 'Give yourself a break, before you break down' ought to have been the singer's advice to himself back then, in view of the way he had almost worked himself into the ground.

'Certain People I Know' and 'You're The One For Me, Fatty' were released as singles in Britain (respectively charting at numbers 34 and 19). The former, coupled with 'Jack The Ripper', had a Linder Sterling cover photograph taken at Hoxton Market in London's East End, close to where the Krays had been born. The video was filmed in South Chicago on the shore of Lake Michigan, and is a feast of homo-eroticism, with the gang giving the impression yet again that they are on the 'pull', save that it was filmed at a very unromantic 5 a.m. when there was no one around to pull, and everyone looks half-frozen to death! Because Tim Broad was by this time too ill to travel, it was filmed by George Tiffin. Morrissey, barefoot and bare-chested under his jacket, wanders along the beach, ever sure of himself. 'And when I swing it so it catches his eye,' he sings, and one wonders whether this is gay locker-room parlance as a topless Spencer Cobrin strolls up to him, swinging a branding iron. It all seems like harmless fun, though it very nearly ended up with Morrissey losing one of his musicians for good when he tried to order them to wear contoured Speedos. Jo Slee includes the instruction in *Peepholism*, part of which reads, 'So: Are you Gazzo, Spenno and Ringo Whyte prepared to risk real mannish trunks as opposed to the usual sexless plywood shorts that you usually wear?' The offended musician later told me, 'This time he'd gone too far. Mozza wouldn't walk around at the crack of dawn getting his nuts frozen, so why should we?'

Margaret Thatcher, politicians, the royals, one or two writers, music journalists in general – these were only dastardly villains in Morrissey's eyes. Then there were the *real* villains: criminals such as Hindley and Brady, who were deservedly loathed. Additionally there were the so-called villains of yore, the ones who had moved into folklore with the passing of time: 'Troubled Joe' of the mid-19th-century Anglo-Irish troubles, referred to in 'A Rush And A Push And This Land Is Ours' – and Jack the Ripper – the subject and title of a fascinating but very much underrated Morrissey song.

In this darkly amusing piece, Morrissey acts as *agent provocateur*, meeting up with the killer, telling him how tired he looks, how his face is as mean as his life has been. He adds that he wants him – 'Crash into my arms!' – even if it is the last thing he will ever do, which of course is what could happen in a real-life situation and for some would make the sex doubly exciting – though the Ripper does not realise that this is, in fact, a trap.

The inspiration behind the song was actually Walter Satterthwait's avant-garde novel *Wilde West* (Collins Crime Club, 1992). This is a fictional recreation of Oscar Wilde's 1882 lecture tour of the American West, during which he had infamously opined at a customs house that he had nothing to declare but his genius. In Satterthwait's rewriting of history, in each city Wilde visits a Ripper-style killer is at work. The police begin to suspect various members of Oscar's weird and wonderful entourage, whereupon the great man himself sets about tracking down and unmasking the killer.

Morrissey's lyric also inadvertently links the 19th-century killer of Whitechapel prostitutes to the Yorkshire Ripper, Peter Sutcliffe – several policemen are known to have disguised themselves as whores in an attempt to trap him. In France the song was compared with *Lily Passion*, an extraordinary musical drama starring Barbara and Gérard Depardieu, which had packed out Le Zénith in Paris in 1986. In 1998, Morrissey included the song on an excellent American album, *My Early Burglary Years*, housed in a sleeve featuring his cover shot from the August 1990 issue of *Gay Times* – and which contained the most astonishing dissection of angst imaginable.

In 'You're The One For Me, Fatty', Morrissey champions obesity, the fact that big can really mean beautiful. The song was coupled with 'There Speaks A True Friend' and 'Pashernate Love' (a take on 'Mad Passionate Love', a hit in 1958 for *Carry On* star Bernard Bresslaw). In Morrissey's reading of this the plum line is, 'Pashernate love could make your sister erupt into wild blisters and boils.' The video, Tim Broad's last, featured celebrity ex-convict Joe Blair and Megan Siller, who later appeared in several episodes of BBC Television's *Casualty*. It centres around the latter's love of food – she even scoffs the flowers he has brought her when they go on a picnic! The actual inspiration for the song came from one of Morrissey's favourite comediennes, Victoria Wood, and her declaration of love for her heavyweight magician husband, Geoffrey Durham. It is a catchy, up-tempo number with strains of Buddy Holly, albeit that the setting is dreary Battersea with its 'hope and despair'. It became one of that summer's most hummable anthems – and was given an absolutely vile review in *NME*, whose anonymous scribe suggested that this 'one-trick pony helpless without its trainer' might be better off exiting pop for good. 'If he's very clever,' he or she concluded, 'he could do a Quentin Crisp and get a gimmick, like refusing to wash his cutlery or his groin for a decade.' What made such remarks unforgivable and hypocritical was that they appeared on page 16 of the publication – while on page 15 there was an expensive, full-page advertisement for the single. 'They took the money,' Morrissey's EMI spokesman said, 'and even then they rubbished him. How shameless can you get?'

Lyrically, one of the best songs on the album, and one of the most moving, is 'Seasick, Yet Still Docked', an allegory of sorts for Morrissey's mistreatment by the press: the fact that he was all too frequently attacked for doing something *before* he did it. He said at the time, 'You can sit in your room for months on end and see nobody, and cry quite bitterly into your pillow because the phone never rings – then you think of those recent weeks, and of your situation, and you burst out laughing at the absolute absurdity of life and expectation.' The song, a long one, links Morrissey with the legendary Belgian singer-songwriter Jacques Brel. In Mort Shuman's adaptation of Brel's 'Amsterdam', poorly covered by David Bowie and brilliantly so by Ute Lemper, Brel says of his sailor, 'He so wants to belch, but he's too full to try.' Morrissey politely declares, 'Tonight I've consumed much more than I can hold,' which may also be interpreted, regarding the detractors, to mean that he is reaching the end of his tether. Moreover, the overall theme of the piece with its ticking clock – time slowly but surely ebbing away – is reminiscent of Brel's 'Les Vieux', with the despondency of unrequited love transferred from the elderly couple waiting to die, to the plight of the sad young man. Morrissey told Les Inrockuptibles,

> All of us are working against the clock in our own way. I tend to have a cheese butty, sit back and relax. Everything eventuates. The day will arrive when you and I are not on this earth. People who have a sense of time and therefore urgency are quite fascinating! I've been accused of paying too much attention to death, but what's wrong with that? It's a pretty serious matter, especially when you're lying under the wheels of a double-decker bus!

All is not, however, doom and gloom, and the precognitive dream – that all will turn out well if this is what one wishes for – holds good with the penultimate song on the album, 'I Know It's Gonna Happen Someday', a work of considerable strength and emotion – and, like the earlier Brel song, subsequently covered by David Bowie.

On 25 May, Morrissey arrived in Los Angeles and checked in at the Sunset Marquis Hotel. With him was thirty-something Peter Hogg who, Morrissey claimed tongue-in-cheek, he had acquired courtesy of 'Rent-A-Chap' – and who was later described by Gary Day in a Guardian interview as 'a real detested troublemaker'. The two-week sojourn should have been a private affair, though the fans and the press soon put paid to this. The pair were photographed cycling on Venice Beach, shopping in the San Bernadino mall, and dining at Johnny Rocket's restaurant in Westwood. On 30 May they showed up at Fashions Nightclub on the Redondo Beach Pier, where a Morrissey/Smiths evening was in progress. Hogg was asked to judge a T-shirt and Morrissey look-alike contest – the prize, five minutes of 'intimate conversation' with the singer in a backroom.

After his vacation, tired of the lack of airplay in Britain and holding EMI partly responsible for not 'pushing' him, Morrissey chose to promote the album in person elsewhere. On 4 July, three weeks before its release, he appeared on the bill of Les Eurockéenes, one of the most prestigious events in the French calendar, staged annually at Belfort. His *vedette-américaine*, as supports are called on the Continent, were an uninspiring Ned's Atomic Dustbin, whose late arrival on stage almost prompted a riot from fans who were interested only in Morrissey. To calm everyone down the promoters sent out for several vanloads of flowers – chrysanthemums, which in France are traditionally sent to funerals! These were handed around, ready to be thrown at Morrissey. He took to the stage at midnight, wrapped in a huge Union Jack, and opened wholly without controversy with 'Glamorous Glue'. He played the introduction to 'November Spawned A Monster' himself, tremulously, on a violin borrowed from rock-chanteuse Catherine Lara. He also sang his own arrangement of 'My Insatiable One', a song by a then little-known group called Suede, whose Morrisseyesque frontman, Brett Anderson, gave everyone the impression that his outfit would soon be hailed as the new Smiths. Not surprisingly, perhaps, Suede's reign would be brief. The lines, 'On the escalator/You shit Paracetamol as the ridiculous world goes by' were frowned upon by many French fans for not being in keeping with Morrissey's clean-cut image. Neither was it deemed appropriate for French admirers to applaud and scream, American-style, while a song was in progress. Even during high-spirited performances by Eurockéenes regulars Barbara, Johnny Hallyday, Jean Guidoni and Veronique Sanson there had to be decorum so that audiences could listen to the singers and the messages of their songs. Morrissey was reminded of this by *Les Inrockuptibles'* Emmanuel Tellier. 'At times,' he responded, 'I would love nothing more than to sit at the edge of the stage and sing to a respectful silence with the applause coming only at the end of my songs. Then the other side of me tells me that if this happened, I would probably feel that I had failed.'

A few days after Belfort, Morrissey participated in the equally prestigious Festival de Leysin, in Switzerland, where even the foul weather and an on-stage tumble failed to rob the evening of its magic. Afterwards, he and the musicians spent a few days in Paris, where at the Hotel Bristol he was interviewed by *Q*'s Adrian Deevoy. Afterwards, as had happened in Berlin, everyone went walkabout – around the Pigalle-Blanche red-light district, where photographer Hugh Dixon snapped him against a background of neon Durex signs and sex-shop windows. The actual interview, however, was not quite the light-hearted affair Deevoy had expected, as he explained:

> The general atmosphere, and perhaps a little too much booze, had made us all giddy. There was devilment in his eyes, so I tweaked his eyebrows and asked him if they were real. 'No,' he said, 'they're held on with Velcro!' Then, just acting the fool, I asked him what he would do if I reached my hand under the table and stroked his knee. He said, 'Why don't you do it and see what happens?' I decided to change the subject, and jumped out of the frying pan by mentioning Vic Reeves and asking for his opinion about the sketch ['The Morrissey Consumer Monkey'] which had offended him. He glared at me and said, 'It was meant to be hurtful. Vic Reeves is a person who can't shut his mouth for three seconds because he feels he'll disintegrate into a bowl of dust. He's completely loathsome!'

On 26 July 1992, the day before *Your Arsenal* was released in Britain, Morrissey embarked on a brief non-singing tour of the United States, promoting the album by radio appearances, in-store signings, walkabouts and by generally just being there. He was also paving the way for a forthcoming tour that would see a repeat of the mass hysteria of his previous visit. He and Peter Hogg booked into the Sunset Marquis, where he was extremely cagey about speaking to the press. He had agreed to be interviewed by David Thomas of *You* (the *Mail On Sunday* supplement), but certain conditions were imposed: Thomas must refrain from mentioning The Smiths, Johnny Rogan, or Morrissey's sexuality. Effectively, therefore, the interview covered very little ground, though the subsequent feature was accompanied by some rather nice photographs taken in and around the hotel pool by Eddie Sanderson. Thomas later observed of his subject:

> He seems incapable of trusting either himself of anyone else enough to form a satisfactory relationship. His emotional life is a self-fulfilling prophecy that parallels his complaints about professional publicity. He wants to be written and talked about, but makes it incredibly difficult for any journalists to get close to him. He wants to be loved but behaves in a way that makes it impossible. This would not matter in the slightest were it not for the fact that, underneath all the rock star flim-flam, Morrissey is actually a very nice chap, excellent company, perfectly willing and able to talk about any subject one cares to throw at him.

Where Peter Hogg was during the interview is not known, but if Morrissey had imposed a ban on personal questions, he was soon titillating and teasing again, by repeating how he had acquired Hogg through 'Rent-A-Chap'. There were also rumours about other men in Morrissey's life but whether they were just fans who had a crush on him or whether their adoration was reciprocated is not known. As always, no one said anything.

A midnight appearance at a record store on 28 July made the television news. President Bush was in Grand Rapids at the same time, but the press attention was diverted to the bequiffed British singer's arrival at The Vinyl Solution, where he was mobbed by 2,000 screaming fans. The excitement continued with a surprise tie-in party at a rock club across the way. Twelve hundred people turned up at Houston's Record Rack the next day, and there were other gatherings in Chicago, Los Angeles, San Diego and New York.

Morrissey also appeared in a radio phone-in show with Tom Calderone of Long Island's WDRE-FM. The questions, from giddy fans, were rarely less than silly. When a woman called Nancy asked, 'As a psychiatrist, I just wanted to know why you left the lyrics out of this album?' Morrissey glibly responded, 'Well, as a *psychiatrist*, why do *you* think I did?' Put in her place, Nancy hung up. The tour ended on 5 August, when Morrissey's musicians flew out to join him on New York's *Hangin' Live With MTV*, where he sang 'You're The One For Me, Fatty' and 'Certain People I Know'. Several hundred fans had camped outside the entrance for 48 hours to acquire tickets for the ten-minute event.

On Saturday 8 August 1992 took place the first of what should have been two concerts at London's Finsbury Park. Topping the bill were the recently re-formed Madness, whose many fans included a small but potentially troublesome element, while Morrissey had been added to the bill at the last moment.

During the afternoon, the National Front – the movement which had appropriated the Union Jack as its own symbol – had coincidentally organised a 'British Troops Out of Northern Ireland' rally through the streets of neighbouring Islington. Trouble was expected once skinhead extremists, the worse for drink, began mingling with the Madness crowd. The instant Morrissey and his musicians took to the stage, the skinheads began hurling whatever missiles came to hand. Hundreds of genuine fans were there too, but their cheers were drowned by heckling and hoots of derision from the mob. Morrissey now made his big mistake – it was an error of judgement, no more – draping a large Union Jack about him during his second song, 'Glamorous Glue', and parading in front of the huge Derek Ridgers backdrop depicting a pair of seventies suedehead girls. He had done this before, to a more civilised crowd, at the Eurockéens festival at Belfort on 4 July. The drunk and disorderly element at Finsbury Park, however, were unable to see beyond their own agenda.

Then Morrissey erred again by performing 'The National Front Disco'. Hoodlums began pelting the stage with sharpened coins – proving that the violence was premeditated and that exactly the same would have happened with any support act. Finally, following a half-hearted 'You're The One For Me, Fatty', Morrissey walked off the stage.

He immediately dropped out of the next evening's concert, realising that this would upset hundreds of fans, en route to Finsbury Park from all corners of the globe and unaware of what had happened. Murray Chalmers, the press officer at EMI, issued an official statement:

> Morrissey is extremely disappointed that Sunday's planned performance could not go ahead due to the abysmal behaviour of a small group of loathsome yobbos. His management have requested the promoters to refund fans' money. A Christmas show is being scheduled for those fans who really want to enjoy without the aid of stimulants.

But Morrissey's detractors now had enough ammunition to prepare their most vitriolic attack yet.

There had already been controversy over 'Bengali In Platforms' and 'Asian Rut'. The former was a reworking of a Smiths song taped before their split but not released. Morrissey had commissioned Stephen Street to compose a new melody, and included it on his *Viva Hate* album. Queen frontman Freddie Mercury adored the piece and was convinced that it was about him. Though he had been born in Zanzibar and raised in Bombay, he liked to think that Morrissey had based it on his 'glam rock piss-take' of Gary Glitter during his pre-Queen phase when he had been known as Larry Lurex. The song was a classic case of 'shooting the messenger', for one does not have to delve too deeply into the lyrics to work out that the narrator is *anti*-racist. 'Shelve your plans,' he tells his young immigrant friend, speaking from personal experience as the descendant of immigrants himself, 'Don't blame me, don't hate me because I'm the one to tell you that life is hard when you belong here.'

What he meant, of course, was that in his opinion, with its current political climate life in Britain was not easy, socially or financially, even for those who had been brought up here – let alone being expected to conform when one had been brought up in a completely different culture. Morrissey had attempted to debate the issue with *Sounds*' Shaun Phillips during the spring of 1988. When Phillips audaciously asked if the song was meant to have a double-edge, after a deliberate pun that had seen the anti-Band Aid Morrissey contemptuously referring to the song as 'Bob Geldof In Platforms', he replied, 'No, not at all. There are many people who are so obsessed with racism that one can't mention the word Bengali. It instantly becomes a racist song, even if you're saying, "Bengali, marry me." But I still can't see any silent racism there.' Phillips recalled the much-discussed, much-misinterpreted line, arguing that if this was implying that Bengalis did not belong here, then Morrissey was not really taking a global view of the world. He was of course baiting him and trying to put words into his mouth. Morrissey finally shut him up with, 'If you went to Yugoslavia tomorrow, you'd probably feel that you didn't belong there.'

'Asian Rut', from the *Kill Uncle* album, was a tender lament deliberately misinterpreted by the music press, whom by this time Morrissey had declared 'not massively equipped upstairs'. To the spellbinding accompaniment of a raga-violin, he champions the plight of the Asian boy who has turned up at school, toting a gun and so calm that he must be on drugs, to avenge the murder of his best friend – a mission that fails when he is run down by racist cowards who only have the guts to operate when they are in gangs. The lyrics could not have been clearer, yet *NME* still accused Morrissey of 'playing games, gently stoking the fires, dodging behind words and trying to get up noses'.

Mark Nevin who composed the music for eight of the *Kill Uncle* songs, told me,

> The first time I heard Morrissey speak the words aloud, I came close to tears. How can anyone call the song racist when it's so blatantly *anti*-racist? Does that mean you aren't allowed to mention Asian people without being called racist? I thought it the best song on *Kill Uncle*, just as 'Bengali In Platforms' was my favourite song on *Viva Hate*. Life really is hard when you don't belong here. And what you said about Morrissey is right. He really does climb into the other person's skin.

Now, in the wake of Finsbury Park, and in what was the start of one of the most vitriolic smear campaigns against a show business personality since the AIDS-related deaths of Rock Hudson and Freddie Mercury, a spokesman for *NME* read out a statement on Radio One:

> Following more controversial lyrics on Morrissey's album, flirting as that song does with right-wing imagery, going on stage in front of a largely skinhead audience, waving a Union Jack – there are questions that need to be asked in the house, so to speak, and we've asked them. We are the People's Friend. He's flirting with danger.

Morrissey never submitted to this pressure, simply because he felt there was no need to. To his way of thinking, there was nothing wrong with being proud of one's country. *NME* reacted by publishing a photograph of the flag-enveloped Morrissey on the cover of its 22 August issue – which just happened to be the anniversary of the Battle of Bosworth Field, where another maligned individual, the last truly English king, Richard III, had died at the hands of his oppressors. The banner headline read: MORRISSEY: FLYING THE FLAG OR FLIRTING WITH DISASTER? Within, spread over five full pages, were the lesser headlines: CAUCASIAN RUT: THIS ALARMING MAN, accompanied by more 'evidence' – another flag-waving picture, one of Morrissey proudly showing off his England lapel badge, two more of him holding up a skinhead T-shirt.

The Jam, we were reminded, had also adopted the Union Jack some years earlier, but they were excused because at the time they had explained that they had been reclaiming it from the Far Right. Obviously, it had not crossed anyone's mind that Morrissey might have been reclaiming it for the England he loved.

In charge of the Inquisition were Dele Fadele, Danny Kelly, Andrew Collins and Gavin Martin. It was a piece of one-sided journalistic propaganda: making the accusations now in anticipation of the subject coming forward to explain his side of things, by which time of course ('There's no smoke without fire . . .') the damage would already have been done. Morrissey was approached, but rather than waste time speaking to people who had so obviously set out to destroy him come what may, he issued a brief statement: 'My lawyers are poised. *NME* have been trying to end my career for four years, and year after year they fail. This year they will also fail.'

An *NME* insider informed me that as a 'safety precaution', the whole exercise had been supervised by a Morrissey-friendly journalist with a sound knowledge of the legal system – without whose help there might well have been a lawsuit.

Even so, it was bad enough, peppered with 'Morrissey quotes' pulled from any number of publications over the previous decade – printed out of context of the original interviews and appearing harsher than Morrissey had originally intended. Referring to a gay-bashing incident with James Maker that, it was claimed, may have been carried out by National Front supporters, the journalists asked, 'Has he changed from the persecuted to the persecutor? Or is he fascinated by the idea of racism, by the look of violent skinheads, to the extent of being oppressed so much, he falls in love with his oppressors?'

Next, the editorial ran through a catalogue of 'dubious' or 'nationalistically pointed' songs, deliberately not pointing out that their contentious lines had been mostly in quotation marks, delivered by the songs' narrators and not by the singer himself. His detractors might have argued that, after all, he had supplied these words in the first place, but this would have been rather like holding William Shakespeare responsible for the horrors of *Titus Andronicus*, when all he had done was dramatise them. Also used as evidence, unfairly because it was yet to be published, was a quote from a forthcoming issue of *Q*: 'I don't want to sound horrible or pessimistic but I don't really think, for instance, black people and white people will ever really get on or like each other. The French will never like the English – that tunnel will collapse.'

Morrissey was expressing an opinion, and anyone should have seen that. Yet at the very end of this diatribe, providing the reader/fan has not ripped the paper to shreds by now, one finds the First Inquisitor opining, far too late, 'For what it's worth, I don't think Morrissey is a racist. He just likes the trappings and the culture that surround the outsider element' – which, of course, we already knew.

NME went on to attack Morrissey for letting down his fans, a reference to his cancelling of an appearance at Glastonbury and the final dates of his last American tour. *NME* themselves had announced that he would be participating in the Glastonbury Festival during the weekend of 26/28 June: a huge number of tickets had been sold, and only days before the event a further 'press announcement' had declared that, following a bust-up with one of his musicians, Morrissey had decided to pull out. Needless to say the fans had been disappointed, genuinely thinking that he had deliberately let them down – until they learned that he had never agreed to the event in the first place. Though, to be fair, *NME* may have been misinformed about Morrissey definitely being booked for the festival, their feature included a 'special section' detailing how much the regular Morrissey fan had spent over the last year for not seeing him twice – 'an astonishing £189.60 for nothing but disappointment'.

The backlash was not just obscene, but bordering on the defamatory. *NME* claimed to have received hundreds of letters of support, though the ones they published came from the very worst of the lunatic fringe detractors. There was an 'open letter' feigning support from the despised (by Morrissey, anyway) Johnny Rogan who soon afterwards collaborated with the Mancunian band Family Foundation on an offensive track entitled 'Red Hot'. This was little more than a 'musical interview' with the former presenter of Channel 4's *The Word*, Terry Christian, who claimed to have known Morrissey at school. The track sarcastically 'debated' the Finsbury Park debacle; to add insult to injury, Rogan and Christian roped in former 'wronged' part-time Smith Craig Gannon to help with the music. Rogan then challenged Morrissey by way of an interview in *Select*, 'Give me a ring and we'll talk it over.' He was, of course, ignored. More vitriol followed from a newly founded Morrissey fanzine, *Miserable Lies*, apparently only interested in filling its pages with derisory remarks and ignoring Morrissey's music.

Morrissey finally spoke out during the summer of 1993, when the commotion had died down somewhat. He stated for the record that the aftermath of Finsbury Park had not perturbed him at all because he had never been guilty in the first place. Opening up more freely to a foreign journalist he trusted – a common feature in these prejudiced later years – he told *Les Inrockuptibles*' Emmanuel Tellier:

Not all skinheads are racists. Skinheads and the National Front are two
different things. Skinheads are emblematic of the British working
classes. I have no ties whatsoever with racism. I do like boxing! Does
that make me violent?

And on the subject of 'The National Front Disco', Tellier told me,
Morrissey added in a 'low voice but with clenched fists':

Anybody who listens to the entire song the way I sing it, and the vocal
expression, knows only too well that I'm no racist and glorifier of
xenophobia. The phrase 'England for the English' is in quotes, so those
who call the song racist are not listening. The song tells of the sadness
and regret I feel for anyone joining such a movement. And how can
the English flag upset anyone? The Union Jack belongs to *everyone*,
not just to the extremist parties. *I am not guilty!*

He was absolutely right. The athlete Sally Gunnell had recently
wrapped the flag about her shoulders after winning her Olympic gold
medal; the officiating soprano at the Last Night of the Proms had done
so before leading the audience in the most roisterous 'Rule Britannia' in
years. Yet the only British journalist to defend Morrissey was Tony
Parsons, writing in the *Daily Telegraph*:

Personally, I don't think Morrissey has a racist bone in him. I can't
believe anyone who can write a song like 'Suffer Little Children' isn't
on the side of the angels. My great fear is that Morrissey will become
the Sarah Ferguson of pop, driven into exile by the cruel and uncaring
media. Let us pray it doesn't happen. It would be a tragedy if the
crown prince of pop suffered the same fate as the Sloane who fell
from grace. Put down that flag, Morrissey. Your country needs you.

*

Morrissey rested but briefly at home before embarking on the American
leg of the *Your Arsenal* tour, a gruelling 53-date schedule that would
keep him busy until the end of the year, and which opened on 12

September at Minneapolis's Orpheum Theater. Supporting were Gallon Drunk, a rockabilly/electro-punk band fronted by James Johnson: they had recently signed with Sire, Morrissey's US record label, and their biggest hit so far, 'Some Fools Mess', had been named Single of the Month by *NME* the previous November. By and large they would prove unreliable, and towards the end of October attempts would be made to find a replacement support. Kirsty MacColl was approached, but declined. 'I'm used to people coming to see *me*, my own fans,' she told me. 'Much as I admired Morrissey, I would never submit to being an also-ran.' Buffy Sainte-Marie was also contacted, and not surprisingly would have nothing to do with the idea. Feelers were again put out for Jobriath – people still did not know that he was dead. Finally, he settled for a Los Angeles-based outfit, the grandly named but not so grandly talented Big Sandy And The Fly-Right Boys.

The Edith Sitwell backdrop had been dispensed with – over the coming weeks Morrissey would be alternatively surveyed by Diana Dors, Elvis, Charlie Richardson, and the suedehead girls featured at Finsbury Park. The first concert was memorable only in that it ended prematurely due to a stage invasion, and this was almost repeated three evenings later in Toronto when there was a recurrence of the problem that had happened last time around at the Pauley Pavilion – i.e., folding chairs, which should never have been there in the first place. During 'The Girl Least Likely To', Morrissey was rugby-tackled to the floor by five fans, one of whom ripped open his shirt to kiss his heart. These were dragged off him, taken to the wings and handed over to the police. Morrissey walked off the stage just in time to see the fans being charged with public order offences, which meant that they would have to spend the night in jail. He kindly signed their release documents, tore strips off the bouncers, ensured that they would be fired, and the show continued. Afterwards he was confronted by a reporter from *Entertainment Weekly*, 'shocked' over the way he had lost his temper. He told her, 'I don't like it when people think of me as a wimpy, poetic, easily-crushed softie. I'm quite the opposite. I'm a construction worker!' The reporter from the *Toronto Star*, also witness to the tantrum, observed, 'Morrissey sings like a choirboy – one who was abandoned at birth and raised by a family of bikers.'

At El Paso, Texas, a young man leapt on to the stage just as Morrissey was in the process of whipping off his shirt: the fan did likewise, the pair danced for a whole minute, flailing each other with their discarded shirts before swapping them, footballer-style, then walked off the stage arm-in-arm! Three evenings later in San Antonio, in a fairly relaxed atmosphere, Morrissey told the audience between songs, 'You know that no one can legally hurt you!' He then pointed at a mean-looking bouncer who had made a move as if to attack a fan, and sang louder than usual, 'I'd hate to be like certain people I know!' Then, when the bouncer did step out of line, he stopped the band and growled, 'Excuse me, Mr Security in the red T-shirt. Leave him alone!'

In Houston, Texas, several hours before performing at The Summit, a 5,000-seater basketball stadium, Morrissey was interviewed by Robert Chalmers of the *Observer*. Chalmers told me of how he had been vetted, that getting to speak to Morrissey was almost as difficult as meeting a senior member of the Royal Family, but doubly exciting: finally, after studying the journalist's credentials, Morrissey had given him less than a day's notice to fly the ten hours from London – and then cut their interview time by half! Again – once The Smiths' split, the Rogan book and the ongoing feud with Mike Joyce had been dispensed with – the key topic was Morrissey's sexuality. 'I'm not running ahead and leaving clues behind bus-stops, as it were,' he said. 'One of my physical encounters was with a man. That was ten years ago. It was just a very brief, absurd and amusing moment. It wasn't love. I've *never* experienced that!' Chalmers then grasped the bull by the horns and asked him ('Seeing as my time was up anyway, I felt I had nothing to lose!') if he had ever slept with a woman, half expecting to be shown the door as had happened all those years ago when Antonella Black had crossed the line. Surprisingly, he did not:

Yes, I feel completely open. If I met somebody tomorrow, male or female, and they loved me and I loved them, I would openly proclaim that I loved them, regardless of what they were. I think people should be loved whatever their gender, whatever their age. I am open to everything. I accept that my experience is different from that of most men, but I feel reasonably normal. I don't feel like a freak. My world is bigger. I never lived in a small town with small morals.

Throughout the tour, Morrissey's musicians maintained a 'toughie' image, which in some ways demonstrated that they were no better than some headbanger groups of a previous generation. In Gainsville, on 16 November, Gary Day went haywire and trashed his guitar after 'The National Front Disco'. In New York, Spencer Cobrin trashed his drumkit with a microphone stand. Obviously, besides inciting violence, these people had money to burn: Cobrin and Alain Whyte were denounced by one journalist as 'like a couple of juvenile delinquents looking for a purse to snatch'.

In Charlottesville, Virginia, on 20 November, Morrissey played to his smallest ever American audience – just five hundred high-school students at the Performing Arts Center – but the performance was no less restrained than in the bigger arenas. Neither were there problems with security. Not so in New York, four evenings later, where his concert at the Limelight Club was delayed by several hours and the support act failed to turn up. The 1,200-strong audience contained a large proportion of gay fans from Greenwich Village, and tension was running high between these and a contingent of hecklers when Morrissey tore off his shirt to reveal the words 'SLIP IN' scrawled across his chest. Halfway through his set the Fire Department arrived and halted the proceedings: the 'official' reason was overcrowding, and this time Gary Day smashed his guitar to bits in a fit of pique.

The New York concert attracted only the worst kind of publicity when Day's antics turned up in a television news report, which helped overshadow the highlight of the tour – the first of two performances at the 13,000-seater Hollywood Bowl, which had sold out in just 22 minutes, eight minutes faster than the record held by The Beatles. The concert in San Antonio a few evenings later started off well enough. When a fan yelled, 'Morrissey for president!' he shouted back, 'Me for president? Then who'll vote for Ross Perot?' Such good humour was short lived, however, when he was forced to stop the show and rebuke a group of bouncers for hitting fans. He told Loraine Ali of *Alternative Press*,

If I see somebody manhandled, I become infuriated. I go slightly out of control. They treat them very aggressively, and when I consider that *I* pay the wages of security, I don't think it's fair. The only aggression that ever occurs at my concerts is *purely* from security.

In the same interview, Morrissey hit out at the American press for their lack of support by declining to interview him – effectively biting the hand that fed by omitting to mention that he had repeatedly refused to speak to them:

They'd rather interview Yoko Ono or talk to Julian Lennon. That's what makes American music quite sad – this enormous capacity not to recognise anything until it's gone. That's the history of the American rock press. They're never quite there. They were never there for Patti Smith, or for The New York Dolls.

The tour ended at the Tower Theater, Philadelphia, on 28 November, and the next day Morrissey and his musicians flew home. One week later, the American gay/fashion magazine *Details* published an interview that had taken months to set up, and which had apparently been granted only on condition that it would appear after Morrissey had left the country – the reasoning behind this being that if he allowed one carefully vetted journalist access into his private sanctum, others would expect to follow suit. 'Life's a bitch, and then you interview Morrissey,' David Keeps began his feature, 'Homme Alone', the title itself smacking heavily of Polari. 'He is a journalist's nightmare: infinitely quotable, but endlessly press-wary.'

Keeps, apparently as fond of titillation as his subject, had successfully petitioned for an interview during Morrissey's last stay at the Sunset Marquis, but this had been cancelled by Peter Hogg at the last minute. A second meeting had been arranged to take place in London on 10 August – the theory being that, if the senior editor of *Details* was so interested in speaking to the singer, then crossing the Atlantic to do so would prove no stumbling block. In the wake of Finsbury Park, this too had been cancelled. Anyone else would have given up, and rightly so, but on the morning of 18 September Keeps had received a call from Jo Slee: he was to report to Morrissey's hotel suite at once.

Reading the transcript of the interview, one is reminded of the interview some years earlier with *Melody Maker*'s Frank Owen – of two men who seem to have an affinity with each other. With strict attention to detail, Keeps described his subject as if no one had seen him before: hair, clothes, complexion, jutting jaw ('like Dudley Do-Right's'), eyes and mannerisms. Morrissey rapped at Keeps not to sit in his favourite chair, then promptly strolled across to the window to be told, 'It's no use jumping. I've got you, now!'

For several minutes without speaking, Keeps stared at Morrissey's face – enough to put anyone off – until Morrissey stuck out his tongue and burst out laughing. Assuming a Noël Coward accent, Keeps demanded, 'What *is* this thing with your tongue, sir? You stick it out rather a lot' – bringing the equally light-hearted response, 'My mouth doesn't close properly. It never did, and I suppose my tongue just falls out. It's like leaving the garden gate open!'

The ice had been broken, enabling Keeps to be bolder than he might normally have been: it had taken him a long time to get this far, and he wanted to ensure a memorable account of the proceedings, not just your standard interview. The on-stage kissing was discussed. 'More romantic than sexual,' Morrissey quipped. 'It's quite personal, and I love that. Wouldn't you?' When Keeps retorted that this would depend on the one doing the kissing, Morrissey raised one eyebrow and posed, '*Would* it?'

Partially tracing the source of this admiration to loneliness and unhappiness, which he considered the major problems faced by the youth of today, Morrissey linked this to his near-permanent depression. Admitting that he had sought professional help, but to no avail, he added, 'And when you're depressed, it is so enveloping that it actually does control your life. You cannot overcome it, and you can't take advice. People trying to cheer you up become infuriating and almost insulting.'

Upon hearing this, Keeps moved on. The pair discussed the 'evils' of the meat industry, and Morrissey's 'redefining of manhood' in the way that he and his songs had 'captured the angst of male adolescence and turned his sensitivity into strength'. And of course, with the emphasis being placed on the word *male* it did not take long for the topic of sexuality to enter the proceedings – or rather, Morrissey's fabled non-existent sex-life, allegedly restricted to the odd urge ('the first at twenty-eight') which of course no one really believed, especially when he claimed (as he had in his interview with Nick Kent) that love, for him, had always been unreciprocated and associated with pain – of how he *had* propositioned lovers, but that they had always turned him down. He concluded, 'If you're asking me if I've ever spent the night with someone in a loving way, the answer is no, I never have.'

This, of course, was *not* what Keeps was asking; neither was Morrissey confirming that he did not have sex. Admitting that he had always found it harder to say 'I love you' than 'I'm sorry' – the former pronouncement, he believed, equating to the death-knell of intimacy – he managed to maintain his composure when Keeps asked in the next breath, 'Are you still friendly with Michael Stipe?'

The conversation moved on to Morrissey's musical tastes. Did he like jazz? No: it was boring and he preferred something more spirited. Did he like gospel, then? This brought a wry smile and the response, ' "Oh Happy Day", sung by hundreds of people who are living in dire poverty in Birmingham, Alabama? No thank you!' (The British music press, of course, would have had a field-day with this one and twisted it into another example of racist stereotyping on Morrissey's part.) Did he like heavy metal, and had he been to a rave? Did he like classical music? Yes, he said of the latter. He liked Jacqueline du Pré, though he had to explain to the bemused Keeps who she was. Then, out of the blue, Keeps asked the question that he believed was on the lips of every Morrissey fan:

KEEPS: Is it true you sleep in the nude?

MORRISSEY: Yes, I do. I like freedom of movement, especially in the event of a fire.

KEEPS: (not getting this) Does that mean boxer shorts for day?

MORRISSEY: Are you asking me what kind of underwear I wear? I didn't until about a month ago.

KEEPS: Did you have some untoward incident?

MORRISSEY: No, I just suddenly decided that I wanted to. I wasn't involved in any political royal scandal. So I tried Calvin Klein. The briefs. White.

KEEPS: It's of compelling interest . . .

MORRISSEY: I couldn't doubt it for a split second.

Keeps had his answer, but at the expense of being allowed to ask any more questions. Minutes later, Morrissey gave the excuse that he had to leave for a sound-check – and allegedly to get his own back for being cut short, Keeps swapped the Morrissey cover he had planned for one of model Cindy Crawford. And in New York, stores reported a surge in the sale of white Calvin Klein briefs.

6

On Ne Badine Pas
Avec l'Amour

'Are you sure you understand the touch of his hand? Does his touch
mean so much to you? . . . Love either finds you, or love either blinds
you to the danger of a heartbreak ahead.'
— Joan Regan, 'Danger Heartbreak Ahead' (Stutz/Barefoot), 1955

Back on home territory, Morrissey and his musicians barely had time to
catch their breath – appearing on several television shows to promote
the new single, 'Certain People I Know' – before embarking on a brief
British and European tour organised by his new manager, Nigel Thomas,
a stalwart individual who had handled the affairs of Joe Cocker and
former Kinks frontman Ray Davies. There was also a brief but pleasing
video compilation, *The Malady Lingers On* (title courtesy of Lancashire
comic, Les Dawson) – and Linder Sterling's lovely book, *Morrissey Shot*.
Many of the studies here were posed for, and are as arrogant as they are
artistic, yet still equal anything to be found in The Kobal Collection.
Many more were not, proving as with Garbo and Valentino that there
was no such thing as a Morrissey bad angle – even while he is asleep.
Linder captures his every mood: pensive, cynical, smiling, irate,
despondent, in tears through the sheer emotion of it all. There is an
inadvertent study of what the French *réalistes* call 'Le miroir, la lampe et
la rose' – the mirror symbolising self-analysis, the lamp symbolising the
warm glow connecting the artiste to the public, the rose symbolising
love. And of course, there are the obligatory exercises in narcissism:

Morrissey hanging half-naked from iron railings; the 'oxters' shot from San Diego, which Kris Kirk only just lived to see; Morrissey in his bath or having his nails painted. And flowers everywhere.

A cold, wet Sheffield opened the eight-date British leg of Morrissey's tour on 12 December 1992. Concerts followed in Birmingham, Newcastle and Manchester – where on 15 December he played his first solo concert in his home town. At the Glasgow Barrowlands the next evening, he ducked as a bottle of water was hurled at his head, and must have been reminded of Finsbury Park. This time he accused the culprit of being an *NME* journalist. The publication had audaciously tried to secure an interview and failed; to 'compensate' for this, in the free pack of playing cards they issued shortly afterwards wherein each suit represented a musical decade, Morrissey was depicted as the Queen of Diamonds – in brackets next to his name was printed, 'The Queen Is Dead'.

The next evening, at Bristol's Colston Hall, Morrissey took another swipe at his least favourite rag by announcing just before 'The National Front Disco', 'If you think that this song is in any way racist, then I suggest that you do yourselves a very big favour. *Give up the NME!*' At London's Alexandra Palace, there were ticket concessions for those who had missed out on Glastonbury and the second day at Finsbury Park. Kirsty MacColl had changed her mind about supporting him – 'We were on home ground and it made a vast difference!' – and included in her repertoire was The Smiths' 'You Just Haven't Earned It Yet Baby'. Towards the end of her spot she was joined on stage by Shane MacGowan, and most unusually for a Morrissey warm-up they brought the house down with their massive hit, 'Fairy Tale Of New York'.

The tour closed on 20 December at the 1,600-seater London Astoria, the smallest venue on the circuit. Rumour preceded the event, on account of his persistent hounding by the music press, that this would be Morrissey's last ever concert on British soil. As such it was filmed for future audio/video release.

Two evenings later, Morrissey played the 6,000-seater Le Zénith, in the Pantin district of Paris. For him and myself, the wheel had turned full-circle. I had first become aware of his music in Paris some years before.

In January 1986, along with Catherine Deneuve, Yves Montand, Juliette Gréco and Melina Mercouri, I had been personally involved with Le Zénith's opening. The out-of-the-way venue had been especially constructed for Barbara – she and Gérard Depardieu had starred in forty performances of her musical drama *Lily Passion*, a vehicle that would have suited Morrissey down to the ground. David (named after myself) is a young serial killer who follows Lily around the tour-circuit: each time he has heard her sing, he goes off and kills someone. Eventually, Lily achieves her heartfelt ambition – like the hero of Morrissey's 'Jack The Ripper', she invites the killer into her arms, and David stabs her after a last song!

Only Barbara and Johnny Hallyday have actually sold out Le Zénith, notoriously difficult to fill, but the fact that only five hundred tickets remained unsold for Morrissey's appearance was a mighty achievement. The concert was recorded, released in May 1993 under the title *Beethoven Was Deaf*, and reached number 13 in the charts. For copyright reasons, two of the songs were replaced by ones from the London Astoria show.

The period between the close of Morrissey's tour (Düsseldorf, 23 December) and the album's release was for him fraught with sadness. On 27 February, Tim Broad died of an AIDS-related illness. The director of his finest promotional videos and one of his closest companions had been just 37. 'Tim had extraordinary patience, kindness and benevolence. The cut-throat politics of the music industry never affected him,' Morrissey reflected. A few weeks earlier, his new manager Nigel Thomas had succumbed to a heart attack and Morrissey had said at his funeral in Gloucestershire, 'Ours is not a very dignified business, but Nigel managed to make it so.' Cynics have suggested that, had Thomas not died so suddenly, like all his predecessors he would not have stood the test of time. The same might have been said for Mick Ronson, who died of liver cancer on 29 April, aged 46. Most of the obituaries were accompanied by the controversial photograph most associated with him – the infamous shot taken by Mick Rock of Bowie as Ziggy Stardust 'fellating' Ronson's guitar some years earlier during a concert at Oxford's Town Hall. *Your Arsenal*, Morrissey's definitive album, had served as

Ronson's final testament, though according to Morrissey the pair had planned an even more involved follow-up. He told American journalist Dave DiMartino in February 1994, 'Mick spoke to me a few days before he died. He was very happy, very enthusiastic about writing songs with me and getting back into the studio. He was very positive about his health. Then three days later his wife telephoned me and said, "My baby's gone." It was so incredibly painful and sad for me. I'd become so attached to him that I couldn't attend the funeral.'

One may only imagine how deeply Morrissey was affected by these tragedies, one on top of the other. Prone to bouts of deep depression, easily mistrusting, it must have seemed like the bottom had dropped out of his world. He became more reclusive than usual, later confessing that things had been so bad at one stage that he had not left the house for weeks. Then, in May 1993, came the shock announcement to *Les Inrockuptibles*' Christian Fevret that his forthcoming album, *Vauxhall And I*, would be his penultimate . . . indeed, it might even be his last:

I'm not interested in taking a break. When I stop, it will be for good. I'm starting to foresee the moment when I'll have expressed all that I want to express. An artiste's longevity isn't necessarily the proof of his worth. Are groups like The Stones of any use? I don't want to hang around just to prove that I can. There would have to be a worthwhile reason for doing so.

Throughout his entire career, Morrissey had denounced whatever had been the current musical trend: paltry Manchester pop ensembles, tuneless rap, too many rock dinosaurs, fabricated dance music, a severe lack of talent within whichever discipline one cared to mention. The time was nigh, he now declared, to search for new horizons. He had, he said, been approached with cameo roles in two major (unnamed) film productions – portraying Charlie Richardson in a gangland drama, and the part of a redoubtable playboy in an Andy Warhol biopic starring Lili Taylor. His pessimism had plunged to an all-time low:

I want to do photography, to travel, to write, but I've no desire to be recognised in the street any more. I don't really appreciate people. The ones that I care about are unreliable. I no longer believe in human nature. The human race no longer interests me. I don't care any more about the environment. People *deserve* to die out. I'll be content when all the tigers, rhinos and elephants have become extinct, then they'll no longer be persecuted. Humanity deserves nothing more than to go up in smoke.

Two days before Mick Ronson's death there had been another demise that may or may not have affected Morrissey, but which also may have caused him to breathe a sigh of relief. Kris Kirk, who had worshipped him from afar since the very beginning, succumbed to AIDS, aged 43. Almost until the week of his death, Kris had been working on a kiss-and-tell, *The Vinyl Closet*, which had threatened to send shockwaves through the pop-rock community. Keeping well within the law, Kris had been about to name names, and had more than enough proof to support his claims. Morrissey's interview with Nick Kent for *The Face* in 1990 (see page 129) was just the tip of the iceberg so far as Morrissey was concerned. Now, the unedited script lies in a vault somewhere, waiting for the day – until then we must content ourselves with *A Boy Called Mary: Kris Kirk's Greatest Hits* (1999, Millivres, edited by Richard Smith), which contains fascinating chapters written in Kris's inimitable style about Morrissey, Boy George, Dusty Springfield, Pete Burns and other gay icons.

During the summer of 1993, with the threat of retirement or abandonment hanging over his fans' heads like the Sword of Damocles, Morrissey shut himself away in a secluded studio and beavered away with fellow collaborators Alain Whyte and Boz Boorer. Of the fifteen songs completed, eleven would be selected for his alleged penultimate album, the others would be set aside for B-sides of CD and 12-inch singles. Besides these songs, there was at least one cover version of someone else's past hit, the Johnny Mercer-Henry Mancini classic 'Moon River', which had been 'crooned' in the 1961 *Breakfast At Tiffany's* by Audrey Hepburn. Danny Williams had topped the charts with it the same year: Mancini himself and Gracie Fields had had hits with it. Morrissey's rendition is passable, though the extended CD version seems to drone on endlessly. He also committed the unforgivable crime of 'massacring' a standard by changing the words – the line 'It's waiting round the bend, my Huckleberry friend' was omitted completely.

Far, far better was a cover version of a French *chanson*, Georges Delerue's haunting 'Interlude', composed in 1968 for the film of the same name. This had originally been included on the B-side of the Franco-Italian singer Dalida's 'Hurt', and had appeared in English for the first time on Timi Yuro's *Something Bad On My Mind* album in 1971:

> Let's hold fast to the dream that tastes and sparkles like wine . . .
> Who knows if it's real or just something we're both dreaming of?
> What seems like an interlude, now,
> Could be the beginning of love!

Morrissey recorded this song as a duet with Siouxsie Sioux, singer with seventies punk ensemble The Banshees. 'Move over Kate Bush and Larry Adler,' *Gay Times* enthused the following September, upon the song's long-delayed release. 'This month's Odd Couple Award goes to punk priestess, the mother of all Goths, Siouxsie Sioux, and Quiff o' the North Morrissey. It's like the Sex Pistols never happened.' In fact, the coupling worked extraordinarily well: the blending of the gentle baritone and the indigo tones of the neo-torch singer make one lament that the pair stopped here.

For these new sessions, Spencer Cobrin and Gary Day were gone – the latter, it is reputed, after some very heated set-tos in the studio – though the pair would turn up again, once the dust had settled. The replacement bassist was Johnny Bridgewood, the ex-Stingray who had played on 'Sing Your Life'. The new drummer was Woodie Taylor, formerly of The Johnson Family, who had played on two of the London dates during the *Kill Uncle* tour. Also there was another short-lived manager, Arnold Stiefel, an all-powerful American whose current stable included Rod Stewart.

The album – of which Morrissey said, 'It's the best I've ever made' – was produced by Steve Lillywhite and its title, *Vauxhall And I*, had music press cynics pointing out that the area around London's Vauxhall Bridge was the hated Johnny Rogan's 'patch' – forgetting the jacket blurb on *The Severed Alliance* stating that the author was forever changing his address. The area, of course, was most famous for the Vauxhall Tavern, the legendary gay pub in Kennington Lane – renowned for its good pint, its drag queens such as the real Dockyard Doris, and above all for its hospitality. The building was immediately added to 'Morrissey's London' and one may only wonder what the patrons of the Vauxhall Tavern have to say about the bequiffed, inquisitive and largely uninitiated individuals who wander through its portals, camera in hand, without knowing what to expect. Kanako Ishikawa, that delightful but painfully shy little Japanese lady, was still reeling from the shock two days after visiting the place when she described to me how the infamous – and regrettably no longer with us – Dockyard Doris lumbered up to her and boomed, 'Come on inside, duckie. We ain't gonna bite yer, gel!'

'Hurrah, praise him, sing hosannas, the Mozzer is back!' is how one reviewer announced the first taster single from the album, 'The More You Ignore Me, The Closer I Get', which peaked at number 8 in the charts in March 1994. This was a rare love song, the most personal to date, in which the lover – Morrissey himself – is not only completely in control of the situation, he is the one doing all the seducing, telling the deliberating object of his desire that indifference will only make the situation more appealing. 'Whether you care or do not . . . *I've* made up your mind,' he declares before warning, just in case his amour decides not to give in, 'Beware! I bear more grudges than lonely high court judges!'

The subject of the song was widely alleged to be 28-year-old Jake Walters, Morrissey's new companion: a photograph of the multi-tattooed, burly suedehead's hirsute six-pack appears on the sleeve of the single, with the word 'MOZ' mock-tattooed in large letters across his middle, the 'O' encircling his navel. Clutching a camera, he appears on the sleeve of the promotional single – this time it is Morrissey who is topless, one fist bunched as he grapples Jake in a stranglehold. Jake, who moved in with him at around this time, also features on the *Vauxhall And I* cover – or at least part of his bare shoulder and his '1 oz' medallion does, caressed by Morrissey's hand, identifiable by his signet ring.

The single was backed by two equally remarkable B-sides. Even more personal is 'I'd Love To', which makes us wonder, given the intense privacy of Morrissey's earlier years, if we should really be hearing this *chanson* that finds him ripping his heart wide open. Obviously he feels we should, as he reveals that true happiness may only be bought with tears. Before declaring that he has had a lifetime of nights he cannot bear, he confides, his voice little more than a whisper to the lover beside him, 'Gay, I lay awake and I cried because of ways I'd love to, but only with you . . . and time will never wipe you out.' [In the alternative version of the song that appears on *My Early Burglary Years*, he begins, '*Again*, I lay awake . . .'] For those fans desperately trying to come to terms with their own sexuality, such lyrics coming from a man who had been seen as fighting his demons for years were an absolute godsend. The second B-side, 'Used To Be A Sweet Boy', had a lush arrangement by Alain Whyte. Here, Morrissey again opens his insular heart and grants us access to his burdening regret as he wistfully pronounces of his childhood, 'Something went wrong, and I know I can't be to blame.'

Vauxhall And I, released on 14 March, was unanimously applauded by the critics – indeed, there was not a single adverse review even from the tabloids – and in less than a week it topped the charts. It is a gentler, lyrically and spiritually more rewarding collection than any of its predecessors, an absolute work of art. 'An inordinately beautiful record, certainly the most gorgeous that Morrissey's ever done,' Andrew Harrison told me, adding in *Select*, 'If he keeps making records like this, you won't want The Smiths back.' Writing in *The Times* the previous November upon the re-release of The Smiths' entire back catalogue by WEA, the frequently catty Caitlin Moran is reputed to have infuriated Morrissey by describing him and his former partner, 'This pouting, lisping son of Oscar Wilde, almost vindictively effeminate and laying claim to the traditional "privileges" of womanhood – passivity, preening and put-down air . . . Manchester's anaemic James Dean figure, together with the vaguely ferret-like greased rocker, Johnny Marr.' Music journalists have always been notoriously two-faced, and now, with the release of *Vauxhall And I*, she attempted to redress the balance by enthusing in *Melody Maker*, 'This is magnificent, made in Gorgeous-O-Scope with supporting roles by Sarah Bernhardt and God.' Terry Deal wrote in *Gay Times*, 'The muddled miserabilist's self-pitying cries are at their most powerfully convincing, adult and human . . . not only the album of the month, but possibly Morrissey's finest hour.' The *Irish Sunday Independent* declared it, 'As homoerotic and darkly celebratory of things homosexual as anything the late Derek Jarman ever put on the screen' – which was perhaps going a little too far, for uncalculated blatancy had never been Morrissey's forte.

The eleven songs proved that, in a complex world viewed through the eyes of the all-embracing poet, Morrissey's well of inspiration showed no sign of drying up. The opener, the catchy 'Now My Heart Is Full', centres around one of his favourite films, *Brighton Rock* (1947, US title: *Young Scarface*), a heavyweight tale of gangsters and 'loafing oafs in all-night chemists' written by Graham Greene. These are referred to by name: Dallow, Spicer, Pinkie and Cubitt – to which he adds himself, the 'jammy Stressford poet' who is amorous of Bunnie. Yet amid the vibrancy of it all there is the lingering undercurrent of loneliness – the fact that, barring 'some rain-coated lovers' brothers', the narrator is still friendless as ever. And again, the fans rushed out to search for the film.

The effervescent 'Spring-Heeled Jim' has scattered among its lyrics snatches of dialogue of youngsters debating capital punishment in the seventies television drama-documentary, *We Are The Lambeth Boys*. Again, there is sexual ambiguity concerning the alleged ageing member of the Richardson gang who will 'do' but never be 'done to', yet who has had 'so many women, his head should be spinning'. And, for the man who in his heyday was afraid of no one, now that he is past his best bravado begets regret and he can only lament, 'Where did all the time go?'

Perhaps the most articulate song on the album is 'Billy Budd', the title of yet another film, based on the novel of the same name by Herman Melville, and subsequently adapted into an opera by Benjamin Britten. In the story, the First Mate has a crush on the Beautiful Sailor (portrayed by Terence Stamp in the film), only to betray him and see him hanged. Melville's biographer, Edwin Havilland Miller, was of the opinion that the tale was based on Melville's own unrequited love for novelist Nathaniel Hawthorne. Morrissey's all-too-brief song draws an ingenious parallel not just between the Beautiful Sailor's demise and his own wished-for demise by some sections of the media, but in the prejudices experienced by gay couples who, thwarted by homophobes, are unable to find work. The song ends, curiously, with a line from the 1948 film of *Oliver Twist*, in which East End actor Anthony Newley, as the Artful Dodger, begs Alec Guinness's Fagin, 'Don't leave us in the dark!'

NME's Stuart Bailie described 'Hold On To Your Friends' as 'like Noel Coward with a harpsichord'. Morrissey told *Details*' William Shaw, 'It was written about somebody I know, in relation of their treatment towards me.' In it, he decries this anonymous user, who only calls him when he needs support, while the rest of the time he is impervious to his friend's feelings. Morrissey reminds him that there are enough people to attack in the world without attacking those one cares about, and portentously concludes, 'There just might come a time when you need some friends.'

In 'Why Don't You Find Out For Yourself', on the other hand, Morrissey makes a futile attempt to warn a would-be artiste-friend of the perils encountered by trusting mentors with the money he or she might earn. It is a case of learning from the experiences of one who knows – one who really has found 'the glass hidden in the grass' – though when there is still scepticism from the other party, Morrissey more or less throws in the towel and concludes with a shrug of the shoulders that he has been stabbed so many times in the back that he has no skin left, and adds, 'but that's just the way it goes.'

In 'I Am Hated For Loving', Morrissey once more regresses into intense, crippling gloom: he feels unwanted – save by himself – alone and unloved, attacked from all sides, not specifically belonging any-where. 'I am falling,' he opines, 'and there's still no one to catch me.' Morbid irony, however, resurfaces in 'Lifeguard Sleeping, Girl Drowning', performed in a breathy falsetto. Death is played in the minor key while the elements are in the major in this *goualante* of the self-centred attention seeker who this time goes too far – a cross between Stevie Smith's 'Not Waving But Drowning' and Byron's lament for Shelley, with a dash of Jacques Brel's 'La Fanette' thrown in for good measure. 'She deserves all she gets,' declares the overworked lover who, when his girlfriend swims too far out to sea and gets into difficulties, casually lets her drown.

'The Lazy Sunbathers', the only politically controversial song on the album, epitomises *Les enfants de novembre* at its most potent. Though written in the wake of the horrors of Sarajevo, it harks back to the early days of World War II and the development of the Office of Strategic Services – the courageous American package of stars that sailed for Europe to entertain our troops at the front, while their so-called peers saw fit to lounge in the sun and continue with the good life as if nothing was happening. 'They thought the war was nothing to do with them,' Marlene Dietrich told me, 'so they just lounged around all day doing nothing, whilst innocent people were getting butchered.' In his song, Morrissey reminds us of the callousness of these cold-blooded people.

'Speedway' is the lengthy, fashionable thoroughfare that runs through Santa Monica. During the early fifties, with its wealth of uncloseted leather bars, gay clubs and bath-houses, it formed a part of the cruising area that was a mecca to the likes of James Dean, Montgomery Clift and Rock Hudson. When he wrote the song, it was one of Morrissey's favourite sojourns, a locality where he felt at peace with himself, safe from the sniping British music press. 'Speedway', the symphony-in-miniature that closes *Vauxhall And I*, begins *colla voce* and appears to be heading towards the tenderness of 'There Is A Place In Hell For Me And My Friends' – until the ear-splitting revving-up of a chainsaw directs it into a scurrilous attack on Morrissey's worst oppressors – the tabloid Shylocks hungry for their pound of flesh, who try to break his spirit and fail to do so only because he has nothing left to break. He confesses, too, that he has allowed the charade to continue in order to prevent one person in particular, maybe a clandestine lover, from being implicated in scandal. And, he concludes, he may be fighting a losing battle as he declares that these enemies will not rest until the hearse has claimed him, silencing him for ever. When later asked by Stuart Maconie whether the song was about 'gentlemen of my profession', he shot back with, 'I've never met any gentlemen of your profession.' Touché!

On 15 March 1994, the HMV store in London's Oxford Street was witness to scenes of unprecedented hero-worship when Morrissey held his very first signing session. The shop had estimated a crowd of around 500, as had happened with Cliff Richard and Tina Turner. Over 3,000 fans turned up, not just from all over Britain but from France, Belgium and the United States, many of them camping out overnight on the pavement. Morrissey breezed in on the proceedings wearing his usual denims and Doc Marten boots, and the badge on the lapel of his tweed jacket read FAMOUS WHEN DEAD. His quiff, observed the *Guardian*'s Jim White, '. . .was like the dorsal fin of a killer whale in captivity.' Casually, or so it was meant to appear, he tossed a bunch of gladioli into the crowd – and hit, not just by accident, one of the music press photographers.

The scene, with the same number of admirers, was repeated two days later at the HMV store in Manchester: he remained on home territory for over four hours, signing autographs and chatting non-stop amid scenes of frequently uncontrollable emotion. One big, very butch-looking lad had to be revived with a security man's hip-flask after kissing Morrissey on the cheek and receiving a hug and a few warm words in return. Bill McCoid reported the 'pilgrimage' in the *Manchester Evening News*:

> The fans are let through the barriers, the last steps towards their Holy Grail in total awe of their idol. This is worship, the paying of respects. Morrissey is hugged, kissed, revered. He wrings their hands. It's not unlike the Pope giving an audience. This is as near religion as you can get without the religion. Homage (and money) has been paid. Their lives are complete.

*

In the spring of 1994, several sharply contrasting Morrissey interviews and features appeared on both sides of the Atlantic. The British music tabloids were no longer interested in him – not that Morrissey lost much sleep over this – but the monthlies still held him in high esteem and found him accessible. He met Stuart Maconie, this time writing for *Q*, not in some clandestine location but in a spit-and-sawdust Battersea pub on a busy Friday evening. Effectively, Maconie was lucky to meet him at all: either Morrissey was incredibly thick-skinned, or he had not been shown the journalist's earlier review for the *Live In Dallas* video.

As had happened in Berlin, the talk was matey and Northern. Though the cover of the magazine proclaimed, MORRISSEY: 'Yes, I Am Pregnant' – MR CHUCKLE-TROUSERS UNZIPS HIS LIP, and though the accompanying photographs had been snapped atop Hollywood's Griffith Observatory (the location for the closing scenes of *Rebel Without A Cause*, though even James Dean had been terrified of straddling the balustrade, as Morrissey does here), the intro of the actual interview read, 'Goodbye, big-bloused flower-fondler; cheerio, depressed devotee of deathly doom; toodle-oo, teetotal football-fearing perma-hermit; we'll sithee, bespectacled Billy No Mates.' This, of course, was what Morrissey was all about: a cross between George Formby Sr and Norman Evans, with liberal dollops of Robb Wilton and Frank Randle. 'It never goes away,' he proudly declared of his Northernness, 'that indelible working-classness.'

Neither was the singer alone: he had brought along his new companion – who, it appears, knew his place. 'A small, bedenimed skinhead personage who answers to the name of Jake,' Maconie observed. 'Affable and barrer-boyish, Jake's role seems unclear: driver, gofer, mucker. Whatever, he busies himself with the pinball machine as Morrissey indicates a dark corner of the tap-room where, seated incongruously at a video game table, we begin.' Jake may have kept in the background for whatever reason, but this did not prevent the magazine's editor from sneaking an uncaptioned photograph of the pair into the finished feature – of the two of them getting into Morrissey's car – for readers to draw their own conclusions.

The topics of conversation were current. Of the *EastEnders* actress Gillian Taylforth's 'Did-she-didn't-she?' oral-sex episode, splashed all over the tabloids, Morrissey said, 'I think even if she did, it doesn't really matter. Do the staff of the *Sun* not do it? . . . It's very old-fashioned and very Victorian to me . . . I feel nothing but sympathy for her.' On the state of British football, now that the disastrously ineffective England manager Graham Taylor was gone, he said, 'It does seem that the current England squad is bereft of real stars. I've never been convinced by Gascoigne . . . I went to see Chelsea recently . . . I thought seeing Dennis Wise and Ian Rush and Neil Ruddock, I'd be in awe and I wasn't at all. I thought I can play better than this.' So, Maconie asked, did Morrissey actually play football? 'Yes,' came the response, 'I played football a few weeks ago . . . and I scored four goals. I should add that the game was against Brondesbury Park Ladies.'

Maconie then asked the usual chestnuts. Did Morrissey get drunk, have sex and take drugs? 'Yes,' he replied to the first part of the question, 'I have a great interest in alcohol and as time goes by I find it more comforting, although I'm not by any means an alcoholic so please don't blandish that in heavy upper case.' As to the second part of the question ('I had to ask, what with him bringing his mate along to the interview, and all,' Maconie told me afterwards) the response was a definite, 'No, I don't.' Morrissey may have been starting to come out of his shell, but some topics were still sacrosanct, even though the replies were getting less and less credible.

A little more of the Morrissey–Jake 'mystery' was unravelled with the publication, also in April 1994, of his intense, inadvertently revealing interview with William Shaw of *Details* (an edited version appeared in *Ray Gun*), which had taken place in Shaw's hotel room in Los Angeles at the beginning of the year. The first thing Shaw noticed was Morrissey's '1 oz' pendant, identical to the one Jake Walters wears on the sleeves for *Vauxhall And I* and 'The More You Ignore Me'. 'That's my secret,' he retorted when asked to elaborate, 'I do a lot of baking.' Much of the interview, a far cry from his previous one with the magazine, centred around Morrissey's depression, the fact that if there was love in his life at last, he did not give the impression that he was particularly happy.

Shaw referred to Morrissey's recent lengthy self-imposed incarceration in his London home, when for weeks he had refused to see anyone. He had tried medication and counselling, he confessed, but to no avail, and he had now learned how to live with his state of mind. 'It doesn't really matter how people try to uplift you,' he added, 'within me it's an immovable, strange, genetic medical condition that I have never escaped from.' Taking this and Morrissey's much-publicised, troubled upbringing into account, the fact that he was a survivor from a broken home, Shaw asked him if he would like to have children. Morrissey reverted to his customary pessimism – not that the conversation had been uplifting to begin with:

> Only in an ideal world [because] I'm not sure what it is about life that is supposed to make it worthwhile. I've never really enjoyed life. I've never known how. I seem to have such unbearably high standards that I set for myself that there's not really any way in which I can win. I'm not really frightened of death. It's not a particularly horrendous thing for me. I feel sad for other people, but not for me.

'Not even if it's a complete full stop?' Shaw wanted to know, bringing a wry, 'That's fine by me' in response.

Morrissey must have liked this interviewer, for when they were interrupted by Jake, come to collect him – 'He is shy and avoids my gaze,' Shaw observed, interpreting Jake's body language – Morrissey invited himself back to Shaw's hotel room the next day. He was 'delivered' by Jake, who this time hovered outside the door throughout the interview. Today the talk was of the tough new world he had begun inhabiting, probably introduced to it by his new companion. Morrissey was now a boxing enthusiast, an aficionado of the eccentric Chris Eubank. 'An astonishing machine,' he told Shaw. He also confessed to having been in a few fights himself, which he had won – whether he was speaking allegorically and referring to the British music press again is a matter for conjecture, though Jake later boasted to friends that Morrissey had actually sparred in the ring and found the whole experience rewarding, even getting hurt. Shaw's interview, however, started to take on an edgy tone when he began questioning the singer about his sexuality – a topic that today seemed especially relevant, he felt, on account of the ubiquitous Jake. The answer was a slight variation on the stock response, 'Sex is *never* in my life, therefore I have no sexuality.' Then Shaw blotted his copybook by making comparisons between Morrissey and the sex-and-self-loathing Kenneth Williams, posing the question, 'You must have had sex at some time in your life, so for that moment at least your sexuality becomes fixed.'

There must have been some sort of signal, for before Shaw could drive him further into a corner, Jake had come to the rescue. 'Simply a prearranged escape,' Shaw concluded. In the photograph he submitted for the finished feature we see the pair reclining: the younger man shirtless, the word MOZ again mock-tattooed across his bare middle – while Morrissey, feigning sleep, has an arm wound about Jake's thigh and his head resting on his crotch.

The new image was criticised in a For/Against local celebrities debate chaired and reported by Rosemary Barratt of the *Manchester Evening News*. While musician Vini Reilly praised Morrissey to the hilt and placed him in the same superstar league as Freddie Mercury and Mick Jagger, Len Brown was convinced of his sincerity, and Johnny Rogan still respected him despite the 'fatwahs', others were unimpressed. John Robb, formerly with punk outfit The Membranes, but now a member of the music press that Morrissey loathed, had been at Finsbury Park, found the whole thing amusing, and therefore had nothing flattering to say. Barratt herself concluded of this 'new' Morrissey, 'No longer portraying himself as a weak and feeble wallflower, he's flexing his pumped-up pecs and courting some rather undesirable company.'

Mark Hadfield, of the techno band Rhythm Quest, had taken great exception to Morrissey's attacks on dance music, and his self-appointed stance as spokesman for the youth of Britain. 'Dance music is made by ordinary people for ordinary people,' Hadfield said. 'Recently he's been selling records simply because of who he is and what he says, not because his music is any good. He's just not that important any more.'

Hadfield was wrong, of course, begging the question a decade on, Does anyone remember Rhythm Quest or any of the other dozens of minor celebrities who went out of their way to attack a man who today remains an active, working legend? He was and still is important, important enough for magazines and periodicals to fight to get his face on their front covers, mostly not because the editors themselves are admirers, but because he boosts circulation figures. Again, with most of these people it was purely a matter of sour grapes.

Elsewhere there was further criticism from Patrick Fitzgerald, the Manchester-raised frontman with Kitchens Of Distinction who had 'outed' himself in an interview with *NME*. 'I hate lying,' he subsequently told *Gay Times*' Richard Smith, having said that he and Morrissey had much in common, coming from the same backgrounds but above all speaking the same language, 'there's no point in doing what I do if I'm going to lie. That was Morrissey's strength on the first Smiths album and it's his weakness now. He was never out.' Richard Smith concluded,

> Morrissey's changed, too, and is now more interested in thuggery than buggery. His stylings are increasingly masculinist, both in terms of his recent records' harder guitar edges and blatant racism, and his scrapping of his fey ways in favour of professing a predilection for boxing, skinheads, the Krays, tattoos and Herman Melville. Of course, they're all as gay in their own way – though from a different tradition – as Oscar Wilde, gladioli and *A Taste Of Honey*. But one wonders if La Mozz realises how ridiculously camp his association with all these things appears? Or does he think he now comes across as one dead butch homi?

The image was toughened up further for the benefit of Morrissey's interview with Andrew Harrison of *Select*, which appeared in May 1994. The cover shot revealed him baring his teeth and wearing a knuckleduster: the subtitle proclaimed him, 'Unbeaten in ten years as World Feather Duster Champion, the man they're calling the Vauxhall Villain – Steven "Bonecrusher" Morrissey.' The photographs accompanying the feature were taken at the York Hall gymnasium in Bethnal Green – a former Krays hang-out, now one of Morrissey's preferred haunts, after he had allegedly been introduced to the place by Jake. Here, he added glamour to the somewhat spartan surroundings by posing in the ring with several prize fighters – including super middle-weight champion John 'Cornelius' Carr, whom he dwarfed. 'For me it's the sense of glamour that's attractive,' Morrissey told Harrison, 'the romance, but mainly it's the aggression that interests me. It has me instantly leaving my seat and heading for the ropes to join in.' Not long after the Morrissey feature appeared, and reputedly inspired by the photographs, the location was used for the setting of *Angels With Broken Noses*, an adult video that starred half a dozen East End twenty-somethings 'unwinding' in the locker-room after slogging it out in the ring. It would subsequently win the *Gay Times* Erotic Video Award of 1996.

To gain access to Morrissey for the actual interview itself, which had taken place at Hook End Manor on the eve of the album's release, Harrison had had to get past Jake: 'A stocky ex-boxer at the 20s-30s crossroads, with a skinhead crop, a white Fred Perry-style shirt and hard blue eyes.' According to Harrison, Jake was in a bad mood because Julie Burchill had penned an unflattering piece about 'the gaffer' in that morning's *Sunday Times*. 'He warned me,' the journalist said, 'if this piece was going to be a similar stitch-up to the Burchill story, then I'd better watch my step.' 'A very unpleasant young man,' one of Harrison's colleagues told me, 'Jake's loyalties were in the right place, but Morrissey was doing himself few favours having him trail around after him like a lap-dog. His attitude wasn't unlike that of some of the bouncers at the rougher concerts. Maybe it was a good thing for Morrissey that it didn't last.'

Morrissey risked raising his detractors' hackles by declaring during the interview how baffled he was that, despite having been the subject of several recent television debates, the National Front were yet to be given a platform to air and discuss their views. When Harrison posed the question of whether this was for the best, seeing as the National Front and the British National Party seemed intent on pursuing their political objectives through violence, Morrissey offered another logical suggestion:

If they were afforded television time or unbiased space in newspapers, it would seem less of a threat and it would ease the situation. They are gagged so much that they take revenge in the most frightening way by hurting and killing people . . . part of that is simply their anger at being ignored in what is supposed to be a democratic society.

The interview brought about the usual flurry of protest from angry readers and supplied the tabloid hacks with more ammunition for attacking him. Now he was accused of 'sticking up for the democratic rights of racists' and the issue of Finsbury Park was again regurgitated.

The rest was fairly unrevealing. '*Vauxhall And I*,' he confided, 'it's a reference to a certain person I know who was born and raised in Vauxhall.' Few doubted that this was Jake, the reason why Morrissey was self-confessedly relieved to be no longer seeking inspiration for his songs from old films and other Smiths-related sources. 'It's like being told that you've been cured of chronic tuberculosis or housewife's knee or something,' he added.

At around this time (though there is doubt as to the actual date of its submission) a script contribution by Morrissey ended up at one of the management-script meetings for *Coronation Street*. A producer's assistant told me,

> The script wasn't as ridiculous and contrived as some of the earlier efforts Morrissey had submitted. Suzie [Birchall, played by Cheryl Murray who had appeared in the 'Everyday Is Like Sunday' video] breezes into The Street looking like a younger version of Bet Lynch, but with real diamonds. She gains affection by soft-soaping everyone, and puts in an offer to buy the Rover's Return – well, we couldn't have allowed that, though had the script come later, who knows? Then, after reverting to her usual bitchiness, she suffers serious injury trying to save Betty Turpin from falling into the canal, and ends up in a wheelchair. The story was turned down, though had we known that Bet would be leaving so soon . . .

The sweat and sawdust of the provincial boxing stadium was foremost in Morrissey's thoughts during the autumn of 1994 when he entered Olympic Studios in South London to record five songs with pugilist themes. One of these was 'Sunny', released after a great deal of deliberation in December 1995, and suffering the indignity of becoming the first Morrissey record not to chart. ' "Sunny" is Moz's lament for Jake,' one of his musicians told me. 'He cared for him a lot . . . and was terribly cut up when they parted company.' It seems almost certain that Morrissey was referring to Jake in his February 1995 *Observer* interview conducted by his friend, Michael Bracewell. Under the heading, 'A Walk On The Wilde Side', Bracewell drew the time-honoured comparisons between the Stretford bard and his alter-ego:

Both are Anglo-Irish artists, both have been feted by the English media, then savaged by them; each has been accused of the worst crime of their respective eras: homosexuality for Wilde and fascism for Morrissey. Both too have had a relationship which was as destructive as it was creative. Making a rare allusion to his private life Morrissey admits, 'I have had a relationship which opened up a crucial area in me. There is something unstoppable about the Wilde story, and my own.'

'We're really missing you,' Morrissey opines in this lovely song, 'My heart goes out to you . . . So I offered love, and it was not required. What else can I do?' The first single release from the Olympic Studio session, however, was not quite so sympathetic. 'Boxers', backed with 'Have A Go Merchant' and 'Whatever Happens, I Love You', was released in January 1995 and reached number 23 in the charts. The promotional video, by Morrissey's friend James O'Brien, was shot at York Hall in monochrome and featured new fighting buddy Cornelius Carr, then regarded as invincible by his supporters. Whether this was Morrissey's way of getting back at Jake for whatever he is supposed to have done is a matter for conjecture, given his past treatment of friends and colleagues who have erred. In this sorry vignette, Carr is seen pulverising Sunny, his opponent, a wimpish young man (which Jake was not) last seen in a television commercial for Pot Noodles – while the camera offers fleeting glimpses of Morrissey, the pugilists' hero, displayed on posters on the walls of the training room and locker room. The closing scene, where Morrissey strides into the room to console the loser – in slow-motion and unconventionally chomping gum – had even the most ardent fans cringing.

'Boxers' was feted by the *Guardian*'s Pat Kane as, 'One of the loveliest melodies and narratives Morrissey has yet penned, an acting tragedy of working-class hardness and celebrity.' Its sleeve featured a photograph of Billy Conn, who had fought the legendary world heavyweight champion Joe Louis for the second time on 18 June 1946 (the date of the photograph) and very nearly stripped him of the title he had held since 1937: Louis had kayoed him in the eighth round. Within the CD release, Morrissey continued his fascination with hirsute midriffs by including one such shot of the defeated fighter.

'It's a pity he took on this phoney tough image,' Kirsty MacColl said. 'Not that I'm saying Morrissey was a wimp, because he wasn't. I'm pretty sure he would know how to handle himself in a fight. But in pretending to be something he was not, rather than sticking to the *Arsenal* and *Vauxhall* trusted formula, he was preparing himself for an almost certain slump in his career.'

7

Sweet and Tender Hooligan

'Violence isn't a hobby of mine. I would like it to disappear entirely from life. But when people treat me as if I'm abnormal, as if I'm not like they are, isn't that already the beginning of violence?'

– Morrissey

The Boxers tour would be the most uncommercial so far: few official posters, programmes and T-shirts on account of a dispute with the merchandising company, hardly any backstage passes because of increased problems with nuisance fans. It opened on 3 February 1995, a wet and miserable Friday, at Glasgow's Barrowlands. Supporting were Joe Moss protégés Marion, a five-piece outfit from Mansfield – from their opening number onwards, the fans yelled for Morrissey. Their frontman, Jamie Harding, later complained about this and was offered an option: put up with being regarded as second-best like any other Morrissey support, or leave the tour. They stayed.

For this tour, the ear-shattering squealings of Klaus Nomi had given way to the equally tuneless rendition of William Blake's 'Jerusalem', as delivered by the borstal boys in *The Loneliness Of The Long-Distance Runner*. The backdrop was a thuggish shot of Cornelius Carr – whose face also adorned the sleeve of the just-released midprice compilation album *World Of Morrissey*. Gone too were the diaphanous/samite/satin tops, replaced by the more serviceable but less flattering 1960s collectors' items Ben Sherman checks, which mostly stayed on during this tour. 'Compared to the pectoral majesty of his album cover on *Your Arsenal*, the singer kept his dark bumfreezer jacket on till the end,' observed the *Guardian*'s Pat Kane. 'It was eventually shrugged off in the surly manner of a reformed Chippendale.' The denims too were 'antiques' – dating from 1944 and costing a cool £2,000 a pair.

There was also another Morrissey first: complementing his new image, he was seen on and off the stage sporting an impressive collection of fighting 'injuries' – provided by his make-up lady, and which looked so realistic that many people meeting him thought that he really had been beaten up. 'Looking like a man who's thrown himself down the stairs of his Primrose Hill residence – a music-hall vision of a Victorian boxer,' was how *Vox* described the wealth of black eyes, split lips, bruises and scars. Morrissey however was the first to realise that by making himself appear overtly ridiculous, he had played straight into the hands of his detractors – telling Christian Fevret of *Les Inrockuptibles* when it was all over, 'At the time I considered those photographs very beautiful. Now, I don't know *what* to think.'

In Glasgow, Morrissey opened the show with 'Billy Budd', worked his way through most of the new album – a collection of mainly laddish B-sides, with nothing pre-1991 – and closed with The Smiths' 'Shoplifters Of The World Unite'. The next evening, in Motherwell, this 'blast from the past' was aborted halfway through due to an aggressive stage invasion, bringing the concert to an abrupt conclusion. 'Proactive and relentless, the stage-invading became a kind of theatre in its own right,' observed David Cavanagh of *Q*. Asked by Cavanagh why he had chosen a Smiths song to end with, Morrissey grandly responded, 'It's just as much mine as anyone else's. I wrote those words. It doesn't belong to some fictitious brickie from Rochdale. It actually belongs to *me*!' David Sinclair of *The Times* caught up with him on the road, and during their brief chat reminded him of what I had written in the preface to *Morrissey: Landscapes Of The Mind*: 'He is an authority on the human condition, quite probably the most influential entertainer of his generation.' 'If such a role is thrust upon me, I'll take it and stick it on the mantelpiece,' he replied, 'but I'm not really trying to be the Lord Mayor of Pop or anything like that.'

Craig McLean, who covered the trio of Scottish concerts (the third was in Edinburgh) for *Spectrum*, observed,

> Like any god, Morrissey has his disciples. Like any disciples, Morrissey's feel compelled to record their own gospel and spread the word. The fanzine culture that has sprung up around the arch-Hulmerist is an international industry. Their mutual love of one man is why they're all standing in a car park in Scotland in the middle of winter.

A major cause for concern amongst these fanzine editors was Jake's departure. Those who had a tough job managing their own lives believed that Morrissey was as weak as themselves, and therefore on the verge of breakdown. Others handled the situation in such a way that some readers actually believed Jake had died. The French *Lonely Planet Boy* printed the lyrics to 'I'd Love To', and a photograph of Morrissey sobbing at the edge of the stage. *Wilde About Morrissey* (USA) and *Drive Me Home* (Spain) included the lyrics to 'Sunny' – the latter alongside the head-on-lap shot from *Details*. Others printed black-edged pictures. *The Mighty Quiff* (Belgium) underscored the lines, 'With your jean-belt wrapped around your arm/And with a needle pressed onto tight skin.' Though photographs of Morrissey, taken by Jake, would appear on promotional material for a while longer, allegedly the singer now had a new companion – wisely, perhaps, kept out of public view for the duration of the tour.

Meanwhile, on 7 February, fans entering Sheffield's City Hall were handed leaflets – written by a former fanzine editor on behalf of the anti-fascist magazine *Searchlight*. Headed, 'Morrissey's Dirty Laundry', these detailed his non-existent political views and urged fans to boycott the concert; they ended up where they belonged, scattered across the theatre steps. The concert, introduced by an overweight Dockyard Doris lookalike drag queen, was filmed by James O'Brien – as was the one the next evening in Blackpool – and later released on a video, *Introducing Morrissey*. Not dissimilar to the earlier *Hulmerist*, the concert footage was interspersed with clips of the more 'interesting' Morrissey fans: Matt, a young skinhead who (in view of Jake's absence) was paid £150 to walk into Blackpool's Empress Ballroom with a copy of *World Of Morrissey* tucked under his arm. Then there was Libby, a pink-quiffed admirer filmed backstage at Birmingham's Aston Villa Centre on 11 February, holding aloft a card inscribed I BLAME YOU, while Morrissey posed on the couch behind her. I met Libby soon afterwards: the singer had autographed her arm, and she had had this tattooed over. 'It's a lasting reminder of the most important day of my life,' she said.

Morrissey went on to play Cambridge, Birmingham, Ilford, Portsmouth, Hull, Bradford, Ipswich (where he rattled a tambourine inscribed SHAG), Cardiff, Croydon and Brixton. At each venue, in addition to 'Jerusalem', he was introduced on stage by Gorecki's Third Symphony, a work composed as a eulogy to those who had died during the Warsaw Ghetto Uprising, which had effectively ended the Nazi occupation of Poland during World War II. This stunning piece, which had topped the British album charts in 1993, also closed the show. In Bradford, despite suffering from the flu and sweating profusely throughout his set, the performance was faultless. 'I'm afraid that I picked up something nasty in Hull,' he announced. When someone yelled, 'Who was it – Jake?' he sniggered and replied, 'Thank you, from the heart of my bottom!'

In Newcastle, on 17 February, there were problems with security, which Morrissey solved by yelling at the bouncers – bringing about a huge wave of fans who rushed the stage and knocked him off his feet. The tour ended in spectacular fashion at London's Theatre Royal Drury Lane on 26 February, where the concert was recorded and the guests included then Morrissey favourites Echobelly, Adam Ant, Blur, P J Harvey, The Pet Shop Boys, Gianfranco (the aforementioned gay porn star), my wife and myself. In terms of location, timing and sheer vocal brilliance, this undoubtedly was the finest moment in Morrissey's career: his Piaf at the Paris Olympia, his Judy at Carnegie Hall. He was in sparkling form.

Touts were selling tickets for £300 a pair – this was how much I was offered for my own in the royal box, organised by his manager. The support was McAlmont – to my way of thinking just a horrendous noise, which was why Jeanne and I headed back to the bar (missing Morrissey, who came up looking for us!) where we spent half an hour chatting to a 'displaced' musician who confessed that though he was looking forward to the show, he had no intention of meeting the man afterwards. 'The last time we met,' he added, 'Moz got so bloody mad, I thought he was going to deck me. But I still think there's nobody like him. Moz is like a drug. The more you take, the more you want, even though you know it's fucking you up!'

Tonight, Morrissey was more loquacious than ever. 'You can either be as playful as you like, or you can be your own boring self,' he announced before attacking a wild and nifty 'Spring-Heeled Jim', and he would not be disappointed. Taking advantage of the unusually relaxed security, and encouraged by a tuxedoed young man named Darren – pretending to be a security man – the stage was assailed by admirers. A leggy, leonine blonde hitched her flouncy red dress up to her thighs, wrapped these around Morrissey's middle and 'grabbed a handful'. A handshake with another female in the front row went purposely wrong and saw him all but dragged headfirst into the crowd. Emerging from this melée, minus his shirt and proudly flaunting an enviable, glistening physique, he slyly remonstrated, 'That was very enjoyable!'

After 'The More You Ignore Me, The Closer I Get' there was more wit and a huge roar of approval when Morrissey pronounced, weighing each word cautiously as if wondering whether he would get away with a few deserved expletives, 'You may have noticed that I didn't get a BTI Award last week – and I was so relieved!' He was actually referring to the BRIT Award for Best British Male Singer, which had gone to Paul Weller. The previous year, Morrissey had received a Q Award for Best Songwriter and had commented during his acceptance speech, 'I would like to thank the people who have stood by me and bought the records over the years. It can't have been easy!' He did not, of course, need such over-hyped accolades – which outlived the recipient's popularity in the world of five-minute wonders – to prove his worth.

Although a not-unprecedented flurry of over-excitement from a group of fans (clambering on to the stage and almost flattening him) caused Morrissey to abandon ship seconds into his 'Shoplifters' finale, the climax to the evening had occurred earlier when, after 'The National Front Disco', Morrissey had performed 'Moon River' and stood stock-still throughout an astonishing seven minutes of multi-strobed, mind-blowing feedback – 'In silhouette, like a noble savage', Max Bell had enthused in the *Evening Standard*. Bathing majestically in the silvery spotlight, as he had all those years ago at the Eldorado, he reminded me of the tragic French actor Gérard Philipe in Alfred de Musset's *On Ne Badine Pas Avec L'Amour* – no mere 'savage' arrogantly savouring the love but, 36 years on, Perdican reborn.

In Newcastle, Morrissey had been interviewed by *Les Inrockuptibles'* Emmanuel Tellier – but only after the journalist had convinced security that he was there on official business. He told me:

> That's the trouble with some of today's entertainers. They themselves are usually charming, but first of all one has to get past some of the horrid people who look after them. These people are often too big for their boots and end up giving the stars a bad name. Eventually, after some deliberation between this thug and Morrissey's hairdresser, I was escorted into his dressing room where the stench of vapour-rub was overpowering, almost unbearable. Morrissey looked white as a sheet. He could hardly stand. This was the face of a man close to death, yet the moment he stepped on to that stage, he seemed to shrug off his illness like an old shirt. The transformation was amazing!

The conversation centred around the forthcoming album, *Southpaw Grammar*, Morrissey's first for RCA now that his contract with EMI was almost expired. Work on this had already begun, in the South of France at the Miraval Studios. Pointing to the mock scar across the back of his hand, he declared, 'These new songs are tougher, more aggressive, frightening and disturbing than anything I've ever done before.' French footballer Eric Cantona had recently hit the headlines with his kung-fu attack on an abusive fan at Selhurst Park, resulting in a six-month ban from the game. Speaking of him as though he was a friend, which he was not, Morrissey said, 'There's no place for me in the pop world. I'm lonelier, lonelier than ever. The only person I feel close to is Cantona. I've so much compassion for him. He responded to aggression and if such a thing had happened in the street, no one would have been shocked. I understand Eric only too well. I'm the Cantona of rock!' Then, as if to make a point, Tellier recalled how he had shouted for his tambourine and scrawled CANTONA across the vellum in large letters. A few evenings later, the tambourine would be inscribed ERIC . . .

The non-obligatory British interview was granted to Stuart Maconie and appeared in the September issue of *Q*. Clearly by this time regarding himself as some sort of neo-Ronnie Kray figure – minus the actual violence, but besotted with thuggery, things tough, gangland duffers and 'bovver' boys – the heading to the piece this time was an atypically aggressive Morrissey quote: DO YOU FUCKIN' WANT SOME? The accompanying photographs, by Andy Earl, were in keeping with the new image: immaculately groomed as usual but sweaty with 'bruised' cheeks, fake slash marks across his forearm and the mock tattoo SOUTHPAW GRAMMAR, the words ENGLAND SWINGS 'carved' into his chest – alternatively posing in a collector's item Ben Sherman shirt, and an Eric Cantona T-shirt. The sub-heading was also his own: ON LIFE, DEATH & ANTHEA TURNER.

When asked the touchy question of why he had moved to RCA, Morrissey quipped, 'I was in the [EMI] building so often that I was surprised they didn't give me a janitor's bucket!' (Replying to the same question a few weeks later, posed by Christian Fevret of *Les Inrockuptibles*, he would less flippantly reply, 'Because I wanted to work under my own steam, without being told what to do all the time.') Of actor Hugh Grant's infamous oral sex episode on Sunset Boulevard, he professed of Grant's actress girlfriend – whose own career had taken off like a rocket as a result of the publicity – 'If I was Elizabeth Hurley and he *hadn't* done anything, I wouldn't stand by him. He's so overrated. All he seems to have is an English accent.' Liam Gallagher, the laddish lead singer with Oasis, regarded by some as 'yet another bunch of Smiths challengers', was dismissed with a gruff, 'Very runt of the litter. You can tell that he'd run off with the fillings from his grandmother's teeth, but that doesn't mean he doesn't love her.' Later, he would revise his opinion after meeting Liam and brother Noel in Australia: the newspapers, he declared, made people out to be monsters when in reality most of them were 'terribly sweet'.

Of the other show business names currently making the news, Morrissey was able to sympathise with Kurt Cobain over his suicide, but expressed only loathing towards the ever-smiling television presenter Anthea Turner, currently fronting *The National Lottery Live*. If *she* handed him a cheque for £20 million, he said, he would hand it back. 'That fixed smile, that fraudulent jollity,' he added. 'If she were telling you that a planeload of children had died in the worst Air India crash ever, she would *still* keep on smiling. Her happiness actually makes me depressed.' Next up were the stock attacks on 'elderly' rock stars, politicians, and a professed indifference towards wealth: 'You may be a billionaire, but if you contract cancer you may as well live in a bedsit in Birmingham – the poor remain poor. *Someone* has to work in Woolworths.' And of course, in keeping with this new Morrissey there was overt praise for Eric Cantona and the boxing ring.

Morrissey's interest in thuggery, of course, had always been there and evenly spread across the board – whether this had been his championing of murderers and gangland heroes, or lesser rapscallions such as rough trade, skinheads and big-headed sportsmen. 'My songs are but a reflection of life,' he had confessed to *Les Inrockuptibles*. This passion for the tougher, seamier side of life reached its zenith in August 1995 with the release of *Southpaw Grammar*, generally regarded as one of Morrissey's poorer albums, though any successor would have been hard put to supersede *Your Arsenal* and *Vauxhall And I*. Paul du Noyer commented in *Mojo*, 'If only Morrissey's tunes were as good as his titles, he would be the Burt Bacharach of his generation.' Housed in a sleeve featuring a long-forgotten boxer named Kenny Lane, the album reached number 4 in the charts, but dropped out of the best-sellers list after just three weeks. Many fans and most of the critics accused Morrissey of short-changing them by including just eight songs – two of these running in excess of ten minutes. This problem might have been avoided had he, say, waited a little longer and added some of the songs that were subsequently relegated to B-sides – though one, 'Whatever Happened To Love?', appears to have disappeared altogether.

A superb song recorded at around this time was 'Swallow On My Neck', one of the B-sides (the other was the lacklustre 'Black-Eyed Susan') of the 'Sunny' single. One of the best *chansons-propres* Morrissey ever wrote sets out to be a hymn to self-outing: 'I have been smashed again with the man from the Old Valhalla Road crematorium,' adding, 'He drew a swallow on my neck . . . and soon everyone knew.' This had the more impressionable fans, the ones who had sacrificed their quiffs for 'Jake' haircuts, rushing to the nearest tattoo parlour, not always aware of the motif's gay implications: Marc Almond had a tattooed swallow on his neck, and Morrissey sports a mock one on the *Vauxhall And I* sleeve. The fact that this little masterpiece was actually left off the album almost constitutes a crime. Paul Goddard of *Grooves*, for whom Morrissey could do no wrong, gave the new album a very definite thumbs-down:

> Once upon a time This Charming Man had us all Reeling Around The Fountain with admiration. We thought his talent was a Light That Never Goes Out and we were wrong. These days, The World Won't Listen – and of the evidence of this, who can blame us? To borrow a baseball term, Bigmouth Strikes Again!

'*Southpaw Grammar* is the school of hard knocks,' Morrissey had told Stuart Maconie, 'it's coming up the hard way and taking your bruises with you.' The cynics, of course, were quick in pointing out that 'southpaw' meant fighting with the left hand – and in gay parlance, 'batting for the other side'. The opening track, 'The Teachers Are Afraid Of The Pupils', has as its central theme Shostakovich's Fifth Symphony, therefore brevity would be deemed inappropriate. Morrissey had certainly done his homework. The great Russian composer, himself castigated for his views (accused by the Communist Party of having anti-democratic tendencies) and a chronic depressive on account of this, had composed the piece in 1937, giving it the subtitle, 'In Answer To Just Criticism'. It had re-established his reputation in the Soviet Union, and like the later Gorecki piece was a firm favourite amongst pacifists. Morrissey's lyric was effectively a complete volte-face from 'The Headmaster Ritual' in that, whereas teachers had once been allowed to discipline their charges and had frequently gone too far, nowadays they were virtually prohibited from disciplining them at all, resulting in classroom anarchy. In Morrissey's schooldays, as in my own, the maxim had been, 'Don't tell your father you got a clout from the teacher, otherwise *he'll* clout you harder!' Now, no matter what the child has done, the riposte from the parents is, 'Say the wrong thing to our children, and we'll have you!' And the teacher, hinting at retirement or perhaps even driven to the point of suicide by all of this, can only opine, 'To be finished would be a relief!' The phrase, however, was double-edged, as Morrissey explained to *Les Inrockuptibles*: 'On a more intimate level, it's about my life and career. Going away would effectively be a relief – no longer feeling the pressure, being allowed to breathe a little more freely.'

The criticism continues in 'Reader Meet Author', a bouncy attack against biographers, and more specifically Johnny Rogan and some members of the music press who, according to the narrator, fail to scratch beneath the surface of their subjects – a point that all reputable biographers would fervently disagree with! It also contains a rare silly line from Morrissey, 'You don't know a thing about their lives/Books don't save them, books aren't Stanley knives.'

The next, much better track on the album – 'The Boy Racer' – is reminiscent of Edith Piaf's 'L'Homme A La Moto', the inspiration behind Twinkle's 'Terry'. It returns the singer to the more familiar territory of gay fetishism. 'Morrissey as the man in the mac', is how *Select* described it. 'He thinks he's got the whole world in his hands, stood at the urinal,' Morrissey declares, confessing his jealousy of the beautiful, Brandoesque youth who has too much money, too many girlfriends. Then he vehemently concludes, indicating that if he cannot have the young man then no one will, 'I'm gonna kill him, he's just too good looking.' Earlier, Stuart Maconie had asked Morrissey, leaving the most personal question until last – as others had done so as not to jeopardise the interview – 'Do *you* ever stand in front of the urinal and think you've got the whole world in your hands?' The gentle reprimand had been, 'I don't need to walk to the urinal. I already know. And *you* should know better than to ask.'

One of Morrissey's musicians told me, 'Two of the new songs were Mozza's way of getting Jake out of his system, once and for all.' In 'Best

Friend On The Payroll', Morrissey gives no indication as to who pampered whom – 'More breakfast in bed, and I'll bring the paper in later' – but he is very firm when declaring, 'No, it's not gonna work out.' In 'The Operation' he laments, 'You fight with your right hand and caress with your left hand . . . sad to say how once I was in love with you.' Before we hear this, however, we are party to the most thrilling chunk of percussion work in any Morrissey recording since Andrew Paresi's contribution to *Kill Uncle* – two and a half minutes described by *Mojo* as, 'Like waking up with a hangover, stumbling out of bed for some Paracetamol and discovering the Boys Brigade are marching through your kitchen, while the Orange Lodge are coming in from the lounge.' 'Jake started off as a very nice guy,' the aforementioned musician told me, 'but he took his position far too seriously. It went to his head. He became bossy. I guess that's why he had to go.'

The most engaging song on the album is 'Dagenham Dave', a brief tale of envy brought about by suppressed homosexuality, the saga of the loveable Essex rogue (thought to be a rare Morrissey-friendly music journalist) who walks through the streets, 'Head in the clouds, with a mouth full of pie' – and who has transfers of his girlfriends' names on his windscreen, possibly to fool his friends. This, however, is a Morrissey song and as such the veil is soon torn aside to reveal how, 'He'd love to touch, but he's afraid he might self-combust.' By comparison, the album's closing tracks, 'Do Your Best And Don't Worry' and 'Southpaw' were, according to the majority of critics and fans, lyrically dull for an artiste of Morrissey's standing.

The launch party for *Southpaw Grammar* took place at England football coach Terry Venables' Kensington nightclub, Scribes West – the sleeve of 'Dagenham Dave' has an unflattering shot of Venables with his tongue sticking out, taken in 1964 when he was a twenty-year-old striker. As for the guest of honour, Morrissey was conspicuous by his absence – he claimed because he had wished to avoid the 'undesirables' from the music press who had been invited against his wishes.

As had happened with his previous album, there were near-hysterical in-store signings: the Virgin Megastores in Dublin and Belfast, and the huge FNAC under the shadow of Paris' Montparnasse Tower, which saw

Morrissey travelling through the very Chunnel he had so often vowed would cave in. Here, thousands of fans were in attendance for what *France-Soir* called, 'A papal visit without the purple robes.' Some had jetted in from Japan, Australia and the United States – dossing down in shop doorways, sleeping in parks, going without sustenance for a twenty-hour wait in a seemingly endless queue, a rushed embrace, and thirty seconds of their idol's time. One couple from Canada told of how they had remortgaged their house to raise the funds for this particular trip! The tattoo parlours around the rue de Rennes also reported good business, working over the various slogans and scribblings on arms, shoulders and hearts. There was also a new breed of fanatic, an adherent of the faction that had attempted to trash Morrissey's name a few years earlier in Chicago. Nicknamed 'The Girl Racer' for obvious reasons – the theory being that if *she* could not have Morrissey, then no one else would – this young American woman had begun by bombarding Morrissey with expensive gifts, including jewellery and a Cartier wristwatch. 'The gifts became so costly,' bassist Johnny Bridgewood said, 'Moz thought it wouldn't be right to accept any more.' This was the same fan who had been searched at Drury Lane after she had boasted to another fan that she had been carrying a knife. One of the FNAC employees told me,

> We were told of an incident outside Morrissey's dressing room, when this woman had become hysterical and threatening after he had refused to see her. It wasn't his fault she'd used up her savings to fly out for a handshake. His management were terrified that she might turn out to be some female Mark Chapman, so as soon as she was pointed out to us, we collared her and escorted her out of the store. She was extremely abusive and lucky not to have been handed over to the police.

Christian Fevret and Emmanuel Tellier of *Les Inrockuptibles* were party to what may now be regarded as Morrissey's most portentous interview. Under the heading, 'My Bitch Of A Life', he appeared on the cover of the magazine's 6 September issue – photographed by Eric

Mulet 'en pleine crannerie' ['in full swagger'], squatting between two huge, slobbering Rottweilers. Time and time again these journalists had proved that they could be trusted to quote his comments verbatim. He explained why he had dispensed with the services of his high-flying American manager, Arnold Stiefel: 'He organised a series of concerts in New York which sold out like lightning. Unfortunately, he forgot to check if I was free to do them. That's one of the great regrets of my life, that I've never had anyone intelligent enough to represent me. Such a person doesn't exist.' What he did not add was that these concerts had been at the city's most prestigious venue, Carnegie Hall, and that – whether or not it was true that Stiefel hadn't checked with Morrissey first – cancelling such engagements for any reason other than sudden death invariably led to the doors of other major American establishments being unceremoniously slammed in faces.

On a personal level, such gaffes aside, Morrissey was this time truly seen to be wearing his heart on his sleeve. No British journalist would have got away with asking him if he held his parents responsible for his permanent state of sadness! His mother, he confessed, had been forced to contend with his 'unsatisfied state' for years. 'She would love to see me happy and in full bloom,' he added. 'Therefore she can't be blamed for the way I am.' The mere mention of his father's name, however, brought an adverse reaction. Emmanuel Tellier told me, 'He turned very pale and grimaced. Then he signalled for me to switch off the microphone. The silence was crippling. I could have pursued the subject, but we both respected his feelings too much to even try.'

In this interview, Morrissey spoke of his desire to form another relationship. He had written 'Now My Heart Is Full' when there had been love in his life, and now he was alone again, though strangely at peace within himself. One of the problems associated with finding someone, he said, was that would-be suitors were always too much in awe of him to let themselves go. Another fault lay with himself: he spent too much of his time arguing with people, he could be just as cruel towards women as he could towards men, he was ever on the alert. Also, he added, he was surrounded by people who thought solely of their own agenda and never tried to understand *him*. He concluded, seemingly finding it no longer necessary to conceal his light under the proverbial bushel:

> It's become, as it were, impossible to meet someone profoundly generous, someone capable of offering his feelings, his emotions. Most of the people I meet always say the same things. And what's the point of seeing people if you know *exactly* what they're going to say, if every move's premeditated and regulated by rules?

This, of course, was a classic malady of the superstar loner: because they are so big, because they rarely settle for anything less than having all their own way, they render themselves feared and unattainable – they needlessly put themselves through the mill and actually enjoy the process, they spend much of their lives alone, and inevitably die likewise. Emotionally and psychologically, Morrissey fitted into the same bracket as Garland, Piaf and any number of post-war torch singers whose lives were lived in the full glare of the media and the public. He might easily have shared a theme song with Judy: 'The Man That Got Away'. When asked about long-term relationships – the enemy of the torch singer in that, if lasting love is found and all the soul-searching stops, the performances themselves have no meaning – he responded, 'If such a relationship was a reality for me, it would no longer be fascinating. I'm drawn towards what I can't have. Accessible things are of no interest to me. If I find calm and serenity, doubtless you would never see me again. That would be the end of my career.'

Morrissey was also by now utterly obsessed with violence. 'It's a macabre fascination,' he told *Les Inrockuptibles*. 'It's *not* a hobby of mine, and I wish it would go away. But for me, violence is a daily part of my routine. People treat me like I'm abnormal, and *that's* also the beginning of violence.' But, his interviewers wanted to know, had Morrissey ever met the woman of his dreams? His response was suitably acerbic, but honest:

> More often than not I've met the woman of my *nightmares*. *Most* women are nightmares, physically and mentally. There again, I was

never very interested. Even as a child I found it easier to fall in love with photographs. I find the whole idea of attraction embarrassing, whether it's attraction towards a man or a woman. So if I bump into someone I find attractive, I flee in the other direction. What's the point in telling him you think he's attractive when you know it's never going to work out? I get those kind of letters from some fans, but if they ever found out what I was *really* like, they'd soon refrain from desiring me.

Emmanuel Tellier put to Morrissey that, as a handsome, healthy 36-year-old male he must get sexual urges. How, therefore, did he control these?

I don't have that many. Honestly! I have no sex life, therefore I don't *get* urges . . . and whenever the hormones start to manifest, I have a shave! I've never known sexual satisfaction, but right now I *want* to have a sex life, to find out what it's *like* to feel satisfied. I'm working at it! It's my greatest wish!

Like William Shaw of *Details*, Emmanuel Tellier had observed the Morrissey–Jake body language. He told me, 'When they were together, Morrissey looked happy, like a child on Christmas morning. But there was something about Jake. He was a very polite young man, but his mannerisms were too affected for my liking. Somehow I was given the impression that he was more attracted to the celebrity and all that went with it than he was to the man himself.' For the benefit of his readers who might not have known, Tellier therefore asked, 'When was the last time you were in love?' Jake is said to have been upset by the response, 'Very recently, but it wasn't the real thing – more like a kind of dream. He was solid and real enough, but our love affair was impossible.'

A few weeks after this interview, Morrissey announced that he would be augmenting David Bowie's Outsiders tour at the end of the year – not on equal billing, but as Bowie's support. Dates were scheduled for London, Birmingham, Belfast, Dublin, Exeter, Cardiff, Aberdeen, Glasgow, Sheffield, Manchester and Newcastle – an 'unlucky' thirteen shows, most of these not in the smaller, more intimate venues Morrissey preferred, but in the impersonal arenas he had always sworn he would never set foot in. The term VERY SPECIAL GUEST was used in the publicity material, but only Bowie's photograph appeared on playbills, therefore it is not difficult to imagine the response from fans of both camps, who predicted a mighty clashing of egos and a fight to the death for artistic supremacy between these undisputed icons of differing generations.

The music press – no real surprise here – labelled Morrissey 'Bowie's underdog' from Day One. So why, then, did he agree to do the tour in the first place when he was well aware that he would be positioning himself for the music press's most vitriolic attack since Finsbury Park? 'He wanted to give his enemies a good kick in the balls,' one of his closest friends informed me. 'It's like the John Major thing. You know, when the PM decided to resign so that he'd be re-elected, more powerful than ever? That's how Moz sees himself.'

Morrissey's victory over the 'adversary' he had elected to take on, to prove a point, would prove almost tragically pyrrhic.

On the eve of the tour he was interviewed for the *Observer* by Will Self, a gravel-voiced, towering six-foot-six presence, and photographed in intense close-up by one of Britain's most eminent photographers, Jane Bown: the result was a candid, beautiful image of an attractive, pensive young man whose penetrating gaze bespeaks a mélange of wisdom and mocking wit, the faint lines of stress just starting to show, along with the odd grey hair, which gave him a look of Byronesque distinction. 'Life finds Morrissey in mature mode,' Self observed. 'Has the boy outsider become an adult and joined the rest of the human race?'

Aware of Self's reputation, like Julie Burchill, of being a law unto himself in the journalistic world, Morrissey got in the first punch by telling him, 'You've actually got the face of a criminal I've met.' Self had his own way of interpreting this. Describing his subject as 'very attractive in the flesh' he asked his readers, 'Is this a man tortured by his own sexuality and that of others? His body language is far from craven. Setting aside the context of this remark, it struck me that this was not the sort of thing that someone intent on denying corporality would be likely to say.' However, when Self broached the subject of Morrissey's so-called 'vexed sexuality' he was very quickly put in his place: 'It doesn't vex *me*. I don't exactly think it vexes other people. I don't think people *assume* anything any more about me. I'm sort of classified in a non-sexual, asexual way, which is an air of dismissiveness which I quite like.' Self summarised this by quoting Oscar Wilde: 'Celibacy is the only known sexual perversion.'

From sexuality, the natural progression for Self seemed to be – via linking the singer with campology and Kenneth Williams – whether or not Morrissey wanted children. This was no doubt a sly way of asking him (from a man who reprimanded a *Gay Times* reporter, ten years later, with the comment, 'I'm not *that* straight!') if he liked sleeping with women, and anticipating some remarkable confession. The response was a variation on the one he had given to *Details* a few years earlier, 'What happens when your child turns around and says, "Look, I don't like this world. Why did you bring me into it?" ' – enabling Self to draw his own conclusion:

> I get the feeling that these kinds of sallies are a form of bluff for Morrissey, and that he throws them out in much the way that aircraft in World War II dropped strips of metal to fool radar. If his interlocutors rise to such chaff, then they're not really worthy of consideration. But he's also adept at side-stepping the conventional psychoanalyst thrusts of the interviewer . . . He is responsible – among other things – for encapsulating two hundred years of philosophical speculation in a single line: 'Does the body rule the mind or does the mind rule the body? I don't know.' He told me he could 'do anything'. I certainly hope he does. England needs him.

The tour opened on 14 November with the first of four concerts at the Wembley Arena. Ticket sales had been poor on account of the prices: two top-notch stars did not come cheap, and fans found themselves paying twice as much to get in as they had earlier in the year. Even so, with the same musicians and Cornelius Carr backdrop, Morrissey easily proved that despite the 'stiff competition' he was still a force to be reckoned with. The *Independent*'s Ryan Gibney described this opener as, 'His most startling performance in years, launching himself at the songs like an Exocet missile.' Will Self, invited to the show, went a step further, writing in the *Observer*, 'The band crashes into the opening chords of "Reader Meet Author", and Morrissey begins to flail at the air with the cord of his microphone, pirouetting, hip-swivelling for all the world like some camp version of Roy Rogers.'

Yet behind the bravado of verve, vigour and general bonhomie there lurked much apprehension, particularly when he drawled after this first song, 'Good evening, we are your support group.' He also looked tense towards the end of his set, the first time since The Smiths' early days that he had been officially listed second fiddle on any bill, when in an attempt to silence the Bowie hecklers he announced, 'Don't worry, we won't stay *too* long!' – before flinging himself into 'Dagenham Dave'. Manuel Rios of the Spanish *Drive Me Home* fanzine witnessed the spectacle from the front of the half-full auditorium. He told me,

> Morrissey *looked* great, in a designer suit and plain shirt. Along with his medallion, his bracelet, his whiskers, his ring and such a cool band behind him, he looked like somebody in a Tarantino film – that is, a sort of gangster. His singing was brilliant, but he seemed *bored* at times and the atmosphere was far from being what it usually is. And you know just how essential that is for his performances.

The non-gutter press were generally sympathetic, but almost certainly contributed to Morrissey's burdening neurasthenia and, looking back on the period, his encroaching breakdown. David Bowie's performances were not up to his standard, either, and saw large sections of the audience walking out on him along with the Morrissey fans. 'Next to Bowie, Morrissey is a parochial pleasure, but at least he has a coherent sense of himself,' observed Roy Wilkinson of *Select*, 'and the rousing "Now My Heart Is Full" that comes at the end of the Moz set is a more affecting evocation of *The Long Day Closing* than all of Bowie's *fin de siècle* poltroonery.'

Tristan, of *The Mighty Quiff* fanzine, was more direct, saying, 'Most of us who stayed to watch Bowie fell asleep.' David Sinclair reported in *The Times* how Bowie had emerged from behind the drumkit:

Singing and walking as if in his sleep . . . the show seemed mired in a joyless aesthetic. Poor Morrissey. He sang well enough, but performing too early, on a borrowed stage to someone else's cold audience, the man with the rapidly thinning quiff fell flat as a pancake. It is hard to imagine Morrissey putting up with this level of indifference for the whole of a lengthy tour.

The Outsiders fiasco chugged around the circuit, and at each venue the response from the media and fans was the same. Then on 29 November, only minutes before he was due to go on stage at the Aberdeen Exhibition Centre, Morrissey was taken ill in his dressing room and the audience were told, in lieu of his performance, that Bowie's would be brought forward. The next day, some of the tabloids ran stories of a supposed backstage bust-up between the two singers, while Morrissey 'insiders' fed the music press with a variety of fabricated stories. The truth was, Morrissey had been driven to the city's privately run St John's Hospital, where a few days later his condition was explained to me – as much as was permitted, anyway – by an off-the-record spokesman:

Yes, it's potentially serious. That's why we're expecting to keep him under very close observation over the next few weeks. But as you know, Mr Morrissey is a strong, hefty laddie, and we have every confidence that he'll make a splendid recovery.

It was rumoured that he had a complete mental breakdown and friends felt it was too much for him. Kirsty MacColl told me, 'He should never have done that tour, Morrissey is far too great a star to be supporting one of the rock dinosaurs he's persistently slagging off.'

Whatever the cause of his condition, within the week, apparently ignoring the advice of doctors and friends but promising to take care of himself, Morrissey discharged himself from hospital. Everyone expected him to recuperate at home for several weeks, then rejoin the Outsiders tour's European leg, scheduled to begin in Lyons on 11 February 1996. He had absolutely no intention of further humiliating himself, however, and is thought to have personally made up for any losses and refunds. For some time now, despite the horrors with security the first time around, he had been wanting to return to Japan. Accompanied by the companion who had got him through the worst of his illness, he flew to Tokyo for a 'stationary' tour – four concerts in different Tokyo halls (Shinjuku, Kawasaki, Ebisu, Tokyo Bay) on 13, 14, 16 and 17 December. Each was a sell-out, there were no problems with security, and the sojourn appears to have done him more good than any psychiatrist's probing, enabling him a swift return to normality. He even managed a few words of Japanese between songs! Then he flew home, hopeful of placing the anguish of the last two months behind him. And to what seemed like semi-retirement . . .

8

I Will Live My Life As
I Will Undoubtedly
Die . . .

'I do feel I'd be disappointed if I got to fifty. It would show a lack of
resolve, or something.'

– Morrissey

Andy Rourke, Mike Joyce and Craig Gannon, despite the hysterical
ambience of Morrissey's 'rebirth' at Wolverhampton in 1988, had for
years claimed that he and Johnny Marr owed them money. In March
1989 – with *Viva Hate* selling like hot cakes around the world – Stephen
Street took out an injunction on Morrissey's single 'Interesting Drug',
preventing its release until his particular financial beef with the singer
had been settled. Prior to this, Rourke and Joyce had been told by
Morrissey and Marr that they were not entitled to the quarter-share of
Smithdom they had demanded (extant of songwriting royalties) because
the group, contractually, had not extended beyond Morrissey and Marr.
The two of them had been told they were each legally entitled to 40 per
cent of mechanical royalties (revenues largely from record sales), which
left the remaining 20 per cent to be shared by Rourke and Joyce – and
by Gannon when he had tagged along. Hoping to resolve the situation,
Morrissey and Marr had proposed an 'ideal solution' – 10 per cent of the
group's general royalties. This had been rejected and the pair threatened

with legal action. The royalties war would rage for years, seriously threatening Morrissey's reputation, though in the dew-kissed eyes of the fans he could have committed mass murder and still been put forward for beatification.

'The Fifth Smith', Craig Gannon, had been the first to take the plunge, challenging the might of Morrissey during 1986's autumn of discontent. Gannon had been fired from the group not just because he had accused Morrissey and Marr of under-paying him during The Smiths' last American tour, but because, he claimed, they had short-changed him by not paying him co-writing royalties for 'Ask'. A few years later – hypocritically perhaps, because he had worked with Morrissey in the interim period – Gannon took the matter to court and won. Denouncing the case as 'heartbreaking, deeply sad and an outrage of public justice', a somewhat smug Morrissey told *Vox*'s Len Brown in November 1993, 'Everybody involved knew he didn't have a leg to stand on yet, through some perversion of justice, he walked away with £42,000 . . . but my opinion is that Craig Gannon didn't really win because he's still Craig Gannon. Ha ha!'

On 3 December 1996 the *Daily Mail* – whom Morrissey had once suggested might publish a photograph of Prince Charles wearing his mother's wedding veil – ran the headline, 'Smith Versus Smith'. After almost a decade, Mike Joyce was taking his former 'employers' to the cleaners. The accusation: Morrissey and Marr had, he claimed, 'swindled' him out of thousands of pounds.

His was a lone stance. In 1989, Andy Rourke had accepted an out-of-court settlement of £83,000, plus 10 per cent of The Smiths' future mechanical royalties. Even so, he was summoned to give evidence. Joyce's lawyers estimated that, in view of the recent abundance of Smiths re-releases, his client was entitled to at least £1 million – along with a full 25 per cent of future mechanical royalties.

There were many who thought Joyce might have been on to a hiding over nothing. The press were reminded of Morrissey's interview with *NME*'s Danny Kelly in June 1985, when Kelly had asked, with regard to Morrissey and Johnny Marr's perception of the other group members, 'You must be aware that the drone Smiths seem like session men?'

Morrissey had replied, apparently without the slightest hint of malice, 'Yes, but I positively know that they're not as upset about it as people think they should be . . . they have their position and they know what it is. We all have our roles. We all know our limitations.'

In Berlin, during the spring of 1991, *NME*'s Stuart Maconie had asked Morrissey, quite likely with Joyce in mind, 'Do you love your enemies?' – bringing the Machiavellian response, 'I *sympathise* – and then I arrange to have their heads kicked in. I *do* have friends in high places. Tower Hamlets, for instance.'

More recently, there had been Morrissey's self-righteous outburst to the *Observer*'s Robert Chalmers: 'I believe that if Andy Rourke and Mike Joyce had had another singer, they would have gotten no further than Salford Shopping Centre.' 'He almost *spat* that out,' Chalmers told me. Joyce had since bumped into Morrissey, demanded an explanation, and in lieu of 'chinning' him had accepted an invitation to go for a drink. Subsequently, Morrissey had come up with the excuse that he had been 'misquoted' – not possible with Chalmers who, as I know from personal experience, tapes everything to ensure there is no comeback.

The London High Court hearing lasted seven days, and did Morrissey few favours, for here he was subjected to criticism not from educationally challenged music press journalists, but from a wily, no-nonsense QC, Nigel Davis, and Mr Justice Weeks, who was not in the least interested in trying to 'decipher' some of his Wildean phrases. Indeed, both are alleged to have never heard of Morrissey or The Smiths until preparing for the case.

The proceedings opened with QC Davis explaining to the court how Morrissey and Marr had persistently denied that Mike Joyce had been a partner in their company, Smithdom Ltd – until November 1995, when they had offered him £273,000, which he had refused, preferring to sort out the matter legally. While The Smiths had been in existence, no formal contract had ever been drawn up about the sharing of profits; neither had there been any verbal agreement to do this. It was avowed that Joyce had been sent a copy of the company's accounts in July 1986, but that with no knowledge of figures, and trusting Morrissey and Marr, he had shoved this into a drawer without even looking at it.

QC Davis added that Joyce had subsequently showed this to a friend who had a knowledge of accountancy, and that after taking advice from this friend, he had decided to take the matter further. Neither Morrissey nor Marr attended the first day of the hearing, but QC Davis explained to the court how Morrissey had described Joyce and Rourke as 'mere session musicians as readily replaceable as the parts in a lawnmower'. He summarised,

> Mr Joyce says he is entitled to 25 per cent of income, deriving from the group's activities, except for activities of songwriting. Mr Morrissey and Mr Marr say he is only entitled to 10 per cent. Mr Joyce never agreed to 10 per cent. On the contrary, he thought he was getting 25 per cent. Morrissey and Marr place the greatest possible emphasis on how much more important they were to the group. They had the highest profile so far as the public were concerned, but it would seem that they would go further and claim they are much more talented. They seek to downplay the importance of Joyce and Rourke. It was Mr Joyce's perception throughout that all the real decisions were made by Morrissey and Marr. In particular, the financial decisions were made by Morrissey. Mr Joyce was happy to do so because he trusted them. Morrissey now seeks to disparage Mr Joyce and Mr Rourke by saying they were mere session musicians.

Morrissey and Marr's effective undoing, so far as QC Davis was concerned, was that in offering Mike Joyce a large sum of money the previous year, they were admitting that there had been at least a verbal partnership agreement. At once, public sympathy was on the side of the apparent underdog. In the 8 December issue of the *Sunday Times*, John Dugdale denounced Morrissey as 'an insecure miserablist' and called Joyce, 'An innocent who has apparently idolised the songwriting duo,' adding, 'He had the great attraction of doormat-like docility. Until last week, that is.'

Not all the subsequent sessions were open to the press, allegedly because 'personal accusations and comments were in danger of being levelled by one side or the other'. So far as is known, Morrissey made just the one appearance in court, looking every inch the star – immaculately dressed and groomed like a Hollywood matinee idol of yesteryear, smiling shyly. What was said is on file, accessible, but under embargo and not always pleasant. One of the few snippets released to the press was Morrissey's admission that he had 'kept back' almost £500,000 in royalties because, he said, the other group members 'weren't interested in business'. He and Johnny Marr sat close to each other for the first time in over nine years. When the question arose that Mike Joyce should have studied the Smithdom accounts sheet before assigning it to a drawer, QC Davis declared that even if he had, it would have been too complicated for him to comprehend. When Mr Justice Weeks reached his verdict on 11 December, Morrissey, surprisingly, was not in court, though he was closely informed of the outcome by his solicitor. Joyce won his case. In his summing up, Mr Justice Weeks delivered his assessment of the four group members, working his way downwards:

> Morrissey, the oldest and more assertive member of the group, held the purse-strings. He and Marr signed the accounts on behalf of The Smiths. Morrissey was more complicated and did not find giving evidence easy or a happy experience. He was devious, truculent and unreliable when his own interests were at stake. Marr was a more engaging, reasonable character, probably the most intelligent of the four, but seemed to be willing to embroider his evidence to the point where he became less credible. Joyce and Rourke impressed me as straightforward and honest, unintellectual and certainly not financially sophisticated or aware.

The cost to Morrissey and Marr would be phenomenal: as Mike Joyce's lawyer had predicted, £1 million plus interest dating back to the spring of 1983 to come out of their own pockets, along with costs in excess of £250,000. Johnny Marr, snapped leaving the court ashen-faced, declined to comment. Morrissey's solicitor issued a statement on his behalf, 'I am disappointed and surprised at the Judge's decision, particularly given the weight of evidence against Mike Joyce. I will be considering the terms of the judgement with my solicitors to assess possible grounds for an appeal.' Joyce told a hastily assembled press-conference outside the court, 'This was never about money. It will not change my lifestyle, but it will secure the future for my wife and children. I still have the highest regard for Morrissey and Johnny, but I always knew ten years ago when I started this action that I would win. And I always believed that I was an equal partner with The Smiths.'

The newspaper headlines the next day unanimously contained the words 'devious' and 'truculent' (Morrissey claimed the latter word had been spray-painted across his mother's front door), along with some variations of The Smiths' song title, 'Heaven Knows I'm Miserable Now'. Almost all of the accompanying photographs were of Morrissey: of the national dailies, only the *Guardian* published one of Johnny Marr.

For a man who could probably win any battle with words, revenge should have been sweet. In the wake of the Joyce affair, Morrissey penned a song that makes one shudder and sympathise with the badly-done-to drummer – not for winning the case, but for being apparently so loathed as to have become the central subject of 'Sorrow Will Come In The End', a tremendous piece of theatricality so barbed in its attack that, next to it, 'Margaret On The Guillotine' and '*The Queen Is Dead*' seem like nursery rhymes. A spokesman for Island Records told me, 'Mozza was informed, "Sing *that*, and you'll end up doing time!" So he tried to get round the problem by *speaking* it!' Even so, the song was banned from appearing on the *Maladjusted* album and is unlikely to ever be released in Britain. In brief, the song's narrator – who has recently lost a court case – wishes a hex on his oppressor, concluding the piece with the foreboding lines, 'I'm gonna get you . . . You think you've won. Oh, no!' Beastly, but brilliant.

Against a force more powerful than himself – justice – Morrissey was a poor loser, though being relieved of a half-share of £1.25 million arguably would have sent anyone over the top. Johnny Marr settled his debt promptly, but Morrissey lodged an appeal, and in April 2003 – using the newly founded *Word* as his sounding-board – he launched a blistering attack on Mike Joyce, listing a catalogue of the drummer's supposed calumnies. According to Morrissey, not sure how to actually get the damages he had been awarded, Joyce had taken to turning up at the stage-door after Morrissey's concerts to ask for money. On top of this, claiming that Joyce had put a charge on his only British assets – his mother's and sister's houses – he scathed, 'He is a purely evil person and he has persecuted my mother, my sister and my nephews, but he presents the public face of a person who's hard done-by and has been thrown to the wayside.'

Morrissey then went off on a tangent, proclaiming how benevolent he and Johnny Marr had been to their former protégé: Marr was alleged to have designed Joyce's drum patterns for him; Joyce had never had to attend business meetings, or even fill in his own tax returns. The supreme accusation, however, was that the court had only sided with Mike Joyce in the first place because Mr Justice Weeks had been 'primed' on Morrissey's character through his former press attacks on the Queen and Margaret Thatcher! 'It's likely that Thatcher had appointed the judge,' he concluded, 'so I was not a very sympathetic character, whereas Joyce was playing the part of the wounded soldier.'

Mike Joyce was either not asked, or denied any attempt to defend these accusations, doubtless because the appeal was close at hand and prudence of the essence. The hearing took place on 22 July 1998. Morrissey lost and immediately lodged a re-appeal.

To date, Mike Joyce is apparently still waiting for Morrissey's portion of the settlement, and in June 2004, ironically speaking to *Word*'s Andrew Harrison, seemed distressed that he might not receive a penny in the wake of Morrissey's having transferred most of his business affairs to the United States. And finally he was offered a platform for his grievances, enabling him to deny Morrissey's claims of the previous year. 'I've got a fair claim on Morrissey's own property and he owes me a lot of money,' he declared, 'but I don't want to throw anyone out of their house.'

It seems unlikely that Morrissey will refrain from denouncing his former drummer at every opportunity – besides 'Sorrow Will Come In The End', at least two Morrissey songs have been 'dedicated' to Mike Joyce. As Kirsty MacColl had said to me some years earlier, 'As a friend, Morrissey is one hell of a guy. But as an enemy – well, you wouldn't want to know.'

*

In July 1998, at the time of Morrissey's appeal against the £1.25 million judgement awarded to Mike Joyce, many of his so-called peers (who had and always would pale in the shadow of his sun) regarded Morrissey as a redundant enigma. He had no record contract. For whatever reason he had hardly ever been capable of holding on to a manager. His 'downfall', it was said, was the result of almost paranoid perfectionism, a mercurial temperament – and greed, the fact that he reputedly would not consider any recording contract under $2 million.

Even so large a sum should have been chickenfeed for any major company to have one of Britain's biggest ever stars on their books – one of almost twenty years' standing who, unlike the Justin Timberlakes and Britney Spears of the fickle pop world, was no here-today-gone-tomorrow sensation. However, because he had always been against the 'down-your-throat' publicity such acts attracted – the tabloids' and weekend supplements' tittle-tattle about their sex-lives, which in any case would have caused him and his clandestine coterie of companions untold grief – most record companies did not know quite how to market him. Such a problem, of course, could have easily been resolved, with decent media advertising and his fair share of airplay. Subsequently, his last album had been largely left to chance: the fans had bought it out of loyalty and force of habit, but there had been few fresh recruits to the Morrissey fan base as had happened with its predecessors.

Then there was the rumour that struck a chill in the hearts of his admirers: Morrissey did not want to go on singing and end up a 'rock relic'. In the spring of 1988, when Shaun Phillips of *Sounds* had spoken to him after a Shirley Bassey concert and posed the question, 'You'll be taking the Shirley Bassey route to stardom, then?' he had exclaimed, 'Good heavens, that means that I'll have to stay alive for another twenty-two years. Could you imagine that? It's a ghastly thought – all those Christmas Morecambe and Wise shows?' On a much more serious note was the rumour from one source very close to Morrissey that he planned to die at 46, like his idol Oscar Wilde.

Had there *really* been a suicide attempt in November 1995, as one of Morrissey's friends had reported to Kirsty MacColl? Indeed, would a true friend have imparted such information before excommunication from the

Morrissey camp? He certainly had not balked at the suggestion of a violent exit from the world when speaking of Kurt Cobain's death: 'I felt sad and I felt envious. I admire people who self-destruct,' he had told Stuart Maconie in the autumn of 1994. 'They're refusing to continue with unhappiness, which shows tremendous self-will. It must be very frightening to sit down and look at your watch and think, in thirty minutes I will not be here.'

Vauxhall And I had been effectively an ode to newfound love and had shimmered with optimism; the fans had shared Morrissey's happiness, and this had been reflected in sales. Much of *Southpaw Grammar* had been a lament for lost love, and this had also been reflected in sales, effecting a curious reversal of attitude by some fans. 'I feel so happy having the flu now that he's got it,' a young Frenchman had told me after Morrissey's Bradford concert – while an inordinately good-looking American fanzine editor who could have had the pick of the crop confessed at Drury Lane, 'I tried sex with a girl and didn't like it much, so I tried sex with a guy and I still didn't like it. Then when I saw the picture of Moz with his head on Jake's lap I tried it again with a girl and a guy and it was like, WOW! Then when I found out that they were no longer together, all of a sudden sex was such a turn off!'

The autumn of 1997 was marked by several show business anniversaries: twenty years since the deaths of Elvis Presley, Maria Callas, Joan Crawford, Marc Bolan and Bing Crosby – and ten years since The Smiths' demise. Morrissey was expected to mark this in some way, but for him there was no going back and he brought out his ninth solo album – *Maladjusted*, better perhaps than its predecessor, but still several rungs down the ladder from *Your Arsenal* and *Vauxhall And I*. Alan Jackson of *The Times*, while enthusing that Morrissey was in 'better voice than ever', still wanted to know,

Where are the searing melodies, the chiming guitars, the deftness and grace with which a complementary band leavened the bequiffed one's famous tendency towards mordancy and introspection? Such virtues are in short supply here, as is another old-fashioned commodity, the tune that can be whistled.

Richard Smith of *Gay Times* was similarly unimpressed:

> The songs are more sprightly than those on *Southpaw Grammar*, but
> they're just as slight, and just as before I've no idea what most of them
> are about. *Maladjusted* largely is the sound of a man who has no
> interest whatsoever in modern life. And to paraphrase some old
> queen or other, to make one boring album may be regarded as
> misfortune, to make two in a row looks like he couldn't care less.
> Maybe Morrissey shouldn't be surprised if these days people care less
> and less about him.

The *Guardian*'s Caroline Sullivan disagreed. Recalling Mr Justice
Weeks' 'devious, truculent, unreliable' accusation, she declared, 'One
must take exception with that "unreliable". In the past few years,
Morrissey has been the soul of reliability, turning out one lachrymose
record after another. This is his ninth, which makes for a pretty
formidable canon.' Suzie Mackenzie, writing for the publication's
weekend supplement, was more enthusiastic: 'The whole album –
elegant, elegiac, with nods to the past to The Smiths – is in fact a hymn
to himself. Morrissey burbling dolefully on like a sad but resilient saint
inventing his own religion.'

The focal point of the album should have been 'Sorrow Will Get You
In The End', the brilliant, unforgivable attack on Mike Joyce, not
surprisingly removed for legal reasons. Even so, aside from the weak but
catchy 'Alma Matters', the confusing 'Ammunition' and the rather silly
'Roy's Keen', there are a few gems. The album opens with the title track,
an explosion of guitars and with Morrissey's lyrics more in keeping with
those of Michael Stipe or even William Burroughs. He takes on the
persona of the 'working girl' (in gay parlance, this could refer to either
sex) who runs away from home 'with a soul full of loathing for stinging
bureaucracy' and ends up in a rough district of London. The song, however, is too long and there is too much repetition of the musical stanza
that is redolent of the Frank Sinatra standard, 'It Was A Very Good Year'.

'Ambitious Outsiders', the most moving song on the album, is also
profoundly disturbing, a brave subject even for Morrissey to tackle for it

deals with the threatened kidnapping of children. What makes it more chilling is that it is delivered in the same minor register as the missing 'Sorrow Will Get You In The End', drenched with shimmering strings. The narrator takes pleasure in being an acquaintance of his victims, who are blithely unaware that he is the one terrorising them. He warns that though they may take whatever precautions they see fit to protect their offspring, he knows 'when the schoolbus comes and goes'. And he arrogantly concludes, 'It's your fault for reproducing – we're just keeping the population down.'

The stimulation provided by difficulties emerges in the very lovely 'Trouble Loves Me', the fact that the narrator feels more comfortable with his problems because these have always proved more reliable than any lover may hope to be. For this reason, love is always best when paid off – among the rough trade of Soho. Lyrically, 'Papa Jack' is reminiscent of the earlier 'Spring-Heeled Jim': the unloveable rogue who never wanted his children when they needed him ('Papa Jack just pushed them away') and now he grieves alone, desperate to turn back the clock. The ambiguously titled, self-deprecating 'Wide To Receive' returns us to more familiar Morrissey territory, and opens with him plagiarising his own work – a musical stanza from 'The National Front Disco'. The narrator is logged on to an Internet chatroom, yet even unseen he fails to score and can only opine, 'I don't get on with myself, and I'm not too keen on anyone else.'

'He Cries' has Morrissey rising phoenix-like from the ashes of attempted destruction – 'Stoned to death, but still living' – while the final, and finest song on the album, 'Satan Rejected My Soul', sees him defiantly proclaiming that such has been his life, the Devil himself wants nothing to do with him ('As low as he goes, he never goes *this* low!') and, as heaven is similarly out of bounds, there is nowhere else to go. Superb!

The album's release coincided with the first Gay & Lesbian Morrissey Convention taking place at the ICA, in London. The event was organised and hosted by Amy Lamé, the owner of Duckie, a gay pub in South London, and covered by the *Independent*'s Bunty Clynch. Four hundred revellers participated. 'Gladioli were shipped in,' Clynch reported, 'as were NHS black-rimmed specs (without lenses), hearing aids, and two hairdressers equipped with enough hairspray to coif a few hundred quiffs.' Inevitably there were straight gatecrashers, some of which nevertheless headed straight for the venue's central feature – a large bed 'where fans were encouraged to writhe around and dream of Morrissey'. Asked to sum up the evening in a few words, one of these repeated the Morrissey gospel, 'People who wade through happiness all their lives don't know what pain is.'

The interviews this time around were more selective, the concerts rather thin on the ground. 'I'm in exile, I'm box-office poison as far as I can gather,' the singer told *Big Issue*. Under duress, it would appear, he 'granted an audience' with the *Guardian*'s Suzie Mackenzie. 'God forgive that I should be normal,' he told her, before asking her if she had any pets – and if she had, would she consider *eating* them? Then he threw a confusing spanner into the works by 'confiding' that he and Johnny Marr had first met not in 1982, but three years earlier at a Patti Smith concert, when Marr would have been sixteen. Otherwise, he spoke mostly of nothing in particular, perhaps because in this instance – interviewed away from the pub, gymnasium or similar laddish environment, and face to face with a woman who might easily to his way of thinking turn out to be another Antonella Black or Julie Burchill – he felt out of place and did not know what to talk about. He no longer wanted to discuss celibacy: 'Can't think why I ever did. It's incredibly boring.' He offered a rare vote of disapproval for the Church, explaining how as a child he had been forced to go to Confession and, to please the priest, invent sins he had not committed:

> God forbid that [priests] feel redundant. It is probably the worst thing you can do to a child, to make it feel guilty, and guilt is astonishingly embedded in Catholic children without knowing why. It is a ferocious burden to carry. How evil can children be?

What impressed Mackenzie about her subject was that he was no longer the wilting wallflower of yesteryear, but now perceived as the 'supreme survivor'. 'Don't ask me how,' he admonished, 'but if a plane crashed at 38,000 feet, I'd be walking on the ground. And if there were eight survivors and one had to be eaten, it wouldn't be me.'

The quills were sharpened for this undisputed survivor when, on 10 December 1997 (as part of a two-event deal with a venue in Chester), Morrissey gave a concert at the unlikeliest of locations: Battersea Power Station. The last two albums had been savaged by some critics, often for the sheer want of something or someone for them to attack. Therefore, would this performance suffer the same fate? The answer was No, because by and large the event was ignored by the tabloids and music press. Stephen Eastwood of Channel 4's text service was enthusiastic: 'Appearing in front of a *Carry On*-style "homoerotic" backdrop, saucy old Moz greeted all the "sexy Londoners" who had trudged through the mud surrounding the Power Station to view their idol. All in all, the show proved there's life in the old Moz yet.' The unsigned reviewer from London's *Eye On Friday* was surprised how the singer had filled out since he had last seen him: 'The rampaging sweaty buffalo of a man careering around the stage was not the Morrissey we know . . . The physique suggested that he now does his moping around in the gymnasium rather than the library. What's more, he was positively jubilant.'

Morrissey was in tremendous form, though many among the audience might have been happier had he ditched some of the *Southpaw Grammar* songs and stuck to the standards. The wit was also razor sharp. 'Hello, you sexy Londoners,' he boomed, as the flowers rained down on him, 'I love being petalled!' This last observation brought guffaws from some of the scene-queens next to the stage, who knew exactly what the term meant. Then, before 'Paint A Vulgar Picture', here given its first airing since The Smiths' split, he announced, 'As some of you may know, I used to be the drummer with The Smiths!'

The *Guardian*, having enjoyed a brief Morrissey-friendly period, incurred his wrath in July 1998 when it published Dave Simpson's very disturbing feature, 'Heaven Knows He's Miserable Now'. Simpson barely drew the line that prevented Morrissey's lawyers from breathing down his neck – what he did not say, he left his readers to work out for themselves, throwing in plenty of double-edged clues along the way. This was the Morrissey the fans did not want to know about: the Howard

Hughes-like unemployed and unemployable manic depressive, deserted by The Gang, a fallen idol who spent much of his time dabbling with prescription drugs, who smashed up apartments, who consorted with 'hard-looking characters beating a pathway to his door'. One 'East Side informant' had reputedly told Simpson, 'Morrissey? He's evil in a way damaged people are.'

Simpson appears to have coaxed friends and colleagues to speak unusually openly. They were only too willing to hammer nails into his coffin before the seemingly inevitable suicide. Former Smiths soundman Grant Showbiz was more dramatic than most, declaring, 'I suspect it'll be the lonely garage with the poison.' Gary Day explained how Morrissey had fired him, how he had loathed the male companions, particularly Peter Hogg. Jo Slee, blaming his depression on 'repressed feelings, repressed pain and emotions', added, 'He's childlike, very extreme in his emotional reactions to people . . . not in touch with the consequences of his actions.' Slee also confirmed his breakdown during the Outsiders tour: 'He was very ill, coming apart at the seams.' Jake dismissed him as, 'The hardest character I've ever met.' Vini Reilly mentioned 'physically wrestling' with Morrissey and also referred to their 'sharing of anxieties'. Such was the severity and finality of Simpson's feature that one imagines the obituary writers already scribbling away. Only Michael Bracewell, now Linder Sterling's partner, seemed to have anything worthwhile to say. Counteracting the suicide predictions, he told Simpson, 'I think he'll be like the heroine in *Far From The Madding Crowd* – where she says, "I shall awake before dawn and astonish you all!"' But it was left to former manager Gail Colson to 'sum' Morrissey up:

> It's so sad. He's his own worst enemy. He's cut everybody out and is back where he was before fame, only stuck in a hotel room, not a bedroom, with his mother running everything. Everybody yearns to love him but he is incapable of receiving affection.

Such adverse criticism, of course, was nothing new to a man who over the years had, or so he liked everyone to believe, forcibly developed the hide of an ox. No matter how tough he was, or appeared to be, some of these comments must have hurt, and now he had had enough. In September 1994, Stuart Maconie had asked him, 'If you were forced to leave England at gunpoint, where would you go?' 'Jersey, Guernsey – anywhere with a decent postal service,' he had replied. 'Not Los Angeles?' Maconie had posed, bringing the response, 'No. I need grit and struggle, and Los Angeles is terribly nice, but people once they get there cease to be real.'

'That was Moz playing Johnny Opposite again,' one of his musicians told me. 'He's done it all the time I've known him. Saying he's ugly when even a blind man can see he's anything but. Saying that he's unloved when everyone worships the ground he walks on. And don't believe all that rubbish about his genitals being a joke, either. He's more than regular in that department!'

Morrissey *was* living with his mother when Simpson wrote his feature, but only because he was in the process of relocation. For a reputed $1.25 million he had bought arguably the gayest property from Hollywood's Golden Age, the former Lincoln Heights home of screwball comedy actress Carole Lombard. The self-proclaimed 'Queen Of Fag-Hags', Lombard had purchased the neo-Hispanic house in 1934 and employed disgraced actor turned interior designer William Haines to completely refurbish the place. Lombard and Haines went back a long way: the biggest silent movie star after Valentino, his career had ended abruptly after he had been arrested by the vice-squad, caught out with a marine in the notorious gay cruising area around Pershing Square. The original plans for refurbishment included the instruction, 'Must be light, feminine and slightly screwball like myself.' Haines had not charged for the work, knowing that if a huge star like Lombard 'put the word out', he would have a solid business foundation, which is exactly what happened. At the time of his death in 1973, Haines had been worth millions.

During the refurbishment period, the promiscuous Haines had brought many of his lovers to the house, including Clark Gable, whom Lombard subsequently married. She was killed in a plane crash during a war-bonds tour, and for a while the grieving Gable had held on to the house as a shrine to her memory. Subsequent owners or leasers have included P G Wodehouse, Joan Crawford, film director John Schlesinger, F Scott Fitzgerald – and Tallulah Bankhead who once observed, 'Willy Haines laid more men in Lombard's house during the six months he was doing the place up than he laid carpets in the next thirty years!' Such were Haines' powers of 'persuasion' that he is even alleged to have seduced Boris Karloff, who lived next door. When Morrissey moved into the house, it only vaguely resembled Carole Lombard's mini fun-palace: stripped of most of William Haines' furnishings, it looked more like the interior of a Roman villa, its walls bare but for the huge portraits he hung of Steve McQueen, footballer Billy Wright, and The New York Dolls. Even the massive stone fireplace in the living room – allegedly purloined by a previous owner from San Simeon, the Randolph Hearst mansion – looks out of place. 'Morrissey has turned the place into a mausoleum,' Kirsty MacColl said.

Amongst the first visitors were Michael Bracewell and Linder Sterling, commissioned to provide text and photographs for a feature about the relocation. By now these British press interviews were starting to become boring, even when conducted by friends, constantly regurgitating the same tired topics: The Smiths' split, Mike Joyce, Finsbury Park. The novelty here was the revelation of Morrissey's interest in things Mexican. 'I spend hours just driving around the small rundown Mexican areas of Los Angeles,' he said, 'that is, the areas where the small, rundown Mexicans live.' The area was notorious for its poverty-inspired relaxed morals. Sixty years earlier, Errol Flynn and David Niven had patrolled its streets in search of what Niven called in his memoirs 'San Quentin Quail' – underage partners of both sexes. 'I really like Mexican people,' Morrissey later declared in a television documentary, 'I find them so terribly nice. They have fantastic hair and fantastic skin and usually really good teeth. Great combination!' He used the neighbourhood as an inspiration for his work – resulting in 'Mexico', though no new songs would be brought back to Britain for his brief tour at the end of 1999.

Morrissey had received rave reviews for his latest batch of American concerts, yet the instant he stepped on to British soil, the hacks were out in force, reopening the familiar wounds. 'He arrives on stage to "Who

Wants To Be A Millionaire?" and leaves, impeccably, to "My Way".
Against all odds, his way sounds irresistible all over again.' This was the
Guardian's Dave Simpson, the man who had effected the biggest
character assassination since the *NME*'s Finsbury Park attack – too late
to make amends, and reminding us yet again of the events leading up
to Morrissey's press-enforced exile. And why on earth these people
assumed him incapable of performing without a manager or record label
was ludicrous. It is no small wonder that he ever chose to visit Britain
again, though of course his absence would only have punished the fans
who had stuck by him through thick and thin. Some of the broadsheets,
too, had now sunk to tabloid level, notably the *Independent*'s Stephen
Dalton, who saw Morrissey at Nottingham's Rock City and accused him
of having 'an unhealthy fixation with a homoerotic fantasy underworld
of racist thuggery'. Indeed, Max Bell of the *Evening Standard* might
almost have been putting the singer's thoughts into words when he
concluded, 'As far as Morrissey is concerned all of Britain can die from
BSE and stuff the gladioli where the sun don't shine.'

Morrissey, like many of us, is said to have been traumatised by the death
of Kirsty MacColl at the end of 2000. Like him, she had recently
discovered a new source of inspiration – South America and Cuba – the
latter the subject of an eight-part series for BBC Radio Two, which she
had just completed. A few years earlier she had called and asked me for
a copy of *The Piaf Legend*. 'Morrissey has a copy,' she said, 'and Piaf and
I have a little in common. The same tragic make-up. A few more hours
and I would have been born on the anniversary of her death.' How ironic
then, that on 18 December – the day before what would have been
Piaf's birthday – Kirsty and her teenage sons were swimming off
Chamcaanab Reef, just off the Mexican coast, when she was struck by a
speedboat that should not have been in the swimming-and-diving-only
area. Its deck hand, Juan Jose Cem Yam, would subsequently be fined a
paltry $100 for negligence. Her death was harder for Morrissey to deal
with because he had been the one, he told *Word*'s Andrew Harrison,
who had got her interested in Mexico in the first place. 'She is
irreplaceable to me,' he said.

*

1498 North Sweetzer Drive – the Lombard house, as it will eternally be known no matter who lives there – has become Morrissey's refuge, a safe haven from which he emerges from time to time to remind us that the wit and sparkle of his interviews and performances have not diminished. As the new millennium dawned, however, there was evidence that lethargy and lack of willpower not just from the record companies but from Morrissey himself were winning the battle that might have ensured that his glory days were behind him – which would have been tragic, for though he was now the same age as some of those rock dinosaurs he begged to 'get off the stage', he had so much more to offer.

When he arrived in Britain in October 2002 for a rare visit – two sell-out concerts at the Royal Albert Hall, and a handful of others including Bradford, Blackpool, Dublin and Glasgow – he was interviewed for Radio Two by Janice Long, and lost no time in cynically denouncing the industry that had turned its back on him, as it had many other major stars in favour of the 'fast-buck' *Pop Idol* boom. He had, he said, a certain amount of sympathy for the kids themselves, fabricated and pushed towards uncertain stardom mindless of the stress wrought upon them by money-mad executives who always stayed in the background when such enterprises failed, leaving the inexperienced singers themselves to suffer the humiliation of having it all blow up in their faces. These artistes were the subjects of the first of three new songs he performed live in the studio: 'The World Is Full Of Crashing Bores'. There is no doubting that the line 'Lock-jawed upstarts [later amended to 'pop stars' for the album version], thicker than pig-shit' referred to *Pop Idol* contestants – yet Morrissey is even more irreverent towards taxmen, and to policewomen, whom he addresses as 'uniformed whores' and 'educated criminals', and in the next breath adds himself to this undistinguished list because he is unloved.

In March 2004 Morrissey would still be denouncing the all-too-obvious lack of originality within *Pop Idol* contestants, telling New York's KROQ Radio, 'They should be put in a cage and sent out to Thailand. They think all they have to do is sing an old Diana Ross song, and suddenly they're a pop idol.' The following month, a little hotter under the collar, he would tell *NME*'s Alex Needham, 'They're worse than terrorists . . . they're idiots. It's just the hideous process of wheeling them on, stripping them down and throwing them off. It's just so degrading and sad. You actually do feel pity for them, and you can only shudder at the working mind of the young people who enter the competition.' To which Needham's colleague, Mark Beaumont, added the comment, 'I think that's a No to the duet, Gareth!'

In the meantime, when asked by Janice Long to name one crashing bore in particular, Morrissey jauntily replied, 'Elton John, because he's pushing his face in all the time and telling us about his private life. Nobody's interested. He's incredibly rich and I think he should just go away.'

'. . . Crashing Bores' was a collaboration with Alain Whyte. Despite recent press reports, and despite some of the barbed comments they had made, Whyte, Boz Boorer and Gary Day were still working with Morrissey, though Spencer Cobrin had been replaced by Dean Butterworth. The second song he performed, complementing a new speech affectation (pronouncing the word 'any' as 'annie', Irish-style) was the sublime 'Irish Blood, English Heart' – 'The components that make up my tubby little body,' he told Long. In this the narrator is Morrissey himself, the rebel who fearlessly declares, 'Irish blood, English heart, this I'm made of/There is no one on earth I'm afraid of' – and who yearns for the day when standing beside the Union Jack will no longer be deemed shameful or racist, and for the time when Englishmen will 'spit upon the name Oliver Cromwell/And denounce this royal line.' 'And', he concludes, 'I will die with both of my hands untied.' When later asked by *Sonic*'s Sebastian Suarez-Golborne if the number was a comment on Anglo-Irish relations and the failure of the British parliamentary system, he would say, 'It's a comment on the whole British monarchy. Oliver Cromwell was no more than a general, but he behaved like some of them by slaughtering thousands of Irishmen just to get them out of the way. As for British politics, the only choice you have is between the Tories and Labour, neither of which are spokesmen for the people. It's an age-old, ridiculous circus.'

Janice Long asked Morrissey if the rumour was true that he had begun writing his autobiography. He affirmed that he had, but that the book might never reach the shelves on account of the large number of injunctions it would attract. She asked if there would ever be a Smiths reunion, and received the humorous reprimand, 'Janice, I'm going to head-butt you in five minutes. The Smiths may reform, but not with me.' Finally, she wanted to know what was happening in his love life, if there was anyone special to give him a cuddle when he wanted one. As usual, he was keeping schtumm, though he did confess that he was no longer celibate. And, hinting that there may have been someone special, he finished with 'I Like You', the ode to the lover who gets away with so much because he likes him, albeit that this object of his affection is not always nice to know: 'You're not right in the head/And nor am I'!

Two other new songs introduced to British audiences at the Royal Albert Hall (where there was a reported one-night-only reunion between Morrissey's parents) were 'Mexico', an anti-racist ode to the difficulties frequently experienced in that country by poor, non-white migrant workers – and 'First Of The Gang To Die'. Here, Morrissey transfers his attention from East End skinheads and riff-raff to the Latino hoodlums of East Los Angeles and the luckless Hector, the 'silly boy' with the gun in his hand whose ultimate reward for thuggery is 'a bullet in his gullet'. There was also an excellent cover version of the 1970 Gilbert O'Sullivan hit 'Nothing Rhymed', one of David Bowie's 'Drive-In Saturday', and new arrangements of 'There Is A Light That Never Goes Out' and 'Hand In Glove'.

Morrissey was riding the crest of a potentially enterprising wave on Good Friday, 18 April 2003, when Andrew Harrison interviewed him at his Los Angeles home for the recently founded *Word* magazine. Harrison told me,

He was in such good spirits. Talkative, the perfect host, ever vain about his appearance. We drove around in his flashy Jag, and he insisted upon taking a change of clothes for the photographs. 'I don't want the people back in England thinking I've only one shirt to my name,' he said. He changed in the back of the car – so yes, I got very close to the fabulous Morrissey torso!

The general air of bonhomie centred around Morrissey's delight over being 'three dotted i's' away from signing a reputedly very lucrative contract with Sanctuary Records – actually his fourth in recent months, though he claimed he had rejected the others because the companies had wanted him to ditch his musicians. Sanctuary were reported as having assigned him the former reggae label, Attack, for his personal use – and to permit him to acquire its extensive back catalogue of music he had mostly denounced in the past. Launched in 1969, the label's luminaries had included Family Circle and Gregory Isaacs. Morrissey's first album for Attack, according to a shaky press report, had been scheduled to go into production that summer.

He proved as eccentric as ever – eschewing the latest rock sounds to play Andrew Harrison of *Word* magazine a John Betjeman interview full-blast on his car stereo, discussing the problems encountered in this most modern of cities buying decent vegetarian cheese. There was the obligatory dig at the latest over-hyped music sensations. Of Radiohead and Coldplay he observed, 'If you fail with that amount of promotion you must be pretty atrocious. The music mystifies me because I don't understand why I have the monopoly on the word miserable. Both of these bands sound very unhappy, with not a sign of a witty lyric.' Morrissey was similarly unimpressed by Robbie Williams, whom he felt had been 'foisted' upon the Americans. 'Personally,' he added sarcastically, 'I think that almost everything about Robbie Williams is fantastic – apart from the voice and the songs.'

Morrissey had been wholly accommodating of Andrew Harrison: the interview had been set up with little fuss; unlike most of its predecessors, the time and location had been adhered to. A few weeks later he was interviewed by Manchester's *City Life* magazine, who wanted to know if living in Los Angeles had given this most English of Englishmen a different perspective as a songwriter. One gets the impression that he still felt he did not belong here:

Slightly. It's a very nervous and frightened city. If you brush against someone accidentally on the street, they jump five feet into the air because they think you're going to kill them. If you wave over to ask someone directions they run off in the opposite direction without answering you – whereas in, say, Dublin or Copenhagen you can literally sit on a complete stranger's knee in the park and they don't especially mind.

Not surprisingly, Morrissey would have nothing to do with *NME* when, in June 2003, it published *The Smiths Special 20th Anniversary Souvenir*, a glossy commemorative magazine which, though generally laudatory, could not resist ruffling a few feathers. Within was an extraneous feature that depicted the 'archetypal' Morrissey fan: an Asian youth, transformed from a beer-guzzling, hamburger-munching yob into an aesthetic Oscar Wilde apostle of ambiguous sexuality. There were over-the-top eulogies from minor pop stars, the 'stigmata' photograph of Morrissey, a selection of his 'wit and wisdom' quotes and letters to the editor, and naturally a reference to the Finsbury Park incident – which, of course, had not involved The Smiths.

Far better was the sixteen-page tribute in *Record Collector*, penned by Simon Goddard, detailing twenty essential Smiths songs that had come about as a result of Morrissey's and Johnny Marr's 'borrowing' from artists who had influenced them – described by Goddard as, 'A near flawless body of work from one of the greatest British guitar bands of all time.' Thus we learned, among other snippets, how 'Hand In Glove' owed much to Leonard Cohen, that 'Reel Around The Fountain' had been inspired by James Taylor's 'Handy Man' (the mind boggles), and less gallantly, perhaps, how 'Panic' had been modelled on T Rex's 'Metal Guru'.

Morrissey had also just completed his first television documentary since The Smiths' *South Bank Show* – effectively, his first major celluloid interview in sixteen years. *The Importance Of Being Morrissey* opens with the claim, 'At last, the record is going to be set straight' – but ultimately tells us little that we do not already know. The other Smiths and two former lovers were asked to appear, but not surprisingly declined, and one gets the impression that the celebrities who do appear and have little or nothing to do with Morrissey are here simply to make up the numbers: a giggly J K Rowling, belying the fact that she possesses any intelligence at all, Michael Bracewell, Ron and Russ Mael, Alan Bennett declaring that Morrissey has 'an interesting face', Chrissie Hynde, Morrissey's nephews, a somewhat nervous Alain Whyte and a copiously vulgar Kathy Burke, who describes him as, 'A good-looking bloke who don't fuck – very cool!' Fortunately his musical contemporaries offer a sensible insight into his genius. Bono, quoting 'Girlfriend In A Coma' as an example, gently denounces the detractors who accused Morrissey of being miserable: 'They're just miserable people that don't get the humour!' Noel Gallagher says, 'Whatever you put down in a lyric to define your love or hate for anyone he'll do one better because he's the best lyricist I've ever heard.' Gallagher further denounces the racist slurs about Morrissey in his own no-nonsense manner: 'If he was, the fucking *News Of The World* would have uncovered it first. Forget the fucking *NME*!'

Soul-mates Linder Sterling and James O'Brien speak of Morrissey's depression. O'Brien, who lived nearby in Los Angeles, observes that when Morrissey comes knocking on the door in the early hours and is wearing spectacles (as opposed to contact lenses), the conversation is guaranteed to turn heavy. Whether Morrissey approved of such comments from those closest to him is not known. He had not been shown the rushes for the film, and with no post-production input from himself was certainly unhappy with much of the finished result, as he explained to *City Life*:

> I did some lengthy interviews with them that were great, but they only focused on all those tired old subjects such as celibacy and racism. I was embarrassed because it looked as if this was all I could talk about. Also they kept filming me from the chin, which made me look as if I've got no teeth – and they positioned the lights every time to give me a greenish-white deathly pale look. In the Australian clips, for example, I actually had a great tan, but the Channel 4 camera technique made me look as if I'm just coming round after emergency surgery. I think it was a deliberate ploy to make me look grey and miserable. But, that's tabloid telly.

Morrissey is seen on stage: the lithe, androgynous creature of yesterday being kissed and hugged at Wolverhampton – the Morrissey of today, stiff-shouldered and burlier but no less charismatic, still sending the mostly male fans wild with emotion and desire as they join in with the chorus of 'There Is A Light That Never Goes Out'. As Gianfranco, the gay porn star, told me, 'The expressions on their faces leave little doubt that they really would lay down their lives for him.' He is seen attacking the archetypal British Bulldog in his London hotel: 'How many people did he send to their deaths, just to make up the numbers?' he asks, punching a bust of Winston Churchill in the suite that bears his name – a precursor to what he would say later in the film about other politicians and the royals.

On the tour circuit, Morrissey meets an Australian fan who has been waiting years for this moment after winning a competition to meet her idol. She tells him, 'You've made me and so many people so happy' – and he responds, humbly and without so much as a hint of sarcasm, 'I didn't mean to!'

The 'exclusives' here are the briefish conversations with Morrissey himself in and around the Lombard house or at his Mayfair barber's shop, filmed over a six-month period. He alternates between looking suave in neat-fitting shirt, and not so icon-like in denim jacket and cheap spectacles. He speaks lovingly of The Smiths ('Like launching your own diary to music') but is contemptuous of their drummer: 'I wish the very, very worst for Joyce for the rest of his life.' He likens meat-eating to child-abuse and admits that he felt smug about mad cow disease – the animals getting their revenge at last. Linking this to one of his least favourite people he pronounces, 'Bring me the head of Elton John, which would be one instance where meat would not be murder!' He says of the hierarchy he has left behind, 'It seems I'd have had a better chance of being struck by lightning than I had of being accepted by the British music industry.'

Elsewhere in the film, Morrissey 'receives' Nancy Sinatra, play-acting for the camera's benefit, and now looking and acting very much like the poor man's Mae West. Yet almost in the next breath he is denouncing David Bowie as a has-been, recalling of their ill-fated tour, 'You have to worship at the Temple of David when you become involved. He was a fascinating artist – 1970, '71, '72 – but not now.' As for those fans who had been horrified to see Morrissey posing in Speedos, they are said to have been mortified to see him visiting a heterosexual strip-joint and seemingly enjoying the experience, while gay fans delighted in watching the filmed footage of Linder Sterling photographing the 'oxters' shots that had featured in her book. Of course, this all leads to the usual, in this instance off-camera questions regarding Morrissey's sexuality – followed by the snappiest put-down ever, 'I'm not telling you. I can't see that it's anybody's business. People can think what they like!'

Coinciding with the documentary, Morrissey had consented to a 'Questions & Answers' interview with *i-D* magazine for its July 2003 Beat Issue – one of his most entertaining and provocative for some time, and yet another missed by many fans because of its inclusion on the back page. The entire magazine was given a similarly 'unadvertised' Smiths/Morrissey theme: computerised advertising mock-ups featuring Alain Whyte, mock-ups of Morrissey at Cadogan Gardens, and re-created Smiths record covers (Dallesandro, Davalos, Morrissey, Fury, Marais) turned into an attractive fashion spread, handsome androgynous models masquerading as Dilly Boys, and various related chapter headings such as 'This Night Has Opened My Eyes', 'I Know It's Gonna Happen Someday', 'The Boy With The Thorn In His Side', etc.

The questions were set by Ben Reardon, who asked, 'What would be your perfect Friday night?' – hardly anticipating the response, 'I'd like to give sex another go.' Then on, this being a fashion magazine, the conversation moved on to clothes. Morrissey had gone a long way since ill-fitting denims and Evans Outsize Shop blouses, and now preferred Helmut Lang and Gucci. 'I have a few pleather [mock leather] jackets,' he added, 'but people keep pinning notes on the car saying "How the fuck can you wear leather, you hypocrite?" . . . So I don't feel quite right in pleather because some very caring and gentle folk think it's the real thing.' Reardon wanted to know how friends addressed him – Morrissey, Steven, Mozzer or Moz? He replied the former, adding, 'I've asked people to stop calling me Moz. It's like something you'd squirt on the kitchen floor.' The wittiest anecdote, however, came when Reardon demanded, 'What is the freakiest thing one of your fans has ever done?' Recalling an earlier incident when a 25-year-old American fan had been arrested for plastering Morrissey's car with photographs, then masturbating over it, he told Reardon, 'He took all his clothes off and danced in the road outside the house. I think he was trying to tell me something. Somebody called the police . . . I believe they charged him with being too happy and enjoying his body too much.' Then it was back to titillation when the journalist brought up the two names that had hogged the British tabloids' headlines for as far back as most cared to remember: 'Posh or Becks?' – i.e. which might Morrissey have preferred sexually? 'I'll take them both and leave them howling,' he replied, 'I often form the third part of a very messy triangle.'

Morrissey's new album (at that point untitled) was recorded off and on at the Sarm Studios in Berkshire, and at Los Angeles' Conway Studio. The producer was Jerry Finn, who had worked with big-selling pop-punk outfits Green Day, AFI, Bad Religion and Blink-182. Again he was backed by Alain Whyte, Gary Day, Boz Boorer and Dean Butterworth – and completing the line-up was Roger Manning, the keyboard player from Jellyfish who had also worked with Blink-182 and Beck.

There was a supposed embargo on interviews, but two reporters from American magazine *Index* slipped through the net: James Murphy and Tim Goldsworthy of the New York record label, DFA. These proved fawning, their queries amounting to little more than blasé chit-chat, and from Morrissey naturally there were the inevitable put-downs. Of Christina Aguilera and her ilk, much favoured by the American pair, Morrissey denounced, 'The most successful singers in pop music can't sing! They make a meal of every note, they chew it to pieces, but that's not singing.' Then he introduced one of his own favourites into the conversation, a performer who, technically and vocally, many might have argued was little better, albeit that he had been a pioneer of sorts: Jobriath, for whom Morrissey had been asked to compile a *Greatest Hits* album (though Jobriath had had no hits!) for the Rhino Homemade label. Morrissey's own forthcoming album was scarcely touched upon, other than that he was apprehensive over how it would be received by some sections of the media. He concluded, with a shrug of the shoulders, 'But I never made music in order to please. I know I don't fit in. Nothing has changed for me in that regard. I don't fit in, and don't want to.'

Early in 2004, Morrissey announced the title for his new album. Tauntingly, he told *i-D*'s Ashley Heath, an impressionable young man who had first flipped his lid over the Smiths at fourteen, '*You Are The Quarry* is actually a title aimed at one person who – no – I won't name. It's not the obvious person, though it is aimed at my audience in general, saying they are a target for me to win their affection now.'

Sanctuary Records issued a somewhat grandiose press release that opened with Morrissey's declaration, sure to have the detractors sharpening their quills in advance, 'This is the best album I've ever done.' Producer Jerry Finn left himself wide open to future comment by describing the album as 'creamy' and 'just purely organic' – and gave every impression that he was criticising the singer's proven working methods by concluding, 'I think *Quarry* is Morrissey's best work because of how it was recorded.' He was referring to the fact that, for the first time ever, Morrissey had eschewed his usual way of supplying the vocals for his musicians to work around and had this time joined everyone else in the studio – suggesting, many thought, that his previous albums would be inferior to this one. Neither did the anonymous writer of the press release do himself any favours by proclaiming, 'As lead singer for The Smiths, arguably the best alternative act of the 80s, Morrissey blazed a trail for dozens of modern day alternative rock acts including The Strokes, The Raptures and The Skins amongst others' – outfits who had yet to make their names outside the parochial pages of the music papers. Worse still, in mentioning the snippet that Nancy Sinatra had recorded Morrissey's 'Let Me Kiss You', he 'upped' her status by calling her 'a legendary chanteuse' – which she was not. Morrissey issued an additional statement that he had assigned Sinatra to the Attack label, along with old pal James Maker.

Recording the album appears to have been a happier experience for Morrissey than usual, on account of the way he was treated by Sanctuary. He told *Les Inrockuptibles*' Jean-Daniel Beauvallet how, on the day he signed the contract, the head of the record company had presented him with the white Vox Teardrop guitar formerly owned by Johnny Thunders, along with a huge basket of fruit. 'It's the first time ever that a record company thought about making me feel welcome,' he added.

In the meantime, with little publicity, two new books appeared. Privately denounced by the singer, Mark Simpson's *Saint Morrissey* had taken several years and at least one change of publisher to reach the shelves. Floridly written and hailed by its author as a 'psycho-bio', its pages revealed nothing new and it was attacked by *Uncut* magazine's Simon Goddard as, 'Fawning hagiography posing as highbrow criticism . . . a strangely boring read (considering its endlessly fascinating subject) which reveals nothing about Morrissey that hasn't been suggested more eloquently before.' Goddard's own book, *The Smiths: Songs That Saved Your Life*, is on the other hand a work of art, luxuriously unsparing in its attention to detail and one no Smiths or Morrissey enthusiast can afford to be without.

On 4 March, having decided not to be interviewed at home again, Morrissey met *Esquire*'s James Medd at Los Angeles' Viceroy Hotel. He was photographed in a Venice Beach car park – feeding the birds and sitting cross-legged in front of a Salvation bus – by Mischa Richter, who enthused, 'He is genuinely lovely. He is totally into animals and made us stop the car to let some pigeons cross the road.'

With his flair for surprising utterances – to put interviewers at ease, or merely to confuse them – Morrissey greeted Medd by asking him if Sanctuary's marketing people had brought him the bread he had ordered – 'Warburtons, the one with the yellow wrapping.' Humour persisted throughout the interview. 'Did you think you'd still be doing this at forty-four?' Medd asked, bringing the response, 'I didn't think I'd still be doing it at twenty-four. I thought I'd be floating face-down in the nearest canal.' Speaking of his disappointments, and the people who had harmed him over the years, he added, 'I think the human race is extremely overrated, and the older I get, the more I feel that way.' Medd wanted to know how he was faring with his autobiography. 'It's bubbling,' he replied, 'but I don't think it will ever see print because when the proofs are distributed I'll probably be immediately assassinated.'

Many believe, of course, that the closest one will ever get to Morrissey will be by listening to his songs, that certainly there will never be such a book during his lifetime because this would only defeat the objective of his very existence: Morrissey, stripped and laid bare for all to see, would no longer be of interest because it is his mystery that attracts the most.

And, Medd asked, would he ever consider returning to live in Britain? 'Only if I'm given a prison sentence,' Morrissey quipped. Then it was to the obligatory 'dig of the day', aimed at one of America's current top box-office draws. When asked if he had seen any good films of late he shot back, 'I'm sorry, I only have to catch a distant glimpse of Jim Carrey's teeth and I'm in agony. I never go to the cinema.'

Also in March, Morrissey announced that he would be celebrating his 45th birthday (on 22 May) by giving a concert on 'home ground' – for 18,000 fans at Manchester's G-Mex. His contract contained a clause stipulating that no meat products be sold at the venue while he was rehearsing, performing or merely visiting. The tickets all sold within forty minutes. Then a press statement announced that he had been appointed curator of the South Bank's prestigious Meltdown Festival, to be held in June. Morrissey declared a list of pencilled-in hopefuls – an eclectic, frequently bizarre mixture that included the three surviving New York Dolls, Gene, Maya Angelou, Jane Birkin, ageing French crooner Sacha Distel (subsequently dismissed by Morrissey as 'an Egyptian cabaret singer'), Nancy Sinatra, Françoise Hardy and Brigitte Bardot – along with 'contemporary sensations' The Libertines, and friends Linder Sterling and Alan Bennett. Much of this may have been wishful thinking, and one may only imagine Morrissey's fans' reaction to Angelou, or Birkin's sublime interpretations of late husband Serge Gainsbourg – indeed, if they had ever heard of them. The final line-up announced in *Time Out* was only slightly less surprising. Morrissey would be topping the bill, naturally, with three concerts at the Festival Hall; Birkin would be plugging her new album and singing Gainsbourg – supported by James Maker, who would also be working with The New York Dolls. Loudon Wainright III, Sparks, Italian impressionist-mine Ennio Marchetto and Alan Bennett would have shows of their own. Linder would be supporting Nancy Sinatra, gay playwright Neil Bartlett would be directing

An Evening With Oscar Wilde, and there would be 'special appearances' by The Cockney Rejects, The Ordinary Boys, Lypsinka and The Libertines.

Morrissey was also booked for the Leeds Carling, Reading and Glastonbury festivals and immediately expressed his dislike of one of the supports, The Darkness, regarded by many detractors as the poor man's Queen. He told New York's KROQ Radio, 'I've never been interested in heavy, soft or medium metal. It's not my bag!'

Over the long weekend of 19/21 March, Morrissey 'held court' in his plush suite at London's Dorchester to around a dozen journalists, admitted single-file, and most of them led to believe that they would be getting that all-important exclusive. His 'official' reason for being back in England, he told one of these, was to help his mother move from one Manchester home to another. His first visitor was the *Sunday Times'* Robert Sandall, who told me that the singer was so jet-lagged, the interview was virtually a waste of time (indeed, much of his piece was packed out with anecdotes from myself). When Sandall hinted that Morrissey might have been on the comeback trail, he was met with a waspish, 'I'm not coming back to anything, but a lot of people might be coming back to me.' Tackling the subject of why he had left England to live in America in the first place – according to the journalist, to make it harder for Mike Joyce to pursue the court settlement – Sandall added, allegedly incurring Morrissey's wrath, 'One aspect of LA living that might appeal to him, you might imagine, is its gay scene. Morrissey is widely presumed to be gay though he has never said so directly . . . He has been seen around with a number of male companions, notably a photographer, Jake Walters. But nobody has ever kissed and told.'

Dorian Lynskey of the *Guardian*, said to be Morrissey's favourite British broadsheet, fared only slightly better – resulting in his subsequent feature being padded out with the oft-repeated lesson in Smiths and Morrissey history. Lynskey described his subject as 'a verbal fencer, thrusting and parrying', 'thin-skinned but hard-headed', and interpreted his body language as 'a choreography of discomfort'. 'He fidgets around the sofa, crossing his arms, chewing his lip and wearing a curious smirk that could either mean he's having a high old time or that he's never hated an interview more,' he concluded. Alternating between the maudlin and the sarcastically enthusiastic, Morrissey bypassed his seven 'lost' years since *Maladjusted* – 'I went through great gulps of doubt wondering whether there was actually any point to it' – before stepping on to his podium, arrogantly declaring of his immense popularity, 'I think if I was shot in the middle of the street tomorrow, a lot of people would be quite unhappy. I think I'd be a prime candidate for canonisation.' Yet in the next breath, he was on the attack again: 'I'm not really that hot on the human race, to be honest. Very few people have anything to offer . . . the world . . . [or] themselves.' And, was he still lonely? Morrissey hedged on this one. Loneliness, he opined, was a privilege that permitted him to develop. 'You don't when you're with someone else,' he added, 'you put your own feelings on hold and you end up doing things like driving to supermarkets and waiting outside shops – ludicrous things like that.' And of course, the interview could not end without bringing up the topic of Morrissey's sexuality. Having been assured that his subject had 'skirted' love on a few occasions and even 'plunged in', Lynskey asked, 'Were all these people women?' The response was an ambiguous, 'They seemed to be, as far as I knew. They would all be women if they had a choice!'

Next in line was *i-D*'s Ashley Heath, writing for the magazine's Drama Queen Issue, though Morrissey's alleged wish to grace the cover was denied – it was primarily a fashion publication, and he had to make do with his name appearing in small print beneath a photograph of a gurning teenage Japanese model. As such, the impressive ten-page spread was overlooked by many fans.

This particular journalist was more interested in discussing the homoerotic aspects of the Morrissey persona than the new album, and the piece was the brief conclusion of an interview that had ended abruptly the previous week at Los Angeles' exclusive Alexandria Hotel. Here, according to one unsubstantiated Internet press report, Morrissey had actually asked to be photographed in the Rudolph Valentino Suite. The piece declared that this was his way of asserting that I, as Valentino's biographer, was aiming to claim Morrissey as a gay cultural icon the way I had the Italian actor. Utter tosh, of course. The fans had done this long before I appeared on the Morrissey scene. He did, during the course of the interview, refer to my new biography – announced that week – which met with a torrent of abuse from the same 'bedroom Google whackers' who had done their best to bring Morrissey down in the wake of his aborted 1992 American tour. 'It's unsettling to read supposedly factual accounts of you and your life from people who have never come within twenty feet of you,' he observed. Needless to say, he was forgetting how he had once written supposedly factual accounts of his idols (James Dean, The New York Dolls) without knowing or meeting them – and he should have been well aware that reputable biographers do check their facts, if for no other reason than not to be sued!

Since seeing The Smiths in Brighton during their *Meat Is Murder* tour, Ashley Heath had carried a torch for their former frontman and felt he could ask him anything, before being asked to leave by Morrissey's manager. Even so, he got him to open up more than any predecessor since Nick Kent before being ejected. Of his interest in James Dean, Morrissey confessed, 'It was purely physical obsession, certainly nothing to do with his films or the art he may have striven for.' There was another icon from his youth, never mentioned until now: an exceedingly hand-some model/gay pin-up named Michael Schoeffing, whose chiselled features and hunky physique had frequently adorned the cover of the American *GQ* magazine during the late seventies, when the publication had only been available in this country on import. 'He was an absolute hero to me, and I used to write to this magazine claiming I would be the next Michael Schoeffing,' Morrissey told Heath, adding cockily that he had also forwarded unsolicited glamour shots of himself to the editor.

Suffice to say, this confessed fascination for beautiful men (Morrissey also observed how, years before it had wound up on the sleeve of 'William, It Was Really Nothing', the *GQ* photograph of the male figure sitting on the bed had held pride of place on his bedroom wall) led Heath to pose the question that caused Morrissey's new manager to see red: 'Were you in love with Johnny Marr?' The response now came over tea at the Dorchester with a muted, 'Why doesn't anyone ever assume Johnny Marr was in love with me? That perhaps Johnny Marr was in fact madly in love with me, but didn't feel he could act on that – or that he didn't have the courage to ever take it any further?'

The following month, *Mojo* would publish a rarely seen photograph of The Smiths, part of a Stephen Wright collection of prints about to be sold on the Internet, and which may have added credence to Morrissey's claim. Snapped at the University of Leicester in February 1984 and captioned, 'Used to be sweet boys', it shows a smiling Johnny Marr taking obvious pleasure in clasping a similarly gleeful Morrissey in a bear-hug from behind. In all probability it is all very innocuous, gung-ho clowning around, but it led to Johnny Marr being asked some rather awkward questions by the press.

The surprise interview – and an act of extreme hypocrisy on both sides, considering how the magazine had tried to end Morrissey's career, and how he had never stopped publicly slagging them off in the twelve years since Finsbury Park – was granted to *NME*. Morrissey was interviewed by Alex Needham, who began his two-part feature with such cloying sycophancy, one is hard-put to determine whether the journalist is being genuinely laudatory, or taking his subject for a ride. 'Rock 'n' roll has seen many heroes,' Needham observed, 'but one stands quiff and shoulders above them all.' And as if this and the opening paragraph were insufficiently syrupy, the magazine cover boasted the subtitle, 'New Mozza Express'.

The interview was no great shakes, other than that it enabled both adversaries to profit handsomely: the magazine's circulation soared, as per usual, through having Morrissey on its cover – and he received invaluable publicity for his 'comeback'. Why he had submitted to an audience with *NME* in the first place was of course high on Alex Needham's agenda. Claiming that the people working for the magazine were 'a different breed' than back in 1992 – as he believed they were generally within today's music press now that 'the nasty old guard' had disappeared – Morrissey concluded, 'It isn't the smelly *NME* any more.' This topic, and the essential regurgitation of Finsbury Park, were quickly brushed aside: Morrissey had moved on, if the publication had only pre-tended to have done. He spoke of his current favourites, The Libertines, though in the age of five-minute wonders not without reservation for their future: 'I think if they can possibly keep themselves together, which is a long shot really, I think they'll take a firm place in history.' Well, maybe. Two months later, the group's frontman, Peter Doherty, would enter the Priory rehabilitation centre for treatment for drug addiction – two weeks after this, he announced his departure from the group.

Yet again comparing Tony Blair with camp comic Larry Grayson (and with *NME* supplying side-by-side photographs to 'prove' this point), Morrissey declared his hatred of the British prime minister: 'I think people liked Blair initially, but in the end – those teeth. I think Blair is just a bumbling fool as well as a liar. I mean, surely he's doomed? Surely people are not going to vote for him again? How can anyone gaze at that face and be optimistic?' Earlier at the Dorchester, he had accused Tony Blair's ally, George W Bush – in the wake of the recent terrorist attack in Madrid – of making the world a more dangerous place to live in, adding ominously, 'I am sure there will be bloodshed in Britain now. It's bound to happen. There will be explosions at a shopping centre – very soon, very likely.'

Well aware that he would only get an honest answer – perhaps the response he might have received from every other man or woman in the street, yet one which would spark controversy – Needham posed, 'What do you think of the current furore about asylum seekers?' The response was a logical, 'Well, it's a question of how many people you'll continue to allow to flood into the country, regardless of where they're from or why they're arriving. It's a question of how it affects the people who still live here. It's a question of space.' Morrissey was not in any way making a racist comment, and he did conclude, 'It's very difficult when people are being persecuted.' Even so, he had opened the floodgates for the obligatory attendant detractors, and *NME* reputedly received scores of letters of protest. Unusually perhaps, the magazine's Asian letters editor, Imran Ahmed, half-defended him (though only after assuring his readers, 'Speaking personally, I was also uncomfortable with Morrissey's comments') by observing, 'I think it's important to see Morrissey's comments in such a context . . . Like most of us, I think Morrissey is guilty of ignorance over the issue of asylum, rather than any deep-rooted prejudice.'

In his interview with Alex Needham, Morrissey enlarged on an incident, the previous year, when a passport mix-up had led to him being apprehended by the Los Angeles airport police and incarcerated in a cell for three hours – hence the attack on the establishment in 'The World Is Full Of Crashing Bores'. 'I was put through the whole process of tagging and searching,' he confessed. 'It was harrowing . . . they thought I was a threat to national security.' The interview ended on a frivolous note – more probing into Morrissey's love life, when Needham asked him if people were queuing up to have him as a boyfriend or partner. Of affection, he quipped, 'It comes in and out, but it's not something I ever speak about because it isn't lasting.' Then he turned the tables on his interviewer, discovered that Needham was still unattached at 29, and doubtless cheered him up no end by advising, 'Buy yourself a nice budgie. That's my advice to you. You've been roaming the planet for twenty-nine years, and if it hasn't struck you on the head by now, I think you'd just better get used to that television set and get yourself a nice comfortable armchair.'

Even more sycophantic was Swedish journalist Sebastian Suarez-Golborne, interviewing Morrissey for *Sonic* in advance of that summer's Hultsfred and (Danish) Roskilde festivals. Declaring that Morrissey fans were the closest one could get to *übermensch* ('supermen', as defined by Nietzsche in *Thus Spake Zarathustra*), and vulgarly attacking anyone who dared criticise their demi-god (this author included) he asserted, 'If someone is a Moz fan on a credible foundation, you can assume this person is intelligent and beautiful with a good sense of humour – that all these features are most probably imbued by a profound hatred against Mankind and an everlasting self-hatred.' Oh, dear! And as for the actual interview, this was such a non-event that its content is scarcely worthy of mention.

Similarly inane, certainly by the time it had been edited for the finished feature, was Morrissey's interview for Flemish-language magazine, *Humo*: more attacks on Mike Joyce, regurgitated stories about Morrissey's likes and dislikes and the disbanding of The Smiths – tedious subjects by now. Journalist Serge Simonart also revealed that the singer had a new companion: 'During our conversation, the woman from the Gucci shop called to ask if they could deliver . . . Jed's new outfits. Morrissey fled into the adjacent room for a while, looking rather embarrassed. Then he returned, and our interview continued.'

Next in line was *Les Inrockuptibles'* Jean-Daniel Beauvallet, who got to spend more time with Morrissey than anyone else – primarily because he was trusted more than the others not to read too much between the lines and jump to his own conclusions. Some years earlier, Morrissey had told the French magazine that he had found it necessary to set aside a few hours each day to practise being Morrissey. Now, he said, the fresh air of California and being allowed to jump into his car and drive for hours on end had liberated the prisoner within the Morrissey persona: 'Even if I ended up in Bangkok, I would still be Morrissey. I'm no longer play-acting. I never considered myself the prisoner of some caricature. I feel free.'

Having earlier confessed that he had had lovers, he now denied that there was anyone special in his life: 'I'm my best friend. I sleep with myself, I wake up next to myself, we'll never get divorced, and we have our moments. I'm a lucky man!' He further denied ever having set foot in a gay bar, and when Beauvallet quipped that no Morrissey song had ever evoked homosexuality quite so much as 'All The Lazy Dykes', he cajoled, 'Doubtless because that's because I myself am a lesbian!'

Having discussed his harsh upbringing, choking back the tears when his father's name had entered the conversation, he now declared, 'No one in my family ever had a drink problem, and there was never the slightest hint of aggression back home – only outside, in the streets of Manchester.' And finally, he was similarly contradictory on the subject of his alleged autobiography, claiming that as an acknowledged storyteller, he had already discussed his personal life in the hundreds of songs he had written – 'It's necessary that a whole slice of my life should run to no more than three minutes fifty seconds,' he concluded, 'I've never got stuck working to that format.'

Morrissey's final visitor to the Dorchester was Keith Cameron, of *Mojo*. Having confessed that he was submitting to this seemingly endless stream of interviews on account of pressure from his record company – 'I'd rather say nothing. I'd rather absolutely let the music speak for itself and do what it can do' – Morrissey cut the session short, but promised to meet Cameron again in Los Angeles three weeks later.

Cameron had duly turned up, only to be informed that the singer had just been discharged from hospital: according to their spokesman, a viral infection had developed into meningitis. 'Uncharitable it may be, but one's instinct is to feel sceptical,' Cameron wrote in his feature. 'For him, the importance of being Morrissey is ensuring no one knows who Morrissey really is, or what he does (and with whom). Which is, of course, one of the reasons for his enduring fascination.' One week later, speaking to the journalist on the telephone, Morrissey confessed that he had been stricken with meningitis, that additionally he had suffered a five-day migraine, and that he had undergone two brain scans. Yet with typical irony, he added that his greatest ordeal had occurred when the doctors had left him alone in his room, strapped to his bed and connected to a drip – while loud hip-hop music had been playing in the background!

It is hard to determine which parts of Keith Cameron's interview were conducted where, and how. Though much of the eleven-page spread is padded out with historical anecdotes and Kevin Westenberg's stunning photographs of a pensive Morrissey, there were some treasured quips. Of his last two largely critically unacclaimed albums, Morrissey was disapproving only of the artwork, declaring, 'I made such a holy mess of *Southpaw Grammar* that I left *Maladjusted* to be pieced together by the record company – and it was even worse than *Southpaw Grammar*. I've got Tony Blair's hairline and I look as if I'm sat on the lavatory crying my eyes out.' And if this was a comeback, he said, then it should be compared to Frank Sinatra's triumphant return from the wilderness (in 1953, when Montgomery Clift had persuaded the producer of *From Here To Eternity* to cast him in a major role). Then he went on to criticise *Q* (and implicitly *Mojo*, for it was the work of both magazines) for their soon-to-be-published The Smiths & Morrissey special edition. 'Rounding up all those little left-over people who met me on the stairs in 1986 for an hour,' he expostulated. 'So boring!' And of The Smiths, he confessed to having had a friendly chat with Johnny Marr the previous summer, only to add, portentously, 'The whole story is so black and twisted, I'm convinced the story will only end with . . . a murder. And you're talking to the potential corpse!'

'Irish Blood, English Heart' was released on two separate CDs (along with a vinyl EP) on 10 May. It shot to number 3 in the charts, his highest entry ever: it was his best single in years, and the B-sides were exemplary. 'It's Hard To Walk Tall When You're Small' sees a Mexican gang member boasting that, because of his diminutive size, he must fight dirty. In 'The Never Played Symphonies', the dying narrator reflects upon his life but can only recall the negative points: the people who cared but whom he can no longer visualise because they cared, the lover who flitted in and out of his life but whose memory still haunts him. He therefore concludes that death will be a merciful release. As for 'Munich Air Disaster 1958', this is doubtless Morrissey's most moving song since 'I've Changed My Plea To Guilty' and was similarly wasted on a B-side. Dedicated to Manchester United's 'Busby Babes', who died in arguably the worst disaster in British sporting history, and backed by the droning of a plane's engine, it brings to mind the newsreel footage of the time and a tearful team-mate's admission, 'I wish I could've died with them.' When Morrissey sings, 'I wish I could have gone down – gone down with them to where Mother Nature makes their bed,' slanting his notes like a torch singer, it breaks your heart.

It was a grave mistake for Morrissey to appear on *Friday Night With Jonathan* Ross (pre-recorded before a studio audience and broadcast on BBC1 on 14 May), though he should have been well aware of the chirpy host's offbeat, frequently smutty interview approach. Matters were made worse by the inclusion of arch-camp television personality Dale Winton, first on the bill – introduced by Ross's houseband, Four Poofs And A Piano, all wearing Morrissey T-shirts and belting out 'Boy Racer'.

Almost at once, the conversation turned to gay sex, and Morrissey was seen cringing in his Green Room corner seat when Winton blurted out that he was 'crazy' about Morrissey's straight drummer, Dean Butterworth. 'He's warming you up, Dino. Watch out!' Ross pronounced as the camera zoomed in on the embarrassed young man. Then, after telling Winton to return to the Green Room and 'work his magic', Ross added, 'All I ask is, if anything happens, come back on the show as a couple and tell us all about it.' His next guest was newly crowned snooker champion Ronnie O'Sullivan (a few weeks earlier, The Smiths'

'This Charming Man' had played over the television credits for the championship as he had received his trophy), who now came on to 'The Last Of The Famous International Playboys' – and was asked by Ross if he shaved his pubic hair. All of this was hugely unsettling for Morrissey, about to give his first television interview in seventeen years, and no doubt terrified of what humiliating questions Ross might have been about to fling in his direction.

Morrissey looked striking in his vermilion jacket, but was tremulous during the first few bars of 'Irish Blood, English Heart' despite the rip-roaring welcome from the audience. He quickly got back into his stride, though, and gave a dazzling performance. Unfortunately, from this point it was downhill most of the way. Half-expecting Ross to interview him on the stage and no doubt keen to get it over with, he stalled before being invited to the sofa, where he fidgeted constantly, tugged at his hair, often seemed short of breath on account of his frayed nerves, and persistently glanced off-camera as if in search of the nearest escape route. He managed to get in an early dig at President Bush, and received a mighty cheer from the audience of mostly non-fans when, after Ross asked him if they might be friends after the show, he responded, 'I don't think so.' When the host mockingly addressed him as Steven and, failing to raise a smile from the singer, demanded if there was such a thing as Morrissey turning on the charm, he replied just as drily as before, 'There is no Mozza charm.' Then he criticised Ross for calling him a performer – 'What I do is real. Only seals perform.'

By now looking every bit as uncomfortable as his guest, and having been rebuked for not taking Morrissey's vegetarianism seriously – 'Would you eat your cat?' – Ross asked him if he was a fan of Britain's cult Saturday night television show *Stars In Their Eyes*. 'Why would I be watching *Stars In Their Eyes*?' he asked, before cringing again – covering his ears – at the footage of comedian Harry Hill murdering 'This Charming Man'. Then the real, absolutely inimitable Morrissey showed everyone how it should be done, closing with a stupendous 'special' version of 'Everyday Is Like Sunday', complete with new introduction. 'I can't understand why my life has been cursed, poisoned and condemned/When I've been trying every night to hold you near me,' he sang, drawing a welcome curtain over quite possibly the longest 25 minutes of his career.

You Are The Quarry was released on 17 May 2004 in an unprecedented blaze of mostly positive publicity. Even the cover was innovative: Morrissey, looking like a spivvish Chicago gangster of yesteryear, levelling a machine-gun as if about to mow down any detractor who might dare challenge the unwritten proclamation, 'I'm back, and this time I'm back to stay, so you'd better beware!' 'For a nation that seemed sick of Morrissey back in the late 90s, there's a remarkable amount of folk dying to get their hands on his mammary glands once again,' enthused *Gay Times'* Jo Heaney, nominating it the magazine's Album of the Month and issuing a proclamation of his own: 'Morrissey releases new album! It's almost too much excitement to deal with. A hundred thousand gay men across the country dive into their local record shop and shell out £16.99 to find out what their great leader is up to!'

Referring to the singer's so-called 'lost years', and linking Morrissey with the reclusive has-been star from Billy Wilder's cult film *Sunset Blvd.* (though portrayed by Gloria Swanson, not Greta Garbo as the journalist seemed to think), *NME's* Mark Beaumont wrote, 'He was big – it was the music that got small.' And referring to the latest musclebound pop comeback sensation (courtesy of an appearance on television's *I'm A Celebrity, Get Me Out Of Here!*) he added, 'Eat Keats, Peter Andre: the true Comeback King has arrived and this proud chest can't be inflated by footpump . . . This is no cap-in-hand shuffle back into the limelight; as if taking bloody revenge on a world that allowed him to fall, Moz deals out the poetic spite-fire like a Uzi-toting renegade holed up in a reference library.'

Victoria Segal made an even more potent comparison in *Mojo*, declaring, 'Morrissey's very own '68 Comeback Special proves that despite the demons, rumours of his death have been much exaggerated' – a point she supported with a brilliant mock-up portrait of the singer (by Paul Slater) recreating the infamous Elvis pose while these demons peer through the letters MOZ spelled out in huge red neon lights. And after using every superlative in the book she ended her review, 'The knives might have been out, but for Morrissey the Ides of March are long since gone. The king is not dead. Long live the king.' Segal's colleague, Keith

Cameron, would observe in the same magazine's next issue, 'What makes his seventh album such a treat is it has the musical flair to match his lyrical blunderbuss . . . not a bullet is wasted . . . There's wit and passion and pathos in every meticulously measured line.'

Morrissey's one-time friend David Peschek erred by writing a double review feature in *Uncut*, covering *You Are The Quarry* and the latest offering by Prince – the two had absolutely nothing in common. 'Morrissey sings better with every passing year,' he observed, though he was generally dismissive of much of the album. And did we really need to know, 'They were born 11 months and 3,876 miles apart'? The wittiest observation, one which one imagines Morrissey would have appreciated, came from *Times Online*'s Ian Watson who wrote, with reference to the Morrissey/Marr/Joyce court hearing:

> If the Morrissey of The Smiths was a Tom Courtenay character, misunderstood and aching for love, then the Morrissey of the 21st century is a Bette Davis monster – spiteful, egotistical, outrageous and utterly compelling. Seven years of being shunned has sharpened the ogre's teeth and he's back on fearsome form . . . being devious, truculent and unreliable has never sounded so good.

From my own point of view, there was absolutely no doubting the fact that it was Morrissey's best album by far since leaving the Smiths, proof of the fact – as in the case of Barbara, Brel and Sinatra – that absence, and the recharging of one's artistic and inspirational batteries, do make a significant difference.

Of the twelve songs, several have already been mentioned. 'Well, America, you know where you can shove your hamburger,' Morrissey expostulates in the album's opening track, 'America Is Not The World'. 'Not since "Margaret On The Guillotine" has Morrissey been so deserving of an FBI or MI5 file,' quipped Mark Beaumont in *NME*. Indeed, the biting lyric is hardly the kind of thing one should be singing when, technically, one is a guest of Uncle Sam. Morrissey does of course have a point in denouncing this so-called land of opportunity, whose president has 'Steely-blue eyes with no love in them' and 'a humourless smile', where bigotry ensures, 'the President is never black, female or gay'. And only Morrissey could repeat the line 'You fat pig' time and time again and make it sound so harmonious. Yet after making the attack he did offer an apology of sorts, telling *i-D*'s Ashley Heath, 'I can't live with the notion that America is George W. But simply because I can't live with that doesn't mean that I despise the place, because I don't.'

Despite Morrissey's claim, in the album's press release, that 'There are no links to the past', 'I Have Forgiven Jesus' furnishes the listener with the first of several. In this disdainful prayer of sorts, made delicious by the wonderful key changes as the drama of the song rises, he harks back to his unloved-and-unwanted phase, recalling how as a dutiful Catholic boy he withstood humiliation and condescension to attend church, 'Through hail and snow I'd go/Just to moon at you.' Religion, he declares, instilled within him so much love to give – while, on the other hand, there has never been anyone there to love him. Even so, he concludes, 'I have forgiven Jesus'.

The theme of loneliness persists with 'Come Back To Camden', lyrically reminiscent of 'Everyday Is Like Sunday', where 'taxi drivers never stop talking/Under slate-grey Victorian sky' in the dreary setting where Morrissey pines for his lost love. From Roger Manning's simple piano opener to the song's gorgeous, heart-wrenching falsetto finale, the song has one wondering just how much sadness one man can withstand. Indeed, 'Come Back To Camden' is superior to the earlier piece – quite probably Morrissey's best song ever, a classy excursion in which John Betjeman meets Judy Garland for a suburban reworking of 'The Man That Got Away'. Recalling the initial intimate moment between two lovers – 'Your leg came to rest against mine/Then you lounged with knees up and apart,' Morrissey issues a plea that may have come from either party, 'Come back/To Camden and I'll be good.'

Many drew the conclusion, rightly or wrongly, that the song was a *cri de coeur* to Jake, particularly when Morrissey told *i-D*'s Ashley Heath, 'The song is about a particular person. I have a history, yes. And that whole time in my life is a very emotive period for me.' If it was about Jake, then one cannot begin to imagine how special this young man must have been to have left such a void in the singer's life, albeit one that inspired a veritable masterpiece.

Sexual ambiguity and confusion form the central theme of 'I'm Not Sorry'. Plangent once more, but brazenly unrepentant over the break up of his relationship, Morrissey pronounces over Dean Butterworth's feisty drumbeats, 'I'm not looking for/Just anyone', then almost throws in the towel by asking, 'When will this tired heart stop beating? . . . Existence is only a game.' Harking back to an earlier French interview when he had skittishly confessed that most of the females he had encountered had been nightmares, he affirms, 'The woman of my dreams/Well there never was one'. Then he blames his attitude on a wild man in his head before the song ends, unusually but pleasantly, with a fade-out flute coda, not dissimilar to the one that closed Marianne Faithfull's 1965 B-side (of 'This Little Bird'), 'Morning Sun'. It was the *Guardian*'s Dorian Lynskey who asked Morrissey if this song was his 'Je Ne Regrette Rien' – prompting at least one Internet 'authority' whose musical sphere progressed no further than Morrissey to pose, 'What's a je ne regrette rien?' As for Morrissey, he merely added to such people's confusion by responding, 'No, it's my Chirpy Chirpy Cheep Cheep!'

Alain Whyte's feisty guitar playing – described by *NME*'s Mark Beaumont as, 'like a flame-thrower burning the stalkers out of the Chez Moz bushes' – dominates 'How Can Anybody Possibly Know How I Feel?' This is Morrissey at his most self-deprecating. 'I've had my face dragged in/Fifteen miles of shit . . . and I do not like it,' he growls, only to contradict himself by declaring it incredible that anyone should like him at all. The woman who said she loved him must be insane; the man who wanted to befriend him cannot possibly know him; and absolutely everyone who observes his pain just walks away. He therefore takes his frustration out on the authoritarian figure to whom he is telling his tale, concluding, 'as for you in your uniform . . . you think you can be rude to me . . . but even I as sick as I am/I would never be you'. Brilliant!

Morrissey is only slightly less critical of himself in 'Let Me Kiss You' – according to Mark Beaumont, 'The first evidence that Morrissey has working genitals and the will to use them.' Opting for the maxim

'Everyone has a someone, somewhere,' he tells the person he believes to be his heart's desire, 'Close your eyes/And think of someone/You physically admire' – only to remind them that, when they open them again, they will be seeing someone they physically despise!

In the so-called age of 'renewed queer culture', which has seen the gay and lesbian communities embracing formerly homophobic terms such as 'faggot' and 'dyke' to neutralise their insult level, 'All The Lazy Dykes' backfires on Morrissey because he has hinted and teased, but neither willingly confessed nor denied being a part of this community. The song purports to be about a female friend, trapped in a conventional marriage, who is personally urged by Morrissey himself to 'come out' by visiting a lesbian club – The Palms, in Santa Monica, a favourite haunt of Hollywood's so-called 'Girl Titans'. Questioned by NME's Alex Needham about how he knew so much about the establishment if he had merely driven past it, he replied, 'The clientele were all spilling out on to the pavement and they looked absolutely fascinating . . . very, very strong women who know who they are, what they want, where they're coming from and where they're going.' Even so, it remains the most offensive song in the Morrissey catalogue, an unnecessary tirade from an acknowledged communicator who should know better – a song that, despite its attractive, plaintive melody, leaves an aftertaste of bitterness and one that may bring him grief in years to come.

The album closes with 'You Know I Couldn't Last', Morrissey's criticism of the detractors who have plagued him over the years. Rumour, he says, may hurt but it is the irrevocable printed word that causes the most damage. Hence he seeks revenge. 'Don't let . . . the blue eyes fool you,' he warns, 'They're just gelignite/Loaded and aiming right between your eyes'. He speaks of himself as a meal-ticket for many – 'There's a cash-register ringing and/It weighs so heavy on my back'. Then, having avowed that adverse publicity unwittingly only brings success, he laments the pitfalls of this and attacks those who steal his hard-earned cash: the 'evil legal eagles', 'accountants rampant' and 'the Northern leeches [who] go on/Removing' – a comment that seems very like a thinly disguised dig at Mike Joyce and the court case.

Morrissey performed 'Irish Blood, English Heart' on *Top Of The Pops* on 21 May – he and the band sported matching black Jobriath T-shirts; for some reason he also wore a sprig of eryngium on his jacket lapel. Two days on, and the single had dropped from three to eighteen in the charts: nothing had changed in the respect that once the hordes of die-hard fans had rushed out and bought the latest record on the day of its release, few others were interested.

The next evening, Morrissey headed a particularly dire line-up on BBC2's *Later With Jools Holland* – the most painful of all, to this writer's ears, being future supports The Ordinary Boys. He took up 25 minutes of the hour-long show, and was in sensational vocal form, performing the single and two songs ('First Of The Gang To Die' and 'Let Me Kiss You') with another newly acquired affectation – a habit of rolling his r's like Piaf. He proved no less nervous in an interview with Holland, however, than he had with Jonathan Ross. He twitched, fidgeted and refused to respond to Holland's attempt to raise a laugh with a 'knock-knock' joke, telling him, 'I'm not in. I refuse to open the door.'

Sitting next to Morrissey at the piano, and apparently wondering how to tackle an edgy subject who obviously did not want to be sitting there, Jools Holland seemed exasperated and at one stage, after Morrissey had made a quip about life flying past, was heard to mutter, 'This is flying past!' Morrissey eased up only slightly during the course of the interview. Asked if he liked Los Angeles he replied, 'It's a very pleasant place as long as you don't meet people.' And when asked what he missed about Manchester he retorted, 'I miss the kind of things that nobody could understand why they could be missed. I miss the grey slate of the sky. But you're Southern – you wouldn't understand. When you're Northern, you're Northern for ever and you're instilled with a certain feel for life that you can't get rid of.'

Morrissey, of course, was not being completely honest here. One of his earlier predecessors, Gracie Fields, had said almost the same thing many times when asked what she missed about Rochdale, after spending most of her life living in luxury on Capri – whereas everyone close to her knew only too well, as with Morrissey no doubt, that she would never want to return. The situation was saved by Holland leading the audience into a rousing 'Happy Birthday' (just after midnight on

22 May, though the show had been taped three days previously), and with Morrissey declaring that the ideal birthday gift would be for George W Bush and Tony Blair to exit the political arena – to make way for himself! Then, doubtless pleased that it was over, he closed with a cracking rendition of 'There Is A Light That Never Goes Out', disappearing during the applause as he did at the end of his concerts.

During the early summer of 2004, Morrissey, who had castigated the powers behind *Pop Idol* for placing personal appearance before artistic merit, went out of his way to fanfare latest-flavour-of-the-moment Franz Ferdinand, who would be supporting him in the near future. He had told *i-D*'s Ashley Heath,

> They have that 'It'. Physically, they're all the same height so their eyes are always meeting each other, and they seem to be the same weight so they look fantastic stood together. I think all groups should be like that. The 'It' factor is everything in life, isn't it?

Named after the Austrian archduke whose assassination had sparked off World War I, the four-piece outfit hailed from Glasgow, and their half-Greek frontman, Alex Kapranos, certainly belonged to the Morrissey school of self-promotion when it came to making extroverted statements. 'We are a proper band who are totally apart from the pop industry and have done everything on our own,' he would tell the *Sun*'s Jacqui Swift in May 2004, adding, 'We have no stylist, hairdresser or make-up artists.' Unfortunately, this showed during their earlier television appearances. Hobnobbing with these new-kids-on-the-block was without question infinitely good for the Morrissey image, proving that despite his seven-year absence he had kept in touch with the latest trends. Therefore what better way of adding a younger element to his fanbase of mostly ex-Smiths aficionados than to be seen with Franz Ferdinand, sharing the cover of *NME*?

Previously, some time in March 2004, *NME*'s Alex Needham, allegedly in an attempt to woo Morrissey back to the magazine he despised, had arranged a meeting 'between pop heroes as sharp of mind as they are of trouser' in a Paddington hotel – ostensibly a gathering of egos for a feature which, though unrevealing, was a brilliant publicity exercise. 'The Mozfather was meeting his heirs,' Needham observed. And on 22 May 2004, Morrissey's 45th birthday, this 'fusing of talents' was put to the test when Franz Ferdinand opened for him at the *Manchester Evening News* Arena – 'An event which came very close to ruining the evening,' claimed 'Mozza superfan' Mark Nicholson. 'He's opened with some pretty bad supports in the past, but these took the biscuit. They were completely lacking in the three requisites that make a decent band – they couldn't play, they couldn't sing, and they totally lacked charisma.'

The local media made a meal of this latest 'Morrissey Mania', this 'private party for 18,000 plus one,' with the *Manchester Evening News* devoting its front page to the city's biggest ever star under the banner headline, BIRTHDAY BOY MOZZA IS BACK WITH A SMILE. The other three Smiths had reputedly been invited to the party, sparking rumours that they might join Morrissey on the stage – as if! Only Andy Rourke took advantage of the publicity, showing up at the Salford Lads Club to stage an impromptu performance, including a clutch of Smiths songs (with singer-songwriter Vinny Peculiar) for the benefit of around a thousand fans. Asked why he had elected not to attend Morrissey's concert, Rourke told the press, 'I would have loved to have gone, but it would have been chaotic and too distracting for all parties concerned.'

Journalists had fought and back-scratched to be given the opportunity to interview Morrissey, mindless of the fact that the Jonathan Ross fiasco was still at the back of everyone's mind. The 'winner' was DJ/columnist Pete Mitchell, who got to spend a few minutes with Morrissey, though the latter appears to have been edgy and as non-loquacious as he had been with some of those summoned to the Dorchester. The questions and answers were routine. It was only when Mitchell asked him if returning to Manchester was like coming home that Morrissey seemingly warmed to his interviewer, responding, 'It does indelibly feel like home. I was born and raised there, and for better or worse, it made me. You can rally against the negative things that you don't particularly like about yourself, and you can easily blame Manchester for that. The only thing I blame Manchester for is my terrible education, not because of anything else.' Cynics may remark that in stating, 'I was born there' and not 'here', giving the impression that he was not speaking in the city of his birth, Morrissey did not come across as altogether sincere.

Sincerity, however, was the essence of the evening of 22 May. The Manchester concert, even more so than Morrissey's first official comeback at the Dublin Point, was all that it had been hyped up to be – and more. Replicating Elvis Presley's 1968 comeback special and the Judy Garland recitals of the previous decade, his name was spelled out in twelve-foot-high red neon letters. There was a 'Je Ne Regrette Rien' fanfare of sorts, followed by a voiceover pronouncing modern maladies: Tiananmen Square, cancer, scandalmongering and the Liverpool comedian Jimmy Tarbuck. Wearing a dark blue jacket, and with a strand of ivy dangling over the front of his trousers, Morrissey walked on drawling a couplet from 'My Way' – 'Regrets, I've had a few, but then again too few to mention' – perhaps less a link with Sinatra than with Dorothy Squires, whose theme song this had become in Britain after the litigious years preceding her 1970 London Palladium comeback.

The audience, some of whom had paid as much as £300 for tickets on the black market, went wild. 'His elevation to national treasure status has made it easy to forget just how nuts Morrissey's diehard fans are,' quipped the *Guardian*'s Alexis Petridis, 'but tonight provides a handy reminder.' The *Manchester Evening News*' Eric Jackson enthused, 'He was among family. Thousands of mostly fellow Mancunians for whom this was more a spiritual rally than a mere pop concert.' Morrissey was, of course – and despite his own categorising himself thus – much more than a pop singer because he had progressed way beyond the Robbie/Elton/Rod megastars stable to join the ranks of the *monstres sacrés*: Leonard Cohen, Bob Dylan, Jacques Brel and a very small band of brothers.

Beginning with 'First Of The Gang To Die', Morrissey performed nineteen songs – working his way through most of the new album, and throwing in a few Smiths classics for good measure: 'The Headmaster Ritual', 'A Rush And A Push And The Land Is Ours' (the perfect companion-piece for 'Irish Blood, English Heart'), 'Rubber Ring' and 'Shoplifters Of The World Unite'. He sang an obscure number by the group Raymonde (James Maker's 'No One Can Hold A Candle To You', from their 1987 *Babelogue* album), and 'Don't Make Fun Of Daddy's Voice', recorded for *You Are The Quarry* but left off. Blasts from the past included 'Jack The Ripper', 'Hairdresser On Fire', 'I Know It's Gonna Happen Someday' (crooned wonderfully to the mirrorball) and the obligatory 'Everyday Is Like Sunday'.

The waspish wit and inevitable put-downs were in plentiful supply. Britney Spears was referred to as 'Satan' before Morrissey ploughed into 'The World Is Full Of Crashing Bores'. The pair of sparring ex-lovers and five-minute wonders who had swapped top spots in the charts (with the expletive-peppered 'Fuck You, I Don't Want You Back' and 'Fuck You Back' – a level to which Morrissey would never have sunk) and thereby relegated Morrissey's single to number 3 were denounced with a sarcastic, 'How very nice and right it feels to be in the British Top Ten again – alongside such major talents as Eamon and Frankee.' When the crowd chanted 'Happy Birthday' he shot back, 'Manchester, you've made a happy man very old. I can't believe I'm twenty-nine. Where did the years go?'

The proceedings were rounded off, after three shirt changes and a flash or two of still finely honed torso, with an even more emotional than usual 'There Is A Light That Never Goes Out', and half of the auditorium were in tears after Morrissey's pronouncement, 'Whatever happens, just don't forget me.' 'It was as if he was saying goodbye, absolutely and finally, despite all the gigs he had been booked for that summer,' Mark Nicholson said.

Other fans believed the same – worse still, that after his recent brush with meningitis, Morrissey might have been ill. Whether there was a reason for the utterance, or whether Morrissey was merely play-acting or carried away by the excitement of the whole thing, would remain to be seen. For the time being, the *Independent*'s Fiona Sturges concluded,

> Just at the point when pop music seems lost to bimbettes, the erstwhile frontman of The Smiths has chosen to come out of exile and show them how it's done. It's clear that this most eccentric star won't be content with anything other than world domination.

*

In 1986, Morrissey had posed for two photographs that recalled James Dean's comment, 'Die young and make a beautiful corpse.' In the first, clutching one of George Formby's ukuleles, he reclines on top of a grave the headstone of which bears the inscription, MORRISSEY 1959–1986. In the other he is half-naked, prostrate on a mortuary slab and looking almost ethereal. Asked what he would like his epitaph to be, he had discounted the former picture and told Martin Aston, apparently very seriously, 'I think I'd have a jam jar instead of a headstone – saying, "He lived, he died." That says enough, really.'

Two decades later, in *The Importance Of Being Morrissey*, Noel Gallagher pronounced – as only he could – 'He's fucking revered, man! His records'll be listened to until George Bush blows up the planet!' It was Morrissey himself, however, who provided the best eulogy, just before the recently deceased Nina Simone sang 'Please Don't Let Me Be Misunderstood' over the documentary's closing credits:

> I've left my fingerprints somewhere. That's good enough.
> I'm my own person and that's good enough.
> I stand my ground. That's good enough.

Discography

The following represents Morrissey's complete recorded output as a solo performer from 1988 to the present day. Bootlegs are included and are of variable quality, some having been issued more than once on different labels. Flexis and trade promos are not included.

1988

'Suedehead'; 'I Know Very Well How I Got My Name' (HMV POP 1618 7-inch)

'Suedehead'; 'I Know Very Well How I Got My Name'; 'Hairdresser On Fire' (HMV 12 POP 1618 12-inch); the CD POP 1618 also contains 'Oh Well, I'll Never Learn'

'Everyday Is Like Sunday'; 'Sister I'm A Poet' (HMV POP 1619 7-inch)

'Everyday Is Like Sunday'; 'Sister I'm A Poet'; 'Disappointed' (HMV POP 1619 12-inch); the CD POP 1619 also contains 'Will Never Marry'

Viva Hate: 'Alsatian Cousin'; 'Little Man, What Now?'; 'Everyday Is Like Sunday'; 'Bengali In Platforms'; 'Angel, Angel, Down We Go Together'; 'Late Night, Maudlin Street'; 'Suedehead'; 'Break Up The Family'; 'The Ordinary Boys'; 'I Don't Mind If You Forget Me'; 'Dial-A-Cliché'; 'Margaret On The Guillotine'. (HMV [CD] CSD 3787)

1989

'The Last Of The Famous International Playboys'; 'Lucky Lisp' (HMV POP 1620 7-inch)

'The Last Of The Famous International Playboys'; 'Lucky Lisp'; 'Michael's Bones' (HMV 12 POP 1620/CD POP 1620)

'Interesting Drug'; 'Such A Little Thing Makes Such A Big Difference' (HMV POP 1621 7-inch)

'Interesting Drug'; 'Such A Little Thing Makes Such A Big Difference';

'Sweet And Tender Hooligan' (live) (HMV POP 1621/CD POP 1621)
'Interesting Drug'; 'The Last Of The Famous International Playboys'; 'Such A Little Thing Makes Such A Big Difference'; 'Lucky Lisp'; 'Michael's Bones' (EMI-Toshiba Japan, CD CP15-5889)
'Ouija Board, Ouija Board'; 'Yes, I Am Blind' (HMV POP 1622 7-inch)
'Ouija Board, Ouija Board'; 'Yes, I Am Blind'; 'East West' (HMV 12 POP 1622/CD POP 1622)

1990

'November Spawned A Monster'; 'He Knows I'd Love To See Him' (HMV POP 1623 7-inch)
'November Spawned A Monster'; 'He Knows I'd Love To See Him'; 'Girl Least Likely To' (HMV 12 POP 1623/CD POP 1623)
'Piccadilly Palare'; 'Get Off The Stage' (HMV POP 1624 7-inch)
'Piccadilly Palare'; 'Get Off The Stage'; 'At Amber' (HMV 12 POP 1624/CD POP 1624)

Bona Drag: 'Piccadilly Palare'; 'Interesting Drug'; 'November Spawned A Monster'; 'Will Never Marry'; 'Such A Little Thing Makes Such A Big Difference'; 'The Last Of The Famous International Playboys'; 'Ouija Board, Ouija Board'; 'Hairdresser on Fire'; 'Everyday Is Like Sunday'; 'He Knows I'd Love To See Him'; 'Yes, I Am Blind'; 'Lucky Lisp'; 'Suedehead'; 'Disappointed'. (HMV [CD] CSD 3788)

1991

'Our Frank'; 'Journalists Who Lie' (HMV POP 1625 7-inch)
'Our Frank'; 'Journalists Who Lie'; 'Tony The Pony' (HMV 12 POP 1625/CD POP 1625)
'Sing Your Life'; 'That's Entertainment' (HMV POP 1626 7-inch)
'Sing Your Life'; 'That's Entertainment'; 'The Loop' (HMV 12 POP 1626/CD POP 1626)
'Pregnant For The Last Time'; 'Skin Storm' (HMV POP 1627 7-inch)
'Pregnant For The Last Time'; 'Skin Storm'; 'Cosmic Dancer'*; 'Disappointed'* (HMV 12 POP 1627/CD POP 1627) *Live in Utrecht.
'My Love Life'; 'I've Changed My Plea To Guilty' (HMV POP 1628 7-inch)

'My Love Life'; 'I've Changed My Plea To Guilty'; 'There's A Place In Hell
   For Me And My Friends' (HMV 12 POP 1628/CD POP 1628)
'My Love Life'; 'I've Changed My Plea To Guilty'; 'Skin Storm' (SIRE USA,
   941276-2)
'My Love Life'; 'The Loop'; 'Skin Storm'; 'That's Entertainment';
   'Pregnant For The Last Time'; 'I've Changed My Plea To Guilty' (EMI-
   Toshiba Japan, CD TOCP-6909)
Morrissey At KROQ: 'There's A Place In Hell For Me And My Friends'; 'My
   Love Life'; 'Sing Your Life' (SIRE USA, CD 940184-2)

Kill Uncle: 'Our Frank'; 'Asian Rut'; 'Sing Your Life'; 'Mute Witness';
   'King Leer'; 'Found, Found, Found'; 'Driving Your Girlfriend Home';
   'The Harsh Truth Of The Camera Eye'; 'The End Of The Family Line';
   'There's A Place In Hell For Me And My Friends'. (HMV [CD] CSD
   3789)

1992
'We Hate It When Our Friends Become Successful'; 'Suedehead'* (HMV
   POP 1629 7-inch) *Live at the Hammersmith Odeon.
'We Hate It When Our Friends Become Successful'; 'Suedehead'*; 'I've
   Changed My Plea To Guilty'*; 'Alsatian Cousin'* (HMV 12 POP/CD
   POP 1629) *Live at the Hammersmith Odeon.
'We Hate It When Our Friends Become Successful'; 'Suedehead'; I've
   Changed My Plea To Guilty'; 'Pregnant For The Last Time'; 'Alsatian
   Cousin' (SIRE USA, 12-inch, CD, Cassette 940560-2)
'You're The One For Me, Fatty'; 'Pashernate Love'; 'There Speaks A True
   Friend' (HMV 12 POP/CD POP 1630)
'Tomorrow'; 'Let The Right One Slip In'; 'There Speaks A True Friend';
   'Pashernate Love' (SIRE USA, 940580-2)
'Certain People I Know'; 'Suedehead'; 'Our Frank'; 'November Spawned
   A Monster' (USA, CD 8803652)
'Certain People I Know'; 'You've Had Her' (HMV POP 1631 7-inch)
'Certain People I Know'; 'You've Had Her'; 'Jack The Ripper' (HMV 12
   POP/CD POP 1631)

Your Arsenal: 'You're Gonna Need Someone On Your Side'; 'Glamorous
   Glue'; 'We'll Let You Know'; 'The National Front Disco'; 'Certain
   People I Know'; 'We Hate It When Our Friends Become Successful';
   'You're The One For Me, Fatty'; 'Seasick, Yet Still Docked'; 'I Know It's
   Gonna Happen Someday'; 'Tomorrow'. (HMV [CD] CSD 3790)

1993

Beethoven Was Deaf: 'You're The One For Me, Fatty'; 'Certain People I
   Know'; 'The National Front Disco'; 'November Spawned A Monster';
   'Seasick, Yet Still Docked'; 'The Loop'; 'Sister I'm A Poet'; 'Jack The
   Ripper'; 'Such A Little Thing Makes Such A Big Difference'; 'I Know
   It's Gonna Happen Someday'; 'We'll Let You Know'; 'Suedehead';
   'He Knows I'd Love To See Him'; 'You're Gonna Need Someone On
   Your Side'; 'Glamorous Glue'; 'We Hate It When Our Friends Become
   Successful'. Live at Le Zénith, Porte de Pantin, Paris. (HMV [CD] CSD
   3791)

1994

'The More You Ignore Me, The Closer I Get'; 'Used To Be A Sweet Boy';
   'I'd Love To' (1) (PARLOPHONE CD, CDR 6372)
'The More You Ignore Me, The Closer I Get'; 'Used To Be A Sweet Boy';
   'I'd Love To' (2) (SIRE USA, 941276-2)
'Hold On To Your Friends'; 'Moonriver' (extended) (PARLOPHONE CD
   CDR 6383)
'Interlude'*; 'Interlude' (extended)*; 'Interlude' (Instrumental)
   (PARLOPHONE CD CDR 6365) *Duet with Siouxsie Sioux.

1995

World Of Morrissey: 'Whatever Happens, I Love You'; 'Billy Budd'; 'Jack
   The Ripper'; 'Have-A-Go Merchant'; 'The Loop'; 'Sister I'm A Poet';
   'You're The One For Me, Fatty'; 'Boxers'; 'Moonriver'; 'My Love Life';
   'Certain People I Know'; 'The Last Of The Famous International
   Playboys'; 'We'll Let You Know'; 'Spring-Heeled Jim'. (PARLOPHONE
   CD 7243-8-32448-2-9)

'Boxers'; 'Have-A-Go Merchant'; 'Whatever Happens, I Love You' (PARLOPHONE CD 7243-8-81888-2-1)

'Dagenham Dave'; 'Nobody Loves Us'; 'You Must Please Remember' (RCA CD 7432-1299-802)

'The Boy Racer' (1); 'London'*; 'Billy Budd'* (RCA CD 7432-1332-942) *Live in London.

'The Boy Racer' (2); 'Spring-Heeled Jim'*; 'Why Don't You Find Out For Yourself?'* (RCA CD 7432-1332-952) *Live in London, courtesy of EMI/PARLOPHONE (both).

'Sunny'; 'Black-Eyed Susan'; 'A Swallow On My Neck' (PARLOPHONE CD CDR 6243)

'Now My Heart Is Full'; 'Moonriver'; 'Jack The Ripper' (SIRE USA, 94100-2)

Southpaw Grammar: 'The Teachers Are Afraid Of The Pupils'; 'Reader Meet Author'; 'The Boy Racer'; 'The Operation'; 'Dagenham Dave'; 'Do Your Best And Don't Worry'; 'Best Friend On The Payroll'; 'Southpaw'. (RCA CD 743-212-99632)

1997

Maladjusted: 'Maladjusted'; 'Alma Matters'; 'Ambitious Outsiders'; 'Trouble Loves Me'; 'Papa Jack'; 'Ammunition'; 'Wide To Receive'; 'Roy's Keen'; 'He Cried'; 'Satan Rejected My Soul'. (ISLAND CD CID 8059)

'Alma Matters'; 'Heir Apparent'; 'I Can Have Both' (ISLAND CD CID 667)

'Roy's Keen'; 'Lost'; 'The Edges Are No Longer Parallel' (ISLAND CD CID 671)

'Satan Rejected My Soul'; 'Now I Am A Was'; 'This Is Not Your Country' (ISLAND CD CID 686)

'Suedehead' – The Best of Morrissey: 'Suedehead'; 'Sunny'; 'Boxers'; 'Tomorrow'; 'Interlude'; 'Everyday Is Like Sunday'; 'That's Entertainment'; 'Hold On To Your Friends'; 'My Love Life'; 'Interesting Drug'; 'Our Frank'; 'Piccadilly Palare'; 'Ouija Board, Ouija Board'; 'You're The One For Me, Fatty'; 'We Hate It When Our Friends

Become Successful'; 'The Last Of The Famous International Playboys'; 'Pregnant For The Last Time'; 'November Spawned A Monster'; 'The More You Ignore Me, The Closer I Get'. (EMI CD 7243-8-59665-2-1)

Viva Hate: 'Alsatian Cousin'; 'Little Man, What Now?'; 'Everyday Is Like Sunday'; 'Bengali In Platforms'; 'Angel, Angel, Down We Go Together'; 'Late Night, Maudlin Street'; 'Suedehead'; 'Break Up The Family'; 'The Ordinary Boys'; 'I Don't Mind If You Forget Me'; 'Dial-A-Cliché'; 'Margaret On The Guillotine'; 'Let The Right One Slip In'; 'Pashernate Love'; 'At Amber'; 'Disappointed'*; 'Girl Least Likely To'; 'I'd Love To' (1); 'Michael's Bones'; 'I've Changed My Plea To Guilty'. (PARLOPHONE CD 7243-8-56325-2-5) *Live in Holland.

1998

My Early Burglary Years: 'Sunny'; 'At Amber'; 'Cosmic Dancer'; 'Nobody Loves Us'; 'A Swallow On My Neck'; 'Sister I'm A Poet'; 'Black-Eyed Susan'; 'Michael's Bones'; 'I'd Love To' (2); 'Reader Meet Author'; 'Pashernate Love'; 'Girl Least Likely To'; 'Jack The Ripper'; 'I've Changed My Plea To Guilty'; 'The Boy Racer'; 'Boxers'. (REPRISE USA, CD 9-46874-2)

2004

'Irish Blood, English Heart' (1); 'It's Hard To Walk Tall When You're Small' (ATTACK CD ATKXS002)

'Irish Blood, English Heart' (2); 'Munich Air Disaster 1958'; 'The Never Played Symphonies' (ATTACK CD ATKXD002) Also issued on vinyl EP.

You Are The Quarry: 'America Is Not The World'; 'Irish Blood, English Heart'; 'I Have Forgiven Jesus'; 'Come Back To Camden'; 'I'm Not Sorry'; 'The World Is Full Of Crashing Bores'; 'How Can Anybody Possibly Know How I Feel?'; 'First Of The Gang To Die'; 'Let Me Kiss You'; 'All The Lazy Dykes'; 'I Like You'; 'You Know I Couldn't Last' (ATTACK CD001)

'First Of The Gang To Die' (1); 'My Life Is A Succession Of People Saying
Goodbye' (ATTACK CD ATKXS003)

'First Of The Gang To Die' (2)*; 'First Of The Gang To Die'; 'Teenage Dad
On His Estate'; 'Mexico' (ATTACK DVD ATKDX003); this release
contains a photo gallery which plays during the audio tracks. *DVD
version.

Bootlegs (Author's Choices)

Morrissey (untitled): 'Stop Me If You've Heard This One Before';
'Disappointed'; 'Interesting Drug'; 'Suedehead'; 'The Last Of The
Famous International Playboys': 'Sister I'm A Poet'; 'Death At One's
Elbow'; 'Sweet And Tender Hooligan'. Morrissey's first solo concert,
recorded at Wolverhampton, 22/12/88.

Posing In Paris: 'Interesting Drug'; 'Mute Witness'; 'The Last Of The
Famous International Playboys'; 'November Spawned A Monster';
'Will Never Marry'; 'Pregnant For The Last Time'; 'That's
Entertainment'; 'I've Changed My Plea To Guilty'; 'Everyday Is Like
Sunday'; 'Piccadilly Palare'; 'Suedehead'; 'Trash'; 'Cosmic Dancer';
'Disappointed'. Recorded at the Elyseé-Montmartre, Paris, 29/4/91 by
Bernard Lemoin and featured on José Artur's France-Inter *Pop-Club*.

Higher Education: 'Mute Witness'; 'Will Never Marry'; 'Pregnant For
The Last Time'; 'Everyday Is Like Sunday'; 'Cosmic Dancer';
'Disappointed'; 'Our Frank'; 'That's Entertainment'; 'I've Changed My
Plea To Guilty'; 'Piccadilly Palare'; 'Sing Your Life'; 'Asian Rut'; 'King
Leer'; 'The Last Of The Famous International Playboys'; 'November
Spawned A Monster'. Recorded in Utrecht, Holland 1/5/91.

Morrissey: London 1991: 'Interesting Drug'; 'The Last Of The Famous
International Playboys'; 'Piccadilly Palare'; 'Trash'; 'Sing Your Life';
'King Leer'; 'Asian Rut'; 'Pregnant For The Last Time'; 'Mute Witness';
'Everyday Is Like Sunday'; 'November Spawned A Monster'; 'Will
Never Marry'; 'There's A Place In Hell For Me And My Friends'; 'That's

Entertainment'; 'Our Frank'; 'Suedehead'; 'Angel, Angel, Down We Go Together'; 'Yes, I Am Blind'; 'Disappointed'. Wembley Arena, 20/7/91.

Nothing To Declare But My Jeans: 'Interesting Drug'; 'Piccadilly Palare'; 'Mute Witness'; 'The Last Of The Famous International Playboys'; 'King Leer'; 'Sing Your Life'; 'Pregnant For The Last Time'; 'November Spawned A Monster'; 'Alsatian Cousin'; 'Will Never Marry'; 'Everyday Is Like Sunday'; 'Asian Rut'; 'The Loop'; 'Angel, Angel, Down We Go Together'; 'I've Changed My Plea To Guilty'; 'That's Entertainment'; 'Suedehead'; 'Our Frank'; 'Disappointed'. Osaka Castle Hall, 28/8/91.

Morrissey In Tokyo: 'Angel, Angel, Down We Go Together'; 'Interesting Drug'; 'Piccadilly Palare'; 'Trash'; 'Mute Witness'; 'The Last Of The Famous International Playboys'; 'Sister I'm A Poet'; 'Alsatian Cousin'; 'The Loop'; 'King Leer'; 'November Spawned A Monster'; 'Everyday Is Like Sunday'; 'That's Entertainment'; 'Cosmic Dancer'; 'Suedehead'; 'Our Frank'; 'Sing Your Life'; 'Disappointed'. Budokan, 2/9/91.

Digital Excitation: 'November Spawned A Monster'; 'Pregnant For The Last Time'; Alsatian Cousin'; 'Interesting Drug'; 'Mute Witness'; 'My Love Life'; 'Piccadilly Palare'; 'Driving Your Girlfriend Home'; 'Everyday Is Like Sunday'; 'Sing Your Life'; 'The Loop'; 'Suedehead'; 'I've Changed My Plea To Guilty'; 'Cosmic Dancer'; 'King Leer'; 'Disappointed'; 'Our Frank'; 'Angel, Angel, Down We Go Together'; 'Asian Rut'. Taken from the Japanese broadcast (WOWOW) of the Hammersmith Odeon concert of 4/10/91.

Dreams I'll Never See: 'Suedehead'; 'Sister I'm A Poet'; 'The Loop'; 'You're The One For Me, Fatty'; 'Girl Least Likely To'; 'Alsatian Cousin'; 'Seasick, Yet Still Docked'; 'Such A Little Thing Makes Such A Big Difference'; 'My Insatiable One'; 'Everyday Is Like Sunday'; 'Interesting Drug'; 'The National Front Disco'; 'November Spawned A Monster'; 'Piccadilly Palare'; 'We Hate It When Our Friends Become Successful'; 'Disappointed'. Leysin Festival, 9/7/92.

I'm A Poet: 'Girl Least Likely To'; 'November Spawned A Monster'; 'Certain People I Know'; 'Sister I'm A Poet'; 'Such A Little Thing Makes Such A Big Difference'; 'Tomorrow'; 'We'll Let You Know'; 'Suedehead'; 'He Knows I'd Love To See Him'; 'You're The One For Me, Fatty'; 'Seasick, Yet Still Docked'; 'Alsatian Cousin'; 'We Hate It When Our Friends Become Successful'; 'Everyday Is Like Sunday'; 'The National Front Disco'. All recorded in Colorado, 1/10/92. 'Glamorous Glue'; 'Suedehead'. Taken from the *Saturday Night Live* television broadcast, October 1992.

Etchings

The following represent the 7-inch and 12-inch vinyl run-out groove etchings (the words scratched into the centre of the records) from The Smiths and Morrissey rarities catalogue. Though taken from the records themselves and from record company lists, they are not thought to be exhaustive.

'Hand In Glove': *Kiss My Shades/Kiss My Shades Too.*
'This Charming Man': *Will Nature Make A Man Of Me Yet?/Slap Me On The Patio.*
'What Difference Does It Make?': *Sound Clinic.*
'Heaven Knows I'm Miserable Now': *Smiths Indeed/Ill Forever, Smiths Presumably/Forever Ill.*
'William, It Was Really Nothing' and *Hatful Of Hollow: The Impotence Of Ernest/Romantic And [ ] Is Hip And Aware.* Reissue of single: *We Hate Bad Grammer.*
'Barbarism Begins At Home' (promo): *These Are The Good Times.*
'Meat Is Murder': *Illness As Art/Doing The Wythenshawe Waltz.*
'How Soon Is Now?': *The Tatty Truth.*
'Shakespeare's Sister': *Home Is Where The Art Is.*
The Queen Is Dead: Fear Of Manchester/Them Was Rotten Days.
'That Joke Isn't Funny Anymore': *Oursouls, Oursouls, Oursouls.*
'The Boy With The Thorn In His Side': *Is That Clever, Jim?/Arty Bloody Farty.*
'Bigmouth Strikes Again': *Beware The Wrath To Come!/Talent Borrows, Genius Steals.*
'Panic': *I Dreamt About Stew Last Night.*
'Ask': *Are You Loathsome Tonight?/Tomb It May Concern.*
'Shoplifters Of The World Unite': *Alf Ramsey's Revenge.*
'Sheila Take A Bow': *Cook Bernard Matthews.*

'Girlfriend In A Coma': *Everybody Is A Flasher At Heart/And Never More Shall Be So/So Far So Bad.*

Strangeways Here We Come: *Guy Fawkes Was A Genius.*

'I Started Something I Couldn't Finish': *Murder At The Wool Hall (X) Starring Sheridan Whiteside/You Are Believing You Do Not Want To Sleep.*

'Last Night I Dreamt That Somebody Loved Me': *The Return Of The Submissive Society (X) Starring Sheridan Whiteside/The Bizarre Oriental Vibrating Palm Death (X) Starring Sheridan Whiteside.*

'Some Girls Are Bigger Than Others': *Noh Girl Like Jaguar Rose.*

'Suedehead': *Dreams Are Just Dreams.*

Viva Hate: *Education In Reverse.*

Bona Drag: *Aesthetics Versus Athletics.*

Kill Uncle: *Nothing To Declare But My Jeans.*

'Everyday Is Like Sunday': *Nineteen-Eighty-Hate.*

'The Last Of The Famous International Playboys': *Escape From Vallium/Return To Vallium.*

'Interesting Drug': *Escape From Vallium/Escape To Vallium/What Kind Of Man Reads Denim Delinquent?/Hosscah!* SPM 29 (one-sided promotional 12-inch): *Motorcycle Au Pair Boy* (plus Morrissey etching of Oscar Wilde with sunflower).

'Ouija Board, Ouija Board': *Art Any Road.*

'Piccadilly Palare': *George Eliot Knew.*

'Our Frank': *Free Reg, Free Ron/Drunker Quicker.*

'We Hate It When Our Friends Become Successful': *I Don't Know Anyone That's Happy, Do You?*

Beethoven Was Deaf: Would You Risk It For A Biscuit?

'Certain People I Know': *Why Bother To Keep Clean?*

Bibliography

Primary and secondary sources

Words by Morrissey (booklet), Robert Mackie, 1980-81; also at www.torr.org/moz/letters.htm.

'Crisp Songs & Salted Lyrics', Cath Carroll, *NME*, May 1983.

'Morrissey', Catherine Miles, *HIM Monthly*, July 1983.

'Sorrow's Native Son', Antonella Black, *Sounds*, April 1985.

'Feast Of Steven: Morrissey: Fallen Angel Or Demi-God', Danny Kelly, *NME*, June 1985.

'A Dreaded Sunny Day', Mishka Assaya, *Les Inrockuptibles*, September 1986.

'Home Thoughts From Abroad', Frank Owen, *Melody Maker*, September 1986.

'Who Do You Do?' Diesel Balaam/Sukie de la Croix, *Gay News*, November 1986.

'Morrissey: The Dutch Interview', Martin Aston, *Oor*, January 1987.

'The Band With The Thorn In Its Side', Nick Kent, *The Face*, May 1987.

'Morrissey', Chris Whatsisname, *Les Inrockuptibles*, July 1987.

'Wilde Childe', Paul Morley, *Blitz*, March 1988.

'Shoplifters Of The World', Anon, *Rock Sound Français*, March 1988.

'Morrissey's Revenge: Homo Hymns For Misfits', Adam Block, *The Advocate*, May 1988.

'Private Diary Of A Middle-Aged Man', Shaun Phillips, *Sounds*, June 1988.

'The Light That Went Out', Keith Cameron, *Sounds*, December 1988.

'Morrissey: I'm A Total Sex Object', James Brown, *NME*, January 1989.

'Johnny Remember Me', Dave Haslam, *NME*, March 1989.

'Paradis Perdu', Nick Kent, *Les Inrockuptibles*, January 1990.

'The Deep End', Nick Kent, *The Face*, March 1990.

'Morrissey: Saint Or Sinner/The God That Failed', Kris Kirk & Richard Smith, *Gay Times*, August 1990; follow-up September 1990.

'Bona Contention', Len Brown, *Vox*, November 1990.

'Wake Me When It's Over', Mark Kemp, *Select*, February 1991.

'The Good Lieutenants', David Cavanagh, *Select*, March 1991.

'La Solitude Du Coureur Du Fond', J-D Beauvallet, *Les Inrockuptibles*, April 1991.

'Marr's On Life/The Best Is Fret To Come', Danny Kelly, *NME*, April 1991.

'Morrissey Comes Out! (For A Drink)', Stuart Maconie, *NME*, May 1991.

'Morrissey', interview with New York WDRE Radio, November 1991.

Morrissey Shot: Linder Sterling, Secker & Warburg, 1992.

'Petite Morte', Johnny Rogan, *Les Inrockuptibles*, July 1992.

'Morrissey: Flying The Flag Or Flirting With Disaster', Various, *NME*, August 1992.

'Mad About The Boy/The Fruits Of Misery', David Thomas, *Vox*, September 1992.

'L'Age Christique', E & J Vincent, *Best Français*, September 1992.

'The Man You Hate To Love', Lorraine Ali, *Alternative Press*, October 1992.

'Morrissey Flowers Again', Robert Chalmers, *Observer Magazine*, December 1992.

'Homme Alone', David Keeps, *Details*, December 1992.

'Villain Canard', Hugo Cassavetti, *Rock Sound Français*, February 1993.

'Saying It All With Flowers', Caitlin Moran, *The Times*, November 1993.

Peepholism, Jo Slee, Sidgwick & Jackson, 1994.

Morrissey: Landscapes Of The Mind: David Bret, Robson Books, 1994.

'Nothing To Declare But Their Genius', David Cavanagh, *Q*, January 1994.

'The Loneliest Monk', Dave DiMartino, *Ray Gun*, March 1994.

'Morrissey: Hello, Cruel World', Stuart Maconie, *Q*, April 1994.

'He's A Love, Isn't He?' Rosemary Barratt, *Manchester Evening News*, April 1994.

'Homme Alone 2: Lost In Los Angeles', William Shaw, *Details*, April 1994.

'Hand In Glove', Andrew Harrison, *Select*, May 1994.

'Klaus Nomi', Rupert Smith, *Attitude*, July 1994.

'Out On Your Own', Patrick Fitzgerald & Richard Smith, *Gay Times*,
November 1994.

'A Walk On The Wilde Side', Michael Bracewell, *Observer*, February
1995.

'This Charming Mandroid', David Sinclair, *The Times*, February 1995.

'Ma Chienne De Vie', C Fevret & E Tellier, *Les Inrockuptibles*, September
1995.

'Morrissey: Do You Fucking Want Some?' Stuart Maconie, *Select*,
September 1995.

'The King Of Bedsit Angst Grows Up', Will Self, *Observer Magazine*,
December 1995.

Joyce vs Morrissey & Marr: London High Court Hearing, 2–6, 9–11
December 1996.

'After The Affair', Suzie Mackenzie, *Guardian*, August 1997.

'Heaven Knows He's Miserable Now', Dave Simpson, *Guardian*, July
1998.

A Boy Called Mary, Kris Kirk (ed. Richard Smith), Millivres, 1999.

'Heaven Knows I'm Not Miserable Now', Michael Bracewell, *Observer*,
November 1999.

'Morrissey,' interview with Janice Long, Radio 2, October 2002.

The Importance Of Being Morrissey, Channel 4 documentary, June
2003.

'Born To Be Wilde: The Smiths 20th Anniversary', Simon Goddard,
Record Collector, June 2003.

'Morrissey I-D I-Q', Ben Reardon, *i-D*, July 2003.

'Morrissey', interview with *City Life*, July 2003.

'Morrissey', interview with James Murphy, Tim Goldsworthy, *Index*,
October 2003.

'The Morrissey Effect', Andrew O'Hagan, *Daily Telegraph*, January 2004.

'You & I, This Land Is Ours', Ashley Heath, *i-D Drama Queen Issue*, April
2004.

'Somebody Has To Be Me', Dorian Lynskey, *Guardian*, April 2004.

'Morrissey: The Guv'nor Returns', Alex Needham, *NME*, April 2004.

'Morrissey: They Thought I Was A Threat', Alex Needham, *NME*, April
2004.

'Morrissey Mord Encore', Jean-Daniel Beauvallet, *Les Inrockuptibles*, April 2004.

'Morrissey', interview with Sebastian Suarez-Golborne, *Sonic*, April 2004.

'Morrissey: Ik Ben Niet De Enige Mens Die Zich Een Zaam Voelt?' Serge Simonart, *Humo*, May 2004.

'Bigmouth Strikes Again', Robert Sandall, *Sunday Times*, May 2004.

'There Is A Spite That Never Goes Out', Mark Beaumont, *NME*, May 2004.

'If I Can Dream', Victoria Seagal, Paul Slater, *Mojo*, May 2004.

'Morrissey: The Smiths Will End In Murder', Keith Cameron, *Mojo*, May 2004.

'Man At His Best: Morrissey's Back', James Medd, Mischa Richter, *Esquire*, June 2004.

'The Band That Dreams That It Never Broke Up', Andrew Harrison, *Word*, June 2004.

'The Inside Story: The Smiths & Morrissey', Various, *Q Special Issue*, June 2004.

Author interviews

Peter Adams, Martin Aston, J-D Beauvallet, Boz Boorer, Johnny Bridgewood, Murray Chalmers, Robert Chalmers, Spencer Cobrin, Gary Day, Andy Davis, Adrian Deevoy, Gianfranco, Andrew Harrison, Kanako Ishikawa, Kris Kirk, Kirsty MacColl, Stuart Maconie, Mark Nevin, Robert Sandall, Pierre Sankiowski, Linder Sterling, Emmanuel Tellier, Nigel Thomas, Alain Whyte.

Index

Introduction

The Penumbra, together with *Maria* and *L'inseparabile*, is one of my dearest books – they are all books about childhood. They almost compose, as it were, a trilogy.

The Penumbra was first published in 1964; it is not a journey in time to recover the past, rather a brief journey in space to my native village. There the adult woman finds herself a little girl again and discovers that she is the same person. This is the meaning of the Proustian title, an integral part of the book, taken from a passage in *Remembrance of Times Past*.

From ourselves comes only that which we drag

from the obscurity which lies within us, that which to others is unknown ... And as art exactly reconstitutes life, around the truths to which we have attained inside ourselves, there will always float an atmosphere of poetry, the soft charm of a mystery which is merely a vestige of *the shadow [La pénumbre] which we have had to traverse.**

So I appropriated the sentence, its better half in fact. Today I know why this book has been especially loved. *The Penumbra* creates a deep communication – almost a communion – with the reader. Each person finds himself or herself there once more, as I found myself again on that visit to Ponte Stura-Demonte. In the persistency of one's own nature are contained all the possible interior adventures of each life – the *us* of Proust.

That, and not the little world of yesterday, is what is revealed in *The Penumbra*. Orchestrated as the visit to the house and the streets of my childhood, it is a journey then to discover my own self.

This book is so much a part of me that I am unable to re-read it. I am jealous of myself. Whoever reads it becomes my childhood companion. I am not jealous of this incredible identification. I write for myself, yet my books – and *The Penumbra* in particular – speak to others.

*Remembrance of Things Past, Marcel Proust, translated by C. K. Scott Moncrieff and Terence Kilmartin; and by Andreas Mayor, Penguin Books

This absolves me from the charge that I have violated the secrets of my origins. For everyone, childhood, even if many people forget it, is in some way a model for life. Life continues to put forward the same fears, the same perplexities, the same alternatives.

October 1994   LALLA ROMANO

Part One

I

The small cell-like room was painted a harsh yellow. The huge bed was made of iron painted in parallel lines to imitate wood. The air smelt of stale smoke and was suffocating. Two flies were walking backwards and forwards like the little spots which dance in front of your eyes when you are ill.

I lay stretched out on the bed, trying to think innocuous thoughts. At every small movement, the bed would groan like an organ.

I had heard people criticizing hotels ever since I was a child. I heard them saying they had fleas. To me this sounded like an advantage that hotels had. If you found a flea at home, they would raise the alarm. Once it had been spotted it would vanish

7

like a mad thing and you would have to skilfully retrieve it so that you could crack it between your fingernails. A horrible practice which I would regard with disgust.

Poor children, friends at school, had a great many little red spots on their necks which were flea bites. This was because they slept with no sheets. Murò sometimes had fleas, too, but dog fleas do not jump on to humans.

Papà had found bedbugs in one hotel. (Bedbugs, even more frightening than fleas, were a rarity, almost a luxury.) Papà had lifted up the pillow to find flat, black bedbugs running around on the sheet. Papà would tell the story slowly, with a mythical precision. I could see the bedbugs like a faraway miniature picture of an army of warriors protected by their shields, marching across a snowy plain.

But perhaps this had not happened in a hotel. Perhaps it had happened at the Sanctuary of Saint Anna of Vinadio where they had welcomed papà as a special guest. He had the right to a room to himself, one belonging to the administration, whilst the pilgrims were all in together.

Papà brought back *abitini* for us children from the Sanctuary. These were small squares of cloth with a picture of Saint Anna, hung on a ribbon of rough black wool, to be worn around the neck under your clothes. But we did not wear them. Papà never came back from a journey without a present. From Turin he brought us bonnets

decorated with little bunches of forget-me-nots or lily of the valley; from the mountains he brought back rare flowers like the Alpine Queen, a stiff blue flower, lace-edged like a jewel.

I had never been in a hotel in Ponte, even relatives who came were put up in the house.

However, hotels did have a place in the village then.

The most familiar one was the Europa, which occupied two floors of our house; we were friends with Lino, the owner of the Tre Colombe, because he was a hunter; then there was the Albergo del Giglio on Piazza Nuova which papà had designed and was rated de luxe.

Now even the Giglio was no longer in the luxury category. I had seen only too clearly in the guidebook that all the hotels in Ponte Stura were in the lowest category.

This had hurt me. Was the village, where papà had been loved and admired, where 'they' had been happy, where 'we had been rich', so poor then? They seemed to me diminished and humiliated. (The actual poverty of the village was for me of no more importance than any other.)

The shocking thing was that Ponte Stura had continued to exist.

Just after we had been moved to another town, I was gazing from it towards the mountains enclos-

ing the horizon and thinking it's over there... but what I really meant was it was over there...

As for our departure, I only know that it was autumn and it was raining. Moreover, mamma was giving all sorts of things away: stuffed animals which she had discovered in the house when she was first married, items of furniture, pictures which were not to be taken to the new house. Perhaps she also gave away then those precious children's newspapers of mine, thinking that since I would be going to the Ginnasio from then on, I would not enjoy them any more.

I do not remember anything else. I know that there was the war – it was the autumn of Caporetto – and that there was an air of defeat about.

We children realized that mamma did not want to talk about Ponte. She would stick out her lip, as if to express contempt. That made me miserable.

We knew that Madrina had been there, that there had been 'the ladies'. (In town mamma no longer paid calls and no longer visited the ladies.) As far as we were concerned, that was nothing. She refused to explain herself. She even maintained that Ponte Stura was not cool in the summer, that there were no shady walks.

But on one of her last days – in a respite from the pain – she suddenly said, 'How happy we were!'

That old happiness, which for mamma had seemed to

be at one with Ponte, I had only perceived in flashes and sudden gleams as a little girl. I think it was a deep current which had nourished my roots, but I was still buffeted by conflicts, uncertainties, fears. I tried to extract direction and sense from them.

The peculiar thing about this attempt is that it dates back exactly to that period. It began then. As soon as I was capable of reflecting I set about distinguishing between a past and a present. In the past I distinguished two phases: one comprised my early infancy and my parents' life, barely glimpsed in allusions; beyond that, extended another, vaguer time which contained the earlier history of episodes from my parents' childhood and youth. (Stories and fairy tales took place in something which was not time, because it was not connected to my existence or my family's.)

That chronology was full and complex and at the same time ordered into late, middle and early Empire.

The dominant feeling was that of having arrived too late, when the most important things had already happened. The marvellous period had been 'the earlier one'.

Certain festivities, which I tried to imagine, belonged to that earlier time. Mamma would hint at their enchantment in the way in which she would mention the places and the people. The names were pronounced with an expression more

ecstatic than nostalgic, yet rapidly as was her custom, so that they would appear and disappear and seem more mysterious.

Papà and mamma had once driven in a sleigh to Festiona.

I knew Festiona very well; it was a village beyond Stura hidden in the woods where one went to gather mushrooms. It was far away, not too familiar, but had nothing special about it, apart from the fact that it was damp, like all places in woods.

As I thought about their departure in the sleigh that winter evening (were there sleigh bells too?) and their return at night (with torches?) it became a remote, legendary place.

They had arrived at Festiona bridge by the main road, not along the paths they would have taken in summer. I saw the journey as an extremely long one which at the same time went by at the speed of a dream.

'Later' they no longer used the sleigh. Why didn't they repeat the journey?

'The Master is dead,' mamma would reply.

I used to know a Master, a neighbour, but I had not known the Master from Festiona; I only knew that he had a beard.

I understood from the way mamma talked about him that he must have been one of those people — they were few — whom she admired unreservedly. I could imagine something chivalrous and unpredictable about him.

Mamma admired the Master's death. For her it was an exemplary one; she always lit up when talking about it as if at the sight of something perfect.

That Master was a peasant too. He was working in the fields when he felt his hour draw near. So he sat down there and then on the edge of the field, took off his cap, made the sign of the cross and died.

Almost all the places in Ponte Stura had about them the enchantment of that earlier period.

Papà used to go hunting in the mountains before I was born, in some famous expeditions with Cino from Cornalè and other hunters. These were expeditions lasting for days from which he returned with an antelope as trophy. Papà still used to go hunting 'later' but the adventures were no longer memorable.

The names of those mountains, with their strange and mysterious sounds as in an unknown language, accompanied these expeditions with their echoes. They were called Tinibras, Nibius, Ischiator and evoked solemn and desolate arctic landscapes. Papà talked about hunting and the mountains as someone who really knew them, and promised me that we would go back there. When I was still small, he did in fact take me up a hill, known as Ortica. But the bigger mountains with their peaks were always facing us, somewhere in the distance. Not that they were unattainable only for me; no one went there any more.

★

And the 'banquets'? They were always happening: the Perosa's party, the Fedio's. Every year, in September. But mamma would make that bored face, papà did not say no but then found he had things to do, and so we did not go.

Except once! Signor Termignon had launched a balloon on the Perosa's fields, a paper balloon of the montgolfier kind which went up with a fire underneath it!

And the picnics in the Castle? Papà had taken a photograph of a group in front of the tablecloth spread out on the meadow. The maids were behind, standing. There were children too: Felicino, dressed like a girl in a bonnet of long lace in his mamma's arms, already had that self-sufficient air so comical in a baby. Idina's papà and mamma were also in the photograph, her papà with his cane under one arm and one shoulder higher than the other, eyes squinting in the light like someone used to the dark. In fact I had never seen them outside the pharmacy; at the very most they were to be found under the porch, sitting playing draughts on the parapet of the arcade high above the road.

I suspected that papà and mamma might have been to the Castle after I was born (when I was in my cradle, perhaps).

The only time which did not cause regrets was the one which was uniquely theirs.

The municipal band had welcomed mamma's

arrival as a bride in Piazza Valloria directly beneath the house. It is easy to imagine how uncomfortable she must have felt, but she had smiled, out of politeness.

That period, to me, was her most secret; and only much later did I think about how it was part of her and perhaps only then when she was dying.

But in Ponte Stura I simply wanted to find mamma as she was then, to forget the end. I have avoided, if I could, saying that mamma was dead.

It was also true that at the end she went back to being so like she was in Ponte: white and slender, with a rather proud smile, shy (of other people) and tender and ironic towards us.

For papà, in one particular sense, the valley was his native one. He had been put out to a wet nurse in Rialpo, a village halfway up a mountain an hour from Ponte, and had stayed there until he was six. The mystery of that long stay did not arouse our curiosity when we were children, and we never knew the reason behind it.

Papà loved his nanny very much; she was already old when she came to see him in Ponte. In the photograph which my father took of her standing on the wooden steps outside her house in Rialpo, that little woman with her hands clasped in front of her is as grave and modest as the saints of old.

She was already dead when papà married, and mamma learned about her from Madrina.

Nanny would come from Rialpo to Ponte to see papà. She would look out for him in the piazza or in the centre of the town and watch him from a distance without making herself noticed, so as not to disturb him. Then she would happily go back to Rialpo without having talked to him.

Such humility enchanted mamma.

All we were told in our childhood about the story of their love affair was that while papà was attending the institute, he did practical work in grandfather's office, and they often handed him my mother, who was a little girl, to take for a walk along the Ramparts (papà was fifteen years older than her). Papà used to say that he had decided then to marry her. This news left us unmoved, while mamma, when questioned, stuck out her lip.

But once, mamma said something very strange.

In the dining room hung a big picture of some fishermen hauling in their nets; their trousers were rolled up to the knee and they wore red and black caps on their heads. Vesuvius smoked in the background. The whole thing was leaden. The painting had been a wedding present; it was not much admired as a painting, but it was precious to mamma because it reminded her of Naples where she had been on a journey with papà.

Once while she was looking at that painting, mamma said to someone, I don't remember who, but it was in Ponte (in the other houses we moved

to the painting had vanished), that she had fallen in love with papà in Posillipo.

How was that possible? Fallen in love after she was already married? I was used to fairy stories and tales in which thwarted love affairs ended in marriage. Love in fairy stories, abstract and cold but also fatal and overwhelming, for me shed no light on the feelings which accompanied it.

Mamma added that it had been 'because' (someone falling in love for a reason was also something which was unheard of) papà forgot to eat – they were in a restaurant – while he was looking at the sea and the fishermen pulling in their nets.

Papà standing as if he were enchanted and gazing with a serious, thoughtful air was familiar to me; I had seen him gazing like that at paintings, at the mountains; I had also understood that since mamma prized beauty above everything, whoever loved it became dear to her for that very reason.

She did not love beautiful things, but she admired certain fleeting moments in nature. Mamma's gaze was very different from papà's – it was rapid. Afterwards, she would seem happy. She would lower her eyes as if she had seen something that other people did not see.

II

I went out on to the road in front of the hotel and breathed in the air. That air is enough for me. It's my air.

In no other valley, near or far, can I find that air. I recognize it from its delicate smell of milk, straw, bitter herbs. But at first it is not a smell.

My need for that air is never exhausted. I think of it when far away and it nourishes me. It torments me, too, as something unattainable but also fatal. For me it is the past, everything that has happened. For me it is also 'them' and I am included in 'them'. The consciousness of them and of me, if not truly distinct then, is even less so now.

★

The long white house behind the hotel was the College of the Immaculate Virgin. Every day mamma took me there and came to fetch me. As I did not have to make the journey on my own, the College did not seem far away as it always did later.

In *Thursday*, the children's newspaper which mamma had read as a girl (the papers were bound in one big volume), there was a long serial entitled 'When I was at College'. The papers were yellowed, the colour of the courtyard in the College. I had not read the story, but I knew the illustrations by heart. I was full of pity for the boy in the kepi (his uniform was that of Moncalieri College). In one little picture he had leaned one arm against the wall and was crying with his head on the other.

When Uncle Andrea was a boy at college he had been beaten until they drew blood. Mamma said that when she met the pale, ceremonious priest she would feel revulsion.

She had been at college in Turin herself. But she had left home willingly; her mother had died.

Her College lay on the other side of the Po, and owned an entire hill. The boarders used to walk under the long covered walks or play croquet. It was a College of French nuns. 'Jamais le couteau à la bouche!' mamma would say at the table, imitating Mother Mathilda.

The boarders at the College of the Immaculate Virgin were also orphans; they were poor and were called Dependants.

The nuns dressed like the nuns at the Nursery School but they were not so friendly; indeed they had a severe, distant air.

I knew that I was privileged in going to the Immaculate Virgin; all the other children went to the Nursery. Even my younger sister, was sent years later to the Nursery School.

I knew that everything my parents did for me was unique and important. Not that they would say so. However, I had observed that in general mamma preferred avoiding places where everybody went, doing things that everybody did.

It was winter, everything was buried under snow. Mamma had dressed in dark clothes and wore a fur hat and muff; she looked like a skater in a fashion catalogue. Her gloved hand was warm.

Mamma was silent, but she would smile with her dark shining eyes.

I let go of her hand and climbed the few steps feeling I had lost my bearings. I knew that she was watching me, but I did not turn round.

Inside was a presence which would not melt ice, but absorbed all my attention – my teacher. Her name was Sister Nazzarena. She was tall, or at least seemed so to me, and her face was oval. Mamma said that she was beautiful, and that her name was like her. Mamma thus suggested a reason for my admiration of her. Even the writing styles which Sister Nazzarena taught had a perfection which

seemed to emanate from her. I tried to imitate those light, slanting, wavy strokes. I suffered from my incapacity to do so.

Later teachers, except for one in the third year who was an exception, held no fascination. Not that I thought so then. But I did not forget Sister Nazzarena and mamma sometimes took me to see her. She must have been shy, in fact she did not talk, but smiled uncertainly; I would take the sacred image from her cold hands.

Until the teacher in the third year, there was no longer that mystical feeling of admiration, but by then I had already had experience of my infatuations and, in a certain sense, passions.

Mamma had intuited that silent worship of mine and respected it. That was also a privilege not to be repeated for my little sister. She in turn adored a nun in the Nursery School, but it seemed funny and they laughed about it at home. Was that cruel? My little sister was treated quite differently from me, though not with a greater severity. She herself called for different treatment, something gayer, lighter.

I was the only one to be ashamed of her. I felt irritated, though certainly not jealous. It was obvious that she was not taken seriously. They had taken on a wet nurse at home for me and then a governess; my little sister had been sent out to a wet nurse in the country; they had not done anything exceptional for her.

On winter afternoons, if it were sunny, we would go to see my little sister. The road was a slippery snowy path into which your feet sank and someone held my hand. We found my little sister ensconced in a little rustic high chair on the dry floor, screwing her eyes up against the sun. There was the smell of milk and stables, mamma was worried about the flies.

I found my little sister a bit repugnant at that moment, because of the smells of bed and dog basket all mixed together; but I did not know that she would be coming home.

When she did come home, it was clear that she was placid, but I think I suffered from the disturbed silence. I used to talk to myself, and mamma let me do that without interrupting me.

My little sister had a rag doll dressed like a Tyrolean, which she would take hold of by the arms and shake, saying endlessly, 'Gee-go, go-gee.' Everyone thought this little song charming.

When she went to the Nursery, she would talk constantly about it. Everything was of such importance: her basket, her egg, the pastille the headmistress gave her.

The nun she liked best was not beautiful; she had a pale smooth face and was nicknamed The Smooth Teacher. I was ashamed of this name, I thought it indecent.

I found my little sister indecent because she was fat; it was then that I realized I was thin. Mamma

was anxious about me because I did not want to eat. My little sister would eat everything; I only liked fried potatoes. I hated milk; my little sister loved milk, even the disgusting skin.

Everyone wanted to kiss her. She let them sit her on their knees and kiss her. I thought she lacked dignity.

I found kisses repulsive because they left your face all wet or they prickled. Mamma and I were the same about that, she could not bear kisses either.

Everyone admired my little sister's enormous eyes. She would calmly open them wide, look directly into people's faces. I usually looked sideways, mainly from boredom and distraction or purposely to avoid looking people in the face if they were looking at me. I felt discomfort, even fear of excessive intimacy; faces were too marked, full of protuberances, hairs, blemishes. I only liked looking at beautiful people who belonged to another species, like characters in the illustrations in books.

I did not want to be scrutinized. Perhaps because I was quiet, I appeared thoughtful. 'She's observant', said Signor Termignon. It was a definition which became famous and was repeated year after year. Signor Termignon, the brother of the one who had launched the balloon at the Perosa party, was a tinsmith and scholar. I can see him now, tall, bald, declaiming poetry.

I did not know exactly what he meant, but I

understood it to be a secret sign of solidarity on his part. Signor Termignon suffered a great deal from not having had the opportunity to study, and he had a fraternal intuition for those he considered contemplative types.

I was anxious to be taken seriously. Both of us little girls had our hair cut in a fashionable page-boy style. My little sister had a beautifully smooth fringe, while mine was always awry. In one place, my hair would not stay flat. They told me it was called the wheel of fortune, but I realized that they wanted to console me. It irritated me that they felt sorry for me, what did my fringe really matter?

My little sister amused everyone with her ingenuous remarks. I felt embarrassed for her and would have liked to make her shut up. They had asked her what the war was – this was during the Great War – and she had answered that it was an iron bar. I reminded my sister about this later; she laughed and added that she had imagined that iron bar placed on a seat in the mountains.

I had said that at school the caretaker put ink in the inkwells; she thought that the caretaker was a bird who put the ink in by dipping its beak into the inkwells. I was amazed by her ability to imagine such things, but I did not appreciate it, because I thought her irrational.

She embodied everything I disliked; compliance, credulity. I certainly did not ill-treat her, but I did have a sort of instinct for corrupting her. Once I

led her by the hand to steal some sweets that mamma kept in a box in a drawer. Not that I was even greedy; I just remember the subtle pleasure of leading the innocent into doing something wrong.

It was only after my little sister was born that I discovered my wickedness. I felt remorse because of it and even fear, because it seemed to me an instinct impossible to overcome.

Not that it was really remorse which had the upper hand, it was compassion. And only on the occasions when I acted as persecutor. I felt that when they found her charming, adults had the idea almost that she was like a little animal and that her docile nature put her at other people's mercy.

I secretly felt compassion for many creatures: for old people, the poor, for dogs and children who were beaten, even for flowers trampled underfoot; but compassion for a creature so close was almost unbearable to me. My intolerance also grew from that rebellion.

On the whole, Piazza Nuova is the same, empty. The ancient chestnut trees enclose it on two sides. It is named after a partisan now, but history of what happened afterwards does not exist for me in Ponte. For me, Ponte is immutable. Like that little man over there, at the bottom of the square.

A little man just like him stood there then as well, posed almost in front of that tall house. (It once had Gymnasium written on it; it belonged to

the barracks.) I always saw him like that, from a distance. It wasn't that he disappeared when you passed near him, you just didn't pay any more attention to him. Even in old postcards there was always the little man on that spot.

Ponte Stura is unchanging, just like that man. Was it the same then too? Perhaps it's because things do not remain unchanged without decaying that Ponte Stura is slowly but surely continuing to die.

But that comforted me. I dream about the immutability which constitutes its real existence: mine.

III

I felt, as a little girl, an anxiety similar to the one I feel now when I have to cross the village on my own. It was not that the unknown had made me anxious; on the contrary, it was the fact that people knew me and so I would be greeted, questioned and so forth. I suppose I was afraid of just such an attack on my freedom. But now? The real reason is the same one as then; I want to avoid people.

My fear of people could become pathological, lead me into a kind of mean-spiritedness. Therein lay the dramas of Sunday afternoons. What did other people do? I did not know, but I would have liked to know. However, I did loathe the way mamma and papà unfailingly chose to take a walk

up to Stura.

I would feel a sense of defeat; it was almost that, in making such a choice, the family voluntarily excluded themselves, made themselves inferior. Sunday afternoons in Stura were part of that period when my parents no longer frequented society.

We would dress up for this walk in rough clothes suitable for the country. I had to put on walking shoes because the paths and fields along the Stura were more or less flooded. My little sister was around by then, but everything always went well for her. She would placidly let them get her ready and I would not even dream of sharing my torment with her, she would not have understood.

I said nothing, but perhaps papà was observing me. I had only a suspicion that he understood. While I was sulking, I was inclined to follow him about. He would say to me, putting the money in my hand, 'Go to Aglietta's to buy *La Stampa*.' To run an errand for papà was usually a joy, something to be proud of, but at times like that it was a heavy burden, the height of humiliation. Clutching the money, I would go out the back way so as not to be seen by the girls from the Europa, then run through the deserted arcades, heart in mouth. I would walk lightly and quickly – not quite running – but the nails in my shoes made a sort of scratchy noise. I was frightened of meeting people, especially school friends, or worse, Felicino Calvi. He would have looked at my shoes, would have

contemptuously called them 'alpine-grass style' and asked smiling in his peculiar way, 'Are you going mountain climbing?' My humiliation at that point had reached such a level that if Felicino were to have taunted me like that I would have been ashamed of the mountains.

The mountains, for me as much as for mamma, meant beauty. People's beauty enchanted but also disturbed me, while in the mountains, with their winds and their silences, I could lose myself. The fact that there might be people who did not like them did not displease me, actually I was pleased about it, for mine was an exclusive love.

It was not that I lost sight of it at that point, but my truer and purer passion was as if overshadowed by another petty, ephemeral one.

I do not think it was altogether trivial, however; there was in it too the pain of other people's intruding, as there is in jealousy.

I would have liked to spend Sundays other than by the Stura. (Besides, the fields along the river were very different from the exciting paths up in the mountains.)

But I suspected that there were meetings – even at the Club – pastimes of which I knew nothing, and for just that reason thought important. I would not imagine them only because I lacked a subject, but also because my feeling was abstract, composed of a vague and almost petulant irritation. That was perhaps its only content.

Papà and mamma were obviously happy with their own company, they were not curious about other people's lives, they even avoided them. This then was my first rebellion against my parents' contented life.

Anxiety about not having the proper clothes goes back to those distant years (before my little sister).

Children in fancy dress would come to the house with their mothers, so that papà could take their photographs. They would wear sparkling costumes, with shawls over their shoulders, cymbals in their hands. The little girls came as gypsies. One was Maria Lazzaro, whom I admired very much. I admired her for two things in particular: because she was an orphan and because she was very beautiful. She had big sad dark eyes, and an aristocratic air which made her seem more of a lady than a little girl. Her presence made the party seem more important, and so I was all the more indignant at being excluded from it.

However, they did propose that I should be included in the photograph; but this invitation exasperated me because it took no account of my unpreparedness and made me begin sobbing again.

The ladies then got hold of some stuff from mamma, bits of material, shawls; they fixed a kind of yellow silk turban with pins for me and swathed me up to the armpits. They said that I was to be an Arab.

Full of disapproval for this improvised costume, I agreed to join the group, standing on a stool behind all the others so that only my head could be seen. In the middle of the other children who were serious and composed, I look angry and out of focus – my eyes flashing and shining with tears – full of humiliation and bitterness.

I felt miserable because of a dress the whole day of my first Communion. I knew that mine was the most elegant by far, made of Chantilly lace (it was the name of a cream, too) but according to fashion (that of Turin) it was too short above the knee, which was the reason for my shame. The other little girls had long starched dresses. My mother really did not care about being like other people!

In the photographs which papà took of me that day, my pointed knees are showing sticking out beneath my dress; there is a look on my face, usually preoccupied or distracted, which instead is direct, almost insolent, with a forced, tight-lipped smile.

It was, vanity notwithstanding, an important matter. The vanity was really nothing.

For another carnival I also had a costume, that of a *Ciociara*. It was of lilac silk with a waistcoat of black material, a little velvet bodice, and a handkerchief positioned flat on my head with the folds falling down on to my shoulders. Yet I was not in the least bit pleased with it, just disappointed and bored. (The parties which I had dreamed about so much were as unbearable to me as they were to mamma.)

31

Since the other children seemed confident to me, I believed my lack of confidence to be an inferiority – only, however, in my relationship with the world. Inwardly I was happy to be the way I was; in fact, when calm, I would consider myself superior.

However, I didn't feel my superiority to be a privilege, but almost a fatal disgrace. It was unimportant to me in one sense; in fact it did not help on the occasions when I did feel humiliated.

IV

Walking down the cobbled street, which I had taken to avoid the arcades, I now wondered if it were the same one where Ciota had led me by the hand to visit her parents.

Ciota's mother, tall and thin with a sharp profile, would come in silently with a little bundle of sticks she had gathered from the pathways. She wore a kerchief knotted under her long chin even in the house. She kept her lips pursed tightly shut and would give you sidelong looks. As she seemed haughty, she overawed me. I was afraid she did not like my being there and felt abashed.

Ciota's father was big and jolly with a white moustache, a trombone player in the municipal

band. So I found it natural that papà said his name was a musician's – Wagner. Ciota's father was dealing with the Town Hall to restore his proper name which had been written down incorrectly in the Register as Waghen. (I thought Waghen Ciota sounded better.)

I could not find Ciota's house which had a steep outside staircase. A little sister of Ciota's, Teresin, had fallen down those stairs and been struck dumb.

The dumb children had a language which consisted of frantic gestures. In Ponte there was a girl whom everyone called The Mute. She would gesticulate and look into your eyes making little squawking noises. The children would shout out, 'The Mute! The Mute!' and flee. I pretended to stay calm, even though I felt cold and my skin crawled. You would usually see her at the Castle, because she was the caretaker's daughter; her figure, which was not unattractive, in fact beautiful but frightening, lent a further fascination to that solitary place.

The many so-called lunatics in Ponte were also dumb: dwarfish, afflicted with goitre, some hairy right up to their eyes like animals, others hairless with wrinkled pale skin like the rind of white figs. They would greet you with joyful gestures, outlining some urgent conversation with their mumbling. You would not try to understand, you would return the greeting. I looked at them more willingly than at other people, because their eyes did not probe.

But Teresin was not a halfwit. She was sweet, and smiling. Yet she had big protruding eyes and was bent, as if she had no bones. Her hands were so soft they seemed made of dough. I felt a bit disgusted, because they seemed dead to me, dead, but warm. Teresin also belonged to that other half of the world (as night is the other side of day).

I had always seen these strange creatures and not been surprised. Actually I thought most adults looked disgusting. There were even animals which provoked revulsion. I distinguished a whole scale of beings who corresponded to a varied and contrasting order. Even beauty, if it were the kind which enchanted, was a sort of monstrosity, insofar as it was unnatural.

Only mamma's beauty, or my aunts' or cousins', seemed right to me.

Did neutral people exist? For example, Ciota, was she beautiful or ugly? I did not think about it. Her face was irregular, nose crooked, freckled, mouth large and mocking, eyes teasing. Was not beauty colourless when opposed to that?

A little earlier I had rediscovered in a wall covered with flat tiles the door to the Nursery. Behind that door was a gravel-covered expanse, a colonnade and a terrace. I had also been there to learn to sing. The sisters in the Nursery would prepare little girls in the primary schools for the Corpus Domini procession. Lined up in rows, we would sing 'Pange

35

lingua' and 'Mira il tuo popolo'. (They were called praises.)

Those choruses rather intoxicated me; the procession excited me too. The women's nasal voices alternated with or drowned out our own. We advanced slowly, in a smell of fallen roses.

Mamma would send me, but she did not come herself. She disliked ceremonies, even religious ones. However, for me, these were the only joyful moments of religion, while thoughts about God and eternal life would plunge me into darkness, into endless questioning.

Mamma would make us say our prayers and would add her own little prayers to the Pater and the Ave Maria, which were rather touching and not very serious, like 'Jesus, bless my little house, send your blessed angels to watch over our peace, health, your holy blessing'. (It also lacked logic; what did it mean to watch over your blessing?)

Everything I knew about religion I had learned from the Catechism. The responses which you had to know by heart and were spoken in a singsong manner were either obvious and repeated the same things as the questions, or they were obscure. There was just one of them on which I had based my whole religion. That was 'God in heaven, on earth and in every place'. I often repeated it to myself and it gave me a feeling of enormous security and sweetness, almost bliss, even if it did not always seem true to me.

A big question was the one about original sin, the fatal nature of which caused me anguish, as it was so irremediable. I suspected they were hiding something from me there as well, just as they did in the mysterious realm to do with birth.

But in the choirs and processions, I felt myself growing lighter, calmer, I was no longer afraid of difficulties. I even felt a sense – new and all-consuming – of devotion.

I would scatter the rose petals, taking them in handfuls from the basket. I did not care about the waste (as I would have done in normal circumstances), I even had the impression of drawing on an abundance which had no limits.

Next to the Nursery there should have been another wall, very high and black, in whose cracks grew maidenhair fern and strange violet flowers. At that dark point in the street it seemed as if you were in a grotto. I could not find the wall again and it seemed to me as if the street now came out earlier into Piazza Valloria.

Before looking at the house I turned around to get the street in its new perspective; in reality to delay seeing the house for a moment. On the gently sloping street another eternal image of Ponte Stura appeared before me against the light – the outline of a cripple.

You could see cripples, the lame and disabled in their abundance in Ponte Stura. They belonged to

a less wretched species than the monsters. For certain people (young girls), being a cripple had something almost charming about it. Suntina, for example, had a very pretty little face; she would laugh wrinkling up her nose and showing her little teeth. She talked very volubly with passionate and at the same time comical gestures. Her speeches would seem mad to me but in the end, her laughter showed that she had wanted to tease.

Hugging her arms about herself to her thin chest, she would say, 'If only I could have one all to myself!' Her passion was for little babies, still at the breast. 'I'd rather have a baby in my bed than a sweetheart!' She prided herself on being the only one who could make them laugh with her little screeches and cries.

I would watch her in amazement and believed that there was a relationship between her extravagance and the fact that she was crippled. When she moved, her long earrings swung against her neck.

Once I tried in secret to imitate her lopsided walk. I wanted to know how it felt, how you would see things, if things danced. In fact they did dance.

Ciota had caught me at it and had shouted, 'You should not make fun of the afflicted!' I had not defended myself; I had believed the imitation really was a mockery and felt remorse because of it.

The cripple was advancing slowly. He stopped, hardly noticing me, then went swaying on again like an insect which has scarcely been disturbed.

He caught up with me, passed alongside me and began to climb the stony slope furrowed just as it used to be by thin rivulets of rain.

His pear-shaped head ended in rough white curls, his shoulders sloped, his feet trailed wide apart, his clothes were threadbare and faded, as limp as if they were empty and in his hand was a bundle of dry twigs.

Suddenly I knew who he was. Battistino Viola. His father, the notary, had taken over our lodgings when we left Ponte forty years ago.

His decline was not unforeseen, nor unexpected in Ponte, yet I was astonished. I also felt remorse, as if it were because of my neglect that the notary's son had become a beggar.

The cripple went under the arcade and seemed to go silently back into hiding.

V

The house is at the top of a small, lopsided piazza, just where you arrive in the village, at the end of a long climb. In all the postcards of Ponte Stura with panoramic views it's the most visible building: long and white, with a long line of windows.

The fact that the house dominated everything was a privilege I accepted as natural, even as if it were inseparable from myself. It arose from an undefined reality, but a precise one. There were other privileges; in the postcard album (which I used to leaf through with delight) there was one entitled *Foro Romano*. Two (or three) fluted, elegant columns which tapered at the top against a fragment of cornice stood out against a confused

background. Those two columns 'were me'. That was also quite naturally true for me, and I never asked for confirmation. I recognized those signs, like someone who is of noble birth learns to recognize their coat of arms.

Except that mine was an original, personal birthright.

The house seemed beautiful to me, but that sense of dominion had nothing to do with wealth.

Besides, as far as wealth was concerned, I had no doubts, except that I suspected that my parents did not consider it sufficiently important, and not only that, almost despised it. I would hear them making fun of certain wealthy and greedy people; for example they would laugh at the mayor who would keep his family in the dark in the evenings to save electricity. They pitied other people who were preoccupied with money as if those with little were happier, more fortunate even. I worried about it. 'Papà,' I had asked, 'do we have a lot of money?' 'Yes, indeed!' he replied. 'All in small change!' I did not laugh, the joke made me feel uneasy.

Aunt Carlotta used to tell a story about me when I was small; seeing me thoughtful once she had asked, 'What are you thinking about?' 'Money,' I had replied. When my aunt brought this up, it put everyone at home in a good mood and they would tease me.

I had no doubts about belonging to a wealthy class. Poor people were respectful towards papà and

mamma, the wealthy treated them as equals. Yet in the way I felt, I was not contemptuous of poverty nor did the certainty of being wealthy make me arrogant. In this I was like my parents who were equally courteous, in fact, friendly with everyone.

I even suffered from the privilege of being rich. Ciota was holding my hand, it was evening and we were walking along under the dark arcades. Perhaps she had come to take me to Catechism; we were talking in fact about eternal life. Ciota said, 'Rich people can't go to Heaven, because they've already got Heaven on earth.'

She had delivered this judgement in a serious, almost reluctant tone of voice; I think she was aware that she was revealing a truth which was kept quiet out of deceit and hypocrisy. She was certainly implying that they do not tell this to the children of the rich.

I was crushed. What were we guilty of? I remembered Adam's sin, which it had always seemed unfair to be involved in, and I was even more disheartened.

If I ever talked about Ponte with my sister, we would still say 'when we were rich'. Because she had believed it too.

When we were grown up, we had learned from mamma that papà earned a hundred lire a month and that we had left Ponte because they would not give him a rise in salary.

When I heard these revelations I was miserable, for a little while, on account of my father's humiliation; but then the positive picture of Ponte would return to dominate me, and with it the privilege of our wealth.

A special class of person existed, people who were pathetic and a bit ridiculous, who they called *travets*. My terror was not that we might belong to it, but that someone in our family could be included. I'd realised that a *travet* was an unfortunate creature who wanted to impress, while my parents, on the contrary, had the opposite failing, they could not care less about impressing.

In one family group which papà had photographed on the road to the Castle my uncle, the doctor, instead of positioning himself like the others, either sitting on the stones or standing in front of the lens, had sat down, as a joke or to be contrary, at the edge of the road so that you saw him hunched over in profile, at the others' feet. What was even funnier was that on his head he was wearing a bowler, what we called a risotto. Mamma laughed and laughed when she saw it, then said, 'He looks like a *travet*!'

VI

The house porch has three deep arches, the one in the middle, the tallest, is roughly Gothic.

I climbed up to the piazza once more and it was my turn to enter the porch, faded now and empty. The two wings had always been different. On the right, where the entrance to the inn used to be, the roof and walls were painted. A travelling artist had covered them with frescoes in Pompeian style, a reed trellis around which vines were entwined and in the intervening spaces, birds in vivid colours.

The same painter had painted the sign outside. Violets and gigantic daisies were interlaced amongst the letters, HOTEL EUROPA. I found the disproportion embarrassing.

The painter made my mother a present of a picture painted on tin, which was then kept in the kitchen. A hand designed with oval muscles (in Byzantine style) held out a bouquet of pansies. On the white background, was an inscription in gold: Homage to the Betrothed. At the bottom was the signature – Pericles. It was a Greek name.

Mamma liked to have such things given to her by her queer casual admirers. They would gaze at her entranced, and forget to thank her for the alms she gave them.

Then mamma got rid of the picture. She would not keep things, souvenirs. If she came across them and they seemed of no importance to anyone, she would burn them or throw them away. I suffered from her indifference; I did not understand it.

The other wing of the porch was always filled with big steaming washtubs, the never-ending washing from the hotel. You would glimpse a steamy interior in semi-darkness through an open door, the laundry room. The air smelled of lye. In the middle of the steam, the hotel-keeper's daughters, faces red as moons, would call out to me joyfully. Why did they have to call out to me? Perhaps because I would go running past, school bag in hand, without seeing them.

The passage leading to the stairs has always been dark. From there the dark staircase descended to the cellar, where you had to have a lighted candle

to walk in the damp penetrating smell. A man had once shut his fussy complaining dog up in there with an onion. The dog had ended up eating the onion, so that he would not die from starvation. (They told me the story to make me eat, and I imagined what had happened down there.)

The first flight of stairs was easy, you could take it at a run. The landing was always strewn with straw and small twigs; there was the coming and going of the stable-boys, the smell of the stables. When do smells evaporate?

The cobwebs have grown thicker, the patches of saltpetre have spread. Through the grating you can see grass growing tall between the cobblestones, stinging nettles at the foot of the wall.

The second flight had a face. The eyes were two black holes under one step; another just underneath in the middle was the nose, then another, the mouth. It was vaguely frightening. I would take the steps two at a time. Along the sides in a groove in the wall was a wooden handrail, which to me seemed a sign of luxury.

The first floor was solemn and a bit mysterious. The air was heavy, filled with suspense. The very high ceiling and the space, as large as a room, got its light from the deep passageway giving on to the courtyard.

The light comes to an end on one side, in front of the intense darkness of a second passageway with

a dead end. There was a door there which was never opened. Where did it once lead, who was it for?

Cavaliere Mattei's door, a warm horse-chestnut colour, shone on the big bright landing.

You would rarely cross that threshold. The interior of the house was dark and shining like the door, and a golden frieze ran around the breakfast-room ceiling.

In spring mamma would make up a bunch of asparagus from the kitchen garden and tie it with a silk ribbon. I carried it, accompanied by Ciota, as a gift to the Cavaliere. While you waited for a biscuit you could gaze at the golden frieze.

Cavaliere Mattei's maidservant was elegant and her hands smelled of vanilla like a lady's hands. When Ciota used to meet her on the stairs she would look at her in her scornful way then say to me, 'Did you see her hat?'

The lady not only wore a hat on Sundays but a feather boa too. And Ciota would sneer, 'Do you see? They don't even wear a scarf like us!'

Us meant the domestic servants, but they? Ciota's conversations often contained allusions which left me puzzled.

The Cavaliere was a widower, his sons at military school. He was a lawyer and secretary at the muni-cipal offices, and so was a colleague of papà. He was extraordinarily imposing; fleshy, upright, his chest puffed out, he had a grey moustache overflowing

his mouth and spoke in a deep voice. If you met him he would say something teasing, but he never came into the house.

Only one summer something new happened. A cousin of the Cavaliere came, a dark-skinned girl with large eyebrows. I was almost as much in love with her as I had been with Sister Nazzarena.

Elsa was not beautiful, but she paid me attention without ever letting her mind wander like other ladies or cousins. She even invented games for me. She promised that she would hold a 'party' for just the two of us 'with flowers'. What did she mean? The word party was already heavy with mystery for me, and how could it be with flowers?

My wait was full of anxiety and delight. Elsa really had picked bunches of hawthorn and all kinds of wild flowers to decorate the balcony over-looking the courtyard with shoots and garlands. I felt a sort of ecstasy. I stayed seated in silence on the balcony for the entire afternoon.

Many years later they told me a story about Elsa, of persecution by her family, and finally the Mental Hospital.

I thought about her leaning against the wall opposite the dark little passage, just as black as it was then and still rather disturbing; I thought that I was still in love with Elsa Mattei.

The tiled floor of the long entrance hall is as

uneven as ever; the tiles are concave, worn away, here and there they have come loose. They are no looser or more worn than they once were. I recognize them one by one, as I placed my sandalled feet on them. Only the dragging shuffle of the cripple and the light step of his old sisters (if they are still alive) have passed this way since.

When the hotel was there, a great deal of coming and going went on: soldiers, boys in service and the daughters from the Europa.

Railings give on to a balcony, at the side of which is the window with the large grille, called the Captain's window.

My little sister had put her head between the railings and did not know how to get herself out, so she screamed. An officer came up smiling and freed her without hurting her. But every time she saw him afterwards, she would start screaming. (Later, though, she confessed that in the middle of her tears and terror she had observed the captain; he wore an elegant black jacket with braided fastenings and he smelled pleasantly of cigarettes and eau-de-Cologne.)

There were always captains in the house, guests of the Europa, engaged in turn to the young ladies. The two eldest were fat and blonde with cheeks the colour of pink powder, and they wore their hair parted in two puffed-out wings. They used to sing on the balcony:

When in May
The cherries are black.

The younger one was dark-haired and prettier, her name was Lisa.

We had acquired a new dog, when Murò was old, a puppy called Lisa, in fact, and mamma told us not to let the young lady hear us calling to the dog. The puppy's real name was Linda, and we had changed it because it had been the name of one of Madrina's daughters who had died young.

Lisa from the Europa really did marry a captain. He went far away from Ponte Stura and later she learned that he was dead.

When the captains went off to war, the young ladies from the Europa grew patriotic; they would brandish tricoloured cockades and announce proudly from high up on the balconies, that they had had letters from the front, from their fiancés.

Now the last flight was in front of me like a wall, the steep narrow stairs like rocks to be scaled. How did the cripple manage?

The white light from the roofs and sky invades the hallway. The door has a square knocker, like Cavaliere Mattei's, but duller, more homely. At one side of the door hangs a garnet-red cord with a big tassel on the end. I did not remember it, but I recognized it; it's the old doorbell.

I don't know if it's gratitude or panic I feel; they are mixed, I think.

Suddenly, the door opens. The cripple appears, half-alarmed, half-irritated. I excuse myself, 'I was looking at the house... ' and I say my name. The cripple lights up; his smile, bristling with big crooked teeth transforms his sharp face and makes it sweet and loveable. 'Come in, come in,' he says.

I had not expected that. I had not even wanted it; I was so sure that I would never have dared disturb the old people, the by now extremely ancient Misses Viola (I had not remembered the cripple) who had always been solitary and suspicious. I had not dared want it; I wanted it too much.

I went down the four steps almost fearfully. Were there entrances like this in other houses? I wondered how I would have behaved as an embarrassed child, and suddenly that seemed strange to me.

You would see visitors from below, which lent them grandeur, almost majesty. I used to see old Tibus like that. Barefoot, thin, in dust-coloured rags which were too big for him, with his gap-toothed smile both joyful and malicious. He would move his thin hands skilfully, describing how he had caught a snake. They said that he ate snakes; yet the admiration was mixed with a certain dismay. Tibus used to heal himself by applying cobwebs to his wounds; mamma was afraid for him and beseeched him to wash himself. The cobwebs did, however, heal him.

Tibus used to carry about a mess tin full of fish

or frogs; he also carried yellow powder to polish silverware. He never wanted payment, so mamma used to put the money in his pocket. Then he would sing to thank her.

The corridor is dark, lit by one lamp, with a glass window at the end, the floor is laid with red and grey tiles.

Papà's guns and field glasses hung on the walls then, the alpenstock (ending in a deer antler) and the fishing rods leaning against them. The cripple walks in front of me, he really does mean to take me around the house. Which room will he start with? At the end of the corridor on the left, mamma and papà's room. He goes to open the shutters. In that corner was the *armoire à glace*.

Mamma was standing in front of the mirror, wearing a brown velvet suit, long, soft and smooth to the touch. (I don't have a memory for clothes; so why do I remember those?) Rinette, the French girl who looked after me said, '*Que vous êtes mince!*' (How did I manage to remember it?)

I am in Rinette's arms and I'm looking at mamma in the mirror. Mamma pins a brooch on her large, feathered hat. Her eyes shine in the darkness; I remember them as sad, even if her face were smiling. (All of her is in that mystery, which I faithfully mirrored as a child, but without disturbing myself with it. Later I explained it, denied it but always found it again.)

In that same mirror she gazed at herself on one of her last days. We tried to turn her aside from it, so that she would not see how thin she was. Her fleshless face surfaced in the mirror, yet she was always mysteriously beautiful. She tidied her hair with one of her deft gestures, and her intense look was as if redoubled in intensity in the mirror.

'I remember her, your mamma. She had curly black hair. She was very ... very ... '

He didn't manage to say beautiful. Out of respect, I think.

VII

I'm leaning over the little balcony with the railing.
The ancient wood, furrowed, dried up, has become
like cork. The varnish (that varnish!) has penetrated
the wood, washed and washed again, dried and
redried.

I leaned out. Beyond the road stretched the slate
roofs of the village below. It's called Borgo Sottano.
It seems deserted, no smoke is rising from the
chimneys as it did then.

I look for Cinto the blacksmith's shop. The steps
in front of the door have disappeared, the door
itself has been walled up; you can see the whitish
traces of it.

Why did I love looking at Cinto's shop so much?

I would catch a glimpse of the smoke from the forge, hear the hammer strike the anvil, surely the most exalting sound it is possible to hear.

From the window looking out on to the piazza you could see another smithy; this one belonged to Cilin, Cinto's brother. The ringing of their anvils would reply rhythmically to each other and filled the mornings with a festive, joyful air. (Why the mornings? Perhaps it was summer and in the morning I was at home, leaning over the balcony.)

Cinto and Cilin were brothers who were enemies; one was good, the other bad. Cinto, the good brother, would come and ask Cilin something; Cilin would shout, especially if he had been drinking, and chase him away. I would see Cinto, thin and a bit bent, turn away from him crestfallen, shaking his head.

Some mornings I would be woken by a confused, yet musical noise. It was a chorus of bleating, and it meant that there was a fair or it was market day. Sheep and lambs had disappeared two by two up the ramp under the house. The bleating seemed very close; the house seemed smaller and more compact. There was a holiday feeling.

A big cobbled ramp led to the Hotel Belvedere. Drunken songs issued from there in the evenings; above this background rose the thumps of a game of *morra*, where one player guesses the number of fingers held up by another; voices that were raucous sang songs which disturbed and made me

sad, though I liked listening to them more than the romantic airs and melodies of the operas on the phonograph, as they issued strangely, from a sadness which was mine.

The soldiers sang in voices which were fresher and not so melancholy. They would sing:

Blonde,
Faithless,
Follower of Garibaldi.

The Belvedere had covered terraces which looked over the main road above the sheer rock wall.

The balustrade was made of squared-off tree trunks set in squat newel posts of tiles topped with a stone. The wind would blow through these airy, luminous rooms.

A path ran behind along the edge of the rock, bordered with pansies and artemisia. These flowers, forever buffeted by the wind, had something strange and particularly beautiful about them. Tavia made a little bunch of them for mamma and added mint and basil to it; the herbs became different, precious, mixed in with the flowers in this way.

Tavia from the Belvedere was tiny, clean and quick. Trume was big and slow, with almost no neck, and always wore a dirty white apron. They were different yet alike; perhaps because they had the same colouring, they seemed like bright watercolours. Tavia's hair, like her eyelashes, shone

like silk, faintly rosy; Trume had little piggy eyes, so meek – or hypocritical? – that looking at him you would have no idea of what he could be capable of at times.

We would hear shouts with prolonged echoes, the noise of blows and Toni and Vigin's stifled screams coming from the house. I would run out on to the balcony and sometimes saw them, hands over their heads. They did not run away.

Mamma, with shining eyes opened wide, would press her hands to her ears and shout out, 'No! No! Not on their heads!' But Trume would not hear her.

If papà were there, he would go down. He always intervened when people were being violent; he used to say that the use of force is an act of cowardice. I do not know if I fully grasped the idea, but I did share it.

Faced with papà, Trume would hang his head. Perhaps this was how he showed his cowardice? Papà would raise his voice, seem to be angry, and he was also rather frightening. 'You should be ashamed of yourself,' he would say. 'You don't realize what the consequences could be!'

The two pale fairish brothers were permanently frightened. They could become dumb, Ciota said. It was lucky, I thought, that papà was so authoritative.

Trume would say sorry, Toni and Virgin were safe (for a little while). Was it not strange that you

completely forgot about it on seeing Trume again all smiles and exchanged the usual greetings? The two boys made me uneasy; it seemed to me that they ought to be ashamed, and I would pretend not to see them.

If he saw someone on the road ill-treating an animal even, papà would threaten him, 'Watch out or I'll denounce you!' That official word was full of authority.

If two people were fighting, he would take out his notebook and write down their names. (But it was just a pretence to frighten them.) The two, mortified, would go off in opposite directions. The fine thing was that papà knew their names and spelled them out while writing them down without their having opened their mouths. (This too was a sign of his power.)

Once mamma had imitated papà in her quick way. She had seen some boys hitting a friend from the balcony; she shouted at them and she also said, 'I'm writing your names down.' She had acted out writing, but on the palm of her hand! I watched, amazed and worried at mamma's daring, and the little wretches had obeyed her.

Besides, mamma, who was the first to get angry over people fighting, would find papà funny when he was being authoritative, and at home she would imitate him and laugh.

I moved away from the balcony and finally looked

at the room. There was a bed, but gas rings and saucepans were lined up on a board against the wall; it was now a miserable, makeshift kitchen. Someone must live here on their own. Was it the cripple? Or one of his strange sisters?

I was born in that room.

'The midwife was drunk,' mamma said in her quick, detached way, as if to rise above the horror. So that she seemed to be laughing at herself.

The midwife was the wife of the parish priest who was called Genio. I did not know what midwife meant (I didn't ask because I didn't want to make my ignorance known); to me the word seemed rather repulsive because of the mystery with which Ciota uttered it, the same mystery with which she talked about bodily functions. However, the midwife was in the house when I was born (that she was drunk was strange only because she was a woman); so when I met the parish priest in the village, I felt rather proud because of the name Genio.

My little sister was also born in that room. Perhaps they did not want Genio's wife again; I did not hear her mentioned at that birth.

I still used to sleep then in the little bed next to the big one. I woke up in the night in a fright; it often happened that I would wake up shouting, sometimes because of a bad dream; papà and mamma would run to help and calm me down. But that time Ciota had come, motioned me to be

quiet, whilst blocking my view. But I had had time to see by the light of a small lamp, that there were people around the foot of the bed on mamma's side. Mamma was sitting on the bed and holding out her arms, as if asking for help. Her mouth was open and her eyes were wide open with an expression of terror. Had there been a scream? No, the scene was soundless.

Might my aversion for my little sister have arisen from that? I do not think so. Much later I realized that it was the scene of her birth, but I never connected her with it. For me it was solely a mysterious torture for mamma and so alien to her, she who was always bubbling over with happiness — or was shy — that I had to relegate it to events which were frightening and unreal. To the extent that in the end I forgot about it.

Mamma never talked to us about her suffering or illnesses. When she was struck by her fatal illness, she apologized, 'I resisted as long as I could until it wasn't possible to hide it any longer.'

'I was looking at the mountains, early in the morning,' she said (she also gazed at those mountains!) 'and I was thinking, "Perhaps I am really ill ..."' Early in the morning, because she was alone and in silence.

I saw again the horror on her face during the crises of the illness; and also a stupor, a questioning, as in the terror of a child. But in the pauses she would accept it in her seemingly proud fashion. 'I

asked it of the Lord. So you might be spared it.' And she would laugh. (She laughed!) She would look at us almost defiantly as if to say 'It's settled'. She was sure she had got what she asked for. But she also laughed because she didn't want to be mourned.

'You're not going to say, when I'm no longer here, "She suffered so much!"'

Mamma had never had that defenceless tone of voice which was there during her last days; and even less in Ponte, which for her too was the time of the *penumbra*.

VIII

In the little girls' room, a covered lamp remained alight all night. Against fear. Only on my account, because my little sister was not afraid of the dark. In the evenings papà would sometimes say, 'A penny for someone who will go and get the paper.' It was a humiliating moment for me. My little sister was only afraid of people in uniform, of Authority. There had been the Captain's window and also a Captains' field. We were with Ciota who was gathering herbs for the rabbits and two soldiers stopped to joke with her on the road. My little sister shouted out, 'The Captains!'

She told me herself that one of her biggest frights had been when she found herself once in the arms

of a Carabiniere (who had picked her up to help her across a puddle). She did not even dare cry, and thought that luckily papà was a friend of the Marshal of the Carabinieri; but whether the Carabiniere knew that was another matter.

For me fear was a void which could open up before me at any moment. I had it in myself – I believed physically – the possibility of being swallowed up, destroyed. It was not suffering I feared, but disappearing. These were the oldest fears which had left a terrible and incomprehensible memory; they were the eternal fears. I fought against them with all my reason, yet unsuccessfully.

My most distant memory is one of fear. And the most terrifying fear, that of nothingness. I see myself again, or rather I know I am on someone's lap, a maidservant's, but not Ciota's. She must have had her back to the light because on the wall in front of me the pointed shadow of her crossed feet is moving, perhaps she's rocking me on her lap. It's precisely that shadow that fills me with terror. I could only understand that it was nothing, no one, who was making the shadow. Much later I reconstructed it as being the shadow of the two feet.

I experienced the same terror another time in a dream. I found myself in an empty room with whitewashed walls which were flaking a little. There were shadows there too, but light ones, like branches trembling on the wall. Suddenly I heard a

burst of applause. My blood ran cold, because I knew no one was there!

A very old fear was one of masks. I am whisked up in someone's arms (we are in the city, at my grandparents'), a familiar person has become a stranger because of the appearance of a mask. The masks are rigid, inanimate faces which suddenly speak, they look, keeping their frightful fixity. They too are no one and at the same time they are.

Fireworks also terrified me. The world was being undermined, and I was the only one who realized it. I shrieked so that the others would understand, but the fact that they comforted me and laughed amongst themselves redoubled my fear.

The last Carnival was the year of the Great War. I was six. There was a dark, menacing excitement about the crowd in the snow. I was afraid, but by now I was capable of keeping quiet about it. Because I was trembling they soon took me home (to my grandparents' house). I was put to bed on the sofa in the dining room. The light stayed on all night. Papà read the paper next to me so as to shield me from the light.

I felt something prick me and said there were crumbs in the bed. Papà said, 'Now I'm going to sweep away all the crumbs' and he passed his hand lightly over the sheet, straightened it and turned it back. But I still felt it and he came back to smooth the sheet with his hands again and stretch it tightly.

After the measles I had grown.

Another fear was windmills. We would go by a watermill when papà took me to hunt for moss for the Christmas crib. When the watermill was not masked by leaves in winter, it was more frightening than ever. You would come upon the enormous black wheels, the white froth of the churning water, and the roar was deafening. The path passed close by it and you felt you could be seized and swept away.

We climbed down beyond the Cant, followed the drystone walls towards Cornalè. The village and the countryside were all black and white. The ravens flew about like in the fairy tales of the Brothers Grimm. Digging about in the snow, amongst the lumps of ice, you would find the damp green moss we called *erba montagnina*. Papà would detach it gently so that the patches would not break into little pieces. His hands were delicate, though awkward when he helped us little girls to dress ourselves, and could not manage to get the buttons through the buttonholes. (When did that happen? Perhaps mamma was ill?)

Papà's hands were dry and hot, and mine disappeared into them; the whole of me seemed to go into them like a nest. I could pass the mill keeping my eyes closed, waiting for the terrible roar to be over.

Another mill, the one in Borgo Sottano, where I went with Ciota, was not so terrible because you

saw the wheels foreshortened above the stream. Inside there was a gigantic void, half in darkness, where everything trembled with a violent shaking and vibration. It was white, but not clean like snow; instead it was more grey like a never-ending rain of dust.

There was another mill, perhaps the most frightening, but in an enjoyable way, lacking danger. You could look up against the light at double images in relief inside a wooden contraption: the Messina earthquake, the Pyramids, Piccadilly and the Moulin Rouge. This one was a windmill round which figures went to and fro with sacks of flour, figures of skeletons with flaming red eyes. If you looked behind at the thin card, the figures would become flat and you could see the red paper stuck behind the eye sockets. But if you put the card back and looked at it again, the fear would return. I called it Hell.

When I was little and was frightened, papà would lift me up and hold me in his arms. But once while I was sobbing on his shoulder I experienced my biggest fright.

I had lifted up my face – perhaps papà was talking to me – and was looking at him close up. I knew papà's face like one of my toys. The game was to comb him. Papà had fine soft hair which you could straighten and part; I would also comb his moustache and his fine eyebrows. I liked to run a finger then along the line of his aquiline nose in

profile, in the crevices of his ears. Papà would let me do this and would stay as still and demure as if he were taking part in some ceremony.

I looked at him and saw his eye very close up. I knew his either gentle or stern grey eyes very well; they were often screwed up because papà was a little short-sighted. But on that occasion, I saw something strange, terrible. There was a yellow spot in the corner of his eye. It was something dead, decayed. Papà could fall ill and die.

I struggled desperately, without saying why.

I already knew about death. First of all, I believed it was agony. A lady was visiting mamma; she was seated on a sofa and rested her feet shod in ankle boots on a padded stool. To drink her coffee she had raised her veil above her nose and held the little cup in two fingers. The lady's voice sounded like a moan. She bent her head back and her gaze slid down over her thin cheeks.

Her child was dead. The lady expressed this in short, unfinished phrases, perhaps so that I should not understand. She had left the child's bed and when she returned, 'It was agony,' she said. The lady made a gesture, lightly brushed her forehead with a feverish hand, pressed her fingers to her temples, sighed. I understood that that act meant agony. In my imagination I saw a crown. I imagined it made of flowers, a little garland, but the flowers were decaying, something corrupt which could even infect a little

child. And I thought that the lady whispered perhaps because of that, as she looked suspiciously at me.

Despite the tender rosy light, I delayed going to sleep.

I was listening. From the barracks behind the house came a long sound, piercingly sweet, the 'silence'. It was a goodbye, a hopeless salutation to someone whom one was leaving for ever.

Then again, the roar, always the same, of the Cant. Flowing, enveloping, without beginning or end. I needed that sound, I would not have been able to get to sleep without hearing it. (At my grandparents' they could not get me to sleep; I could not bear the silence.)

Finally, there was an almost imperceptible, secret sound. It was born between my ear and the pillow; it flowed distinctly, faintly, far away. I called it the violins to myself.

It could have been the buzzing of a meter. But I do not think so. In other houses, at other times, that sound has accompanied my nightly anguish, but it has always been a confused, prosaic sound, very different from the violins which I have listened to only in Ponte.

In the last room — the guest room — the uncles, aunts and the beautiful cousins from Turin would sleep. The presence of relatives gave certain things a particular value. For me the tenor of life became

somewhat worldly. During the remainder of the year I would forget about that period.

Fulvia, the youngest of the cousins, came most frequently; I would go with her to the tree-lined avenue even in the mornings, or make trips with Cavaliere Mattei's sons who were on holiday from military school.

Fulvia was blonde and plump with long lashes which she would lower over sleepy blue eyes. She knew she was admired and that invested her with a peculiar seriousness. She possessed a famous dress, the raw-silk dress, as she would say flattening her r's.

Mamma would look at her with a smile, as if she found Fulvia rather comical.

Elda, with magnificent red hair, was studying painting and she cared for her elegant locks herself.

Uncle Livio, papà's brother, had red-gold hair like Elda and short-sighted, slightly protruding eyes; his pince-nez was attached to his ears with a gold chain. He had soft hands like papà and talked with extraordinary sweetness.

Uncle Livio would accompany me on the little grassy roads alongside the low walls and show me flowers the colour of coral or little leaves whose veining he would have me admire. He took pleasure in images, likenesses. Once he picked an ear of corn and freed a plump grain from its sheath. 'Look,' he said, 'it's the same shape as a little bread roll.' It made me happy because it was true.

Uncle Livio died when we were still in Ponte.

My parents went to Turin, and when they came back I heard them say that the doctor had washed his hands in an earthenware bowl and that had caused an infection. I wondered what it meant and was impressed by the idea of infection.

Mamma told me to write something to my aunt at the bottom of the letter. I was now in elementary school and wrote 'Everyone has to die'.

They commented on this when they thought I was not listening. But I had heard that they thought me heartless.

To me it seemed it would be a comfort for my aunt to remember that truth. I convinced myself that I was pitiless and wondered what I could have done so as not to reveal my abnormality. My parents did not reproach me, though, for that phrase, as if they thought me innocent.

The little aunts alternated with cousins. Mamma was sorry that they were badly dressed in cotton cambric! Grandmother Caroline (their mother) was austere. They made you feel sorry for them, said mamma, because they were pale, looked alike, and were dressed the same. They always had rather damp hands, and mamma maintained that they did not eat enough. They stayed in Ponte for a far shorter time than the cousins, but they were just as happy. They were content to play with me and come with us to Cornalè or go mushroom picking. They were timid and did not have to do with boys like the cousins did.

'Your mamma treats us like real guests,' they once told me, 'she changes our plates at every course.' I was amazed by this. 'At home, they only change papà's.'

Aunt Carlotta, like the little aunts, was mamma's sister. They called her little wretch; it seemed to me more a reproof than a joke – yet mamma and papà talked about her solemnly, in a disappointed way, because she would laugh too intimately with the local magistrate, a gentleman who wore a big ring on his little finger.

Aunt Carlotta would wear lace blouses and ribbons in her hair. My little sister in particular very much admired her, she said Aunt Carlotta's fingers smelled of sweets.

Papà took photographs of Aunt Carlotta with the small Rialto lake as background. The mountains and clouds were reflected as in a little mirror, its grassy banks bordered by willows. In that dreamy landscape, even she assumed a pensive air.

My uncle, the doctor, had a fat wife who was bigger than him. He was tiny and nervous. He was irritable, often sarcastic; he thought that mamma and papà were spoiling us girls. When he sang a song from his student days at University he seemed nicer:

'na vestina
percalina
e 'n nasin volta a l'insu.★

★In dialect: a little dress/in cotton cambric/and a little turned-up nose.

71

Uncle Andrea and Uncle Nicola were still students. Mamma adored them, and felt sorry for them; their grandparents were strict and she wanted them to be happy in Ponte.

She would welcome all the guests with eyes full of joy, and they in turn seemed as if they were bearers of happiness.

Uncle Nicola amused himself with the young ladies from the Europa. I imagined them playing at chasing one another around the rooms in the hotel and it made me embarrassed, I found them clumsy like that. 'It's his age,' mamma and papà would say. But if he came home after midnight papà had to shout at him for disturbing the grandparents. He had to go through the other rooms to get to the end one; he went on tiptoe and papà pretended to be asleep.

One night Uncle Nicola stayed outside sitting on the steps to the loft, because he did not dare come in again. They used to tell this story laughing, then sadly, because he died in the war.

The uncles would come to Ponte during their wartime leaves too. If it were winter, they had fur-lined overcoats. Mamma had made them two hide bags out of the bedside rugs which belonged to her and to us girls. They were sheepskin, as white and soft as silk. The uncles had not received them, however. There was corruption on the supply lines

Uncle Nicola used to amuse himself by teasing my little sister, for example by pretending to steal something from her; she would fall into the trap and

when she realized it had been a joke would sulk.

Then he would tease her and she would start to cry. When she was in tears uncle found her even more endearing.

'My' uncle was Uncle Andrea. Like papà, Uncle Andrea knew how to make the things he did for me wonderful. Every year he would come during the narcissi season and take me to pick them in the fields along the Stura. We made enormous bunches. The smell of the narcissi was so intense that it grew bitter. There was a strange green light in the valley below the dark clouds of the first storms. We fled from the cloudburst and Uncle had the same good smell as the Captains. I felt grown up with him, we were almost equals. I felt bitterness when I heard them say that he flirted with all the young ladies. I pretended not to hear, because I wanted to forget about it immediately.

Uncle Andrea had passionate eyes, the thin face of an Arab. He sent us girls English postcards from the front with a caption under the illustration, which he translated for us. 'I made a black pudding, but Pussy is dead!' said a fat little girl, saucepan in hand, as she looked at an emaciated little puppy.

Uncle Andrea came back ill from the war; he had caught some terrible illness which was surrounded by mystery. I thought again of that picture that mamma had had of him when he was a child at boarding school and they had beaten him.

★

For me the war was made almost unreal because of its distance. The names of the front written down in letters from the uncles and under the little photographs they sent us – on thin dark paper – became familiar yet mythical, exactly in the way that fairy tales were: Pasubio, Podgora, Cormons, Javorcek, and the High Plateau of the Seven Communes (seven, like in *The Seven Crows*).

Papà would consult a big coloured atlas but that atlas, too, crammed with symbols, was unreal. The only thing I succeeded in imagining about the war was that it was happening in the mountains; its heroic side became mixed up with papà's hunting exploits. The adventurous aspect of the war allowed you to let your imagination run riot. Since there were those called the missing, I secretly imagined that there had been a mistake and that Uncle Nicola would come back. I liked dreaming that he would reappear while we were busy with the puppet theatre (perhaps because for me that was the apex of pleasure). We would turn around and there he would be on the doorstep with his broad smile, in his big rough fur greatcoat.

IX

I stood at the window. Opposite, beyond the Borgo, was the Castle. The Castle was a ruined fortress which had been destroyed in ancient wars and was now entirely one with the mountain, an isolated spur of rock covered with woods over the valley plain. At the top lay the caretaker's long low white house (it was once red). 'It's a summer camp,' the cripple tells me. 'The Count left it to the parish.'

What does it matter? The Castle is there, it cannot change. Perhaps the avenue has grown sparser, but that might be because of the drought, the autumn.

Behind the Castle the two great wings of the valley come together in the distance like pincers. It's a huge space, yet it formed part of the house.

The eye would fly over the void and the images enter the rooms, still and wonderful like paintings.

Elda, the painter, had copied the Castle from that window one winter morning. In Ponte Stura the sun and ice played games of mirrors. Her painting was composed of little brush strokes of yellow, blue and white. The caretaker's house was a dark comma. I stared at it avidly, because it was the first time I had seen anyone other than papà painting. Papà used to paint in that room, too, but he didn't paint from reality. His landscapes were natural, but also a little bewitched. It was important to him for the painting to be deep as he used to say. He meant the distance of the background. There was a sure, subtle feel to his paintings, the execution was precise and incorporeal.

Papà had taken lessons from a painter who painted frescoes on pillars; he had learned the technique of painting in oils from him. When a tube was a bit dry, and it was difficult to get the paint to come out, the painter would say, 'It's constipated.'

'Painting's an abominable profession,' he used to say; he had a lot of daughters to keep. In mamma's opinion, he was no good at it, the faces of his saints were all the same. Papà admitted that he was mannerist but defended him by saying that he was accomplished technically. These conversations about painting – in an exciting smell of turpentine – stirred me deeply; I listened to them enraptured.

But the fascination with painting above all consisted in watching papà while he painted: his intent and serious air, the dense, patient, light brush strokes, the imperceptible changes of colour. What colour will he dip into now? And why doesn't he emphasize the outline of the little houses?

Mamma also liked to watch him paint. She always wanted him to stop in time before the painting became laboured. She also thought his handwriting a bit affected; it was delicate, with art nouveau flourishes. She even found his writing style stilted, in her opinion it was too wordy.

Papà's best painting was *Winter*. A snowy mountain, in soft shades of grey and violet against an evening sky the colour of old rose; snow-covered roofs of a village in darkness at the foot of a mountain. The lighted windows were a little orangey stroke. In front was a snowy road and at the sides, bare trees. A little man on the road dragged a fir tree towards a distant village.

It was lovely to imagine arriving there, at those houses. But there were dark windows too; and then you got the impression that you could never arrive.

We had recrossed the rooms and were in front of the glass door at the end of the corridor. The wood is dark, shining with mouldings in relief; a frosted floral motif runs across the glass.

Unembarrassed, the cripple opens up; he proudly shows me that there is running water in the

washbasin. I share his pleasure. I explain to him that papà installed a zinc tub and piping for two purposes. (Papà was for progress.)

The system papà conceived of did function, but it was over complicated. The tub had to be filled with buckets and water was obtained from the fountain in the piazza. It was old Tibus's job.

When he had put down his buckets, he would declaim poetry, one of his funny madrigals. And mamma would laugh and laugh.

The 'place' is still there, a cupboard in appearance. The hoops stuffed with straw were hung inside it. (Madrina kept hers in her room). I hated that place less than the humiliating chamber pot.

The invitation to 'sit on the pot' I felt as an insult. I would pretend not to hear and when they insisted would answer rudely. I even felt dislike for mamma at those times. Mamma was afraid that I would get kidney stones; she asked advice of Doctor Vinaj. 'It will strengthen the bladder,' the doctor reassured her.

I had noticed that when there were guests, the smell of the place was a bit different. I managed to identify the presences who had preceded me. There was a foreign smell which I knew how to identify. This sensation of foreignness, linked with the smell, was much stronger than the one people themselves gave me.

I also distinguished, by the smell, places where I had already been in other houses. The easiest to

recognize, with my eyes shut, was Idina's, because the smell of the chemist's shop which impregnated them all and their house, hovered around her.

Actually, I rarely visited those places; never, if I had to ask a grown-up. But in Idina's house when we played hide-and-seek in various rooms, I chose it as a hiding place. It's true that there was the usual hole, sealed with a wooden stopper and you felt your eyes prickle at the strong smell. But I would forget the smells; the door and walls were papered completely with old print.

I never finished discovering them all. They were illustrations from novels, vignettes taken out of books or magazines from the end of the century. Some had a title or at the bottom a sentence from the novel, but any further text was mostly cut out. The pictures were aligned with no empty spaces between them.

There were Hugo and Parisina (who were they?), The Death of Orlando (I knew that one), Colombo in prison, and others of the same kind.

A sleigh ran across the snow followed by wolves; a man in a heavy fur coat was whipping the dogs, another turned to throw something to the wolves; but they were running and getting closer all the time.

I pondered for a long time over the title of a vignette in which a gentleman in a wig looked through a telescope, while behind him a lady fanned herself and secretly passed a little note to

another gentleman in costume. The title read 'The more you look the less you see.'

I follow my guardian angel. The two rooms seem smaller to me in the half light than they were. They are tidy and shining; perhaps the sisters' rooms? The first used to be the little sitting room, the other the dining room.

When they had visitors, they did not have them in the sitting room but over there. Mamma laughed about it later when we were grown up; but for me that was the last evidence of past grandeur.

I can only talk about two parties. One was in the daytime, therefore unimportant. Mamma offered strawberry ice cream. We children helped make it: the strawberries were sieved, then everything was assembled, the wooden bucket, the iron contraption with the handle, ice covered in coarse salt. Perhaps other children had come too and we had played in the hall and on the inner balcony. In any case by then I was already sceptical, I no longer believed in parties.

The other one, longer ago, I remember better, even if I am unable to say that I saw it. I was unhappy on account of it, because they sent me to bed. And I knew that the general's wife was going to be there too! Above all I think I suffered because I could not succeed in imagining a party. I could only think that it must be rather like a scene from the theatre, since it took place in the evening. The lighted lamps

would excite me on ordinary evenings; I never wanted to go to bed.

Why, I wondered, would they not let me be there, at least for a little while? That children should not be allowed up at night did not seem the real reason to me.

Suddenly I decided. I had to know. I was not afraid of the dark and ran barefoot right up to the door of the little sitting room. I stood on tiptoe and looked through the keyhole. I only saw the lampshade, a shower of white pearls amongst which some red ones made a curious pattern, a kind of flower. That lampshade had always seemed an object of luxury to me. I heard the hum of conversation, laughter, the noise of chairs being pushed back, clinking glasses. It was wonderful and at the same time exasperating.

Then I saw papà's smiling face draw near to the lampshade, he was standing bending over the table. He was pouring something; I distinctly heard him say, 'A drop, or a little cloud... ' It was a disappointment. Papà made that joke even when he was offering something to drink to mamma or Madrina! The unexpected domestic detail suddenly extinguished the longing for the forbidden party.

The dining room was the happiest of all the rooms in the house. Perhaps because it was filled with light.

Mamma always kept the blinds up. The morning sun would come in from the balcony to the east of

the valley, the afternoon sun through the west window. Even if it rained or snowed there was light, a white light with no shadows. In fact, I was a bit ashamed, as if it were neglectfulness, of the excessive simplicity of mamma and the house. Other houses were dark, beginning with Cavaliere Mattei's and ending with the gloomy houses of the nobility. It was a sign of distinction. I used to go into other houses with a feeling of fear, even if I were greeted warmly. It seemed to me that everything ought to be done differently from the way we did it at home.

In other people's houses you would never even suspect there were mountains outside; the glitter of other houses or the shadows of a garden barely percolated through the shutters. Noises did not penetrate or were muffled. You would not hear singing, dogs barking, or quarrelling in the square the way you did at home. The furniture was dark and there was a musty sort of smell. The rooms seemed full of secrets like the people.

I was sure mamma neither knew about nor suspected such secrets, because when other people boasted about them or made them public, she said they were not true. Mamma did not want to know about mysteries. The fashionable way for ladies to talk was in a roundabout way, pausing and sighing. This was very different from mamma's elliptical, rapid speech. When they were playing grown-ups, the children would imitate exactly this cautious, affected manner.

The ladies seemed to want to hide something; something seemed to be hidden in corners behind the sofas, behind the dark curtains. Mamma told the story of a lady who when was she was visiting her had suddenly seized hold of the teatray with the cakes and hidden it under the sofa saying, 'My husband's coming!'

And another one had hidden the letter she was reading out loud to mamma inside her shoe!

But who were these ladies? Mamma would never utter their names. Even when I was grown up I could not make her say precisely. She would only say the ladies and even the madames (as if she were not one herself).

There was only one place in the dining room to hide, under the table. The table had a lot of legs, carved like columns. You could crawl through on all fours or sit upright. If you found a dark mark in the wood, you could scratch it and very fine powder would come out. I had taught my little sister to do this as well, but we were shouted at for doing it. The fact that we little girls would play under the table was a cause for criticism on the part of my uncle, the doctor.

Before my little sister, I used to spend hours and hours leafing through albums, illustrated books, catalogues. I adored the figures. In the postcard album, as well as the *Foro Romano* there were many other places which I regarded as mine. In a London

park, I was a little girl with a hoop and the lady beside her with a man's straw hat on her head was mamma. I was not pretending. I even seemed to remember the red sky behind the enormous trees.

Uncle Andrea had sent landscapes from Switzerland (Interlaken) and Bavaria while he was staying there as a student; they illustrated places in our mountains for me.

The catalogues were also seen as ours. The one from Frette which contained tablecloths (I connected Frette with the Flanders of the linen) decorated with little swallows or four-leaved clover was said to be mamma's. But one – an English one – with hunting and fishing, said to be papà's, was my favourite. There were endless rows of fish hooks, bait in marvellous colours and a range of yellow, red or blue cartridges.

Papà used to prepare the cartridges and I would watch. He would measure out the powder and small shot with a scale, seal the cartridges with a machine which made a round edge as it compressed the stopper. The colours were the same clear intense ones as in the catalogue.

Mamma would read me stories in the afternoons. She liked ones that were a bit comical like the three chickens who went to Rome or the house of chocolate.

I, however, liked the sad ones. With Grimm's fairy tales I felt imaginary pain. The saddest was *The Seven Crows*. The point at which the little girl

discovers at the fountain that her brothers are no longer at her side and she sees a flock of crows who 'were them' soar up into the evening sky, struck me each time with a feeling of hopeless loneliness. I heard the beating of those funereal and simultaneously familiar wings. It was fear, the horror of metamorphosis, but above all it was the sadness of an irrevocable goodbye.

I had learned the word metamorphosis in another fairy story. Joringhel could no longer see his wife Jorinde alongside him in the wood where they were lost. He realized, however, that there amongst the trees were the towers of the enchanted castle and that Jorinde was the little bird singing on the branches of a tree. Joringhel, said the book, 'knew about metamorphosis'. I pored over that part and reread the word, to get to the bottom of it. But it was like a closed door, full of mystery.

A tapestry painted by Aunt Carlotta hung in the guest room. At the bottom ran a stream, with a woman bending over the bank washing, you could glimpse a castle above her through a tangle of branches and rocks. Lacking a story, the fear was vaguer. But the woman washing clothes was not reassuring. She could be someone from the castle, or not be magical at all. Fundamentally, it was the woman's presence which evoked the fear.

With my mother we also leafed through her famous illustrated magazines. They were called *Thursday* and *Innocence*. They were not in colour

like the *Journal for Little Children*; they were illustrated with prints, like the ones in the privy at the Calvi's house. The little girls had skirts, with white lace below, which stuck out. Their little legs were shapely with the rounded calves and slender ankles of a ballerina.

In *Innocence*, there was a handsome naughty little boy who was tormenting his sister. He was called The Little Tyrant and his little sister was sweet and meek like mine. I noted the affinity with dismay.

It was in these newspapers that I discovered poetry. The rhymes in the *Little Messenger* were amusing, but I had never thought of them as poetry. They were considered anacreontic (Anacreonte, old, fat and bald, would gaze at himself in the mirror and young girls, garlanded with flowers, would laugh at him). They had a melody, and it was that which delighted me. One pleased me more than all of them and I read it endlessly to myself. It was about the death of a little bird; I remember only the line 'of laurels, of myrtles'.

Even at night the dining room was joyful. Papà and mamma, elbows on the table strewn with papers, were planning the construction of the villa at the top of the Podere. They would consult a little book called *The Modern Villa*. The villas were art nouveau, decorated with stucco work. Mamma had chosen a Swiss chalet, severely geometric; I was afraid that papà would approve of it. I had made my

choice too. My villa had a little round tower ending in a terrace with a railing of complicated design. On top of the roof was a lightning conductor. One of the crosses I bore was the fact that there was no lightning conductor on our house and that my parents were not in the least worried about it.

But it was some knowledge of science, learned in school, which had made me anxious; and in addition, there was the story Signorina Fichner used to tell. The old lady Fichner used to spend the summer in Europe and come and visit mamma. She said that a little Bavarian girl had been lying stretched out on a sofa near the window. The little girl had fallen asleep; a storm had broken out and the lightning which entered through the window had killed her. I shivered and stared at Signorina Fichner in fascination. Something still prolonged the fear; it was the colour of her earrings which sparkled as she shook her head. They were of a violet stone which had a mysterious name – amethyst.

There was a malign force in nature, snares against which I thought people did not sufficiently protect themselves.

A vignette from the *Little Messenger* used to fill me with dismay. I would re-examine it and gaze at it in horror, the impression it made on me would be repeated each time. It came in two parts: in the first picture a professor was teaching his pupils about the crocodile and pointed his umbrella at the

gaping mouth; in the second the professor had half-disappeared down that throat, swallowed up.

It was above all that lightning rapidity which terrified me. It happened like that in the story about the '*petit navire*', which mamma would gaily read me. When we got to the '*courte paille*' and the little sailor was eaten up, (*tout de suite dévoré*), I used to feel desperate. That rapid, fatal cruelty was inhuman.

Cruel things would happen in fairy stories; but fairy stories began with 'Once upon a time' and for that reason were confined to a faraway realm which made them improbable.

Papà often played his flute in the evening; I thought the sound of the flute was like his name, a lonely sound in harmony with the night.

While he was playing, papà was transformed. He would half-close his eyes, bend backwards and forwards, as if he were miming a fight or a dance. He wore a thoughtful expression, almost one of suffering but joyful at the same time.

Every so often, however, a spitting or hissing would emerge from the flute instead of the sound. Papà would interrupt his playing and say, 'It's dry,' and pour some wine into the tube. Mamma would laugh shaking her head, and I wasn't sure if it was a joke.

Papà had two flutes: one black one with silver keys, the other of red wood. He also had a pipe and an ocarina, but these were for summer evenings when we went to San Marco with Aunt Carlotta.

Papà would play, sketching out dance steps.

I learned from mamma that just after I had been born, papà used to play his flute near my cradle. 'So she'll like music', he said. It was not repeated for my little sister. I felt solemnly proud of being so privileged.

Papà and mamma were in the habit of saying about people, 'He likes' or 'He doesn't like music'.

We had the latest model in phonographs; it was called a gramophone and had a shining brass funnel in its drawer. (At home we would make fun of other people's bell-shaped horns.)

Guests were judged on how they listened to records. Papà and mamma had a predilection for a violin sonata which they called Kubelik's. If the guest seemed to be distracted or bored during its playing, they would exchange glances of commiseration.

Mamma would sing to herself in the morning, in a light, rather harsh voice. She had something indomitable about her: her songs, for some reason, seemed to be songs of freedom. She would often sing a French song:

Nous allons à Vincennes
dîner à bord de l'eau.

Mamma would laughingly defend herself when papà (tenderly) teased her and imitated her wrong notes.

Papà would often play this joke; he would take a school report out of his briefcase. It was a real one, one from her school in Turin; it had mamma's marks listed in columns in the various subjects. At the bottom papà had added, Singing 'nought'. Mamma used to laugh; but she also, quickly, pulled her usual face.

Papà sang Tosti's ballads in his baritone voice. Mamma would listen seriously to him for a bit, enraptured, in fact; then she would laugh at him for his over-romantic emphasis.

I preferred 'Come back, perfect darling' out of all the ballads; even though some passages which were unclear left me perplexed. I liked the phrases 'the lonely room' and 'a new dawn'. Aunt Carlotta very much admired this ballad too. She sent papà a postcard with a wood of dark firs and a pink sky; she had written in the corner in her beautiful sloping handwriting, 'a new dawn! ... '

The dawn reappeared in another ballad described as dressed in white. It said, 'Put on your white dress too!' It re-evoked the summer, but a summer more splendid and somehow rendered eternal.

Papà and mamma used to love Puccini, they thought that Doctor Morini, who was passionate about Verdi, had old-fashioned tastes, but they made an exception of *La Traviata*.

Papà would sing 'Your tiny hand is frozen'. Where it spoke of 'dreams and chimera and castles

in the air – the soul is millionaire' I again imagined the lonely room and thought that he had the soul of a millionaire. I experienced ecstasy, a moment of joy. Then I ended up by feeling uncertain, the usual anxiety that papà was quite happy to be a millionaire in that particular way.

X

The cripple opened the blinds and we leaned out together over the balcony. The valley had always been crossed by winds, and on that sultry afternoon I, too, felt a current of air passing under the house which seemed to lift it up and transport it. There was a relationship between the wind and the roar of the Cant, both were an inexhaustible flow.

The ladies had come visiting. The general's wife was also there and they did as they always did, they went out on to the balcony to admire the panorama. They were disparaging the mountain landscape, 'It's monotonous, unchanging. The sea, on the other hand ... ' I was crouching at the very end of the balcony; I saw the ladies' faces from

below, their necks swathed in lace with little pieces of whalebone. The general's wife looked at mamma through a lorgnette, her little mouth turned down at the corners. Mamma said quietly but firmly, 'The mountains are not unchanging. There are the seasons ... '

It did not seem a pertinent reply to me; nevertheless I was grateful to mamma for defending the mountains. I then looked myself for arguments to support the comparison. I tried to list aspects of the mountains which were moving: the streams, the little brooks and the irrigation rivulets along the slopes, the tall grasses and the fields full of oats and wheat marbled by the wind, the same wind which blew from far away and carried far away. I promised myself I would communicate all that I had reflected on this to mamma so that she could rout the ladies more splendidly; I imagined the kind of apotheosis it would be and at the same time worried that mamma would not want to hear it.

The old parapet on the street beneath the house is now finished with a convex top of cement; then it was covered with tiles. I had proudly walked as a little girl swaying to and fro along those tiles holding papà's hand; later I had dared it on my own, drunk with my defiance of the giddiness.

On that street – once dusty or muddy or frozen – I had taken my first steps.

The child alone on the wet street looks puzzled

at the ground and her forehead – but is this possible? – is furrowed with what the Doctor called the thinker's frown. That little girl survives in papà's photograph (or if not, where?).

I used to run then with my hoop – it ran along lightly and obediently beneath the blows as if it were alive. Poor children (the children of the poor did not play, they used to knit stockings) would use a wheel rim and push it along using an iron wire hook. They would run bent over, intent, and you would hear the rasp of metal. It became a completely different game with something frenzied about it.

When I stopped to get my breath, I had a stitch, I used to hug a telegraph pole and put my ear to it. You would hear a strange music in waves which passed through the pole, and it would vibrate like an instrument. (It had a scientific and therefore dangerous origin.)

In the middle of the bridge over the stream there were two holes on opposite sides. One was half-blocked with stones; through the other one you could see, by bending down, the whirling course of the water. From this one there issued a wind and a roaring, deep booming noise which was frightening, while the blocked-up hole seemed stupid and dead.

Pale convolvulus trailed and wild rye grass grew at the edge of the road. Someone had told me to stick an ear of the rye with the beard downwards

into my sleeve. I knew what was in store for me, but I tried it again hoping that this time nothing would happen. I had firm faith in reason; that there might be something magical about the ear seemed contrary to good sense. The stretch of road from the Cant to my house was long enough for the ear to climb. I felt about and found it again high up in my armpit.

Where the main road broadened out below the house in the curve towards the square, the snow plough sat like an enormous pair of pincers. In winter, it would heap up the snow, sliding heavily along in fits and starts at the sides of the road, the horse droppings steaming in the sun.

Then the snow plough would remain there. The soldiers would sit on it during their nostalgic dreaming; they would gaze at the valley descending to the plain. Or they would have competitions to lift the snow plough with the strength of their arms alone. They would grip it by the two iron struts and grow red with their efforts.

In fine weather papà would go to that space, look up the road and whistle; two notes repeated (a questioning motif) as if he were saying, 'Are you coming?' He was calling mamma to go to the garden.

You can see the garden, looking foreshortened, below the Selve's villa on the land which slopes down in terraces towards Borgo Sottano. (Today

the brief glimpse you get of the garden shows it is uncultivated and neglected.) Perhaps working in the garden was more of a game than anything else to them. Papà would spy on the asparagus bed as the bellying green shoots pushed up: he would have liked to see them actually growing and would gaze at them for a long time.

There was one special delight for me in the garden, to detach the tender curls of damp earth, home to the worms, from the paths and mould them with my fingers. I also liked to look very closely at particular flowers which had a face. The pansies would laugh, the forget-me-nots were astonished little eyes. I also admired the flowers on the vegetables: the creamy-white ones of the potato, and the splendid blue ones of the borage with its hairy leaves. I didn't despise the flowers of the weeds, or even the nettles; in fact when I was grown up I intended to have a garden filled only with humble flowers, wild ones. I revelled in this dream, which was almost one of revenge.

The path to the gardens (I get a glimpse of it exactly as it was) descended steeply and tortuously between high compact walls, the tops of them bristling with black or green glass. Suddenly you would smell an acrid, nauseating stench in waves. (Because of the privacy it offered the path was used as a lavatory; despite his authority, papà had not succeeded in preventing this outrage.) But the fresh smell of the gardens mingled or rather interfused

with the stench and alongside the path ran a fast-moving stream in its bed of cement.

I felt a sense of mystery too during that short cut; it was not so much the walls which had this effect on me as the bolted doors to the gardens. I would imagine wonders in those gardens; and if I could manage it without my parents seeing me, I would glue my eyes to the keyhole, but I did not manage to see anything except insignificant details.

Above our garden was the Selve's, where their *Maman* would hoe. She and mamma would greet each other with little bows and gesture with their hands. On their way back home before it got dark, they would again exchange greetings at the door to the villa. The Selves were from Turin. They used to come to Ponte at the beginning of the summer. The day after they arrived, mamma would dress me up and put on an elegant silk dress herself, don hat and gloves, all of this in silence. Then she would take me by the hand and we would cross the little square. It became a solemn business, almost a journey. To ring the bell you pulled a brass knob. A sort of marble mouth under the knob was fitted into the wall, it was the letterbox. (The entire Selve villa was luxurious.)

We were greeted with exclamations of surprise, hugged and kissed (damply). The house was dark, gleaming, lightly perfumed. We talked in low voices as if someone were seriously ill. Mamma and the

lady grew animated reminiscing about Turin; Mamma said that on Sundays the aunts used to take her to Regio.

Did mamma go to Signora Selve voluntarily? It was the only call she continued to pay after she had dropped all the others. The Signora had a protective, maternal air towards mamma. She warned her smilingly against the other ladies. Mamma would shrug her shoulders uncertainly; her eyes would be laughing, but underneath they were a little dismayed.

I was entrusted to Signorina Stefania who would take me by the hand to the verandah; you could see the gardens and roofs of Borgo very close, but half-hidden by the leaves of the paulownia.

Signorina Stefania was one of my passions. She was tall and somehow transparent; when she flushed, it seemed as though she clouded over. She had ash-blonde hair, soft, fresh white hands. Her way of speaking was slow and languid with French r's. She always seemed half-asleep. What caused discomfort was the fact that her unearthly air produced a painful sensation and made me feel ill. Because of this I never overcame the barrier of my shyness.

The Selve sons who were already grown up were there too, but they did not stay in Ponte the whole summer. They were aristocratic, friends of the general's wife and the gentry.

A little scene took place, I've forgotten what was

said. Massimo, one of the Selves, came to our door and papà and mamma invited him in. He was tall and thin with a clipped moustache and curly hair cut short. I can see his thin face again, his jaw working nervously as he bowed jerkily. He had come to invite papà and mamma to a country party (that was the term they used). Mamma told us this when we were grown up, teasing papà a bit. She used to tease him and at the same time you could see her admiring him.

Papà was quick to say he was sorry, telling him with absolute seriousness that he had received a dispatch and that he had to leave for the city. And the best thing about it was that he did hire a cab and off they went. We never knew if mamma had liked that or not at the time; now she seemed merely amused.

Papà's sense of humour did not always come to his aid as in the invention of the dispatch; sometimes his strong emotions made him angry, with strangers who were innocent (or almost). Aunt Carlotta who had been there on this occasion told us this, and my mother was able to confirm the story although not all the details. 'Don't believe everything Carlotta tells you. She's got too much imagination!'

A young officer had stared, perhaps too insistently, at mamma (they were crossing under the arcades) and my father suddenly stopped in front of him and knocked him down. 'And what about

you?' we asked mamma. 'I wanted the ground to swallow me up,' she replied.

Back home, according to Aunt Carlotta, papà had become desperate but my mother had made her decision. She wanted to leave. Carlotta continued, 'She told me to get you dressed (there was only you then) and I had already put your little white coat on and your bonnet. Then he snatched up the rifle, said he wanted to die.' ('Don't believe everything!')

However, the story had to be true, it tells how mamma backed down when she saw him do this, not because she thought it tragic, but funny rather.

Then there was a party (wine and music!) and papà was content; he had been forgiven. Mamma was still offended, but tempted to laugh.

I could never understand if she were more flattered by other people's admiration or papà's jealousy. Perhaps she was not flattered; there were people she admired herself, especially the Doctor and also the Selves, whose friendship she enjoyed, a little. As for papà's jealousy, it must have made her suffer somewhat, but she understood the profound reasons behind it; and what she must have found offensive, she managed to turn into a joke.

The proud Selve villa stood on the opposite corner of the square, high above Borgo Sottano but lower down than our house. You could see the whole of its broad terrace with its blue and white lozenge-shaped tiles from the balcony. When I read

descriptions of parties in my story books, I would imagine them taking place on that terrace.

I have not been able to find the green and yellow ceramic tiles set all round though, nor the flower pattern stucco work over the windows. They removed it, the cripple explained to me, when they had the house renovated, and they did not replace it.

The Selves were perfect. They even had a lightning conductor on their roof.

'Do you know how Signora Selve ended up? She died in the hospital.' (The hospital in Ponte also meant the hospice.)

And the cripple told me that the daughter-in-law (the last) whom the signora had disapproved of because she did not come from a good family had not wanted to help her.

'There was a war on, it's true. But in the hospital!' The cripple has compassion, I feel it. But I think about what wide-open, frightened eyes my mother would have made.

'The worst thing was that people used to laugh at her. She was a bit senile. She used to put three beans on the table and say that they were the three members of the Holy Trinity.'

The sisters had made their sitting room out of the old kitchen: armchairs by the window, knitting on a little table. Where were they? Gone out? I noticed some framed photographs lined up; in one of them I recognized the notary, looking irritated, just as I

had always seen him. He used to talk jerkily, in a nasal voice. Now he looked out at me from the photograph as if he were waiting impatiently for me to go away.

Where Ciota's room had been they had made a kitchen. We used to read the story of Geneviève of Brabant sitting on the bed. The book which belonged to Ciota was soft and crumpled. On the cover Saint Geneviève was clad only – but completely – in her hair. Or we would read *Maghelona the Fair* or *The Kings of France* (Fioravante mounted a palfrey . . .).

Ciota did not like what I considered my stories. There was only one whose mocking humour satisfied her – *The Ugly Girl and the Fairies*.

A woman had a very ugly daughter but spread the rumour that hers was a rare beauty, and that she kept her hidden only because the sun would spoil her. When we got to the part where the woman let the prince who was wooing her see her little finger all smoothed and perfumed with oils through the keyhole, Ciota would find that passage irresistible and laugh until she cried. It was the same when the prince saw that his bride, once her veils were lifted, was so ugly that he hurled her out of the window. Or when the three fairies, one crippled, one hunchbacked and one wall-eyed, stumbled across the spread-eagled body of the ugly girl.

We turned off into the corridor which was lit by a

small lamp. I noticed that the floor was shining and polished. 'Your sisters keep the house beautifully!'

'Oh, we have a cleaner for that!' (So why then his poor man's little bundle of sticks?) The cripple moved away to close the shutters again. I shut my eyes for a moment and tried in vain to re-evoke that smell.

The first thing that uncles and cousins would say when they arrived was, 'The smell of your house!' For years they would reminisce about it, 'Do you remember the smell?' And I, 'What smell?' 'A special, fresh, good smell. You could only smell it at your house.'

There were distinctive smells for me. In mamma's room, a porcelain phial with a long neck ending in a little queen's crown (papà had brought it back from Nice) held a smell of real violets. However, if you smelled a bunch of violets collected from the hedgerows they had a different perfume; tender, slightly bitter, while the one in the little glass decanter was sweeter, but cold.

Another good smell belonged to a big box of sweets where mamma kept her ribbons. On the inside of the lid was a design raised in relief of a woman's profile with curly hair like little snakes. The smell was of almonds and vanilla, but more delicious; perhaps because it was the memory of the smell.

There were bad smells too. Murò's smell, strong but pleasant, grew acrid when he had been soaked

in the rain. Papà's smell was also a bit acrid when he came back from hunting or surveying. But the worst smell was in Madrina's room, the smell of Oppodeldoc Balsam.

Will he open that door too? He opens it. Here's the big dark room – the only dark one – because of the single window furnished with a grille which gives out on to the courtyard.

'We call it the grey room,' says the cripple. Half-empty, you can see that it is used as a storeroom for supplies; there are sacks and baskets in the corners.

'It was your grandmother's room,' he says. (He knows everything!) So it is true then, as Aunt Carlotta used to say, that 'they gave her the ugliest room.'

'I used to call her Madrina. She was my madrina. Papà and mamma called her *Maman*.'

'She was a very imposing lady. She had lived here for many years with your papà before he got married. She had been left a widow early.'

I hoped intensely for a moment that he would say something that would help me to understand Madrina's mystery.

'She was tall, upright.' And the cripple tried to straighten his little person. 'We used to call her Her Royal Highness.'

'Was she proud?'

'You know how nicknames are,' and he laughs indulgently, shaking his head.

I see Madrina again giving mamma a drink from a little glass. Papà supports mamma by her shoulders as she is shaken by dry coughing.

According to Aunt Carlotta, Madrina would enjoy frightening mamma. When papà was late coming back from his hunting expeditions or inspections of the reserve, she would stand in front of her and say, 'I hope ... '

'What?'

'I hope that he hasn't met some old acquaintance ...'

Mamma was too proud to feel jealousy, but she was certainly wounded by the intrusion, the suspicion.

I had always been afraid that Madrina was not a good person; however mamma never said it, and I considered spite (grown-ups' spite, because I knew that I was spiteful towards my little sister) as a kind of secret illness which was unmentionable.

'Mamma, what was Madrina like?' I would ask.

'She loved you,' she would reply in her elusive fashion, which skipped preliminaries.

'But with you?'

'It's over, it's over,' she would reply and make a gesture, miming the rapid flight of time.

Mamma did not want to talk to us about Madrina but she did admit that papà had shared out their duties very fairly. 'Now the house is her responsibility,' he had decided after Madrina had gone straight to his office to complain.

'After you were born, Madrina changed!'

All that had happened earlier.

Madrina was majestic, but her face was hard. She had lines at the corners of her mouth, and thin lips. That she was papà's mother was incomprehensible; in fact when I was a little girl I never thought about it. She was Madrina and that was that. And I never even considered that she had been young. Although she had a hairy chin, she did not seem really old to me.

Fulvia later showed me a photograph of her as a young woman. She was wearing a crinoline and was graceful and slender. Her expression was not haughty, but nor was it sweet, rather indifferent. She had a high forehead and a long aristocratic face even though she was a tradesman's daughter. In her small town she had been nicknamed Beautiful Italy because she had gone to a party dressed up as Italy (in 1870) wearing a tiara decorated with towers.

However I felt a vague, mysterious compassion for her. I think I intuited that her hardness had sentenced her to solitude.

We used to go on a ritual walk, always the same one, Madrina and I. We would make a long circuit round the village, on the Ponte Cross side, below the Counts' wood and behind the Barracks. We would pick flowers in those wild places; flowers which were very beautiful yet not valued like mullein with its pale yellow flowers and rough leaves and blue chicory. Madrina picked them

because they had stems which were difficult to break.

She was not one of those grandmothers who tell stories. However, she did know one and would tell it in an extraordinary fashion. I remember one part of the story concerning a bridegroom. They played a trick on him, because instead of sending the princess to him on their wedding night, they sent the chambermaid, disguised in the princess's clothes. The carriage crossed over a bridge. Unable to restrain herself, the false princess said, 'Oh what fine water!' (Here Madrina raised her voice at fine water.) 'It would be good for rinsing the washing!' So the trick was discovered. Then they sent the cook. On seeing the stream, the cook exclaimed, 'Oh, what fine water!' (She would repeat the emphasis.) 'It would be good for washing the dishes!' I forget what the real princess said.

I wanted to say goodbye, but the cripple came out with me, closing the door as he was speaking, and as if he knew that I wanted to see everything, he showed me the stairs to the loft.

I would follow Ciota up into the loft and watch her sawing wood. There was a good smell of beechwood, and everything, powdered with sawdust, had the same reddish-yellow colour, even the spiders' webs. Ciota would make me smell the little piece of fat with which she oiled the serrated blade; she thought it had the most wonderful smell.

There were low beamed ceilings and a diffused half-light. The atmosphere made such an impression on me that I still dream about that loft. And in my dreams it becomes a sequence of more enormous, empty, dusty passages which lead to vague places for ever out of reach.

The series of low passages unfolding beneath the roofs had always intrigued me. Ciota refused to let me run through them saying that further on they were bricked up. But she had an air of not wanting to say, or being unable to say, that there was something you should not see. Was Ciota trying to frighten me? I do not think so, at least not in this case. For her the whole world was full of traps and mysteries. Sometimes an old woman would be sitting on the first flight of wooden steps to the loft; these were as broad as a bench and so worn down that they had become crescent-shaped. I have never known who she was or where she came from. Strangers did not frighten me; it was only what you didn't see that could make you afraid! I watched her because she was old, and old people aroused my curiosity as if they were a different species. Often they had a strange smell, like a stench below a layer of earth.

The old woman was sewing; when the thread ran out she did not know how to rethread the needle. I tried to do it and found it very easy because the needle was a very big one. The old woman's blessing gave me the impression that I was part of a fairy story.

XI

On the balcony to the courtyard, Madrina's flowers, pots of saxifrage, were once lined up. They were metallic pink flowers which had something cruel about them because of the name. At Easter she would cut them and make a bunch for my mother. (I would secretly rejoice over this.)

One side of the courtyard is bounded by the cowshed and haylofts (empty now) and the balcony only runs along three sides. You see an enormous mountain close by above the low roof of the cowshed. It's the biggest mountain in Ponte Stura, Montselvaj. Papà and I used to go along that balcony on our way surveying or hunting on the mountain.

It was dawn, and we would hear the cocks calling to one another, hoarse with sleep. We would walk carefully, but our hobnailed boots made a crunching noise on the stones and you could hear Murò's claws scratching as he raced about not whining, but unrestrainable.

We always used to leave from the same side to go to the mountain; we would soon reach the stream by certain small paths, and from there the mule track. The sun in the valleys would already be caressing the gleaming grass at the edge of the ravine. At Barcia we would drink the first icy water falling into a black and slimy hollow tree trunk. A mongrel, curled up, was pretending to be asleep, then up he bounced and growled with hatred at Murò the noble. Murò looked at his master in bewilderment and I too seized hold of my father's hand.

Later the valley became narrow and stony, full of wind; the sky seemed white from beneath the shade.

There were not only meadows smelling of honey on that mountain, but mines as well. They were black holes barred with wooden beams; one was even a gold mine! Papà explained to me that it had been abandoned because it cost too much to extract the ore. But I couldn't manage to grasp that ... I promised myself that I would try when I was grown up.

★

On the edge of the bent, worn balcony railing, lacking nails here and there, I used to drink, by sucking it, the rainwater with its exquisite taste of rust.

I would lean on that balcony and gaze out. The courtyard is still deep, but it was even bigger then. Stable-boys and servants would currycomb the horses, then polish them, brush in hand. The shining coat would flash beneath the currycomb, long shudders run along the rump. The powerful smell of horses and stables rose up, with the good smell of hay and carob beans. Shouts, curses and laughter resounded.

The landlady's laughter was like thunder. Black and skinny, she didn't look in the least like her beautiful daughters with their languid poses. She had a man's raucous voice, a drinker's. She would laugh hollowly with the men, and they treated her as an equal.

While I was sitting on the tiled steps with Ciota who was teaching me how to crochet, Agnesina, Master Musso's daughter, arrived. Agnesina was blonde with a great many pale freckles; she would smile showing her little teeth and screwing up her eyes short-sightedly. She seemed sad even when she laughed; she laughed soundlessly, as if she were sobbing. She and Ciota used to talk in a secret language containing a lot of f's; they would speak very quickly and laugh.

At either end of the balcony were lavatories. The

one on Master Musso's side was always clean as if it were unused, and had a dry smell; the other one, which belonged to the hotel, had such a strong smell that it made your eyes sting and the tears come. Ciota said with a serious air that it was because the men (the soldiers) went there.

Ciota respected all men whether they were soldiers or not. Her predilection for them had an obscure significance which embarrassed me. She would only make fun of women. When she introduced a woman, especially a lady, she would make faces behind her back and imitate her walk.

With men she would limit herself to managing their names if the fancy took her, or inventing a rhyme. It made no difference whether they were very serious people. On the contrary, she even dared to make a joke about the respected name of the Doctor:

Doctor Vinaj
mangia la supa senssa l'aj.*

On the opposite side of the balcony is Master Musso's door.

'It's not many years since he died,' said the cripple. (If only I had come earlier!)

He had been very old. However, he was still slim, upright, and used a stick only as a companion, he would carry it on his arm.

*Doctor Vinaj eats his soup without garlic.

'Even then he would carry it like that.'

'He hadn't changed, only his goatee had turned white.'

Master Musso belonged to a race of wise men. He was sweet, patient, silent. His presence gave me a peculiar sense of protection.

When I did not go to school he would take me by the hand and we would go out together to the cemetery. The road was long and dusty between the fields right up to the foot of the Podio. The Master would stand unmoving before the grave of his first daughter Alfonsina who had died aged eighteen. I knew her from the little photograph on her grave. A small round face, rather sulky-looking as if offended, beneath a dark felt hat with a big upturned brim.

I would then let go of the Master's hand and pick some flowers. These were wild carnations with long thin stalks; I went about gathering them amongst the black crosses and tall grasses covering the cemetery.

Back home Ciota would shout at me, 'You shouldn't touch them! They're the flowers of the dead!' It did not make much impression on me, I could not relate the flowers to the dead.

The Master's wife was, or seemed to be, a bad person. She had a thin bitter mouth and frowning eyes which were growing increasingly blind, so she would move around gropingly. I would slip away from her, go over to the Master and he would give me

illustrated books to look at. These were very beautifully coloured, because they were Swiss or German.

The Master used to get excited when he talked to papà about truly civilized countries, or about poetry and music. He would sit at the piano accompanying himself as he sang. In the village they said the Master was a *barbett* (an old bore). 'He was a socialist,' specified the cripple, and it seemed to me that he said it respectfully.

He pointed out the windows on the first floor. 'They held their meetings there ... '

'I know,' I said, 'the Protestants.'

The cripple turned round to look at me in admiration, 'Do you remember them?'

'There was a long table covered with a green cloth in the room, and men all round it. One of them stood and read loudly from a book. We used to watch them with Ciota and Agnesina; we were quiet and attentive. We would hear the voice but not understand the words.'

'They were reading the Bible. Who knows what those people believed.'

Then he added rather solemnly, 'I took part as well, several times.' Now it was my turn to look at him with admiration.

At the bottom of the other staircase there had been a notice, an inscription in blue on white Evangelical Hall.

'That sign isn't there any more.'

★

The meeting hall is now a squalid empty room; I can hardly make it out through the dirty windows and thick cobwebs.

Before I was born a big lunch had been held there. On that occasion papà had shown himself very attentive to the ladies. Aunt Carlotta had told me about it when I was grown up. Mamma smiled about it rather scornfully; she couldn't have admired my father very much on that occasion.

That lunch, which belonged to that splendid period, the earlier time, I've imagined so many times that now I remember it as if I had seen it; papà standing pouring wine, and the ladies, the Signoras Calvi, Signora Borgo. perhaps the general's wife too?, smiling and raising their heads to look at him, holding up their glasses. The gentlemen gazed at mamma, and she was profoundly bored. She did not like society.

What was it exactly that she did not like? The conversations they had? Or, in that particular case, that papà flirted with the ladies? It certainly bored her that he played games.

Aunt Carlotta told us that when mamma was a young lady (that was the expression they used then), grandfather, after much pleading by her friends, had accompanied her to a ball. But halfway through the party she had left the room, went to grandfather, who was playing billiards in a side room, and asked to go home. Later it was not easy to get an explanation out of her; she finally

confessed that she hadn't been able to bear her friends' envious looks. She had realized that they were suffering because she, more simply dressed than them, had more attention paid her. She did not want to give them pleasure by leaving; she left out of impatience, because she despised taking part in such a competition.

Her antipathy towards society was profound. I now recognize in it her pride, the unaccustomed road to her extraordinary humility.

I heard about another dinner which my mother alluded to in that same room in the Europa. I wondered subsequently if it were a fantasy, not entirely, but in certain details. Yet mamma would not invent anything; on the contrary, she stripped things down, removed superfluities, did not exactly tell a story, rather she would only make allusions. To understand what she was thinking, you needed to see her expression, and even that was secret too, hidden behind irony. There were her exclamations, her shouts of joy, fear, anger. But they were sudden, unexpected, and too rapid.

I think she talked about the dinner precisely because of her imaginative nature. Later on, I did not dare ask about it. (Because I was afraid it was not true?)

Papà had been invited, the only man, to a women's dinner, actually, The Women's Dinner. And who could they have been? Definitely not

ladies. I imagined them as those old ladies who used to wear a stiff saffron yellow shirt on which they would pin a blue *abitino* in the processions. They were known as *Le umiliate* (Ciota called them *Le mule matte*.)

Mamma said that she had been curious to see it too.

'Catlina and I went there, to spy.' (She was nineteen! It happened in the first year of her marriage and Catlina was the servant then.)

'What did you see?'

'Papà had thrown a rug over his shoulders, jumped on the table and was making a speech.'

'And the women?'

'They were clapping.'

Mamma used to laugh as she told the story. However, she also told it another way, or rather bringing out a different meaning, not laughing, but as if she were overcoming some bitterness.

On the day of that famous dinner, a lawyer friend had come from the city to call on papà. The friend was indignant and distressed and when papà came home, he made a scene. At this point, the story became funny again, in fact it was funny to imagine the scene. The friend was Giuseppe Barra, nicknamed Pagiada because he talked very slowly and swallowed his words as if he were talking in his sleep.

The two versions were not different because of ambiguity. My mother would show now one side

of something, now the other without explanation. She really covered her tracks because it did not matter to her whether she was understood or not. But above all, she did not want anyone to be judged because of her stories.

The cripple came down the stairs with me. It seemed as if I had a big bird on the steps beside me, a palmiped which had to walk painfully. He talked and every now and then would stop. I was no longer listening.

XII

We had said goodbye to each other in front of the house; but a bit later when I was coming out on to Piazza Vecchia there was the cripple again, under the last arch of the colonnades behind a pillar as if lying in wait.

I felt embarrassed; I wondered if he were a bit mad, as it was obvious that he was waiting for me. But he greeted me with his enchanting monster smile and I was not in the least afraid any more.

He said he wanted to show me the ancient Parco dei Conti. An offer like that when I was a little girl would have made me delirious with happiness. But now the park is the public gardens. Where there used to be the little tower with a sundial they have

made two flights of steps which lead to the garden. The little avenue of dwarf elms, thinned out and pruned, no longer hides either the paths or the statues which were once invisible.

The cripple does not conceive, nor intuit, that I have no desire to visit the garden which is secret no more. For me the nobility were beings of a finer, rarer species. Their secluded life, their big dark homes made them different. But they belonged more in my fantasies than in the real world. I would dream about them as I would dream about imaginary characters deprived of a real existence (or almost). When my uncle the doctor declaimed:

a sta 'l baron d'Onea
per la 'n t' un castel frust
so pare ven da Enea
sua mare ven da August.*

I would laugh; I did not suffer for my idols. In reality, their actual personages did not impress me much. Count Bolleris was ugly; papà said he was a bear. Furthermore he had been the political opponent of the Doctor, papà's great friend, therefore he was, in a certain sense, an enemy. (Only the Count lived in Ponte Stura, the others would come in the summer like holiday-makers.) In summer I used to see the Marchioness go by

*here's the Baron from Onea/the inhabitant of a crumbling castle/his father goes back to Aeneas/his mother goes back to Augustus.

120

in her gig on her way to the Castle. If the Marquis were there, he would run alongside her; he was so tall that their heads were on a level. (The Count's mother was a Marchioness because she had remarried, wasn't that strange?) The Marquis would always stand, long and severe, in church on Sundays. He had several books piled up in front of him on the bench instead of one. (The other men not only did not have missals, they did not even go to Mass. Not even papà at that time.)

They used to say that the Marchioness dominated the Marquis, and ordered him about like an inferior. During a meeting of the Committee she had ordered him in front of everyone to go and get the dog and take him for a walk. I listened avidly when people talked about them. Not that I approved of the things I heard people saying; on the contrary, I thought common people were incapable of judging them properly.

They also said of the Marchioness that she was extremely mean, that she weighed the eggs. Now what did it mean? Someone added, 'Like Leopardi's mother'. (When I learned that the Marquis had written 'in defence of Leopardi's mother, I thought that he must have meant to defend the Marchioness as well in that way.)

The Marchioness often had two noblewomen from Spain as guests who were known as The Spaniards. They were small and delicate, but they had big heads and dark, hairy, masculine faces, as if

the wrong heads had been planted on their little bodies. They wore white and seemed even darker because of that. I was amazed by the way they looked because I thought that the song which went:

only the Spanish woman knows how to love like this

referred to them.

'Do you know how the Count ended up?' the cripple asked me. Yes, I knew, more or less. He already drank when he was young. It was talked about. 'At the end he degenerated,' he continued. 'He went around filthy. He didn't speak to anyone.'

Since I did not want to visit the park, the cripple proposed an alternative. Would I like to take a turn around the Pasche? This road also skirted a garden belonging to the nobility, the Counts Blanc. The cripple showed me how the garden seemed almost stripped of trees behind the boundary wall. The old Lebanese cedar, teetering now, stuck out a single branch like a mangy stuffed bird with a single remaining wing.

The two little Counts were dressed sailor-style like all the other little boys but their socks were held up by garters. This gave me an impression of something orthopaedic and at the same time particularly masculine. I felt embarrassed when I

caught myself gazing at that black elastic, those hooks.

When I was very small my mother had called on the Countess. I only know that I was on a little balcony and I was bored. At that moment did I not realize that I was in a house belonging to the nobility? Perhaps my passion came later.

Soon afterwards there was a brief intimacy. The Countess had asked papà to take her with us on a pilgrimage to the Sanctuary of Saint Anna of Vinadio. The carriage took us up to a village, then you had to go on foot for hours and stay there overnight.

The Countess held herself a little aloof, at least so it seemed to me. She ate sitting apart from us, but would take and offer things. I was the go-between. The Countess had brought a box of fondants.

I discovered that she really was different when she displayed great fear and emotion at a point where the path had caved in. She used to suffer from giddiness, so she passed the spot leaning on papà and holding mamma's hand, her eyes closed! I thought her very beautiful at that moment and it seemed to me that I was a little in love with her.

I saw their garden, but not during one of our visits. I was passing by there on my own and the gate was open. That was already unusual, so I went in timidly. It was as if I had been invited into an imaginary garden revealed only to me. The

perfume of the flowers, their colours, the buzzing of the bees and even the sun's heat had a greater intensity than usual. And then I had the sensation that it must all have lasted no more than an instant.

The gardener, without saying anything, cut flowers and put them, one after another, into my folded arms. I took them without breathing, not daring to hold them tightly. The gardener finished off the bunch with a spray of blackcurrants. The ultimate luxury – a fruit as if it were a flower!

'Who were more important, the Blancs or the Bolleris?'

The cripple was perplexed. He came to the conclusion that the Bolleris had been the ancient lords of the manor in Ponte Stura, but the Blancs were the more ancient nobility. I thought he had endeavoured to find a reply out of politeness, making it up on the spot.

Below the wall of the park which ended in a sheer drop to the stream, a path led to a shut-up private house, which bore a For Sale sign. It had been built when I was small; I had noticed then how symmetrical it was, like Rubino's houses in the children's newspaper.

'Do you see the two names over the door?'

There was in fact a nameplate in cement with two names in relief: Anna and Giacomo.

'They are the names of a husband and wife, the only ones in the village who were practising Protestants.' (Then someone in the village had been

converted?) 'He was a timber salesman; he had the house built for himself and his wife. They loved each other very much. That's why he had the two names engraved.' For the cripple, the Protestants must have been something like the nobility for me.

Now I could say goodbye; but I hesitated. I continued to climb the Cross road with the cripple, walking carefully over the big cobblestones. I felt as if someone had forced me to have a drink.

Many years ago, when I left Ponte, I had felt similarly upset. The certainty with which I had been born was blurred for a while; in fact I had been afraid of finding it an illusion. But I did not admit it to myself. Now I know that it was jealousy, the shame of a moment of life passing.

While I was walking along with Battistino Viola, I remembered my stupefaction then and partly felt it again. In the dulling of awareness, the pain was becoming detached, becoming subterranean once more. I went through a number of arcades with Battistino Viola. We met nobody. I had an impression of being invisible.

We crossed the two piazzas together in silence, the Old and the New. What was the cripple thinking about? He surely knew that his task was at an end. He said goodbye in front of the hotel.

We made our farewells like two old travelling companions.

★

I went into the hotel and parted the rustling screen of threaded pearls. A corridor led into a room which had remained as it was – a café. Black tables, hunting prints on the walls. In addition, a big radio which did not work, a heap of blankets on a table; it was just a junk room you passed through. And a smell which was both sad and familiar – because ancient – of mould, wine, old grease. That room comforted me, it was something of Ponte.

The odour of stale smoke persisted in the room, the trace of a recent presence. Putting my things into a drawer, I knocked against a little box of tablets.

I began to fiddle with the lamp, a small glass bowl held tight with screws. The lamp would not light. They had explained that you had to give it a vigorous shake. I tried that; at each shake it flickered feebly and immediately went out. I gave up. I chased after some flies, but didn't manage to hit any.

I sat down on the only chair.

Part Two

I

I was leaning on the old parapet, at the spot where the snow plough used to be. The house was facing me, tall and shut up, once more inaccessible, remote. (Restored to order? But I did not want it to be alive.)

Now outside the house I had to go on with the inventory, an inventory of defeat? A slow but painful decline had taken place in me during that period which I now considered divorced from time. Because of contact with the world?

Beyond the house was the world into which I had to venture quite alone. When I had to return home I felt a vague fear that I would not find it there, nor my parents, nor familiar things. I forgot

the fear as soon as I got to the arcades.

But sometimes the house itself was barred to me. However, I was the only person who saw the problem in alarming perspective. To anyone else, even a child, it seemed derisory, nothing.

As I returned home from school I would come running out of the arcades, but on entering the square I would slow down, doubtful and uncertain, paralysed by the sight of two puppies.

They used to be in front of the porch, curled up asleep, usually in the middle of the road; they were waiting for Cavaliere Mattei to come home from the Office. The maid had brought them there. They were mother and son, she was fat, slow, he was minuscule, full of life and jumped about on slender legs like twigs. There was something mechanical about him as if he were some sort of gadget; if he barked in anger, his own voice made his whole body shake.

I would look up at the windows of the house, where both mamma and Ciota would seem oddly intimate, like accomplices. They would make signs for me to come up, not to be frightened, but at the same time they would laugh and that made me despair of any help.

I decided to try another way. I made a half-turn, went by the baker's on the corner. Doing this, which took a while, gave me some respite.

Blin the baker called out to me from the low windows level with the ground and stretched out a

fresh bread stick through the grating to me. Nibbling the bread stick, I would slowly climb the cobbled road. After the baker's came a blind wall; on the other side was a white house with a staircase with two flights of stairs. I peered up at it as I went by, hoping to see something in the doorway which was open on to the dark interior. The daughter of our carpenter lived inside, immobile on a little camp bed.

Mamma sometimes came with me to visit her. She was a very beautiful little girl but it was painful to be near her; a damp heat and sweetish smell emanated from her. Her face was not thin, it was oval, with a muddy pallor, her eyes were black and shining and upset me with a gaze which was too serious like a reproach. That little girl was privileged on account of her illness; mamma would talk about her respectfully and she had a right to judge me.

When I arrived at the Barracks, where the soldier on guard was in his sentry box, I changed direction. There was nothing but walls up to the door of the house halfway along the road; on one side one belonging to the courtyard, on the other the very high one belonging to the Barracks high up on the mountain behind the Belvedere. But at the bottom, in front of the Trattoria, was another dog Blesilla. (Who on earth gave that name to a yellow bitch with a hoarse voice and uncertain temper?)

I had to get to the door without Blesilla noticing me. She seemed to be asleep, but when I thought I was safe, she would spring up and make a fuss, or worse, come up to me. Better the puppies, at least they jumped up and down in one place. I turned back; Cavaliere Mattei was late, the dogs were still there. My mother was no longer at the window. Tired now, I made another desperate attempt from that side.

I can't remember the moment when I would finally get in, heart in mouth, through one entrance or another. Nor even how they welcomed me home, probably laughing and teasing. The teasing was not so much about my fear of dogs in general, as to do with the fact that the dogs in question were very small.

This fear of dogs apparently had a plausible reason, an external one. In reality the dogs' anger stirred some secret alarm in me. The real fear was not of being bitten or attacked but of making some unwitting mistake, as if I had broken some law, had sprung a trap set by an evil power.

In fact the dog which a little earlier had seemed a demonic presence was quietened by his master and came up to me nicely, restored to being what he really was, a poor dog.

This never happened either with Cavaliere Mattei's puppies, however, nor with Blesilla. I never saw them subdued.

They were The Devil in dreams, the smallest

kind, black, almost incorporeal. I would see him trotting about the house, I knew who he was, and I would wake in a cold sweat.

When I was small my best friend was my dog Murò. Murò was a flame-coloured golden setter, as papà would say with satisfaction. He was Maura's son, the bitch belonging to the vet.

Murò was sweet and discreet, as patient when he was playing as papà himself. His thoughtful forehead expressed his constant efforts to understand, to anticipate.

In many photographs Murò looks like my guardian. In one he is at my side in the garden sitting on his back paws, neck erect, proud, conscious of his dignity. There's a resemblance between the dog and the little girl. Both our foreheads, his dark and rigid, the little girl's white and convex, are faintly furrowed, shadowed with melancholy. But Murò's eye is fixed, intrepid and ingenuous, whilst the little girl's seems to be fixed on contemplating something troubling, far away.

Even Murò, like everyone, had once been young and awkward. Once he ate all the *tomini** which one of the Boves had brought.

The first thing the hunters would say about him was, 'That's the dog who liked the Boves' *tomini*!' They took this liberty, but they were very aware of how valuable Murò was when hunting and they had a great respect for him. They talked about him

*Kind of goat's cheese with a pepper rind

with that grave affection which I observed in the hunters when they were praising their dogs.

Mamma and I often followed papà and Murò along the Cant when they went hunting, in particular for birds.

For that lowly kind of hunting, a dog was a nuisance, and I had to hold Murò back. At times like that Murò certainly was not gentle, but he became even more beautiful. He would pull, stretch his head wildly when attracted by a call which seemed to make him beside himself. I would hug him tightly around his neck with my little girl's arms, hang on to his collar. Murò dragged me so many times like a deadweight into the thorn bushes and rocks. He would be howling with desire, and I with impotence. Afterwards, when he was panting and out of breath, I would embrace him tenderly and one by one pick the burrs and bits of straw off his fur.

He grew old and at the end was deaf and almost blind. He would bump into table legs, walk about with his head down, locked inside himself, depressed. Papà said they should have sent him for a while to a breeder who would have cured him.

Was I distracted by other things? Did I manage to overcome that loss? Because I can't remember when I must have understood that I would not see Murò again; worse, that someone must have put him down. (It's possible that I've forgotten the details because it made me suffer so much; so much

134

so that I wanted to avoid thinking about it.)

Murò had borne other humiliations in old age. Papà had got two young dogs with long ears, who took no notice of him; they were forever going about in a foolish, carefree way, and they would devour their broth in a flash. (This always vexed Ciota: the morning's food also had to make do for the evening, so she would take it away when only half had been eaten.)

This was in a period when my little sister was around. She is on a country road in one photograph, surrounded by dogs; she's crying desperately, and looks funny. Murò, mortified, stands on one side. He was no longer my little sister's guardian.

Before he was mine, Murò had been mamma's guardian. Papà could really only have left her on her own a few times, if as she said, Murò had been allowed to sleep at the foot of her bed.

'I even made him jump up on it,' she said with that almost arrogant air she assumed at certain times. 'I was frightened and he gave me courage.'

Could mamma have been afraid? What was she afraid of? Mamma used to shudder, press against papà often, but it seemed a joke, an affectation. Aunt Carlotta had said that mamma had been extremely fearful as a little girl and her brothers used to tease her. As a little girl, but now?

Signora Borgo also confessed to being afraid when her husband, the veterinary surgeon, was

called away at night. He took Maura with him, and so that she would not be left on her own (Bellina was not yet born), she sometimes followed him.

'Just like that, in my slippers, so that I could dash off quickly; but then we had to cross the fields and when I got back home again my slippers were all plashy.' (She meant soaking wet; she often used strange words because she came from Tuscany.) Was it not even more frightening to cross the fields at night? I could not understand mamma's fears.

Perhaps papà's long absences were because he was hunting antelope. He would come back a few days later, perhaps late at night with all his companions (he called them the Moving Squad) and invite them all in. They were muddy, filthy with blood; they would heap their rifles, cartridge belts, knapsacks in the hall.

Ciota was not there, but old Catlina, papà's ancient governess was. Catlina would stay calm, she was already used to such invasions.

To mamma, the antelope seemed an important and noble prey, but she was struck with horror when she saw the beautiful inert head, the veiled eyes.

When she talked to us when we were grown up about papà's exploits, she liked the lies that he would resort to, like a schoolboy, to hide the hunting expeditions from the eyes of some authority or other, or some prominent respectable person.

'I have to inspect a reserve,' he would say with a vague gesture.

That papà would make up stories to have a holiday was incredible; yet it was entirely in character for him to play games with the sort of decent boring person who did not understand, nor even suspect the passion for a day's hunting in the mountains.

The hunt did not always end up with an invasion. They would also gather at the Tre Colombe, Lino's. Lino was one of the hunters, and since he was the owner of a restaurant, he would invite mamma too. She went there several times; she liked Lino's wife, white and soft and constantly smiling, who did not lose her pallor even in front of a red–hot stove. Lino, however, was hairy and clumsy like a sheepdog. When his wife died, he married a taciturn peasant woman who let the hotel decline. (So papà said with regret.)

I used to see Lino in front of the Three Doves, one foot either side of a dirty gutter, or rather a drain in the paving. Lifting his cap, he would scratch his grey head, then put it on again back to front, spit in the drain and sigh, 'It's a dog's life!'

Before mamma he was ashamed. He grew covered in confusion and would take her hand between both his own, recall that in the mountains once she had condescended to drink from his canvas water bottle; then he talked about a little medallion which since I was small I had worn on a gold band around my wrist and he took my four little bones between his great big hands.

Lorenzo was another hunter whom my mother had met at Lino's. Lorenzo lived in the mountains and had to leave the little band before the others. From time to time he would say, 'Gertrude's waiting for me.' The others would praise Gertrude's patience gravely. Then it was mamma's turn. 'Is she your sister?'

'No, she's the mule.'

There was a sadness about mamma when she told those little stories about the hunters; they belonged to the earlier time which was the golden age for me, and perhaps for her had been the most difficult.

All the hunters seemed romantic characters to me, one more than all the rest with a proud cold manner and gentle green eyes. His name was Cometto.

I was already more grown up, in the fourth year at school, when papà took me on a hunting expedition. We left the house when it was still night, and the hunters seemed like bandits on the broad white road beneath the moon. We climbed the wooded Festiona mountain to a chapel, where we had to wait for the dawn.

The moon had gone, we were in the wooded darkness. Lino swore, then apologized to me, almost as if I were mamma!

The one with the green eyes at the others' urging told a story about a hunter (one of the

group? he didn't mention his name), who had shot himself.

'What was she like?' they asked. 'Like a Madonna.' And he added that she was from France, that she had short hair. Then in his deep voice, almost whispering, he explained, 'He leaned the barrel of the gun like this' and he brushed under his chin with the twin barrels of his gun, made a gesture of pulling the trigger ...

The leaves in the wood rustled in the approaching dawn; I opened my eyes wide and my heart swelled with an incomprehensible emotion.

Murò would crouch on the little wall which runs along the steps to the Belvedere whenever mamma and papà went into town and would stay there for a few days. He would refuse to eat or go inside again. Every now and then he would jump up, scrutinize the road carefully, then take up his post again. Everybody would notice and talk about it for a long time, they always remembered it.

It happened before I was born. Later on he stayed in the house because I was there and he had to look after me.

My parents nearly always took me with them when they travelled. But when they did leave me at home, I was frightened they would not come back.

Ciota would try to keep me happy. On one occasion she piled up the coffee service and glasses on the kitchen table, to have a party, she said. But it

seemed an extravagance to me and I was even afraid. Madrina had gone too; only Murò was left to console me.

In a dream I saw myself crouching against the porch wall in front of the door to the house. Papà and mamma were dead. Their ship had sunk in the ocean and I could see the tip of it. The Ocean was the planimetry which I had seen in papà's office and which I liked, because the broad loops of the river were coloured blue. In the dream, and remembering the dream later, the sense of being orphaned was a deep, intense sadness, but like a faraway disaster which had happened a long time before.

II

My little sister was not yet around when we travelled by carriage. You could take the mail coach from Ponte Stura into town but papà used to hire a gig. The coachman would mumble because he was always a bit drunk, especially on the return journey. His eyes would be red and mean, his hair dishevelled and his breath smelled sourly of wine. Mamma was very frightened when we went downhill and would shout out, 'Put the brake on!' The brake was a horizontal handle like the one on the coffee grinder. It made a dry, hollow sound, tac tac tac ...

Those journeys marked out the olden days which perhaps were the happiest (and at the same

time contained the biggest terrors); a period of uncertainties and conflicts, and pleasures which were no longer so intense followed. To be exact, it was my little sister who was the source of these conflicts.

I thought my little sister a superfluous nuisance in the way she had violated the intimacy of the three of us.

On every journey, I used to look out for the Three Trees against the sky high on a mountain ridge. They were a row of three firs or ash trees — one was a bit shorter — which appeared to be holding hands.

'They are papà, mamma and their little girl,' papà would say. That reply would fill me with inexplicable happiness.

We naturally travelled more during the warm months. At one particular point on the road you could see the Poppy Meadow on a crest, a small, uncultivated stony field flaming with poppies in the morning light. Papà had the carriage stop. He would clamber up there and gather a bunch of poppies for me.

The poppies had been a very old passion. As a very little girl (so they told me) I would call them 'wed–owers' (red flowers?). When I saw them I felt ecstatic. Papà would treat that kind of childish passion of mine with respect, he did not tease me.

I would not let them put me to bed one night because I had seen poppies along the San Marco

road and wanted to go and pick them. I remember my convulsive sobbing, the darkness in the room, and that 'I couldn't wait.' Mamma had lost patience with me and gone to bed, soon I would have to be in bed. Papà did not lose his patience. He tried to persuade me, then he satisfied me.

We went out, me holding papà's hand, on to the road which was hardly visible beneath the stars, right up to the field. It was a field shaped like a triangle, bounded by hawthorn. The corn was lightish and the poppies black. I swallowed my tears while papà chose the poppies at the edge of the field. I was sobbing again when we climbed back up. At home mamma was already asleep.

Which were better, the joyful outward journeys or the long, very slow journeys home?

We almost always came back at night. There were a host of delights. I was allowed to curl up behind their backs, I would listen to the trotting and jingling, the slow or the quicker rhythm according to whether the road climbed or was flat.

They would talk peacefully to each other, I would hear the subdued sound of their voices.

I looked up at the stars, I would gaze at one, then another. They had colours: blue, green, gold. I mixed their colours up by opening my eyes wide then closing them. I wanted the journey never to end.

When we arrived home, I was almost fainting

with sleepiness, but I tried to force myself to stay awake because I did not want to be thought a baby.

One journey in particular was different from all the rest, the journey to Monte Carlo. I had never seen a train. On it were red velvet seats covered in white lace. Everything shuddered and trembled, but I was not afraid. We ate sitting by the window at a little tip-up table covered with a white tablecloth. It was as if I were being transported to a strangely easy and magnificent way of living. All my sensations were more acute and at the same time dreamlike.

The sea was visible through the window and papà took a photograph of the sun's reflection on it. When evening came, the train became a sitting room all lit up.

A little drama took place. A lady was sitting on the seat opposite, almost sprawled across it, and was pressing a handkerchief to her face, as if she were crying. It seemed like a scene from a play, even more so because the lady was richly and fantastically dressed (like in the Salon de Paris postcards). The lady's handkerchief fell on to the carpet. It consisted of a tiny scrap of material with a lace border twice its size. I looked at it enchanted. I had never seen anything like it. Mamma whispered, 'Pick it up, give it back to the lady!'

A long moment passed. The lady smiled at me, and she really did have tears in her eyes. She waited while mamma pushed me forward a little, lightly

resting her hands on my shoulders. But I could not. I was paralyzed with admiration. I would have had to cross a void to reach the handkerchief .

I know that I did finally pick it up and hand it to the lady, but I can't re-evoke that moment.

The sky was still light when we arrived in Monte Carlo but the street lamps were already lit. The carriage went up and down broad streets between date palms and white palaces overflowing with towers, balconies, spirals, and already illuminated. The lights were bright and sparkling. (In Ponte Stura, the lights were feeble and sad.) You inhaled the scent of mimosa.

My uncle and aunt's house was high up a mountain. Everything was so new and marvellous that I was not too surprised at strange things. Like the fact that my aunt was combing her long hair – in the evening! – and that her hair was grey when her children were small; nor that my aunt was crying (from joy at our arrival?). Anything could happen.

In my sister's time, the tram already existed. The tram was somehow ours, in that papà was a friend of the owner. He even had a free season-ticket!

The owner of the tram was an elegant gentleman, of a different species from the gentlemen in Ponte Stura. His person exuded a perfumed warmth, his brown eyes had long lashes like a child's. They said he was in love with my little sister. He would tease her like Uncle Nicola did and say

that he wanted her shoes. My little sister was overpossessive of her things; she liked her new shoes, her beautiful little dresses very much, and so she was afraid of this so very amiable gentleman. I kept aloof from these skirmishes which I thought silly, but I was vaguely saddened that I was not an object of attention too. When I was grown up I found this severity, to which I was so attached as a child, rather melancholy.

The tram was luxurious, the seats like armchairs buttoned and upholstered in red velvet like the train to Monte Carlo (however, minus the lace). It had a good coal smell to breathe in. In winter my feet would be freezing, but I could rest them on an iron foot-warmer in the shape of a muff. The tram conductors had jackets with astrakhan lapels and when the trams were leaving they would blow a little brass trumpet. One of them reminded me of the coachman because he had red eyes too; he would drink at each stop but it was not dangerous because he was not the driver.

The tram would announce its passing by whistling shrilly across the silent valley. From the window of the tram the valley seemed different to me. I realized that in this way we were drawing closer to the city, that place of wonders; yet it made me sad. (Was this a presentiment?) I had to leave by that tram the October I left Ponte; from that time onwards it seemed to me I was infinitely detached from it.

The splendid tram grew old with the years; it died, decrepit, in the last war. They told me the conductors were the same ones and still had their lapels of fake astrakhan.

Climbing the valley now in a car, I have rediscovered the placenames and their echoes. Curious names: Beguda, Gaiola and Moiola (sisters?), San Membotto (did a saint with that name exist?). The stops on the journey then sounded full of promise. Now the villages disappear as soon as they are glimpsed; to pass through them like this without stopping seems like an insult. They are stops and stations no more, but reduced to fast-moving backdrops, just as in any other valley.

III

Halfway up the Belvedere steps is an entrance (now closed) for horses and carriages. Once the clowns' caravans had come through it. They erected their scenery on one side of the courtyard in the coach-house; tarpaulins masked the caravans and the bales of hay.

The wait was intoxicatingly long. I gazed at the red velvet curtain which was filled with mystery, but at the same time mobile, almost alive. The lighting was white, trembling acetylene light.

All the happiness ended with that wait. The show, a farce, upset me.

Gianduia was saying 'a humpback!' and they were already beating him, hitting the hump. The

little crowd would laugh and clap each time the hunchback entered; little boys clinging to the steps against the railings shouted enthusiastically. I was seized with terror at that point and papà bore me off.

The memory of an unbearably powerful feeling stayed with me. Perhaps it was all real for me and therefore terrifying. Perhaps it was also the applause and shouts of joy at a scene which seemed to me cruel, which was frightening.

I remember the second play better. However this time I had hardly had a glimpse of it when I was led away by authority. I was only allowed a glance.

I had heard from Ciota and the other girls from the Europa that there was going to be a performance, but it was to take place in the courtyard, not in the house. I was not so little any more, by now I knew my passion. I was in despair, because mamma, who had laughed so much at the strolling players' comedy, showed no interest in this new show. She said neither yes nor no.

My impatience was at its height; the day had arrived and I still did not know whether they would send me to bed that evening with the usual explanation that the theatre, like parties, started late. No one said anything that sounded disapproving, but I intuited it.

When the time came, Ciota accompanied me. We went in up the stairs of the house which led through a door on the first landing. The room was

packed with soldiers in a cloud of smoke. The scene was a garret made of boards which represented, I immediately grasped with delight, a prison. Albina, one of the young women from the Europa, was lying on the straw gesturing desperately. She was dressed in a black silk undergarment with fringes. She was reading a letter and sobbing.

Ciota must have been ordered to take me away at once. But I had taken in the scene with such ecstasy, that I was as satisfied as if I had seen the entire play.

Was it not strange that Ciota did not want to see any more? But she was extremely faithful to orders. I asked her, without hope, what might have happened to Albina and she replied, 'She has been betrayed.' From the seriousness with which she said it, you could see that the theatre was real for her too.

Ciota and the girls always knew when there was going to be a dance at the Town Hall. I thought they would be like a play, and wanted to go. It seemed to me that mamma and papà were laughing about it together, but on this occasion, too, papà had arranged to satisfy me.

Ciota and I went out soon after supper and were the first to arrive. The staircase and the broad entrance hall were in semi-darkness. All around were the usual benches where every day the peasants would sit whilst waiting to be seen in the offices. The large hall, still empty, was also only

dimly lit. Those minutes were agonizing for me because I knew the time limit allowed.

We sat on those benches too, and waited. It was very gloomy. Someone began to dance, but they were girls dancing together and they were not in fancy dress nor even dressed up for a dance. They were girls from the village. Ciota watched them disapprovingly and said, 'Real tarts.'

I was cold and sleepy and when it was time to go home, the party had still not begun.

The theatre was also a puppet theatre, and I was never disappointed by that. It was performed at the Calvi boys' house at the top of the stairs to the loft. One of the puppets was an old woman with rather yellowish white hair (made of cotton?); she talked in a shrill voice and when she got excited, she seemed angry and alive.

She was the Devil's Mother. But that was not what provoked the unease, it was the fact that she looked like Tavia from the Belvedere who was also always excited and had a shrill voice. The likeness was frightening, as if Tavia were really there, in those proportions and with that rage. When I saw Tavia again, I felt uncomfortable at first because I remembered the puppet.

But the painted cardboard backdrop of one scene made the biggest impression on me. It was double; on one side was represented a shady tree-lined road sloping down and gently curving; on the

other side was a steep stony road which led through rocks without a single blade of grass. I called them to myself The Road of Vice and The Road of Virtue. I knew why they troubled and saddened me. The shady path because of the contrast between its appearance and its real nature which was made up of betrayal and wickedness; the other frightening in itself, because it was inevitable that one would take it. It had its own beauty, too, situated precisely in its desolation; but the final impression was even more desperate. It was obviously a road with no exit, and that was the prospect of Virtue.

The fascination with the theatre was essentially nocturnal. I would only see the lights in Ponte early on in the evening during the winter twilight. (They used to put me to bed early.) The evenings made me feel an immense, consuming emotion. The arcades in semi-darkness became higher; here and there they showed feeble, reddish lights. The ones which streamed weakly from the windows and doors made the houses and the deserted streets even more mysterious. They had an aura of silence, of sleep.

In contrast when I went into the illuminated interiors I got an impression of splendid, artificial life.

The Club was more splendid than any house. (Mamma told us later that the famous Club was a

terrible place, a hovel...) I was almost always kept out of the Club. I knew they put plays on there; I was only allowed sometimes to be at the rehearsals, because they took place during the day.

For the most part I was disappointed; I must always have realized that the actors were only playing parts.

I never saw papà acting. I heard that he was very good, but he upset everyone because he would make up lines and other people did not know how to find their place again. As for mamma, she would protect herself and would not hear of performing. The gentlemen insisted in vain.

I saw the rehearsals for a farce in which Doctor Morin, the husband of the teacher of the third year, took part. He played the part of a guest who says he has had dinner and during the night comes downstairs in the dark in search of a bread roll. But in the rehearsal the set was not dark at all and instead of a bread roll there was a bunch of ribbons. Doctor Morin was very imposing; he was a large tall gentleman with a pointed beard and protruding eyes. It was difficult to imagine that he would tell lies and steal a bread roll, so when I saw him hide the bunch of ribbons under his jacket and look around him fearfully, instead of laughing I felt frightened. (Years later, far from Ponte, the Doctor became mentally ill; I saw him again in that absurd position.)

An extraordinary image from the Club was that

of the general's wife in her dress with the train. She was already different, like the nobility; in that dress she was marvellous, almost like the lady on the train to Monte Carlo. The dress was grey with large white stripes, perhaps made of lace. She had had it made for the unveiling (in Florence) of a statue to her father who was also a general.

Her husband, the general, was tall and severe, taciturn. For me generals were privileged beings, I believed them to be so by birthright, just like the nobility. I did not consider the King noble; perhaps because I thought of him as military, the Soldier King.

The final disappointment regarding the theatre was the performance in the Nursery. Everything happened stupidly without any mystery, in the open air and in full daylight!

It was wartime and the little ones were playing soldiers; they mimed actions with wooden rifles, now shouldering, now pointing them, and they sang marches with a military rhythm. Only one little boy had a real captain's uniform, because he was the son of a captain in the war. My little sister was the Red Cross Lady. The little boy captain was wounded, his arm was bandaged and he had a sling around his neck; my little sister was unafraid and said her line prettily, 'A little vinegar for this poor man!'

Only one moment in this despised play succeeded in moving me. In one scene a little girl

(Celina, the daughter of our baker, Blin) played an old lady dressed in a brown silk crinoline with a white wig perched on her head. She was so grave and majestic that she seemed a convincing but above all ancient woman. The little girl had to portray what she would become with time, an old woman, but she was also one from days gone by. That transference of times which I vaguely intuited made me uneasy; it gave me a sense of an elusive reality or perhaps of the true reality which was as yet dark and hidden.

IV

There was a big dark square stone against the last pillar of the arcades; Blin the baker would sit and rest on that stone. You could see him there when he was not at the window of the bakery.

From where I was I could see that Blin's old stone was still there. I was as grateful as if it meant, who knows why, that I had arrived in time. Perhaps because I had forgotten about it.

A man with a rigid gait walked out on to the square; one arm was outstretched and he leaned lightly on a stick; his round hat seemed to rest on a head made of wood. The man walked quietly in the middle of the road, and I was suddenly aware of the silence.

Below the house at the fountain, which still exists but is diminished now, humbled, lacking its basin, Ciota would walk about saying hello, calling out someone's name, while she waited for the bucket to fill up. Cilin's anvil would resound as it was hammered, while Cinto's would respond like a faraway echo. (At the bottom of the square where the blacksmith's used to be is now an electrical goods shop with no sign and one dusty little window.)

And the Cant? The whole time in Piazza Valloria, or in the house, its full triumphant roar had accompanied us. I listened, perhaps I could hear it, but with great difficulty, it was muted, dimmed. Why?

The man, I now saw he was an old man, walked in front of me. His face was gentle and a bit stupid. He smiled at me. That was how I recognized him, it was Blin.

I had always seen Blin covered in flour, his cap with the visor on his head. The fact that he had smiled at me did not mean that he had recognized me, he had always smiled then too. He would take my hand between his, speckled with pastry. Why was he so affectionate? Perhaps when I left Ponte I had not even said goodbye to him.

Blin, I now saw him from behind, walked down with small, mechanical steps (like someone recovered from paralysis). He stopped, turned right around in one movement and then sat down with another jerky movement on the wall, which was

low at that point. He remained there, extraneous, like a child, or as if he were already dead. He fell asleep, his head resting on his chest, now I could see all of his round head, his hands on his stick. That little walk, like the choice of a place to sit, must have been a habit, that was perhaps why they let him take it on his own.

Blin was still somehow a part of the house. The baker at the side of Piazza Nuova was called Parola. 'Go to Parola's and buy some bread,' Signora Borgo would say to Bellina. That was enough to give me an idea of foreign.

The world of Piazza Nuova was the furthest away, in relation to the familiar Piazza Valloria. Besides, even Piazza Valloria in exactly the same way was not completely familiar; there were some places which were more secure, some less. In the same way the arcades, familiar as far as the school, became dangerous after that. The shops which were almost all under the arcades, were a first intro-duction to the world, but were still linked to the house. I would go there with mamma or Ciota, or even on my own on errands for them.

I used to go with mamma to Ninin's little shop. Ninin was so fat that she couldn't bend and was breathless. I was only greedy for two things: marinated eel and Gruyère. While mamma was talking to Ninin, I would slip under the counter and repeat under my breath, 'Gruyère, Gruyère,

Gruyère...' Mamma would make signs for me to be quiet, but I would keep on until Ninin cut off a little piece of Gruyère for me from the round cheese.

There was a small grocer's shop displaying a terrine full of boiled haricot beans on the road leading to the parish church. Every time I passed it, probably on my way to church, I would stretch out a hand to that terrine and with the dexterity of a thief, take a bean. The bean would be cold and insipid, but I would eat it with a special enjoyment.

The shops, had I thought about them, would not perhaps have seemed important to me, but when I went in them they enchanted me. Each one had a colour, a smell; each one was happy or solemn or frightening.

I would never have gone into the butcher's shop on my own. It was small and dark, the walls painted an ox-blood colour, decorated with a motif of stylized lotus flowers which I thought were like cleavers. The thin nervous butcher would sneer and play around with his cleaver making it spin about, to impress me, I think. I pressed myself up against mamma or Ciota.

That stretch of arcades ended in a church. The whole front was covered with a large fresco; I would glance fleetingly at the graceful naked martyr, kneeling crossways and offering his neck to the axe being brandished above him by a short thickset man. The axe was identical to the butcher's cleaver. If I were alone, I would go the long way

around the butcher's. It was a secret fear like so many others; I knew it was one of those dangers which adults considered unimportant.

The most important shop was Nina Basteris' dispensary. It was in the Conti palazzo, near a mysterious doorway. (Sometimes it was half open and I would catch sight of a little dark courtyard.) There was a serious, almost solemn atmosphere about the dispensary. The windows were high, with an embrasure at the bottom like in a fortress. Oblong and oval boxes made of dark wood containing strong-smelling substances like camphor and cinammon were ranged on the high shelves. That smell and the blue of the sugar paper were all of a piece with Nina.

Nina Basteris was imposing. She wore long earrings and had a mass of curls around her brown, purplish cheeks. She wore the yellow shirt of the *Umiliate* in the processions; because of this I thought she must have been one of the ladies at papà's forbidden supper.

There were big glass jars on the counter with small sticks of twisted barley sugar inside; Nina Basteris would give me one and I would suck it slowly. But inside the other jars were strange, unwrapped toffees with beautifully coloured stripes; I thought they were precious like the little Venetian glass balls which you could also suck. I did not even dare want them, heaven knows who they were meant for!

I called Café Bertone Basilio's café, because that was the name of the owner, a tall, rather mysterious man, always wrapped in a huge black cloak. At that time everyone wore cloaks, even papà when he went to the country, but Basilio's was longer; and because he also wore a broad hat he had the air of a brigand about him. He did not bother with the café. His very thin wife would stare with her black eyes, the whites of which shone because they protruded a little. I was rather afraid of her. There was a son, too, a little bespectacled doctor whom I called Emilio Basilio.

The shopkeepers' families fascinated me. I could not imagine their houses, which could not be like poor people's houses but nor like the gentry's. You could have polite conversations with shopkeepers but not exchange calls. They had a protective manner towards me which was even more intimate than that of personal friends, and the result was that they intimidated me, though only when I was near them. Otherwise I never thought about them.

The only time they would ever enter my head was when I was reading fairy stories. These would often conjure up merchants and shopkeepers; I saw them with the faces and the shops of the villagers in Ponte Stura.

They did not always correspond. For example, the merchant in the stories was always rich and clever; the merchant in Ponte Stura was Medeo, a little man with a big head and a tranquil open face.

His long dark shop like a corridor always smelt rather sourly of cotton cambric. You could not imagine Medeo rich, yet he was somehow out of a story. Medeo's wife was small, like poor children's wooden dolls. The scissors hanging from her apron attached by a black ribbon were enormous, almost as big as her. Medeo and his wife made me welcome when I went in; they would smile kindly and seem amused. I was certainly small to them.

The tailor, who in Ponte was Tailor and Barber, as you could read on the sign I saw every day on my way to school, was a pale silent man with a black moustache. I identified him easily with the tailor in the stories, perhaps because when I passed I would see him bent over the clothes he was sewing, more like a picture than anything.

The same went for the cobbler whom Ciota called the Hunchback, the one I thought was the Jasmine of the song:

I am the hunchback
Called Jasmine
Owner of a shop
Owner of my garden.

As she washed the dishes, Ciota would sing another song at the top of her voice:

The pharmacist sells poison
as a balm

and you, you claim
I sell you my love.

I brooded over this impressive content. However, because the verse contained that mysterious
word balm, I did not see the pharmacist as the one
in Ponte Stura, Idina's father. Besides, I never
thought of the Calvi pharmacy as a place where
things were actually sold. The Calvis and the
pharmacy were too serious an institution even if
they were familiar.

The pharmacy was (and still is) in a fortified
position on the highest point of the old arcades;
you reached it from the road by a little steep stone
stairway which was built into the arcades, while
other steps led away from it to the side terraces of
the arcades. This as-it-were fortified position lent it
a commanding aspect.

When the glass door was pushed it shook a little
bell which sounded fretful and made you feel
irritable and uneasy. The pharmacy was narrow,
crammed with old shelves. Santino Calvi would
appear from the depths of the long dark rear, where
there was the white light of a low window at the
end like in a tunnel. He would blink his blue eyes.
He was a little bit taller than me, all of them were
curiously on a scale with the pharmacy, and he
hunched his shoulders, slightly lopsidedly, so that
he seemed crooked. Idina was short compared to
me, and every time her father said to her, whistling

under his moustache, 'You're letting her pass you! You're not growing!', she would retort, 'And what about you? You've never grown very much either!'

Then he would snigger and shrug his shoulders petulantly. These discussions about my height, something which had nothing to do with me, used to embarrass me.

Signora Valeria would also prepare and weigh the powders behind the counter in the pharmacy. Yet she was almost a symbol of the gentry for me; of the gentry insofar as they were strange, evasive, rather unhealthy, different beings from mamma.

Signora Valeria had about her a noble and tragic air like an actress. She held her head, which was large compared with her little body, thrown back, and her eyes would disappear beneath lowered lids. This gave her an air a cross between a queen and a sleepwalker. I always observed her in amazement. She was pale, with the rather greasy pallor of old wax; she had a prominent aristocratic nose, blood-less lips over large teeth. She would smile almost painfully as if the smile cost her difficulty and suffering. She talked slowly and hesitatingly, with pauses and gurgles (which in secret I tried to imitate). At their house, at a table already set, flasks and bottles were lined up, from which a few drops would be distilled into glasses. This was something you never saw at our house and I considered it a sign of importance.

To be invited to lunch at Idina's seemed an

honour. You would eat at a round table in a ground-floor room which adjoined the pharmacy. The food would be a kind of meatball, a croquette flavoured with spices and smelling vaguely of the pharmacy. I would eat it reverently. The Signora would smile with pleasure at seeing me eat. Mamma would then say to her, 'What is so special about what you make that she never eats at home?'

Signora Valeria liked very much to be a success. It was a tradition that when she made her famous 'cisi' soup she would send papà a bowl of it. The maid would come with a covered dish. It did not appear as something domestic to me, but an honour, something which reminded me of a mysterious sentence I had heard, 'When the king sends the wages.'

I suspected a shadow hung over the friendship between my parents and the Calvis. I had grasped that the Calvis were for the nobility, therefore they were the Doctor's enemies; they never in fact mentioned the Doctor in their house. When I learned later from mamma that some people in Ponte had not approved an increase in papà's salary, I was afraid that it was the Calvis. I did not ask about it because fundamentally 'I did not want to know'; besides, mamma would not have answered me.

That they were different constituted a reason for embarrassment, curiosity and respect on my part. The Calvis were not what you would call modern. All the inventions dear to papà, the phonograph,

photography, sport, hunting, fishing, were so
foreign to them that just the idea of our introducing them to these things was laughable.

They never went for walks, in fact they never
even went out. Sometimes I succeeded in taking
Idina to the mountains; when we sat down to eat
near a spring, the stuffy, respectable smell of the
pharmacy would issue from her packet of food.

V

In summer I would withdraw to the balcony in the early part of the afternoon, curl up against the railing and gaze fixedly at the road glittering in the sun, until the three of them would very slowly appear: Idina, Felicino (her cousin) and in the middle of them Tota.

They were all the same height, because Tota was a dwarf. The black lace umbrella dominated the group. Two would look up as agreed. Each time I was afraid that they would not look round. They made no other gesture, nor called me, but they walked on demurely with little steps.

I would ask permission from mamma and each time was anxious, because mamma seemed unhappy.

Why? She preferred people to come to the house, she did not like us going to other people. My passion, however, was the opposite, to be invited, introduced to the secrets of houses, lives. At home I was fine when on my own, and, in fact, visits and the presence of other people would almost destroy my world, so that I no longer knew how to play and grew bored.

At a sign from mamma I would fly down the stairs; I let myself slide, leaning one arm on the handrail, to join the three. Often they had stopped; the old woman seated on a little wall with her feet high off the ground, the children leaning on one side. Tota was having a little rest.

When Tota opened her large grey mouth to speak, you could see her teeth, which followed a line going in the opposite direction to her lips. I stared at her fascinated by this monstrosity. It was that particular thing and not her hump nor her dwarf's stature which seemed extraordinary to me. The afternoons in Tota's garden were long. It took a long time to get there, though there was still a great deal of time to play. It was evening when we went back. Each time Tota told me that she would have liked to send my mother some blackcurrants but they were not yet ripe. I reported this to mamma and she appeared neither indignant nor shocked by the lie.

At the bottom of a very long wall was a door covered with studs. You opened it by turning a key

several times. Tota's head came up to the keyhole. She would turn the large key with her soft little gnarled hand which seemed to wrap itself around the key.

The door gave on to a stone terrace from which a steep stairway descended. The garden was much lower then than the road. I remembered it as limitless, losing itself in the shade of the hazels. The sections, divided by blackcurrant bushes, were kept either as garden or meadow. There were a few flowers, of the aquilegia or stocks variety, dark curled flowers which had something old-fashioned about them.

We would play beneath an arbour in sight of the terrace; Tota would sit up there under another umbrella which was white. She would watch us children and the gardener. We were not allowed to break off even a little bunch of blackcurrants. That brilliant red along the hedges made the garden almost magical.

We played at making sad little meals with grasses and stones; but we also plotted, pretended to run in order to go out of bounds and pull off a small bunch. In our haste, it was more the roughness of the sour taste which stayed in our mouths than the delicious acid flavour of the blackcurrants.

Every so often, to my enormous surprise, the gardener would find a way of getting us near the blackcurrant bushes. I was also frightened of him and excited by his complicity. The man was sullen

and brusque, and we used to say he was Tota's enemy.

There was a house in the garden near the entrance; it seemed enclosed and half-hidden by creepers like Sleeping Beauty's house. At the beginning of summer it was all wistaria blossom. It was only opened up on the last day of the season and the affair was imbued with solemnity. Tota would hold a party.

Mamma did not take the party seriously; it's unsure whether she attended it, with the Calvis. Perhaps only once.

The party seemed magnificent to me. The house, into which the sun penetrated only that day, showed itself as a book filled with indecipherable stories which had been exhumed. The rooms smelled strongly of mould, which was actually how the sitting rooms in Ponte smelled. Thick black cobwebs hung everywhere. To me even they seemed a luxury.

The reception consisted in offering boiled potatoes. (Perhaps this was why mamma used to smile about it.) The boiled potatoes were naturally good, but to eat them like that, leaning one's plate uncomfortably on a dusty armchair, they became something altogether new, a refinement. They were prepared by Modesta, Tota's old maidservant, who spoke in a thread of a voice, as if she were constantly crying.

They said that Modesta stayed with Tota without

being paid. Was Tota rich or poor? Was it true that the Calvi children kept her company to appease her? The fact that Tota was mean was not strange, yet she was mean in a rather peculiar way. I heard people talking about these things and it seemed to me that they formed a part of the garden's importance. If I tried to tell mamma about them, she would not comment; she did not reprove me but she did not encourage me to continue.

I also played statues with Idina and Felicino in front of the pharmacy. I was always amazed when I saw how much better than me they were at miming the actions for the various trades, perhaps because they were more familiar with the shopkeepers. Our dominating house and mamma's tastes kept us aloof from the village.

We also used to play in the courtyard cluttered with boxes and empty flasks; it was a sad but exciting place because it was dusty, untidy, even dangerous. Dark and sordid valleys, tinkling grottoes of little bottles and phials opened up between piles of boxes.

Or else we would play inside Idina's house. The dark stairway smelled of ipecacuanha. The silent house was ancient and noble. The decrepit grandfather, who failed every time to recognize me, used to sit in the sitting room in an armchair. I would stop for a moment to look at him. I would have liked to know, for example, how he felt about being

like that, in that state, which was almost like being a thing. Idina talked to him by shouting, she seemed to know how you should behave towards him. But we immediately forgot about him.

The grandmother was dead and her house was open on the floor above. We used to go there to play; we did not give the grandmother a thought. In a cupboard were her clothes which we used for our theatrical costumes.

Felicino had invented the theatre—cinema. On the wall opposite the sofa was a big mirror, and at the side of the sofa, a door. Inside that empty space the actors played their parts; the audience seated on the sofa would see the action in the mirror. The two little sisters made up the audience, mine and Idina's, the two little sillies.

We also played at theatre in Stura; we were already grown up (it was the final year in Ponte for me) and they let us go there on our own. In Stura you could, actually you had to, play your part at the top of your voice to drown the noise of the river. There were secondary branches to it, which represented, as in my dream, the Ocean. Felicino, standing in the shallow water, would declaim a farewell; he was a father emigrating to America. We, as the children, stayed on the shore.

We had taken our dresses off and the wind (or Felicino) had thrown them into a gutter. We were ashamed to go into the village in our petticoats. Felicino walked at a distance from us holding up

his bucket disdainfully. He said he did not want to be seen with naked women. Huddled up against the back door, we waited for him to decide whether or not to open it for us.

Felicino was ugly, but at the same time attractive (I heard the ladies say so). His wide mouth had a kind of ironic sneer about it, and his eyes were teasing beneath large brown eyebrows. He had a peculiar habit of sucking on saliva in one corner of his mouth: that was also a coquettishness, a pretended shyness. He had pleasant manners which were almost courtly, yet you got an impression of being taken for a ride. He knew how to have a conversation with ladies; he would talk slowly, with hesitations which seemed affected, shifting from one sandalled foot to the other and moving his hands. Mamma would interrupt her sewing at the machine to listen to him. She found him very likeable (as one would find a man likeable, not a child).

Papà did not like him. The men disliked Felicino and the boys even more so; he never played with them. He was always with us little girls. They said about him in the village (Ciota did too), that he was *despiasent* which means unpleasant and offens-ive at the same time. Felicino used to walk about under the arcades leading a chicken on a string and he took her everywhere so that she would peck and annoy the ladies in the shops.

His mother admired him as well as complained about him. Idina and I would tell stories about his

173

exploits, I did it perhaps because I was influenced by her.

Felicino used to go and visit certain old women. To comfort or torment them? There was an old café beneath the arcades of his house. He used to go there, and we did too sometimes, to 'pay a visit to Madama Baruc'.

Bent old Madama Baruc wore a kerchief knotted under her chin like a peasant. She would complain that no one remembered her. The polished tables in the big rooms which no one visited any more reflected the white light from the windows. Bunches of old postcards were stuck in the mirrors, Madama Baruc had been sent them as a young girl. Felicino took one of them and put it in his pocket. When the postman tipped it out on to the counter, the old woman must have recognized it and began to cry. 'You wanted to get some post,' Felicino apologized. Was he malicious or sympathetic? Perhaps both. His act did not seem a good one to me, but I considered it out of the ordinary, the sort of thing you might read about in stories and I admired him for that.

Madama Bunduan was the widow of a *garibaldino*. Her house was completely dark, you would bump into the chairs. She was minute, her little face bristled with white hairs and her eyes, with no eyelashes, were red-ringed. She would welcome us surprised and smiling, then sit down at the piano. She played frantically, accompanying a

thin, inarticulate shadow of a song. Some of the keys were mute.

We would snigger as we squeezed together on a sofa. I would wait with a feeling of faint nausea for what would happen.

'Did you hear that?' and the poor mad old woman would suddenly pause in her strumming. Idina, who could not control herself, would already be laughing. Felicino, with his peculiar smile which was a mixture of flattery and insolence, would say: 'What?' 'Didn't you hear footsteps?' 'Where?' 'At the bottom of the stairs ...' 'Who could it be?' 'One of my admirers!'

She would go and spy at the door then begin to play again, then interrupt herself once more. In the end we would run almost tumbling down the steep staircase. Outside we tried to get excited again by going over the scene and forced ourselves to laugh. I did not tell mamma about those visits.

It was not just in these situations that I had a bad conscience, but every time I played with the others. I felt uneasy, as if I had been split in two, in fact almost as if I were outside myself, and I had a painful feeling of being at odds with myself.

If the others came to my house, however, my interest in them disappeared. We would play tombola with Madrina or I had them look at my books, which no longer seemed so beautiful to me.

Papà would see that I became different in the

games with the other children in a way which he could not have liked; and he would never want me to be too long away from the house.

Mine was a kind of obsession, which led me to rebel even against myself. We used to play at journeys on the terrace of Felicino's house (in a wheelbarrow). The journeys were longer or shorter according to the names of the cities we nominated. Cesco, an older brother, would be the judge. Ciota had come to get me and I refused to follow her. My friends backed me up. This intoxicated me. Ciota went away, stiff, offended (she could no longer bear to see Felicino). She came back later on, saying that papà was angry; it was up to us to believe it or not. It was Ciota, I said, who wanted to interrupt the games!

My friends offered to go home with me to complain about Ciota to papà. We crossed the village. Ciota went on ahead hurriedly, ever more upright and indignant; but she was counting on getting satisfaction. I followed her and behind me came my friends, even Cesco who was already in high school. We walked outside the arcades in the middle of the street, quite a procession.

I was stunned by my unexpected popularity but noticed an uncomfortable feeling, an emptiness in my stomach. I climbed the stairs in terror and when the door opened I heard the noise of my supporters hastily running downstairs. Papà had a sad, distant expression on his face. He did not say a

word and hit me with a single slap. It was a very serious matter; I knew papà disapproved of the use of violence. It was this which upset me; making papà suffer and feeling his disapproval was unbearable to me. I could no longer understand how I could have done it. I did not even cry, I was too desperate.

As a little girl looking at that eye, I had been frightened that papà was going to die; since then I had not been able to bear seeing him suffer. Mamma did not suffer when I was mean to my little sister; at bottom it always amused her a little. And besides she found it ridiculous to make a drama out of things.

I knew that papà's sufferings were more pitiful.

In the song 'When one day in the mountains' which I heard sung at Aunt Carlotta's, the girl who fled with her lover would say '... and I did not even kiss my old father's hand'. I felt very sorry for that old man. A little earlier in the song it said that the mountain air was 'pure – untainted by love'.

What did it mean? Perhaps love was bad? The word tainted made an impression on me.

Signor De Vito had two very beautiful daughters who had made him ill. I had heard papà complaining about this. I used to hear Ciota announcing that 'one of De Vito's daughters has run away again'.

Signor De Vito had a famous garden which I used to visit with papà. In his garden ablaze with flowers, Signor De Vito was pale, grey, in fact; he

seemed like a photograph instead of a living person. He greeted papà unsmilingly and said (like King Lear), 'You have daughters too?'

The rebellion against Ciota was also linked to the dislike which we children had for our maidservant when we were out with other people, almost as if we were ashamed of her.

When we were little, the maids in their little white aprons with the big starched bows would accompany us when we went out. They were Ciota, the red-cheeked Anin, who would go with Bellina, and rarely, Antonia, Idina's maid who was like a nun and fat and surly; you had to be especially respectful of her because she was a widow.

Mamma said that the maids in Turin had rebelled against the uniform and the white apron. 'Because they're a sign of servitude,' she had commented. I accepted this strange information and waited for it to be confirmed. It was true that hostility was engendered during those walks made by the children and maidservants, as if the uniform falsified their usual relationship. At home we were always around them in the kitchen and in their rooms; outside we children were united, and the women similarly. The women would listen to our conversations and make fun of us. We would talk about things which were fashionable amongst the adults: ghosts, making the table rock.

'You silly things,' Anin would say, 'you'll make yourself frightened and then come night-time you won't be able to be on your own.'

'Ciapinot will come and tickle you,' agreed Ciota (Ciapinot was a diminutive of Ciapin, the Devil).

We would talk about ghosts precisely to make ourselves frightened. The day-time fear was delicious, at night it was agonizing.

I found myself unprepared on the subject of the little table, because my family did not take part in séances. Not just that, but mamma would laugh about them with papà. I knew that they had been the first few times, but their scepticism had made the experiment fail. Fulvia told me, in her serious fashion, what had happened to a lady in Turin, not to impress me but because it was a true story. Doors opening by themselves, icy breath on your neck, whispering in your ear.

Mamma's lack of belief was part of her rebellion against fashion and worldliness, but above all it was her taste for intelligible, real things. Ghosts seemed even to me something simultaneously frivolous and disgusting, yet I pretended to be interested.

Other conversations and secrets only took place when the maids were not around us. We had become bigger. Idina confided in me what she had discovered about babies. But she would laugh nervously while she did; that was how her feelings always betrayed her.

The discoveries were suppositions and logical deductions which Felicino had made. He had noted the fact that in the Capuana story it had said the Queen had sired a son. That word, which sounded repellent to me, was used when talking about a cat or a bitch which had had babies. Mothers then made babies.

I listened without showing surprise, because I did not want him to realize that I did not know. Idina and Felicino must have talked in secret about these things whilst excluding me; I had the impression that they thought me a baby.

They would use a rather affected slang together largely made up of mispronunciations; there was something ambiguous and tender in Felicino towards Idina. She would act coy, bluster, annoy him; but she was flattered.

They told me to look at some beggar or another. He was a man with purplish swollen drooping cheeks; one leg dragged and he had a rigid arm which he waved about crosswise in front of him as he limped along.

'Look where he's putting his hand' and Idina could hardly hold back her laughter. The man was already rather repulsive, and that fixed gesture made an obscene picture of him. Why? He was an old man, clumsy and sad, his shame seemed an unjust punishment to me.

Oddly, that kind of thing provoked in me a kind of sadness mixed with unease more than curiosity.

I experienced an anticipation of disappointment, a weariness of life. It was not a fear of violence, but rather an intuition of inevitable, fatal decline.

Even if there were things that adults must know, I preferred to think that my parents were ignorant of them. Ciota knew, in fact she surrounded my parents themselves with mystery ('that' mystery). I almost hated her for that. When I was a little girl I used to climb into the big bed to cuddle up against papà, to play with the pillows, but she, coming in to dress me, would shout at me, 'It's dirty!' (Why?)

In the street alongside Blin's oven which led to the Barracks behind the house, I often used to see a pale, listless little girl, sweet as a madonna, who took care of a small boy. Ciota manifested a kind of disapproval of her and told me not to look at her. I had deduced that it must somehow be linked with sin and that this must affect the little boy; in fact Ciota did feel sorry for him.

The little boy used to scratch amongst the pebbles and once, when he bent over, lifting up his little vest, I saw something sticking out. I thought that it was a little deformity, perhaps an illness which was a result of his mother's sin. I felt shame (I used to feel shame about all illness) but remained troubled because it was new proof of a relationship between birth and sin.

Idina said about her own little sister who was six,

'She's still innocent.'

I was frightened and dismayed (like the time when I discovered that rich people were damned). It seemed perilous that I had lost my innocence without being aware of it; worse, without even knowing what a good thing it was.

Saint Geneviève was innocent; did that mean that she did not know how babies were born? While Ciota was reading me her story I had had that impression because of the particular tone of voice in which Ciota would pronounce the word innocent; yet my reason told me it must mean not guilty.

It was terrifying to have lost my innocence, because once lost, it could not be regained. I envied our despised little sisters who possessed it; I felt bitterness for the lilies, which were its symbol!

I would have liked to leave my confusion and unenlightenment behind. The thought that I had to risk life in ignorance made me dizzy. But I would immediately drag myself away from such thoughts.

VI

Were my school friends, the more quick-witted ones from the village, talking about those things perhaps when they seemed to be plotting something? I never thought that. Such things never entered my head when I was at school.

Twice a day the bell in the Town Hall pealed out its peculiar note: tan-tina ... tan-tina ... gay and impatient at the same time. I was afraid of being late and would hurry but not run. I did run when I was going home though, I would even alternately jump and hop right up to the house, my school bag bumping against my legs. The shopkeepers would tell my mother, 'She jumped down the entire street!' and it seemed to me they were admiring me.

The schools were (and are still) on the highest point of the arcades, where the village slopes down behind them towards the Cant. I crossed the short dark entrance hall, the corridor illuminated by light coming through french windows at the end. I thought the light was cold, and poor somehow. The smell in the latrine is cold too, and it also smells of poverty, and is reminiscent of prisons and hospitals. That was not how I remembered it. Then it had been mixed with other warm smells both acrid and insipid: ink, the stove, and little girls who had their own smell too.

At either end of the balcony are two doors, for the First and Second Forms. The little bolt on the door, in the shape of a cross, is what I would touch when, with heart racing, I arrived late and the classroom buzz, its heat and intense odour, and the teacher's emphatic voice suddenly seemed full of a powerful alien life which I did not dare face.

The teacher in the First Form was called Magnetti. She was dry and ugly (and good naturally). I heard people talk about her unkindly; I had picked up ambiguous looks, silences which had to mean something, but what I could not imagine. I was in agony over it. I thought the Magnetti teacher deserved special respect, she was a Red Cross Lady! The urchins in Ponte Stura would sing in the street:

General Cadorno
made a mistake

he sent Tota Magnetti
to the Red Cross
boom boom boom
to the noise of the cannon.

The teacher in the Second Form, Paoletti (Tota Pinota), welcomed mamma on the first day of school but remained on the platform of her desk so that she could dominate the class; she was very small. Her round face with its turned-up nose, framed with an abundance of rippling little curls, was drawn with her effort to express authority.

She maintained her air of severity with all the mothers and would declare drily, rapping her desk with her knuckles, 'We're not in the First Form any more!'

That year mamma and Signora Borgo used to visit the school, they were the Lady Inspectors. I was very excited. Mamma seemed more beautiful than ever to me, but in a way distant too: even if she smiled at me. I realized that it was all a game for her.

The ladies held the little girls' stockings or exercise books in their beautiful hands, they caressed them under the chin and the little girls would blush and shyly reply. I suddenly realized how humble these little girls were, and they were my friends.

In the terrible winters in Ponte my friends would cover themselves up with only a black woollen shawl which they wrapped around their necks.

Perhaps I had accepted this like everything else, but mamma, who watched me through the window going off to school, had observed the pupils arriving from the countryside many times and talked about it with papà and with us children. She was particularly sorry for three small brothers whom she called The Three Unfortunates. They came from a hamlet beyond San Marco. She would lament their rags, the scarves wrapped around their hands swollen with chilblains.

All the children in Ponte Stura wore clogs in the winter, I had them too. They had a wooden sole and a leather upper with a toe reinforced with brass. Bunches of clogs adorned the shoemakers' doors.

When the boys came out of school they made marvellous slides on the ice, the track was a dark stripe in the middle of the snow heaped up around it.

That winter in the Second Form, one of my friends stopped coming to school, and then we heard that she had died. I do not remember her face any more. Her scarf remained hanging on the cloakstand (the same ones are still there, made of thick roughly planed wooden pegs). When the teacher left the schoolroom the little girls would play with that scarf, they made it whirl around and said it was a serpent. Whoever it touched would be bitten!

When she came back, the teacher gave out a punishment. The little girls knew where she went most regularly, to have a chat with the other teachers, for example to talk about the price of

eggs. The little girls used to laugh; when the teacher reappeared, her little figure erect, her face irritated, they would fall silent, frightened.

She treated me roughly too; but she was not entirely fair, as she was also more considerate to me because I was the daughter of gentry.

Every day the first thing the children had to do was to say prayers, standing behind their desks. The Paoletti teacher made them say absolutely everything: the Hail Mary and the Creed, the Ten Commandments, the Seven Deadly Sins, the Cardinal Virtues and the Theologicals as well as the Church Precepts and the Works of the Misericordia. She meanwhile would go back and forth scrutinizing the little girls' faces one by one.

Immediately afterwards she would climb on to the platform and hammer out, 'Pocket handkerchief and work!'

She used old-fashioned words which made us laugh the first few times, then they became part of her authority and inspired terror instead. The little girls had to put up both hands: in one a handkerchief, in the other the heel of a sock. I often used to forget one or the other; my mother was a bit forgetful at times too. Then the teacher would send me home to get what I had forgotten and would have me accompanied, this was one of the privileges, by a companion.

These companions, daughters of woodcutters or shepherds in the mountains, made me their

favourite. Perhaps they admired me in the same way as I admired the nobility, finer people, a little mysterious. They were generally older than me and because of that they also protected me. They wore their long hair gathered up in plaits at the back of their head, their forehead and neck crowned with light curls. They had a good smell of smoke, hay and the stables too.

After the Third Form I lost them. I recognized one when she was untying some bundles from the mule, behind the house. We greeted each other, I saw she seemed already a woman.

The ones from the village, the shopkeepers' daughters, were different. They were my friends, too, but they usually showed off about something or had secrets amongst themselves. They made me touch the hole they had in their earlobe for earrings. I was ashamed that I didn't have one.

Mamma let me go and pick flowers with my school friends only once. They were not the timid little girls from the mountains, but little girls from the village. They were like conspirators, they grew excited and had discussions; suddenly picking flowers grew into an almost risky business. I discovered that their adventures were more exciting than those of wealthy children. The plan seemed somehow profane to me, we were going to pick narcissi. We scattered about the fields beneath the Castle along the Cant. I was amazed that there were narcissi there as well; we used to go a good

distance along the Stura with Uncle Andrea.

My friends told me to pick sour grass too. When everyone had made a bunch, we climbed up the hill again to the Castle and sat down there in a circle. The bunches were all thrown together; the little girls took the narcissi out of the heap one at a time, quickly split them, sucked the sweet sap and threw them away. I was dumbfounded. I knew too that in the narcissus stem there was a drop of sweet stuff; I too used to spoil some to suck it, but that banquet seemed to me the height of profanity. You had to chew the sour grass every so often to avoid feeling sick.

Two little girls were humblest of all. They were Dependants and came from the College of the Immaculate Virgin. One was blonde and had big protruding eyes of a pale blue which was almost white; she sniffed continually and had rather a bad smell; the other was dark-skinned with red cheeks. They made me feel sorry for them and I tried to talk to them. They repaid my pity by bringing me little scraps of chasuble or other sacred vestments embroidered (by the nuns) with gold thread and silks in precious colours. I liked them very much. For a whole year they promised me a red rose, but they never managed to bring me one.

The Paoletti teacher was once explaining something in her emphatic monotonous way and as

usual I was not listening and did not hear; I only grasped the last bit, the question 'Who wants to go?' I immediately put up my hand and was picked. I was given as companion one of the little girls from the mountains who was almost double my size, in fact almost twice my age too. I can see again that little girl's narrow pointed face, framed by a mass of black curls; her eyes were gentle and her smile extraordinarily meek. She was one of the ones who were devoted to me. It was she who took hold of the reason for the errand, a bundle which she supported in both hands because it was heavy. It was a large knotted kerchief and contained eggs.

When we left the school, we took, as we understood, the direction to the high valley; we crossed the two squares and came out on the main Vinadio road. Every so often I asked, 'Where are we going?' My companion replied in her meek way, 'I don't know.' 'Nor do I!' and we laughed, both of us convinced that the other was joking. We swapped the weight, which was a heavy one for me, from time to time.

The deserted white road unwound, the mountains showed darkly. There was a little house high up on the mountain. 'Shall we go up there?' I said and laughed. The other replied perplexed, 'I don't know.' 'You really don't know?' Then we realized, and got frightened. We turned back. By now we were tired, but we walked quickly, in silence.

When we arrived back in Ponte it was dark. The school was closed, so we took the bundle back to the teacher's house. I do not remember if we were shouted at; memory, at that point, until then intense and precise, fails abruptly.

Again I climbed the stairway which after the first flight splits into two smaller flights, very steep and dark. I went into the Third Form classroom. On one side the windows look out on to an alleyway; the window beside the teacher's dais was opposite my desk. I would watch the snow slowly falling through that window, see the thaw drip from the roofs in the March sun. Its light seemed remote, peaceful, timeless, like the light in a painting.

The desks are made of rough wood, blackened like tables in a tavern, full of deep notches, old ink stains.

My fascination with teachers and ladies was united in the Third Form teacher. She was the municipal doctor's wife and mamma's friend; they were intimate. When I was in her presence I felt that timidity and reverence which were signs of my admiration and which excluded confidence. My heart beat fast when the teacher called me from the dais. Her voice was deep and rather hoarse. I thought she looked like Signora Selve except her skin was dark; they were both thin and supple and their caresses plunged me into the anxious excitement of infatuation.

The teacher was working at her crochet; she called me and without saying anything arranged the lace around my neck, removed it, then sent me back without explanation. Besides her manner was always dry and straightforward. This went on for several days.

The collar was for the teacher's little girl. I heard her say to mamma, 'I took the measurement from your little girl's neck because all the other children's necks are dirty.' I had hoped it was for me, this rather absurd supposition had quite intoxicated me.

Signora Morini had a sister who was a Fourth-Form teacher, she was very different from her. I thought she looked like the hairdresser, to whom she was not even related. They were both tall and thin but they seemed fat because they both had big round stomachs which was the manifestation of an illness they had. They were ill but always lively, their laughter made their enormous stomachs shudder.

I found resemblances useful for categorizing people, making a sort of catalogue. I discovered that if you found one resemblance there would be others. The hairdresser and the Fourth-Form teacher I liked because they were authoritative but good-natured matriarchal figures, yet devoid of mystery and fascination.

The inspector wore his coat even though it was almost summer and kept his hands in his pockets. We little girls stood at our desks, arms folded.

'Which is the most important Food for the Human Body?' the inspector asked. It was a boring subject but the fact that it was an external inspector who was proposing it kept us in suspense, made us anxious. 'The Human Body needs Salt,' said the inspector. Then he discoursed at length on the baneful consequences of a salt scarcity which reminded me of the terrible consequences of mortal sin that I had read about in my Catechism. As usual I was impressed by scientific exposition. At home I talked about it even though I knew mamma would smile, divesting the matter of any importance at a stroke. Which is exactly what happened.

In the fourth year I had a friend. Her name was Rina Ramella, the daughter of a forest guard, one of those who went with papà on his expeditions.

Rina Ramella was top of the class. Mamma asked the teacher, 'In what way are Ramella's essays the best?' 'She adds something,' she replied, 'which is like salt in soup.'

I used to go with Rina to the mountains. Ramella, the guard, already an old man with a grey moustache, would bring his little girl along. Papà not only allowed this, but had asked for it. While they inspected the reserve we always used to play the same game. We would scrape up a bit of earth and make miniature cemeteries, then decorate the little lined-up tombs with flowers and small stones. Ramella had suggested the game.

We only had to follow papà once on a long journey around the mountains because they were working coal in the valley. 'Why?' I nagged. Papà said gravely to the guard, 'I don't trust them. They are *lingere*, good-for-nothings, rotters.' The guard nodded solemnly. And it seemed to me that even Rina showed with a look that she had understood.

It never crossed my mind to question Rina about babies. I did not think it a suitably intellectual subject for her.

Rina lent me a book. It was bound in sheepskin and had thick yellow pages; the writing was dense, with e's the same as f's and it smelled of mould and tobacco. Ciota called it The Missal. I put off reading it. Since Rina had given it to me I thought it too difficult. But I liked smelling it and dreaming about the title *A Thousand and One Nights*.

Rina was tall and pale and had a strange tic. She used to pinch the skin on her long thin neck folding and then unfolding the supple skin with rapid movements of her fingers. Her neck was darker at the spot where she did it. I supposed that there must be some relationship between this nervous habit and Rina's superior intelligence.

Ciota did not like Rina. She thought her tic repulsive and asserted that she was sure I was far cleverer than she was. For me it was enough that she was my friend. I thought it right that Rina was ambitious to become a teacher. I knew my uncles were professors and as Rina said, 'Professors have

authority over teachers'; yet I maintained that to become a teacher was the highest ambition possible.

In the Fourth Form I discovered patriotism while singing 'The Girls of Trieste' with my friends in the choir. At home, papà was hopeful of victory, mamma was worried about her brothers (the doctor uncle was also at the front) and about all the soldiers. She would beg papà to obtain an exemption for those who were fathers of a family (they called it the 'xemption).

Pariotism belonged to the gentry. In the village they used to sing the famous 'If you want to see Trieste, look at it on a postcard' and I suffered a little because of that. But Ciota went even further. She would sing with a gloomy and vengeful air:

And those fine folk
who shouted long live war
and now have a son beneath the sod
shout long live war no more.

I realized that it was impossible to pit 'The Girls of Trieste' against that 'Beneath the Sod'.

We went to Catechism after school (not when we were still in the Fourth Form, however). The girls were at the end of the nave on the right, the boys opposite. The boys came in all together after us; a roar like a torrent of water would go up, their clogs

thundering on the tiled floor.

The Sisters from the Infant School were the teachers of the Catechism. A teacher called Liscia was in charge of the boys. There was greater promiscuity on the benches with your friends than at school. Some friends had a bad smell, they would tell frightening facts, 'If you take Communion and there is a sin you have not confessed, your tongue will turn black and fall out on to the floor.'

The children were gripped with a kind of frenzy when the sisters arrived late. The boldest would sit inside the confessional, others, red in the face from convulsive laughter would kneel behind the grating and say rude words, or at least ones which seemed so to them. I was ashamed later and tried to forget those moments.

The priest would come and make inspections. He was young and tall and restless. I often used to see him playing football behind the church. He had a mobile, mocking face, a little like Ciota's. Instead of asking questions about the Catechism he would ask other ones in fun. The Sisters' faces were more severe than usual, but the little girls would get excited and laugh. 'What month is it when women chatter less?' The Sisters would not laugh but touch their wimples in embarrassment.

On Sundays during Grand Mass I would watch the priest with Idina and Felicino; we found his quick genuflections and nervous gestures funny. He sang the Ite missa est with trills on the 'i' which

seemed extremely strange to us; we were convinced that he had invented them to make us laugh.

One year Idina's mamma was Cresima's godmother. Papà took a photo of her at her godfather's, Doctor Morin, beside the bishop. Signora Valeria had her actress's air, she held her bell-shaped skirt bunched up in one hand; she kept her eyes lowered but smiled at the bishop almost flirtatiously. That bishop had an incredible name for a bishop; he was called Flower. Doctor Morin was in a dress coat with tails.

In another photograph papà portrayed the *perpetue*, the priest's servants and sisters; an idiot with a face completely covered with hair had managed to get into a corner of the photograph and was sitting on the ground laughing.

Another year mamma was Cresima's godmother. I had stayed at home with Ciota. They had also invited Madrina to lunch at the Parish. But someone came to say that I was invited too. Ciota dressed me, made me sit on the kitchen table to put on my white leather shoes, which would not have happened if mamma had been there.

The lunch was in a dark dining room around a very long table; what impressed me most was the soup. Little balls floated in the broth and had a sweetish taste; they were called royal noodles. The food seemed particularly ecclesiastical to me.

★

The little square in front of the hairdresser's is as deserted now as it always was; it only lacks the man with the white moustache who used to sit on the ground against the façade and mend umbrellas.

At the side of the church a road climbs to the Chapel of the Counts Bolleris at the top of the park. I would go there with Ciota on the Day of the Sepulchres. The park remained secret, you were only allowed to stop at the damp dark little church, which was truly sepulchral.

All the churches in those days were gloomy and because of this Ciota wanted to make me laugh. She made fun of the women, imitating the way they walked, tugged at my sleeve so that I would watch the Mute who was gesturing or Falenda, a wandering mad woman, who would embrace and kiss the Cross in an obscene fashion. I used to laugh but tried not to look; I felt it was sinful.

Why did my mother send me with Ciota? For the usual reason, perhaps, that she did not like to go where everyone else was going.

I wanted to see the Counts' pew again where the Marquis had stood up for Mass and had piled up those big books in front of him; our pew, which papà had had made with arms and a high back by the carpenter behind the house, now bore another nameplate.

Mamma brought a big book to Mass bound in red leather as fine as silk which had as its title a strange woman's name, Filotea. At home mamma

would let us look at it when we played, it was full of pictures, souvenirs of College.

For my First Communion I had been given as a present a little white book bound in some hard material and closed with a golden clasp; later I had another one, a real book with a brown cover which I read during Mass. It did not contain prayers exactly, but a kind of meditation on death (physical).

'When my dried-up mouth ...' There ensued an analysis of the torture of thirst, of the difficulty of breathing and speaking.

'When my eyes are ready to close ...' Every chapter was the re-evocation (I saw them all with a bluish or violet tinge) of the final decay of the body and its senses. It ended with an invocation, but I skipped that. I thought it necessary to prepare myself for death and the book succeeded easily in familiarizing me with the spasms of agony. I knew them by heart. I would never think about them, however, except when I read about them.

In that church I never felt the joy of the processions or of my thoughts about the presence of God 'in every place'; since it was precisely there that I was unaware of it.

VII

Was it only because of the Doctor's huge authority
that I faced the Piazza Nuova with a vague sense of
fear as a child? The air you breathed in Piazza
Nuova might be more refined, but less secure and
less peaceful than the one we had at home; was this
because 'God was not present'?

Not to believe in God was madness to me. It was
if you did not believe in the Law of Gravity, but
also, in a certain sense, the opposite. The Laws of
Gravity frightened me, they seemed like a machine
which could get jammed and ruin everything. You
could not not believe in God, however, if he
himself had said, 'I am your Lord God.' It was like
accusing him of being a liar. (The argument

seemed irrefutable to me.) God was reassuring; he only made me a little bit afraid in his guise of the 'eye in the triangle' which I would see in church above the main altar.

A lady (holiday-maker) had asked the veterinary surgeon if he believed in God. I watched him in suspense. He exaggerated his usual bitter sneer and shrugged his shoulders. The lady said portentously, 'Superior men do not believe in God.'

I felt bewilderment, almost fear. Because I knew that the Doctor, too, did not believe in God and the Doctor was certainly a superior man. Was it true, then, was it fatal? Since I was on the side of superior men it was a new condemnation, like being rich and losing one's innocence.

The veterinary surgeon seemed even more vulnerable to me, he was a strange taciturn man, and at the same time dangerous. The Doctor's case was different; papà had faith in him, and mamma admired him.

The world of Piazza Nuova was a complex one. The Doctor lived there and although I almost never saw him, I considered him to be easily the greatest authority. The Borgos lived there. But above all there was the chestnut walk.

The trees of the ancient avenue are decrepit now and even falling down. The dusty earth, unswept, looks somehow crumbled.

Beneath the shade of the once-straight thick

chestnut trees I gathered the scattered flowers fallen from the tall candelabra. The most precious were flaming pink ones, tender as red wax. I was amazed that such a profusion of beauty lay on the ground.

Perhaps had I come in May ... Perhaps they still flower even though the trees are so exhausted; but the ground would now be as neglected as ever and dirty and the shade meagre.

Fulvia used to walk beneath the avenue amongst her admirers. Giglio Gorsin, Madama's son, brushed the strings of a guitar on the Gorsins' terrace. The sizzle of a red-hot iron on a hoof, a pawing and whinny harmonized from the blacksmith's beyond.

We all used to play beneath the avenue: Bellina from the house, Idina and Felicino, Titi the younger son of the general's wife and other children holiday-makers. We would play four corners or other well-behaved games. Meanwhile, the village children would make us envious as they threw carbide into the gutter running alongside the chestnut avenue, and watch it burn in water!

But we had played at one time in a freer, impassioned way, in the Barracks. When could this have been? The Barracks, which we used to call the headquarters, was a long tall building with arcades and a long open space in front. It was open, empty and abandoned as if after a flight.

There were immensely large rooms with high, arched vaults of dirty white; the stairs were strewn with straw, you could smell horses, hospitals and

latrines everywhere. We would make the hallways and vaults resound with our running and shouting. (I saw the Barracks from the last war on the same spot; gloomy sheds with all their blue glass windows smashed in.)

There was jealousy between Idina and Bellina which was to do with me. 'She's coming to me tomorrow!' 'She's coming to me for lunch!' I knew that their two worlds were in opposition, and I did not participate. Yet I suffered as a result; I was afraid that it would end up with my having to announce a preference, which would have seemed unfair to me. I wanted to be like my parents, friends with everyone equally.

Bellina's parents were modern, similar to mine in that respect. Signora Emma was a friend of mamma's; in so far as you could say she had a friend. Their meetings were not calls like they were with the other ladies.

The two mothers who were friends had made identical aprons with lilac stripes, and papà had taken a photo of them together underneath the chestnut avenue. Bellina and I when we were little also had identical aprons. It had a pocket in front on which was sewn a coloured figure, mine was a *bersagliere*, who was making a Turk in a caftan and red fez flee from his bayonet; on Bellina's the *bersagliere* was kicking the Turk. (I was pleased that it was not mine; I thought it brutal.)

Bellina was smaller than me; I had to hold her hand in the Castle because she kept slipping around on the dry grass. We had been friends in the First Form for a while, then they had taken her out of that school.

We used to go to the toilet together. There were two holes in the ground crossed by a grating; it was wet and slimy all round it. Once, to our disgust, we both slipped on that slimy coldness. The teacher helped us and dressed us again. For a long time I felt humiliated because of that.

Bellina would repeat, continually shrugging her shoulders, 'I don't dare … ' and her mamma would reply, 'Blockhead!'

Signora Emma was dark like mamma, but quite different: fatter, more flamboyant. She had a big red mouth, her upper lip was shadowed a little. Her teeth, which she showed often as she laughed, were admired because they were compact and shining. She liked company and gay parties. She used to say, 'My father brought me up like an American!' (I wondered what this might mean.)

Once she said to mamma that both of them had married too young when they knew nothing. She would laugh and sigh and mamma nodded doubtfully. I thought that they were joking, but remained puzzled. If mothers really 'did not know', then life was too risky.

Some afternoons Signora Emma would come to the house to listen to records she liked. Her favourite

was one which went, 'What says the murmuring sea to you?' When she put a record on, mamma was breaking papà's rule. Mamma was rather careless when she used the machine; once she did not lift up the arm holding the needle in time and the record got scratched. I was afraid it was a serious matter but the record was not important and papà said nothing.

Mamma and Signora Borgo would lend each other novels. Their favourite was *My Cousin Guido*. (When we were grown up we laughed at her books from that period and she admitted, 'What little sillies we were!')

Signor Borgo had lines of disdain at the corners of his mouth. I had heard the story of how he had fallen in love with Signora Emma when she was a young girl running about under the chestnut trees, her plait hanging down her back (something I could not imagine and which seemed incredible to me). After he had married her, he reverted to being bored and discontented. He had a magnificent setter, Maura, but he was too lazy to go hunting; papà would say, 'Borgo, cards and his pipe' and shake his head as if he were sorry for him.

I thought he had a sad, mocking air about him as if he were laughing at himself and others, who did not understand why he was sad. He was gentle when he bent down to hug Bettina, but with his wife he was dry and even rude. Sometimes I thought he looked at her angrily. That was very different from the teasing yet affectionate look

which my parents would exchange; and in other houses like Idina's, for example, you were not aware of any kind of look.

Yet I felt compassion for him.

The Borgos were friends with the Doctor especially in the sense that they were on the Doctor's side; they were intimate with Tota.

When you said Tota in the Calvi's house, you would mean the Tota with the garden, while in the Borgo household Tota was the Doctor's sister, Tota Jefina. The other Tota never happened to be mentioned in either of the two houses.

Signora Borgo thought her Tota tiresome. They used to talk about Madrina, she and mamma, and Signora Emma would say, 'I've got a *soscera** too!'

As far as Tota was concerned, nothing was done properly and there was always something to find fault with. She told a story of how Tota had scolded her when she did not bring in the linen immediately after sunset; I did not understand the significance and wondered if there might be some hidden meaning in it.

I had heard that Jefina was jealous of Signora Emma. Was that possible? Her husband was certainly Tota's favourite and Tota addressed him as *tu* and treated him in a brusque protective way. They had been friends a long time, before he was married.

*In dialect: Mother-in-law.

206

Tota Jefina had a garden, too, or rather a vegetable plot. We did not go and play there, yet we could follow her, interrupting our games under the chestnut trees. She would call out in her rather nasal yet strong voice like a man's, '*Masna**!'

Bellina would run and hug her. Even I would be kissed too and the sensation of those kisses was not unpleasant exactly, but strange. Tota's chin would prickle because it was bristling with cut hairs as hard as pins.

Tota was particularly clean, despite her advanced age. Her hair was white and luminous. I liked to look at it, seeing how a rosy light would appear from underneath it, while on the heads of other old women you would discover amongst the small pads of false hair, crusts or dark spots like lichen.

In the afternoon Tota's white head would appear in the ground floor sitting room, bent over the little table at the window. Signor Borgo and his wife, or some other people, never the Doctor, would be with her. They used to play cards and had a sort of gadget to record the scores.

It seemed strange to me because we did not play cards at home. Or at least, not in earnest. Sometimes after dinner we children would play Don Bruschett with Madrina.

The Doctor's house, which looked out on to the chestnut avenue, is closed up now, fallen into decay,

*In dialect: Children

yet it still retains its special air, a certain elegance. There are the tall windows, the steep staircase on the side which disappears beneath an arch (it led to the kitchen) and in front, the short shallow flight which seemed so formal to me with its low semi-circular steps. The border of the roof is still edged with fretted wood which was like a frivolity, a coquettishness in contrast with the severity of the Doctor's house.

I did not find the Roman stone again on which I used to lean against the corner of the house. It was of white, bevelled marble and you could see a palm motif above the inscription .

Inside the Doctor's house was like every house I admired and at the same time found frightening; it was dark and shining. In the kitchen, the severity was lightened by the presence of the servant, who was fat, smiling and bald, as you could see when the kerchief slid off her head. Her name was Ciota too; it was a bit embarrassing, like an unexpected kinship.

Beyond the house there was a little cobbled courtyard. Against the opposite wall inside a shallow niche is a statue of a Benefactor, a spare white marble gentleman in a tailcoat. He is preoccupied and rather bored and looks sideways with his head bowed, like a noble gentleman who behaves correctly in every situation but is lost in thought.

The Doctor also seemed lost in thought but in

quite a different way. He was not sweet and tired like the noble gentleman but proud and absorbed in contemptuous thoughts.

The Doctor loved and detested Ponte. Such extreme feelings were all of a piece with him. He was loved by his few friends in a similar fashion and the poor whom he treated for nothing; but he was loathed by the gentry and almost the whole village. The former loathed him because of his ideas, the latter because of his aristocratic ways.

He really was proud. After his political defeat he drove his gig across the entire village with head held high and the challenging air of a winner. (I heard my parents recounting this.)

The man in the statue was the founder of the Hospital, an ancestor of Count Bolleris. The Doctor had been defeated in the political battle by that same young Count who was supported by the Marquis, his stepfather.

The Doctor had managed the Hospital, then had been moved out because he had spent too much time renovating it. He had been Provincial Advisor (Mamma and Signora Borgo had gone to the city to see his chair); he was not re-elected because he did not want to impose taxes on the peasants. Papà said he was right; he and the Doctor had seen at first hand how the peasants in the valley lived.

I learned how politics worked in Ponte. But it was a quite different era. Now the contenders are no

longer people from Ponte and fight one another with different, noisier methods.

I supposed that papà supported Cassin, a Jewish city gentleman, who claimed that he was continuing the Doctor's political line; yet papà said that everything was quite different now. His opponent on this occasion too was a Count. In the village they used to sing:

Viva Cassin
che Roasend l'e a la fin.*

Papà detested the way they fought, the vulgarity and near violence. On election days we would go to the mountains to pick mushrooms. We could see the sunlit village from the darkness of the woods and make out the bustle of a little crowd on the piazza; from time to time voices and shouts would reach us.

Papà and mamma thought the Doctor a huge enigma. I think they admired him precisely because he was different from the others, contemptuous of pettiness.

My parents' respect for the Doctor was something difficult, but not a reason for anxiety. It rested on a secure basis, my certainty that they were incapable of being mistaken.

They also admired the grand old man's beauty.

*In dialect: Long live Cassin/Roasenda's on his way out.

The Doctor was tall, erect, with thick white hair like Tota's; his two-pointed beard, which had been reddish, had become white. Lots of small red veins reddened his face. He had a keen glance which might be mixed with either affection or irony. One eyebrow was slightly raised and that too seemed a small indication of arrogance.

Papà took many photographs of the Doctor, especially on a sledge in winter. In one photograph he looked as if he was buried beneath the snow. Lumps of snow lay on the blanket and on the fur beret tied under his chin. Fido the horse had a plaid blanket, too, the snow lay on his head and back making him look like a statue. The wall of the Belvedere was behind and the snow formed little mountains on the rocky outcrops. Over everything lay the dreamy and suspended air of winter.

To me the Doctor belonged more than anything to that earlier time, before I was born. But his legend endured in the way mamma and papà talked about him, endured in the person himself. I saw him in front of his house sometimes, sitting upright and frowning in an armchair; he would be reading his newspaper. When he came to our house he was different. He still seemed imposing but as if liberated, relieved of his frown.

Even during her last days mamma would light up on remembering the old friendship with the Doctor. 'It was only us he would voluntarily come to see and stop and talk,' she said, and added with a

211

touch of pride, 'He liked our ménage.'

The Doctor had been papà's friend before he was married, then he became our family doctor. Mamma would quote one of his phrases years after Ponte, 'Medicine should limit itself to diagnosing the illness and letting nature do its work.' Mamma was inclined to agree with that sentence.

As she crossed the Doctor's room mamma had glanced around admiringly, almost covetously (so it seemed to me). We had gone up with Tota and some other ladies to watch the Revue for the end of the Great Manoeuvres from the balcony. She had stared a moment at the famous portrait of Kant which hung at the head of his bed (instead of a sacred image), an old man in a wig who had the same name as my stream (but you spelled his with a K). There were endless books on shelves on the walls, magazines heaped up on armchairs. I knew that they were not only about medicine but also about literature.

Before she went out on to the balcony where the other ladies were standing, mamma turned to the Doctor who was following her and apologized, 'We've invaded your room!'

The Doctor smiled, 'My room has never had such a beautiful ornament!' Mamma remembered that sentence years later; yet she disliked compliments. But it was surely the fact that the Doctor had said it which made it important, and the way

in which he had said it, with that rather stiff solemnity touched with irony which he possessed.

The Doctor was a kind of saint for mamma. How was it possible, I thought, since he did not believe in God? Yet mamma's certainty comforted me.

The Doctor had come to retire in Ponte Stura as a young man because he was ill. He had fought his illness with the healthy mountain air and the life of an ascetic. Mamma once said of him, 'If you had made all those sacrifices for the love of God, you would be a saint.' (What had the Doctor replied?)

He was also a poet for her. He had written a madrigal in honour of mamma in the provincial newspaper, a welcome on her arrival in Ponte Stura. 'The crown of golden jonquils, which we offer up to you ...' Years later, for the inauguration of the tramline the Doctor wrote, 'On the bridge over the Ella, looking through the window towards the abyss, a young woman shudders and turns away ... ' That picture of her was so real that no trace of the madrigal remained.

The Doctor had been a comforter. As he went from one room to the other, he had caressed mamma's cheek; I understood he was consoling her. But for what? Because of Madrina? Because of the ladies?

When he met mamma holding my hand in one of the little country lanes, the Doctor would get down from his horse and holding it by the bridle

would accompany us right up to the house. The ladies would murmur ...

Mamma would stick out her lip disdainfully or smile pityingly.

The Doctor's defeat endured time. Nothing – and perhaps no one – recalls him in Ponte Stura.

By chance I went into the Cemetery. There were monuments leaning against the wall. I went towards a low one, flat as a plank. There was only one name in large detached letters: Giuseppe Antonio Vinaj. Nothing else. How desolate it was, now, that faith in one's own name! That defiance then endured, too, the solitariness which mamma had admired in him. The Doctor had wanted to be cremated. Mamma, when she knew about it, said she would pray for him nevertheless.

A little later I discovered Tommasino Musso's tombstone. His little face with its sad eyes in the little picture under glass is as preoccupied as it always was. I did not know that there had been an inscription:

Tommasino Musso
delicate flower
plucked from his father's garden
transplanted
to the gardens of Heaven.

The signature was GAV, the Doctor's initials! The

style was that of the jonquils, but the garden was real, it belonged to Ponte. And the gardens of Heaven? Neither the Doctor nor Master Musso was a believer. I never knew they were friends, yet it was natural. And their being side by side was a comfort to me, it made the Doctor seem more familiar.

VIII

I had not been back to the Cemetery since I used to go there with Master Musso. Then it was small and wild, planted with wooden and iron crosses leaning crookedly. They gave the place its rather mad air of some macabre dance. But the wild flowers lent it the grace of an abandoned garden.

Now it's no longer wild, it's grown and been reorganized. I seem to remember papà himself doing the work.

Or perhaps I had been back there once, when I was already in elementary school, for a funeral (they say burial in Ponte). I had also sung the beautiful song for dead children 'Beati Immaculati in Via'. So it was the accompaniment for a child.

Who had it been? I remember only the journey there and the song.

They had given me a large key (I had to ask for permission in the Town Hall to visit the Cemetery) and I was afraid that I would not know how to use it. But it turned smoothly in the lock like a house key.

I began to look at the portraits. Perhaps none of the names would be unfamiliar to me, the sound at least; but the enamelled photographs in their little oval frames held the faces and I was sure of recognizing them.

The Paoletti teacher was there with her curls framing her little round face. I noticed her full lips. I had forgotten her; but it was those lips which had frightened me.

I also understood, suddenly, that the teacher in the Second Form had had a respect for me which the other teachers who were friendlier and more affectionate had not had. It was because she was indignant when they called me by a nickame, 'You must not give people dogs' names!' She called me by my proper name (which seemed pompous and strange to me). And perhaps it was from respect for me as a person and not because of my social importance that she had me accompanied.

They talked to me about her in Ponte. She had grown very old, but she was always lively. She never wanted to go to the cinema (there was an auditorium in the Barracks), yet she liked people to

tell her the plots of the films. She would pretend indifference for these stories and then after a few days would suddenly ask, 'Did they get married then, those two?'

The Paoletti teacher had had an admirer. It was Signor Termignon, the erudite tinsmith. Once he had burst out in front of her, throwing his arms wide open, 'You're always magnificent!'

This sentence (like the famous 'observant') was recounted again and again as an example of his style. The quotation was made to amuse, but it also contained a certain admiration for Signor Termignon's imagination. I was uncertain as to whether that magnificent meant very beautiful or alluded to the teacher's hospitality as I understood she had offered him a drink.

I found Signor Termignon's inscription; it was not in an elevated style, he had not prepared it himself.

There was only one picture on the Calvi tomb; the one of Felicino's mamma, whom I had rather forgotten. She had the same eyes as him, teasing. But mamma used to say she was the kindest lady in Ponte. I only remember that for picnics she would spread a special jam (which was very dark and delicious) on the bread.

I was sorry that there was no photograph of Doctor Calvi (who looked like Chekhov). Felicino's father often came over in the evening to listen to records. He was a very attractive gentle-

man with a strange old-fashioned (mamma used to say) manner. He beat time with one booted foot. When he laughed, his pince-nez would fall off his nose. Papà used to call him by his first name, which enchanted me, Celeste.

The Borgo tomb had no photographs. It was the most elegant but the most neglected. Bellina's name was there as well as the veterinary surgeon's. Bellina called herself Flora. She had died (of cancer) aged twenty-six. I had seen her again when she was dying; she was yellow and shut up inside herself, almost shrivelled like a leaf. Someone told me then that Signora Emma was still alive far away, and that she was ill, actually paralysed (news which I found incredible and absurd).

I discovered another little portrait which attracted me. I recognized Celina, Blin's little girl, who had been my sister's friend in the Nursery. She always had a rather grave, hypnotic air. Her eyes, which I knew were blue, gazed knowingly into the distance with an innocent solemnity. Her inscription also read 'Borne away very young by a pitiless disease'.

Alongside the great main doors of Ponte's Town Hall a double colonnade of several arcades opens up, which is closed at the bottom end by a large gate and gives on to a narrow courtyard where the grass grows between smooth cobblestones. All the children in Ponte used to play at putting their heads between the large iron bars of that gate

(perhaps they still do). Some bars seemed pushed to one side, bent as if someone very strong had made a gap with his hands.

In my dreams the Town Hall appears as an enormous complex castle which has been sealed up, like a kind of Kremlin. You reach it by a road which ascends in broad curves (the staircase?). Does it mean that I do not dare visit it? Now it is for me the most imposing place in Ponte Stura, even more than the Counts' palazzo, because it is more real. Perhaps it is because it was there that my father was in authority?

Papà's office was not big, but it was imposing. It was sad and austere, the furniture was black, there was a stale smell of old leather and ink. Papà used to sit alongside a low window which had the same cold wan light as the windows in school. In front of the desk was a tall bookcase which obscured the rest of the room.

I always felt a moment of joy when I entered the office.

I went there very often with mamma and my little sister to claim papà on Sunday mornings as we came home from Mass. There was more activity in the Town Hall on Sunday mornings; it was the day, like market days, on which the mountain people would come down to the village. As we went through we could smell their acrid yet simultaneously fragrant odour.

When we went in papà would lift his head and

look at mamma. I observed in that instant that mamma seemed to shine in the dark office and at the same time was as if embarrassed by her beauty.

Papà gave me one of my favourite steel pens as a present, the ones which were shaped like a heart and had a band at the bottom. Somehow I thought papà produced these pens; because of this I had a special liking for them, while other pens, which were grey, had no narrow part and were shaped like a drinking straw – mine were a beautiful copper colour – seemed foreign and insignificant to me.

Papà could send a messenger from the Town Hall to fetch or carry something. The messenger himself was an important person. He was an old man, tall and severe, with a large grey moustache; the sign of his authority was a special cap with a visor. Mamma would offer him a little glass of liqueur; the messenger would drink it slowly standing up, and I would watch him fearfully.

Papà could also give orders to the road menders. When I was only five papà had taken me up into the mountains; on the way back I was tired and complained, 'There are too many stones!' Papà solemnly replied, 'Tomorrow I'll tell Rico the road mender to come and take them away.'

Again I went up the great staircase of the Town Hall. (I was going to enquire about my visit to the Cemetery.) I could no longer detect the old smell. I turned to a door-keeper, who looked at me

perplexed, then accompanied me to an office. It was papà's office.

I recognized it from the position of the window, the melancholy light. It seemed strangely big to me; perhaps because it was full of low card indexes inside drawers. The dark old furniture was not there any more.

I was suddenly struck by the meaning of that office. I realized, almost for the first time, the lowliness of my father's work, of his life which had seemed so magnificent to me as a child.

Now his life once more seems a fine one to me, but in a sense that I would not have understood as a child. And that certainty is not a comfort now for my incomprehension then.

Besides, the only regret that papà had was that he had never been able to study letters. He dreamed of other things, like a trip to Greece or Palestine, or studying the flute; projects which were left for old age.

I had been almost shocked when I had heard him say that he had done technical studies because of family misfortunes (a squandered inheritance and other mysteries); otherwise he would have chosen to become a teacher. For me the Office and his work were all one with papà. It seemed monstrous to imagine a different papà. And the mountains? And Ponte Stura? I felt a retrospective dismay, as if I could myself have been erased from that possibility.

★

In a dream I saw the Estate as it had been before papà bought it (he had had it for almost nothing from the Town Hall). It was a little hill just outside the village, rocky and wild. Frightening too, because in the olden days a gallows had been erected on the summit. In my dream it was once again bare and wild, windswept. There was the darkness of a storm, lightning flashed and not a sound was to be heard. My heart was beating because I had always complained about not having seen Podere as it was earlier and now I was seeing it like that.

I felt that I might meet someone. But I found Murò asleep, curled up in one of the rocky caves. Silent tremors raised his long hair, his stomach rose and fell in sleep. His presence gave me a sense of security.

A little beyond the hotel, in the bend of the main road, is the Podere hill. Papà had sold it later after we had left Ponte.

Now it was undergoing big changes; they were laying the foundations of a house, not on the summit as papà had planned, but near the road. The Pinnacle is still standing on the summit.

Papà had had built on a narrow bit of level ground, like a symbol of a future house, four slender cement columns with bevelled corners, which upheld a balcony with a railing.

That airy construction, weather-resistant at the same time, might give an idea of papà, of his

optimism. The cousins from Turin would tease him a bit about Podere which they called, I've no idea why, Mount Pleasant.

At the foot of the columns papà had planted climbing roses. I could announce to my friends that one of them was tinted violet (which bordered on the incredible).

The first big task at Podere was the construction of a high boundary wall all around it. Above it small cement columns supported a metal grille; the columns ended in a kind of geometric head which, if you looked closely, had an enigmatic face. Inside the imposing boundary wall the hill was still wild. The other task was to map out the beautiful big road which ascended in two broad curves right up to the Pinnacle. It was to be used by cars. It was edged with white carnations; when you went mushrooming in the woods on the opposite side of the valley you could make out a very white winding thread as you looked over.

The section of road which commanded a view was the steepest; there were caves (where in my dream I had seen Murò). Papà had been able to dig out and prepare the fields behind, more stones than earth, for wheat and potatoes. But papà's real passion was plants. Sparse and stunted fruit trees had not changed the hill's physiognomy in the slightest. Papà's favourite was a kind of ash which bore bunches of bright red berries. It was called birds' poplar because the birds loved to peck at the seeds.

The lavender bushes were still luxuriant between the scorched paths.

The man who worked at Podere was called Pietro. Since the soil of Podere was poor, papà had decided that Pietro could keep what it yielded and bring us only samples. Even those we saw rarely. Pietro was small and slow; he called papà *sur Patrun*. He had a daughter whom mamma and Ciota never called anything but Pietro's daughter.

Each year Pietro's daughter had a new baby in her arms; the one from the year before would cling to her skirt which was shorter in front because of her protruding stomach. Mamma was sorry for her, or rather sorry for Pietro because of his daughter's children who had no father. Ciota said they were many and all soldiers. She said it with a fierce air, and I realized it was a painful, shameful secret.

Pietro's daughter was gentle with her children; she would caress the little head covered in a white bonnet with her big stubby hands. (She pastured goats on the crags of Podere.) At such moments her wild face would express a sweetness.

Her nose was flattened so that the holes of her nostrils were bigger than her eyes, and her thick lips stuck out further than her nose. She did not have her father's humble manner. She would complain bitterly, talking to Ciota, about the other girls from Ponte because she said they sold themselves for furs. Ciota confirmed that they were worse than

her. They named one of them, the mother of one of my school friends. I knew the fur; a moth-eaten fox which she wore round her neck. I thought she was not a girl since she had a child. I always had violent feelings when I listened to these conversations, despite my trying to reduce the facts to something reasonable.

You could walk through Podere on the old paths, between drystone walls and mulberry hedges.

Some capitals have fallen off the encircling columns. The thin fruit trees have not developed much; I could not find the birds' poplar. The fields looked better cultivated to me, but they showed signs of drought.

I know that you cannot feel the wind which blows up there anywhere else. Only a breath reached me on the path.

I especially loved Podere for that wind; you could feel it more at the top amongst the lavender bushes where it carried a little of their intense perfume. I liked to be there at twilight like now, when that wind would come from faraway countries and worlds.

You could see crosses along the paths then: against the walls, under the untidy cascading hedgerows. They were like the ones in the cemetery: black, covered with a little roof of frayed tinplate. The tin plaque nailed to the wood on each one bore a

name and date. They were the names of peasants who had fallen down (drunk) in the snow one evening after a party.

The desolation of those solitary crosses held something sweet and comforting for me. The little villages at the head of the paths have almost all been abandoned. One of those paths was the Madonna of the Pines. I looked for it and saw it emerge at the top of a high spur of the mountain chain, and behind it the church and the old twisted pine tree.

The Hermit used to live up there. People visited him reverentially, they would give him alms. He ate only what he was offered. There were potatoes in a drawer wrapped around and around with a thick tangle of roots like a ball of wool. Mamma was horrified. They would have been poisonous for other people but not for him. Whenever the Hermit felt ill in the night, he would ring a bell and people from Fedio would come running. I liked the word Hermit very much. I liked it in another form too: Ascetic. (Papà had a little book, a School Prize, which Madrina used to look after, bound in violet with gold decorations which was entitled *Teofilo or the Young Ascetic*.)

I found the isolated house again which used to frighten me on those paths. It was a private house, painted a light colour, yet it was menacing: empty, with doors and windows fallen in. Its mystery was even stranger amongst the wheatfields and piles of

stones and therefore more real. The silence surrounding it was not the ordinary silence of the fields but something which had undergone a secret violence.

From far away the house seemed to me to have been repaired; perhaps someone lived there now. When I reached it I saw that it had in fact been renovated and modernized but that later there had been a fire. The damage was not recent, it must have happened during the war; you could see indistinctly relics and things from the war through the doorway.

IX

Podere and the Cemetery were not places to me; the Cemetery was always part of the countryside, Podere, the house. But other places were similarly witnesses and almost participants in our lives. More than this, they had a history which had happened 'earlier' so they had traits and personalities like people. But they dressed themselves up in the ornaments of the seasons, and their history was as if veiled, rendered infinitely distant.

I think that I felt the intimacy of the Castle especially because I saw it constantly from the windows of the house. My parents were fond of it too; it was papà's favourite, the background for his photographs. As a child for me the Castle was

the place of every delight.

It had grown nearly wild again, but not natural at all. You could hear the echoes of old stories there. You would come across signs of civilizations, avenues, spaces, but also traces of military presences, massive high walls, the remains of the demolished fortress. The silence of places which had been battlefields was everywhere, the theatres of forgotten defeats.

The entrance was after the last house in Borgo Sottano, a high gate between two pillars. The gate is open now because nowadays the Castle is open to everyone (and perhaps no one goes there). The cripple told me that it's a school camp in the holidays. The chestnut avenue is as tall, thick and dark as it once was. However the big circle where the first steep climb ends lets in too much light; the ring of trunks is no longer complete. From there the avenue curves and climbs steeply again in a slope which we never crossed. We would stay in the circle.

All around were odd stone seats sunk in the ground which were fragments of architecture: pieces of arches, capitals bordered with mouldings. They looked concave, like armchairs. It was these which evoked the solemn decorative air of the circle, something like that of a stage set.

Then the grass was tender, thick and even, dotted with flowering daisies. Now it's dry, uneven, trampled down here and there. You can detect tyre tracks in the avenue. All the new signs of life are

signs of violence, hurrying decay, ruin. In the Castle then, however, time seemed to have stopped.

I used to play with little stones and horse-chestnuts as I leaned against the buried capitals. Mamma would embroider in silence. Like me she preferred the Castle to the avenue because we were alone. Sometimes a lady on holiday at the Europa would come with her.

A vague fear weighed down from the keeper's house high above. We would not go near it. The Mute lived there.

I once saw her close up when I was older and had gone to play at the very top of the Castle: she was going along the Podio road between the crumbling walls. We had discovered the opening to a tunnel and wanted to explore it, when we found ourselves near the Mute who was making threatening gestures with her hands and eyes. Perhaps she wanted to discourage us; we escaped pretending it was funny, in reality frightened by her presence.

At one point in the Podio road the broad path, along which the Marquis's gig used to run, branched off.

I did not know how to find the Photograph Stone again on the first stretch of road; it must have been pulled up and turned on its side to make it wider for the military vehicles during the war.

At that time the stone used to stick out from the edge and was roughly the shape of a log; it seemed

as though it had been put there expressly for sitting on. I thought of it as papà's.

Papà would compose the group. Mamma seated, a cap placed flat on her curly hair; me with a little white overcoat leaning against her; papà standing behind us with his hunter's jacket buttoned up to the neck and his fur cap. In front of everyone, Murò. In the background the road edged with oaks and thin wild elms.

Papà was serious, rather proud, with the shadow of a smile in his half–closed eyes. Even Murò was serious, but in some photographs he is distracted by a butterfly and has turned his head away. Mamma would gaze rather teasingly with her deep eyes. (She found the business of photographs rather boring.) As a little girl I gazed out with an almost painful astonishment.

Papà would be in the photographs because he could press the shutter with a bulb which he held in his hand behind his back. The bulb was linked to the camera on the tripod by a long thin rubber tube.

Photography, which in Ponte Stura was something that only papà did, was something complex with aspects of magic. It involved secret operations which were done under a 'red' light. I was allowed to be present.

The plates were enveloped in red paper. There were wooden frames with steel springs into which the plates were inserted, small white enamel basins with a blue rim in which you would gently shake

the liquid until the picture appeared. I think I used to ignore the pictures then, for with them the exciting part came to an end.

While he was developing, papà did not talk, but whistled a little tune with flute-like modulations which was also part of the delight of the business.

Mamma was interested in the pictures, but she often got sleepy while she was waiting. She was teased about this; she laughed and told a story about how her brothers used to play jokes on her at home. As a little girl she would fall asleep early in the evening. (To me this seemed somehow ingenuous, and inferior compared with my father.)

Papà took the art of photography seriously, he had his name printed in gold on the red binding of the photograph album with the inscription Amateur Photographer. (Mamma found the whole business funny.) Papà would use this term, which I thought his own, for his activities as a painter and flautist as well, if he happened to talk about them with anyone; but he certainly considered photography to be the easiest art.

The style of his photographs was similar to his paintings. The images were calm and light without deep shadows or any stiffness, captured by a delicate hand. Earlier the poses were a little different. Mamma would hold my little sister on her lap and you could see she was unaware she was in a photograph; I was leaning against my hoop, almost as tall as me, and seemed impatient; papà had a less romantic and

233

livelier air. Mamma was perhaps more contented, more serene. Was that a moment of her happiness? ('Don't I have two beautiful girls?' she said when she was dying, and time no longer existed for her.)

Papà had also taken many photographs at the top of the Castle, always at the same point, with a background of a forked pine tree, its trunk branching in two directions.

In one, papà is leaning his head against mamma's (it's during a romantic period); mamma is preoccupied as if she were alone and is playing with my hair with one hand; I am in front of her, tiny, aged about two or three, with thin legs and that anxious amazement in my eyes which I always had.

But the image which I was now searching for was mamma on her own. She was dressed in white against a background of pine trees, leaning lightly on her little parasol with one hand. Her slender waist was encircled by a wide belt with a silver buckle. If I had not possessed the photograph, I would have remembered only that belt. A grosgrain ribbon striped in pale yellow and pink, with a very high buckle. Mamma gave it to us later to play with. The blouse was lace, the skirt smooth, full at the bottom. The ruffled lace fell softly over her wrist in ample folds. Her wrist was slender, the hand thin and somehow weary.

I held her hand which had reverted to being like the one in the photograph between my own; I

clasped it as it lay on the coverlet. That small hand with its slightly curved little finger had a shy and somehow secret grace. It was abandoned, but it still squeezed a little, and the faint heat which emanated from it was a last, silent gift.

There were women all around; silent, attentive women almost holding their breath. There were often things to be done: cleaning, dusting, changing the flowers. Necessary things. She would praise their work, 'Good, very very good.' Yet she would exchange rueful glances with me; they had interrupted the silence, the contemplation. I would suffer on account of those interruptions, but I was also ashamed of being incapable, unlike the others, of making myself useful. I was happy, of course, to be able to be by her, to look at her face, her thin hands as white and slender as when she was young.

I compared her hands, at first unconsciously, with those of the visitors and the relatives. They were suddenly gross alongside hers, their wrists coarse and massive. They made you think of something hard, they had something heavy and painful about them. And her delicacy seemed defenceless and as if fatal. As if that delicacy were the reason for her dying now.

At the top of the Castle amongst the sparse trees I felt the wind from the valley coming in as it once used to do. There was still an impression of the ancient building in the clearing which had reverted

to wildness, an impression of a proud, unfamiliar grandeur.

The keeper's house had been cleaned, the arcades reinforced. You could not go up close, there was a fence, a closed gate.

I climbed the paths half-hidden between the mimosa again and everything ended in some high netting. Here and there scrap iron, relics of war signalled the passing of the soldiers' stay. It was impossible to get to the caves and the sloping rocky banks; even if it had only been forgotten about, the prohibition was still in force.

All the same, I did find what I had been looking for, that exact point of reference, the cleft pine. Mamma had posed there amongst the prickly junipers which would graze your clothes. The forked trunk had thickened like someone grown heavy with age. The two arms then had been separated like the two arms of a lyre. The ground was steep and slippery because of the dry grass.

The Podio extends with its gentler ridge the high ground of the Castle which is all rock. The road leads on to the slope of the Cemetery, and beyond that the meadows towards the Stura.

The Podio road is paved with dry moss like an old carpet; it runs between humps stripped by the sun, between poor fields white with stones and stubble.

That sense of suspended life, of the road leading nowhere I had always associated with my roads of

Vice and Virtue. But it was too gentle to represent the austere life of Good, too arid to represent the temptation of Evil, so I called it the nothing road. Perhaps I meant of death?

I went down the road again and it still seemed familiar to me and I to it.

A long swift hare went leaping by at the edge of a field and immediately afterwards at its heels a black and white dog (a pointer like our Lisa). It went searching, trembling all over with agitation. The hunter's whistle called it back, the hunting season had not yet begun.

X

The Castle was still home, more solitary and so more intimate for me than the house itself. But absolute intimacy, exhilarating freedom for me was only to be found in the mountains, in the deep cool valleys, on the windswept ridges.

The village, in other words the world, surrounded, indeed almost besieged the house; while the mountains were free of this world.

I really did think the mountains were papà's. He knew everything about them: the paths, the passages, where the springs began, their rare inhabitants.

The little hamlets and the last huts were like the furthest camps on the threshold of another world; they were wretched and privileged at the same time.

The people were like papà's nanny with customs more ancient than memory. Mamma would gaze at everything with an amazement filled with admiration. The women on the doorsteps would spin wool as in fairy tales. The old men would thank her saying 'For the souls!' Sometimes she was also disgusted, as when she saw an old woman blow her nose with her fingers ...

In the legendary earlier time, mamma had gone to discover the mountains. Photographs show her hoisted up on a mule, dressed in white with her lace umbrella and the flowery hat encircled by a veil falling to her shoulders. She appeared a little earlier armed with an alpenstock and with binoculars slung around her neck.

One person from the mountains who also belonged to the house was Simonass, a large bent old man who would come from Fedio to bring ricotta. The ricotta was called *seirass*; that the two names rhymed seemed logical to me. Each time there would be a rather lively scene; Simonass did not want to be paid and would run away, so mamma would have to run after him down the passage.

Ricotta was the food of the gods for me; the lightly perfumed flavour and compact mass bearing the imprint of the stitching from Simonass's little bag, were both delights.

The people in the mountains spoke a particular dialect which was incomprehensible to the people

from the village. Papà understood it, and Idina's papà also knew some words and phrases which he would say to make us laugh. *Chiauta* meant up high and *liamunt* meant below.

During the war Felicino's mother would send him to hunt for eggs in the cowsheds; Idina and I would go with him. 'As cialino tu?' Felicino would ask the little girl in the loft. *Cialino*, *ciabro* (hen, goat) were easy words; the difficult thing was to get the right intonation, which he managed to do.

The shepherds went higher up in the mountains than anyone. One shepherd, having wiped a large stone with a damp rag, placed a white shapeless cheese on it as big as a loaf. If you looked closely at it you could see a tangle of worms swarming like minuscule tentacles.

Papà would lose patience with the mountain people when he had to persuade them to come to an agreement. Since they were stubborn, he would treat them as blockheads; he would say, 'You'll have all your money eaten up by the lawyers!' His function was to resolve their fights; he was the Justice of the Peace.

Some mountain people were hunters and because of this they were different. They and papà understood one another. They were proud, confident; they would plant themselves in the middle of the threshing floor and have discussions with him, moving their hands in hieratic gestures. And the dogs, hunting dogs, would not bark at you.

XI

The first stretch of Trinity road ran high above the deep valley of the Cant. A glance towards the torrent would make you shudder.

Papà had exchanged a few words with a woman cutting grass with a billhook on the bank. The woman, speaking slowly in a singsong voice, told him a terrifying story. Her husband, while he was scything like her, had fallen over backwards, rolling right down to the bottom.

The rustic fence of forked palings with the thick peeled branch resting on top no longer edges the road; instead there is a cement parapet. The road has been widened, improved. But I discovered a woman below the parapet on the steep bank just as

before. Scrawny, dishevelled, dressed in rags with bare legs as thin as sticks, she wore men's shoes which looked as if they were made of iron. She had a goat near her. 'The grass is dry!' I say. She explains to me that it's better because green grass gives the goat colic. Is she not afraid of slipping? She shrugged her shoulders: Alas! She had been a widow for many years; her husband had caught an evil spell in his head. The Parish Priest from Trinity had organized a warrant for compulsory repatriation so that the hospital would take care of him for nothing. (She named the Parish Priest as if he were a person I had met yesterday and as if she knew that I had known him.)

Mamma's admiration for Don De Maria, the Parish Priest from Trinity, was similar to her admiration for the Doctor (although not so romantic): she admired him in another way as she had admired the Master from Festiona and papà's nanny for their religious simplicity.

My parents considered the Parish Priest a free and unprejudiced man. (Did they disapprove of other Parish Priests? They never voiced it.) Compared to the Doctor the Parish Priest was certainly not regarded as a man of science, but he too knew how to take care of the sick in cases of emergency. Both of them would defend the poor; except that the Parish Priest lived almost as they did while the Doctor lived like the gentry.

Don De Maria was the Parish Priest to everybody, as Doctor Vinaj was the Doctor to his friends. To be friends with the Parish Priest was unexceptional; he was everyone's friend. Whoever turned up at Trinity, even a stranger, was welcomed or at least given a cup of coffee.

Usually when you arrived there, you would not find the priest in his house. You would have to look for him, someone would point him out, in a crooked little field above a drystone wall. He would be scything the rye. He would cut it in bunches with a leather knife, explaining why he had to do it that way. He would talk slowly, his voice the rather hoarse one of a smoker, with a delightful preciseness.

While he was working he wore his velvet shooting jacket with poaching pockets. The fields were not his, he was working them for the men who were away in the war at that time.

He seemed old to me. He was a bit bent, his smiling face sunburnt, marked with a few deep wrinkles, his hands were hard and calloused. While he was eating he would collect the crumbs which were scattered about the tablecloth one at a time; mamma would watch him smiling. That also seemed like humility to her.

His house was like the church in that inside it was small but had a very high front. The rooms were luminous and minute, they had thick bulging walls; the floor crunched beneath your feet. There was a smell of dry wood and honey everywhere.

Eagles and other stuffed birds jutted out from the walls of the staircase on shelves and supports. But the little sitting room contained the miracle of miracles: four squirrels were playing cards in the middle of the round table! They held the cards in their deft little paws in front of intent little muzzles.

The second marvel, in another room, was the Tree of Birds. A many-branched little tree in a glass casket supported a host of airy birds in various poses; you expected to hear them sing. All these animals had been stuffed by the Parish Priest.

He knew how to draw out the poison from vipers; he was a friend of the bees, from whom he collected honey. The Parish Priest's honey was one of Trinity's delights, like Marianin's coffee.

Marianin was the perfect complement to the Parish Priest. She seemed almost worldly in my eyes. She was small and very thin, although she had, like an ageing fairy, flat feet which made her hop a bit. Her black eyes gleamed keenly in her pointed face; she had a malicious smile and brusque, but maternal ways. She was always neat, but when feast days came around she would put on earrings and become a little lady.

Marianin was no less respected than the Parish Priest himself. When we came back from hunting, she would wash my feet. I was embarrassed by the honour.

We often went to Trinity to hunt; the Parish Priest was a hunter though he did not have any

dogs, and he was glad that papà would bring Murò along. We used to leave very early in the morning. The Parish Priest would say Mass while it was dark, Marianin was his server. I found it extraordinary that he spoke Latin and that he would even ring the bell for the elevation!

Marianin had a niece and nephew who were orphans, Don De Maria was their tutor. It seemed odd to me that they had a tutor when they were grown up. The girl was studying to be a teacher and because of that always spoke Italian; the brother was a lieutenant in the war. When he was on leave I enjoyed myself with him almost as much as with my uncles. The fact that he joked with me made me feel grown up like Uncle Andrea did. He had a handsome face but was rather fat and slightly lame. He knew all the songs; I liked the one about Pamela:

Pamela, beautiful Pamela
Daughter of the gypsy from Doberdo.

Doberdo was another legendary name from the war.

If the niece Mariucca was there I would stay in Trinity for a few days and sleep in the very small room where they kept the Tree of Birds.

Mariucca was studying English and as she touched things she said their name in English. She assured me that the Parish Priest knew everything; to prove it to me she asked him what lapis lazuli

was (mysterious words which occurred in the song about Pamela). The Parish Priest knew in fact.

Mariucca told a good story. Like the true one about the old tramp who stopped in Trinity as he was going back up the valley. He said he was going all around the valleys in search of the fountain. (Mariucca imitated the old man's way of speaking, how he said 'funtain'). He had been doing that his entire life, but the night he stayed in Trinity he died in the straw where he had stretched out to sleep.

The room was bare except for the bed and the Tree. The window was high up, there was an embrasure at the bottom, and it had no curtains. I woke up one night and saw the moon on my face. In Trinity it seemed very close. But I was not afraid. I heard a faint whistling in the silence; the Parish Priest was snoring.

We usually went to Cornalè towards the evening. We would go there every season but especially in spring or autumn. For long periods in the winter there was no track even, and in summer we went on other walks, had other friends.

Why did we go to Cornalè so often? Then just the name was enough for me. There was no other Cornalè in the world. Was it because we were friends with Gin and Cino? Cino, the hunter, was so ugly that you would never tire of looking at him. His thick chapped lips could not close over his long, protruding teeth; he stuttered a little, and

when he talked his lips would be almost painfully twisted. To help himself over difficult words he would toss his head and shake the thick cap of black curls which fell down over his nose. He used to laugh at papà's little stories, without realizing that they were being told again, something of which I was very aware.

For example, the story about the man who was cutting bread as he was standing with his back against a tree. Papà told it as a warning against cutting bread whilst holding it against your chest. The man in the story had cut the bread, cut himself, and cut the tree he was leaning against. I do not remember if I found it funny the first time; it certainly seemed impossible to me that Cino could laugh convulsively every time, holding up his arms as if to say 'Enough! Enough!'

Gin rarely laughed, she was too proud. Gin was big, coarse, yet beautiful and majestic like a queen of savages. It did not bother mamma that Gin said *tu* to papà. She did not always use it, but when she did, it was to interrupt him, for example. (The people in the mountains only used *tu* or *voi*, never *lei*.)

Mamma told us when we were grown up that before he was married papà had had a loan from Gin of Cornalè. To us this seemed queer and devoid of interest.

Giannetto (the son) was handsome. Mamma would look at him, she would follow him with her gaze and say to Gin, 'Giannetto's handsome!' and in

peasant fashion Gin would shrug her shoulders and say, 'Not that handsome!'

Cornalè is hidden behind the ridge which extends parallel to the valley and forms a little valley crossed by a stream.

This stream was an invisible thread of water between rocks and undergrowth. It was difficult to find the right place to cross it, jumping on stones which seemed to have been lined up just for that purpose. Only papà knew how to find it, it was a secret short cut.

The long road is on a slope between dusty dried-up fields. Thinly scattered stunted old oaks shade the road here and there with leaves already red and burnt.

I could not find the course of the stream in the little valley. I crossed at the narrowest point, holding on to branches. There I found myself before a steep embankment. I was disappointed; I did not recognize the places.

I saw a little convoy going along the high ridge of the grassy embankment. A man was driving a cart full of children, four or five of them. 'Are you taking them to sell them?' I shouted. The man stopped and looked down. I had surprised myself with the joke. I had imitated papà. The man laughed contentedly, he was very old and could appreciate an old-fashioned joke. He said they were his grandchildren. I asked him about Gin's son. 'That one, that one just there,' and the man

pointed an ash out to me, 'is the one which felled Gianetto. He was paralysed. He died a few years ago.' The man then indicated how I could get to the houses.

As I went I collected some little apples from under the stunted apple trees; they were as dry and bitter as if they were poisoned.

I did not recognize the houses as I had always come from the other direction. The little village seemed deserted, abandoned. Roofs had fallen in, there were tufts of nettles in the crumbling walls. A dog barked.

Cino had remarkable dogs, silent and perpetually moving sleuths after hares. There had been a mongrel too; but I was never afraid of dogs in Cornalè. Now the barking sounded angry to me, it gave an impression of being driven off.

A woman shouted at the dogs to be quiet; she turned to me with the old expression, 'They're not saying anything' (which means they don't bite). The tiny thin woman, not very old and still agile, looks at me with lively eyes. I say hesitatingly that I had known someone called Gin. The woman shrugs her shoulders, the way Gin did, and says, 'My *madona**!'

I said my father's name and the woman hugged me, threw up her arms, gave me a welcome.

The kitchen was the same. The vaulted very white ceiling, like a house in Spain, a milky, floury white, the black chimney, the cauldron. Only the

*In dialect: Mother-in-law!

floor was new, made of small tiles. 'My son made it,' the woman said.

It had been beaten earth then, smooth and with humps in it; it seemed that it would make you trip but in fact it was hard and firm, muffling your step like cork.

You would arrive over-heated, the kitchen was as cool as a cellar. Mamma admired its cleanness, as I admire it now. There are even flowers in a glass placed in the middle of the table, gigantic dahlias. (This is a novelty, I do not think that Gin cared for flowers.)

Everything was the same, because they had not been able to buy anything. I wondered, because of Giannetto's accident? He had lived paralysed for eleven years. She was the only one who could work, with a little boy. But now the son is a man, he is clever. Giannetto was depressed, she needed to comfort him. Then the war. People came from Ponte Stura to Cornalè to hide. Even Jews, from far away. Then a fascist from Ponte Stura had denounced them. ('Fascist from Ponte' – I heard the sound of those two words; their being combined made no sense to me.) The woman took out a postcard from a frame, a photograph papà had taken. It was a group of hunters with rifles and dogs and game. It looked like photographs of Buffalo Bill. Broad-brimmed hats, large moustaches, an air of solemnity. Papà, hares slung over his shoulder, had a special rather teasing smile on that occasion.

The woman turned over the now yellowed piece of card. Papà had written the address in his minute, delicate handwriting. 'To Signor Giacinto Verra, Great Hunter, Lower Cornalè.'

'We always used to talk about him with Giannetto. I knew him, too, before I got married. He used to come to my father's house in Fedio early in the morning to drink our cream with all the other gentlemen from Ponte. He used to talk more than all of them, he could talk very well. He was thin, blond. He would smile, look, like you; you smile in the same way.' And the woman stared at me in amazement.

She showed me the little garden in the shade where despite the drought the dahlias were blooming.

'I didn't like it here the first few years,' she said. And she looked up towards the mountain bristling with red rocks. 'Back home in Fedio it's green, it's beautiful.' She ended, 'Now, it doesn't matter to me any more.'

She showed me the right road which would lead to the bridge over the stream. I did not ask her about the secret passageway; perhaps it no longer exists.

The woman had wanted me to have a drink. In the dry smell of the stubble, in the prickling heat of midday amongst the scraping of the cicadas, I felt as if I were drugged.

251

XII

I had come across some houses of a village I did not
know, and like Cornalè it seemed deserted. Houses
falling down, some already in ruins. But one of
them was newly whitewashed, the door painted
light green. A thin old man came out. He looked at
me in astonishment.

'Your house is beautiful.' The old man
brightened. 'Have you always lived here?' 'No, no.
In France.' He had worked there, he said, for forty
years. 'Do you know how old I am?'

'Perhaps you knew my father,' and I gave his
name.

'Of course! And he knew me, too, my name and
my nickname. They used to call me Flag.'

A woman had come out and stopped to look. An old woman, but beautiful, tall and erect. She gazed proudly but incuriously and said, 'What are you talking about? Nonsense.'

'Oh, no. He used to know my father,' and I repeated the name. The woman continued gazing at me as she had done from the beginning. I asked her if she had known him too. She did not reply immediately then she said carelessly, almost disdainfully, 'We were talking about him last night.'

I was afraid that the old woman was joking and was hurt for a moment, then I realized she had something more to say.

'There was never anyone like him,' she said solemnly. 'I was still young then. And he was young, too, but already a man. Not married then though.'

She talked calmly, slowly, lending her speech gravity like this. Perhaps she was repeating what she had said the evening before. The old man listened to her and seemed astonished again.

She told a story of how she and some other girls had gone to the villa.

'It was a holiday. We had walked around, looked at everything. Then we were thirsty. But you needed money to have a drink and we didn't have any. We'd thought of having a cup of clear broth; it cost a *soldo*. Your father was watching us and cried, "Sing one of your songs! If you sing well, I'll offer you something to drink." We sang and he paid for a drink for us.'

She was quiet for a bit, then added, 'And so it's impossible for us to forget him.'

That was papà exactly, his simple yet unpredictable way of doing things; his joking with women (which turned into reserve with time, to please mamma?).

Mamma, so full of joy had made papà grow serious.

'He knew,' she said when she was dying and confided in us in that new way which was simultaneously light and tragic, 'he knew that I could escape him.'

We had never imagined anything in their history. For years mamma had only seemed beautiful and gay; papà in our opinion was more interesting. She certainly became livelier when we were grown up, even if it were in her swift, unexpected way. Mamma's joy when she welcomed us as we came home from school, her running to papà when he came home we used to think ingenuous; while papà, whom we used to see as more serious, almost taciturn during that period in Ponte Stura, we thought was deeper than mamma. This was when we were young girls.

Later our judgement was reversed. Papà seemed too simple to us, we began to glimpse a seriousness in mamma's silences, to be aware of something mysterious in her beauty. Until then our very youth had made us obtuse; indifferent to what they might or might not be. We accepted naturally and

almost uncaringly that they were good, with a sort of indulgence that they were happy.

When papà fell ill, we did not realize that mamma was still quite young; we only knew that he was old. But when she died, we realized that loss with a cruel lucidity, like a surgical operation undergone without anaesthetic.

Now the air has grown really cool again, the sky veiled. The light snow was a useless medicine for the burns of the drought.

At the hotel, the room was no longer so hostile. A little bunch of meadow saffron was doing battle with the yellow of the walls now turning slightly green.

I had picked the meadow saffron (which was once called *frigiolina*, flower of the first frosts) in the meadows below Madonna di Ronvello, a country chapel at the top of a rocky spur, sheer to the valley. Only those who know it can make it out from below. I had climbed up there with mamma as a little girl. The two of us left on our own, papà being already up there. Was he sleeping up there in a barn? Or did he leave earlier? Papà was doing a long survey for the Town Hall. Every day mamma would take him something to eat. It only happened at Ronvello, and later we always remembered it. During her last days too.

I went out by the bridge over the Cant towards the mountain. A path detached itself from the mule

track and climbed bleakly upwards. I stopped, wondering if it would be of any use to me to follow it. Meanwhile a dog overtook me; an old black mongrel, silent as a shadow and swift, almost as if he had some pressing business up ahead. For a moment I was afraid; but dogs have changed and he took no notice of me. The path began to climb steeply. Stones rolled from beneath my feet, loose as in a landslide. It really was the path. And why would it have changed?

Lifting my head, I saw higher up a little girl with a mess tin in her arms on another small track running parallel. Perhaps she was also taking someone something to eat.

'Am I going the right way for Ronvello?' The little girl nodded and pointed out the way. The sweetness of the present made past happiness sting less. I tried to imagine my mother climbing with me, as always, I could only bring back her silent presence. We must certainly have passed the short flat stretch near the fountain where two young women were now doing their washing. They looked at me and said with mocking familiarity, 'Are we going mountain climbing?'

On the last part, the rocky spur on which the chapel stood unfolded. Papà was somewhere near, we waited for him in the meadow. He would arrive smiling in his hunter's jacket and leather leggings; he would wipe away the sweat. We would hug him, sit down in the meadow. He would invite the

people who had worked with him, the 'assistants', to share the meal. They sat a little apart and accepted a glass of wine; they would poke their moustaches into the aluminium cups.

The ruined chapel must have been as it is now. There is graffiti on the outside walls, soldiers' names. Some were written with a piece of coal and have been rubbed out a bit.

The view towards the mountains is of bare fields, rocks, caves, a desert landscape. The vast empty space opens out on to the valley. At the bottom is the flat plain with patches of cultivated fields; in the middle are the two high grounds, the Podio and the Castle; higher still is Ponte Stura, fortified at its entrance by the lateral valley of the Cant. The mountains, lined up like wings in a theatre or backdrops, are the ones with the strange names which used to sound to me like those of a far-off country. They have a northern, ancient and desolate aspect.

The main road beyond is a dark bluish thread. In papà's picture the road was a white thread. The picture with the valley seen from above (from Ronvello?) hung on the wall at the side of mamma's bed. While I sat by her side I would gaze at it.

Papà had painted two shepherds and a goat (he had copied them from a postcard) in the foreground. The Parish Priest on one visit had admired the picture, but had mistaken the goat for a donkey.

'The donkey is very good!' They had excused him, because he was no judge of painting. But how mamma had laughed!

The valley like the house, is inhabited by 'them' and by me as a child. It almost holds the trace of a physical presence. But for that reason, it no longer exists. It cannot in fact contain other lives. That is why when I left, on that distant Autumn day, I thought, 'It was ... '

the penumbra

First published in Great Britain by Quartet Books Limited in 1998
A member of the Namara Group
27 Goodge Street
London W1P 2LD

Originally published in Italian as *La Penombre Che
Abbiamo Attreversato*

Copyright © Guilio Einaudi Editore S.P.A., 1964
Translation copyright © Sian Williams 1998

A catalogue record for this book is available from the
British Library

ISBN 0 7043 8071 4

Phototypeset by F.S.H., London
Printed and bound in Great Britain by Cox & Wyman, Reading

the penumbra

LALLA ROMANO

Translated by Siân Williams

Quartet Books Limited

Lalla Romano, now ninety-one and with a vast oeuvre to her name, is viewed as one of the classic writers in 20th century Italian literature. Her writing enjoys a painterly quality, particularly in evidence in this novel. The first volume of her collected works was published in 1991 in Mondadori's prestigious *I Meridiani* series.

Siân Williams was a publisher of literature in translation for many years. She has translated *Isolina*, a biography by Dacia Maraini published by The Women's Press and *Veronica Franco*, a play by Dacia Maraini for Aurora Metro. She now lives and works in London as a translator and a promoter of literature in translation and literature from Welsh publishers.

Uncle Cam

The story of William Cameron Townsend
founder of the *Wycliffe Bible Translators*
and the *Summer Institute of Linguistics*

James & Marti Hefley

Photo Editor: Cornell Capa

Word Books, Publisher, Waco, Texas

Contents

6   CONTENTS

PART III. NEW BEGINNINGS

Authors' Preface

Every century or so there arises a remarkable Christian innovator and servant of mankind. We believe William Cameron Townsend ("Uncle Cam" to thousands) is the man for this century. Thus we have spent years researching and writing his biography.

The idea of a biography was reluctantly accepted by Uncle Cam— and this only after a trip around the world when he decided that the publishing of his life story might speed the light of Scripture to the remaining Bibleless tribal and minority groups.

This book is not an official publication of the two organizations which he founded. However, leaders of the Wycliffe Bible Translators and the Summer Institute of Linguistics and other close friends and relatives cooperated and made available their recollections and judgments.

In writing *Uncle Cam* we worked principally from primary resource material: interviews with scores of individuals who have known Uncle Cam, some for almost three-quarters of a century; impressions of visits to fields where he worked in the service of foreign governments for Indians; voluminous personal correspondence and reports. Research involved twelve trips to Latin America, a summer's residence next-door to the Townsends in North Carolina, coast-to-coast interviews, even accompanying Uncle Cam for a visit with President Richard Nixon in the White House. The single-spaced typed index of the primary materials runs over 250 pages. The first draft of the manuscript was twice as long as the finished version.

No one can be completely objective in writing about someone they love and admire. However, we have tried to write responsibly and candidly. This effort was aided by the openness of Uncle Cam, his family, and close associates in interviews.

It is impractical, if not impossible, to name everyone who helped make this book possible. Contributors to research ranged from former presidents of Latin American countries to humble jungle Indians; from 1917 classmates of Uncle Cam at Occidental College to his twenty-year-old son, Billy. We thank all of those who helped.

The manuscript itself represents our combined efforts as a husband-and-wife team. Our picture associate was the distinguished photographer Cornell Capa. Mr. Capa, a long-time friend of Uncle Cam's, selected and edited the photographs, including some of his own, for the book. He is without peer in his field. We consider his professional aid a high honor.

Paula Kelly was our dependable, accurate secretary who transcribed hours of tapes and typed the final copy.

The life of William Cameron Townsend is significant for a wide audience. We hope that at least to some extent the telling adequately represents the man and his life.

JAMES and MARTI HEFLEY
Signal Mountain, Tennessee

Part I
BEGINNINGS

1. Poverty's Heritage

Sweating and itching, young Cam Townsend slogged across the jungle marsh. The pack of New Testaments and food rations rubbed his blistered back. Though covered with bites, he had learned it was much wiser not to scratch. His thin body ached for rest, but he knew that to sit beside the trail would only invite more bugs.

Cam daydreamed of plunging into the California surf, then coming home to climb between clean white sheets and awakening to the savory smell of a farm breakfast. He yearned to hear his deaf father reading the Bible at the breakfast table and thought how enjoyable life would be back at Occidental College finishing his fourth year as his mother had wanted him to. Even the army, where many of his classmates had gone, could not be as bad as this.

Suddenly the dark cloud that had been thickening overhead splintered with lightning and seconds later the usual afternoon downpour began. He broke to seek shelter under the spreading branches of a tree.

A half-hour later the storm stopped as abruptly as it had started, and Cam plodded on through a sea of mud, anticipating the smile of the Indian friend who was to meet him at the railroad station.

Actually, there was no question of returning home. He had committed himself to sell Bibles to farmers and villagers along the sparsely populated trails of Central America. "Go ye into all the world and preach the gospel" was the commission that burned in his bones. Neither heat, nor rain, nor chill of night, nor wild animals, nor hostile fanatics would hold him back. The Word of God must be planted. God would give the increase.

It was the year 1917, and the "apostle to the lost tribes" had launched his first enterprise. At the time he didn't dream that over

11

2,000 tribes existed without even alphabets. But as more awareness came, he would "by faith" cross the linguistic frontier of a baffling language and lay the pattern for thousands of future translators to follow. Cameron Townsend would become the most daring, innovative Christian leader of the twentieth century.

As is so often true of milestoners, he was never picked by any institution, denomination, or government agency as one most likely to succeed. His incipient greatness was hidden to most who knew him. Yet the evidences can be found in his own recollections and diaries and the memories of a few aging relatives and friends. The seeds of an audacious faith and discipline were there. But they were simply not recognized by most who knew him as a boy.

The Townsends came originally from England. Three brothers, Quakers, joined William Penn's seventeenth-century colony. But only one remained in Pennsylvania. By the mid-nineteenth century the Pennsylvania Townsends had become Presbyterians and were living about twenty miles east of Pittsburgh.

One of them, William, decided to enter the ministry and enrolled in a Pittsburgh seminary. While still a student, however, he died of pneumonia, leaving a two-year-old son Richard Cameron. Six months later his second son, William Hammond, was born. His widow then remarried and had three more children.

By the year 1876, William Hammond—Will—had grown to a wiry but sturdy five-foot-nine. He held a contract for hauling lumber to Pittsburgh for construction of a building to be used in the centennial celebration. But just before Will was to be paid, the major contractor ran away. Will was left with the bills in his name—and no funds to pay them.

The young man vowed to pay every cent even if it took the rest of his life. Then he said goodbye to his mother and stepfather and headed for the new state of Kansas, where he found work on a wheat farm. His long back-breaking days were brightened only by Sunday services at the local Presbyterian church and by visits to the Cormacks, a Presbyterian neighbor family that had migrated from eastern Tennessee. Mr. Cormack regaled him with tales about the hills and hollows of Tennessee, but Will was more interested in the oldest daughter. Molly, with the merry smile, straw-colored hair, and an infectious laugh, made Will feel that he could whip the world if she were beside him.

Molly and Will were married in 1884, the year Grover Cleveland was elected president. They rented a nearby farm and between dusts and droughts eked out a living. After daughters Oney and Ethel were born, Will wanted to move on in hopes of earning extra money to pay on the debt that nagged his conscience.

But life was little better in the Green Horn Range of Colorado. With two more mouths to feed, Lula and Mary, Will grew barely enough vegetables for the family table. Hearing talk of fortunes being made in California, he decided they should move again.

They arrived in California in 1893, the year of a great depression, and moved into an old farmhouse near Pasadena. With prices dropping and people returning east, Will still had trouble making ends meet. Bad fortune plagued him year after year. If he planted cabbages, they'd sell at an all-time low, while tomatoes were selling high. If he tried tomatoes, the bottom would drop out of that market. Then in the midst of their poverty, Molly gave birth to a stillborn son.

Will felt they could better themselves by moving again—this time to the desert Eastvale settlement east of Los Angeles. Here on July 9, 1896, in an old farmhouse that had only curtains for partitions, a healthy boy greeted the world with a yowl that could be heard above the wail of the hot Santa Ana winds that whipped against the house. They named him William for his father and grandfather and Cameron for his minister uncle.

For awhile the family was concerned that Cam might be spoiled or sissified, being brought up with four older sisters. That worry ended with the birth of Paul two years later. Little Paul dogged Cam's footsteps. Except for his having brown eyes and hair lighter than Cam's, the two boys looked very much alike. But in personality they were quite different. Paul was mechanically minded and enjoyed using his hands. Cam thought it more challenging to figure a new way to do things. Especially if he could talk Paul into doing the physical labor or deciding to do something the way Cam wanted it. On one occasion they had to choose between two puppies. Cam wanted the brown one and Paul the black, but Cam convinced Paul it was really the brown one he wanted. Another time after hearing a Sunday school lesson about Jacob shearing his sheep, Cam took his mother's sewing scissors and clipped off Paul's blond curls. Molly pulled a limb from the quince tree in the front yard and gave Cam a thrashing.

14 UNCLE CAM

Cam was full of fun, sometimes at his younger brother's expense. There were irrigation ditches nearly every place they lived. Cam, agile and two years older, would jump the smaller ones and dare Paul to follow. Time after time, Paul fell in the water and was rewarded with a spanking when they got home. Eventually, though, Will and Molly discovered the real culprit and administered the proper medicine.

But Cam also had his serious moments. One incident seems a portent of his lifelong expectant faith. One night he rolled over in bed and squashed his pet bunny. The next day he and Paul held a funeral and buried the animal in a cracked mason jar under an umbrella tree. That evening Cam couldn't sleep for thinking of the bunny. Remembering from Sunday school that Jesus had raised Lazarus, Cam reasoned that a bunny would be much less trouble. So he prayed. Then he figured that if the bunny did come alive, it would soon die again without air. He climbed out of bed, lit a lantern, crept across the yard and exhumed the dead rabbit.

Poverty and ill fortune seemed to dog the family's footsteps. By this time Will had lost almost all his hearing. He attributed the cause to a rebounding plank that had bounced off his chin back in Colorado. A prize calf swallowed Cam's first store-bought necktie and choked to death. Produce from the tenant farm brought hardly enough income for the family to exist on.

But Will's stubborn, keep-trying, hard-work philosophy made an indelible impression on his children. "You never lose your vote when you stand for what is right," he would say as he continued to vote for the Prohibition Party. He was strict with the boys in the fields and expected instant obedience. "Finish one row before you start another," was a frequent admonition that stuck in Cam's mind. And if Cam did sloppy work, Will would insist, "Do it over until it becomes second nature to you."

Will's deep-seated honesty also left its mark on Cam. Because Will still felt obligated to pay the quarter-century-old Pennsylvania debt, he wrote letters back to Pennsylvania in an effort to locate the addresses of creditors. He even asked a lawyer to draw up a binding legal promissory note, but the lawyer talked him out of it.

When Will went on selling trips into Los Angeles, one of the children usually accompanied him. The first time Cam was allowed to go he felt very grownup and important. As they made periodic stops along cobblestoned Telegraph Road, Cam noticed that the merchants seldom looked at their fruit and vegetables before buying. When he asked a burly Italian grocer about it, he was told, "Your Papa, he say it's good, it's good. We call him the 'honest deaf man.'" The pride Cam felt has remained in his memory to this day.

Will had a very sensitive conscience. Once he traded a horse for a cow and then worried that he had taken advantage of the other man. He had no peace until he evened out the bargain with a precious five-dollar bill.

If Cam got his streak of stubbornness for hanging on to what he felt was right from Will, he received his cheerful disposition from Molly who tried to keep the house bright and happy. There were always flowers around, especially her favorite petunias or Will's sweet peas. She laughed and joked with the children. Sometimes this bothered deaf Will and he would frown and ask, "What's so funny? What are you laughing at?" By the time she had the joke written out, it never seemed quite as humorous.

However, neither Will nor Molly were the type to bemoan their troubles. They prayed for the needs of others, and under no circumstances tolerated disparaging criticism. If they were envious of more fortunate neighbors, the children never remembered it.

All his life Cam has been a man of one Book—the Bible. He recalls how every weekday morning before milking his father would read three chapters—five on Sunday. After breakfast came family devotions—Bible reading, a hymn, and prayers. Despite his deafness, Will loved to sing. When his voice cracked, the children were under strict orders from Molly not to laugh. He always ended his prayers with, "May the knowledge of the Lord cover the earth as the waters cover the sea."

At twelve Cam joined the Presbyterian church. Afterwards, Will took him out to the barn and questioned him concerning his beliefs. Cam wrote down his answers for his deaf father. Will was pleased and satisfied that his son had a firm personal faith in Christ as his Lord and Savior.

The summer Cam turned thirteen, Molly, Cam, and Paul took the train to visit relatives near Fresno. That was a big event for youngsters who had never been farther from home than Long Beach where the family went once a year to swim and watch the ships. While there the boys and their cousins went swimming in a canal. When the others dove in, Cam followed suit and discovered he was in over his head. Panic-stricken because he couldn't swim, he called for help, but went under twice before an older boy saved him from drowning.

The close call was a maturing experience. Cam applied himself more than ever in school the next year. In the spring he completed the eighth grade at the head of his class. But the following year produce prices took a sharp downturn, and it looked as if he might have to drop out of school to help with family finances. The two oldest girls were married by this time and the younger ones were engaged. The idea of Cam's interrupting his education was abhorrent to all of them, and Lula volunteered to postpone her marriage a year and continue her secretarial job to help pay for Cam's schooling. Her fiancé didn't understand the dedication in the close-knit family and broke their engagement.

After a time, Lula found a better job in Santa Ana and the family moved there for her convenience. On their first Sunday, Cam and Lula attended a Methodist church close by. Eugene Griset, Cam's bachelor Sunday school teacher, visited him the next week to invite him back to the class. When he kept visiting regularly, Cam decided his real interest was Lula.

During his sophomore year, Cam biked to the Santa Ana High School. His route passed a pasture where the young aviation enthusiast, Glenn Martin, was developing his first plane. Occasionally he stopped and peered at the plane, daydreaming of someday having the opportunity to fly.

In Cam's junior year both Lula and Mary married, and the rest of the Townsends moved to Clearwater. Cam got a job hauling fifteen schoolmates to school in a wagon for $70 a month, out of which he had to feed the team. He turned most of the profit over to his folks, leaving precious little for personal spending.

Despite the time spent in hauling his passengers, feeding and stabling the team, and regular chores, Cam was involved in many school activities. He edited the 1914 yearbook, took the lead in the senior play, served on the debating team, and with Bob Gillingham won the doubles championship in tennis.

He graduated with the highest average in the class, but being a transfer student he was ineligible to be valedictorian. However, his standing with his classmates was such that the class prophet predicted he would one day represent California in the U.S. Senate.

Above: Downey, California, in 1907 had dirt roads and horse-drawn carts. These were some of the Townsends' neighbors. *Below:* The Townsends lived in this house in Downey from 1902–1909.

The Townsends
in 1902.
L. to r., back row:
Ethel, Oney, Mary, Lula. Front row: Mollie, Paul, Cam, Will.

Above: Cam and Paul at 12 and 10. *Below:* Mary, Oney, Lula, and Ethel. Both pictures were made into postcards.

Above: Cam, with the flower in his buttonhole, was valedictorian of the class at his graduation from grammar school in Downey in 1910. *Below:* Cam and high school friends in Compton, in 1913.

Cam graduated from Compton High School in 1914.

"The greater need is where the greatest darkness is."

2. Siempre Adelante!

Until his last year in high school, Cam had planned to be a teacher. When he began thinking of entering the ministry, Will and Molly were jubilant. His sisters and their husbands all said they would help the aging parents financially while Cam got his education.

Since the ministerial scholarship from the Presbyterian church wouldn't cover all his college expenses, Cam worked the summer after graduation as a bellhop on the S.S. *President*. The big steamship stopped at cities along the Pacific coast from San Diego to Vancouver. Though Cam got seasick and was exposed to rough men for the first time, the experience was invaluable.

World War I had already flared in Europe when he enrolled in Occidental College, a Presbyterian liberal arts school in Los Angeles. During his sophomore year Cam was drawn to the Student Volunteer Band, the local arm of the national Student Volunteer Movement. New joiners had to tell why they wanted to be members. Though Cam belonged to the Debating Club, when his turn came he found it hard to articulate his concern for foreign missions. He could only say, "I'm not sure why I wish to belong."

His interest picked up, however, when John R. Mott, the leader of the movement, came to the campus to speak. Cam sensed the burden of the man and wondered if there might not be a place for him overseas. He was further challenged by the life of Hudson Taylor, founder of the fifty-year-old China Inland Mission. Taylor's faith, pioneering, and adaptation to the Chinese culture appealed to him. He felt that if God should lead him to become a missionary, he would strive to be like this man.

But his Bible knowledge did not complement his budding interest in missions. Beyond what he had learned at home and in church, he took only the Bible courses required by the college: a study in Genesis and Exodus, and New Testament Greek.

Once after Bible class, a fellow student asked, "Cameron, do you know how we're saved?"

"By the life of Christ, I guess," Cam replied lamely.

His classmate looked appalled. "No, by Christ's death! Haven't you studied the theology of the atonement?"

"Well, no," Cam said. "I guess maybe I should."

While managing to make good grades in college, he frankly questioned some teaching methods of the day. He thought memorization a poor method. "College men are too often unable to hold their own in the practical world," he wrote in a theme entitled "The Object of a College Education." "The reason is that the graduate is not capable of applying his learning to the problems of life. He has stored his brain with a great many facts and principles, but he is unable to use them."

A member of the Literary Club, he enjoyed writing essays on varied subjects which oddly enough seemed to forecast his later interests: "Eternal Life," "Many Paths to Mexico's Enchantments" (an armchair travelogue), "True Wisdom," "Language in the Embryo," and "Canvassing as a College Student's Vacation Work." He had had personal experience in the latter as an unsuccessful summer magazine salesman.

In one paper he weighed the relationship between genius and physique: "Success in any walk of life is as dependent upon the body as upon the inspiration. We may never become great but it is the duty of each one to bring to the highest degree of development those powers which God has endowed him with. To do this he must care for his body." Cam was then a skinny 130 pounds. Still he practiced what he preached by playing tennis, wrestling, and getting to bed every school night by ten.

Another lifelong interest surfaced early. His first poems were published in the student newspaper under the *nom de plume* of Eunice Bomsinger. One that illustrates some of the inner conflicts he was having at the time also shows a characteristic that has never left him.

Limitation
Oh hateful word
That halts your aspiration,
That downs your dreams
And brands your schemes

As filmy speculation,
　And says you shan't
　Because you can't
In the face of limitation.

Deceptive word
That means procrastination;
　That bids content
　With every stint,
And pillows lowly station,
　And says, "Just wait
　Till time and fate
O'ercome your limitation."

. . . .

Yes! The challenge word
That dares against stagnation,
　Brings out your stuff
　And frightens bluff
With every consternation,
　And calls for might
　And bids you fight
To climb o'er limitation.

In 1916, Cam's junior year, a National Guard recruiter came to the Occidental campus. The war in Europe still seemed remote to most students. Woodrow Wilson was campaigning for a second term as "the president who kept the U.S. out of the war." When the recruiter told Cam and his best friend, Carroll Byram, of the engineering training available in the Guard, they joined, figuring that if war did come they would be drafted anyway.

That year Cam's parents rented a house near the campus for $6 per month and Cam moved in with them. Will planted barley, and Cam helped harvest it and the wild oats that grew on vacant campus land. Will and Molly kept hoping that Cam's interest in the ministry at home might return. But Cam's bent remained toward foreign missions. "The greater need is where the greatest darkness is," he wrote. "Our orders are to forget self and to give our lives in service for the Master."

In January 1917 Cam heard that the Bible House of Los Angeles wanted Bible salesmen for South America. Having taken Spanish in high school and college, he decided to apply to the Bible House with the idea of returning after a year to finish college. With the country still out of the war, he thought chances were good for resigning from the Guard.

The Bible House accepted his application and assigned him to Guatemala, a country he had not even known was in Central America. But when he told his parents, Molly was dismayed, fearing he might never return to complete college and attend seminary.

When Congress declared war in April, Cam was sure he wouldn't be going south after all. Then a call came from R. D. Smith, director of the Bible House.

"Cam, there's a missionary from Guatemala in the area. I think you should go talk to Miss Stella Zimmerman about the country where you'll be going."

"It's no use," Cam replied. "My Guard unit will be shipping out to France shortly."

"Well, go see her anyway. You'll be coming back from war one day."

Cam agreed and asked his good friend Elbert Robinson to come along. "Robby," president of Occidental's YMCA and ten years older than Cam, was also an enthusiast for foreign missions. Miss Zimmerman, a tall angular blond about Robby's age, was glad to talk to them about Guatemala. After telling them about the rich history and great natural beauty of the little Idaho-shaped country that straddles Central America below Yucatan, and describing the spiritual needs of the people, she asked, "When will you fellows be going to help?"

Cam and Robby looked at each other rather sheepishly. "Well, you see," Robby replied, "Cameron here is a corporal in the National Guard. He'll be going to war before long. I may try to get into officer's training school."

"You cowards!" exclaimed Stella Zimmerman. "Going to war where a million other men will go and leaving us women to do the Lord's work alone! You are *needed* in Central America!"

Her visitors didn't like being called cowards. Robby blushed, cleared his throat, and said, "Well, Cam, let's go to Central America."

"Bu-but I'm in the Guard," Cam stammered. "I've never heard of an able-bodied soldier being discharged in time of war."

"We'll pray that you'll get out," Robby said.

"I'm willing, if that's what the Lord wants."

But Cam didn't leave it at that. He solicited the help of his history teacher, Professor Robert McClellan, who drafted a letter to the captain of Cam's Guard unit. Cam took it to the officer and waited at attention while he read it.

To Cam's surprise, the captain agreed to the discharge. "Go," he encouraged Cam. "You'll do a lot more good selling Bibles in Central America than you would shooting Germans in France."

At the same time Robby had accepted the challenge and had applied to R. D. Smith. He was quickly accepted. "I'm glad you'll be going," Smith said. "You can keep an eye on Cam. I'm not sure how he'll work out."

When Cam told his family, Will and Molly agreed it was a lot better than going to war. His sisters and brothers-in-law again pledged their support to the senior Townsends in Cam's absence, since Will's health was poor. Paul, then a college freshman, agreed to get a job the following year and help support them.

"But just as soon as you can, Cameron," Molly added, "you must come back and finish college and go to seminary."

The Bible House agreed to pay the two salesmen $30 a month each with a three-month advance to help on transportation. But they each had to raise an additional $150 for their passage. As soon as the school term was over, Cam and Robby headed north for summer work on a ranch.

In his first letter back to the "home folks," Cam reported that they had been "pitching hay and pulling weeds for the last three days," and would soon be "heading grain and planting corn. We're accomplishing a good bit with our Spanish. We memorize verses and catechism questions while we work."

Cam celebrated his twenty-first birthday that summer on the ranch. Then in mid-August the boys returned home to pack for Guatemala. Cam's old Guard unit, which included his closest college chum, Carroll Byram, had shipped out the previous month.

On Saturday, August 18, 1917, the Townsend family, with several friends and relatives, saw the two young men off at the Los Angeles train station. They were headed for San Francisco where they hoped to secure passage on a ship bound for Guatemala.

Cam penned his feelings in his log book: "Well, we're off. Left Los Angeles at five o'clock. . . . Had a wonderful send-off. I've got the greatest folks God ever blessed a fellow with. . . . May God help me to be as true as steel to them all. *Adelante*, now. *Siempre Adelante!* Eyes to the front! Forward march!"

"Lord, I'm a failure."

3. Failure

Cam and Robby arrived in San Francisco eager to set sail. But the first booking they could get was first-class passage on the S.S. *Peru*, which was due to sail in two weeks.

"First class" called for more money than they had, so they hired on with Wells Fargo and loaded crates at night for $15 a week to earn the extra. Living largely on poached eggs and milk, Cam complained in his diary that he "didn't like the waterfront a bit."

With the excited pair on board, the *Peru* slipped out of San Francisco Bay on September 15, 1917, Guatemala's Independence Day. Eighteen days after embarkation the ship anchored off Port San José, Guatemala, and Cam and Robby were swung over the deck in an iron basket to a waiting tugboat. Custom officials gave Cam's small suitcase and Robby's trunk hardly a glance.

On board a train chugging toward Guatemala City, an American engineer filled them in on the politics of this little tropical country. "You'll make out fine," he concluded, "if you remember to keep your mouths shut and your bowels open."

As the train rocked along the narrow gauge railway, Cam was enchanted by the scenery. Twin volcanoes, "Agua" (water) and "Fuego" (fire) coned upwards on one side while pristine Lake Amatitlán reflected fluffy white clouds on the other.

Near sunset the train crossed the lake and began climbing towards the mile-high elevation of the capital. When it jolted to a stop in the city, the boys donned their overcoats to ward off the chilly night air. To their great relief, Miss Zimmerman was there to meet them, along with another missionary and a national pastor.

The pastor called a carriage that took them across cobblestoned streets to a five-street intersection, then stopped beside a large brick building. *Iglesia Cinco Calles* ("The Church at the Five Streets") proclaimed a sign. Inside was an auditorium, offices of the Central American Mission, and upstairs rear apartments.

The new arrivals were shown their room in the attic. Tired out from the trip, Cam collapsed on the bed while Robby set to work unpacking. Downstairs the "welcoming committee" briefly discussed the new recruits. "Robinson will do fine," one predicted, "but that skinny Townsend won't last two months."

After breakfast the next morning the young men called on Edward Bishop, director of the Central American Mission work in Guatemala. Bishop had been asked by the director of the Bible House to get them started.

"Our C.A.M., the Presbyterians, and two other missions have divided the territory so we don't overlap in our work," he said in his businesslike briefing. "As Bible salesmen you'll be working with both groups. I'm sure you'll get full cooperation from everyone.

"I'll give you a little history of evangelical missions in this country. The first Bible salesman was thrown out by an autocratic Catholic government. But the great Liberal Revolution in 1871 under General Barrios turned things around. He decreed freedom of worship and established public schools. Then he went to New York and asked the Presbyterians for a Protestant missionary. The Presbyterian board responded quickly and soon founded an evangelical chapel and school where the president enrolled his own children.

"The C.A.M. came later to help evangelize the nation. We have about forty missionaries in Guatemala and as many more in the other four republics of Central America."

Bishop paused and looked at the two eager-eyed recruits. "As Scripture salesmen you boys will sow the seed where there are no evangelical congregations. It won't be easy. But you'll have our prayers and God will help you."

After two weeks of getting acquainted with missionaries in the capital, Bishop felt they needed to get out among the people. "Come along to a Bible conference I'm holding for believers over the mountain in the old capital of Antigua. You can start your Bible selling there."

Bishop went ahead on horseback, leaving Cam and Robby to take the stage. After the heavy rains, the road up the western mountain was in frightful condition. The driver kept lashing his four mules unmercifully while cursing the president for spending public funds on portraits of himself instead of repairing the roads. The old coach creaked by more stalled oxcarts and burdened Indians than Cam could count. Even the children carried loads of firewood. "It looks as if the Indians are the beasts of burden down here," Cam remarked soberly.

Once over the rim the driver whipped the mules into a dizzy gallop, and the vehicle careened and bounced around hairpin turns. They made Antigua before nightfall, where Mr. Bishop and other workers welcomed them with a warm supper. Then after a freezing night on army cots, they set out at 5:00 A.M. to explore the city.

Poking among the ruins of an old church, they left footprints in the dust beside the bones of clergy that lay strewn around broken crypts. At one place they saw ragged people kneeling and knocking on a tomb, pleading to a long dead saint. They were overwhelmed at the sight of pitifully poor Indians dropping coins into an indulgence box.

The friendly caretaker at the old Capuchin monastery showed them relics of the Inquisition. He pointed out one niche that formed a strait jacket where heretics had been fastened while water dripped on their heads until they either recanted or went mad. Further on he stopped at an oven in which he claimed more serious offenders had been roasted alive.

"For two hundred years Antigua was the capital of Central America," he told them. "It was as grand as Lima or Mexico City. But an earthquake in 1773 destroyed most of our city. Now Antigua is only a market center for the valley and a hunting ground for relic seeking.

"Look up there, señores," he said, as they entered the dark gloom of the lizard-infested dungeon. "Those metal rings in the ceiling were used to hang dissenters."

"Those black-robed friars were great representatives of God," Cam commented cryptically.

The caretaker nodded in agreement. Then in a brighter tone, he said, "Come, see what is now on these walls."

"Why, those are Bible verse cards from the Bible House in Los Angeles!" said the astonished Robby. "How . . . ?"

"I put them there," their guide chuckled. "I am an evangelical. The local priests don't appreciate them, but, ehhh!" he said with hands turned up in assumed condescension.

The Bible conference was just beginning when they arrived at the church. Taking their seats, they watched the congregation. The few who could read and write were taking notes while the others listened reverently, straining to retain the precious words in their memories. When testimony time was announced, the response was immediate and enthusiastic.

A shoemaker turned evangelist rose, cleared his throat and declared, "Before I was a believer I was thrown in jail sixty-three times for drunkenness. Now I've been behind bars three times for preaching the gospel."

Other national workers told of similar experiences, including stonings and beatings by mobs. "It's just like the Acts of the Apostles," Cam whispered to his companion.

On the final day of the conference Edward Bishop urged everyone to go out and practice what they had learned. Cam felt his mentor's eyes looking right at him, and he shuddered at the idea of personal evangelization in Spanish. He had never even done it in English.

When the meeting ended he excused himself and hurried up a street alone. He didn't want anyone, not even Robby, to watch. Turning the corner he approached a man standing near the curb. Pursing his lips to speak, he could make no sound and he walked on past with a pounding heart. Twice more he tried, but could not summon the courage to speak. A block farther on he came upon a young man more his age. "Lord, help me," he prayed fervently.

Having read that a good opening question was, "Do you know the Lord Jesus?" Cam asked in halting Spanish, "¿Conoce Usted al Señor Jesús?" The Guatemalan's dark face showed puzzlement. "No, I'm a stranger in town myself," he replied in Spanish. "I don't know the fellow."

Cam hadn't realized that in Spanish señor may mean "Lord" or "Mr." and that Jesús is a common name in Latin American countries!

Feeling a total failure, Cam fled down the cobblestone street to his room. Dropping on his knees and burying his face in the bed, he cried, "Lord, I'm a failure."

4. Cakchiquel Challenge

When the conference ended Bishop assigned Cam and Robby their territories before he returned to Guatemala City. Cam's would be for now around the twin Indian towns of San Antonio Aguas Calientes and Santa Catarina, where there was a group of Cakchiquel Indian Christians. "I'll expect to see you both in the capital for our Thanksgiving conference," Bishop told them.

It was October 23 when they parted. Robby rode away on a horse purchased for $25.00, while Cam left on foot with Isidro Alarcón, the Guatemalan pastor of the Antigua congregation. Though he was still smarting from the failure of the previous day, he said nothing about it.

As they hiked along the dusty road that led across coffee plantations, Cam was full of questions.

How had the gospel come to the Indian towns?

"It's a most interesting story," Isidro replied. "Silverio Lopez, one of the few Cakchiquel Indians who could read and understand a little Spanish, bought a Bible in Guatemala City when he was working there. He found it hard to understand and put it away. Then when he came home one of his children died and another became ill. The witch doctor blamed the sicknesses on the spirits of dead ancestors and told Silverio to buy candles and put them before an image in an Antigua church. The cost of the candles and the witch doctor's fee put Silverio in heavy debt."

The light-skinned pastor pointed to the ground. "On this very road, *don Guillermo,** Silverio found a scrap of paper which read:

---

* Spanish for William. Cam went by his first name since Cameron is very close to the Spanish word for shrimp.

32

'My Father's house should be called a house of prayer, but you have made it a den of thieves.' When he got home he looked up the verse in the Bible and decided to stop paying the witch doctor. He went back to Antigua and bought medicine from the drugstore that cured his daughter's stomach. Then he looked me up and I told him how to believe. That was only six months ago. He has since led forty Indians to Christ."

Cam was curious about the burdened Indians they met all along the road. He noticed that the men wore dark blue togalike shirts tied at the waist with a sash over white trousers. The women wore handwoven blouses of ornate design with long wraparound skirts of handwoven cotton cloth. "You can tell the town a woman is from by the design of her blouse," Isidro pointed out. "That girl up ahead is from San Antonio. The Indians stubbornly hold on to their old ways and languages."

Cam sensed condescension in the tone of his companion's voice. He knew that the pastor was a *ladino,* that is, a mestizo or person of mixed Spanish and Indian heritage, who enjoyed higher status in society.

"Can an Indian become a *ladino?*" he asked Isidro.

The pastor shrugged. "If he can learn to talk and live like civilized people. Few do."

They were over a hill now and Cam could see below the two Indian towns tucked into a saucerlike depression with a small blue lake to the left. Behind Santa Catarina the slope climbed steeply toward the volcano Agua. Two other volcanoes, Acatenango and Fuego, rose south of San Antonio.

A barefoot Indian man met them at the foot of the hill. Isidro introduced Francisco Díaz, one of Silverio's converts. "We're happy that you are here, *don Guillermo,*" the Indian said in Spanish. "You will eat and sleep in the chapel."

The pastor left Cam in a thatched hut with Francisco and some other believers. While struggling to get acquainted in Spanish, Cam took in the new surroundings. The thatched roof rested on a frame of rough logs and bamboo. Vertical cornstalks laced together with vines formed the walls. Chickens clucked across the bare earth floor and a smoky fire smoldered in the center. In a dark corner he spied a pile of thin blankets and mats.

He was finishing his supper of tortillas and soup spiced with eye-watering chili peppers, when the crowd began filling the hut. The men sat on benches while the women and children sat cross-legged on mats spread across the earthen floor.

Silverio, the first believer, lighted a paraffin candle, and they sang two hymns in stumbling Spanish. Then he motioned for Cam to come behind the table that served for a pulpit. Peering into the half-darkness alive with shapes and forms, Cam gave a short testimony of faith and quoted a few Bible verses he had memorized in Spanish.

The next morning, putting his first failure firmly behind him, the young foreigner boldly began a hut-to-hut campaign. He would walk through the opening in a cornstalk fence, present a tract to startled residents and quote John 3:16 with as much explanation as his limited Spanish permitted. Not until a scruffy dog bit him in one yard did he realize it was the Indian custom to call first from the gate.

Toward the end of the first week he entered a sort of beer garden and offered a tract to an Indian who was drinking liquor. "Sorry, *señor*, but I cannot read," the ragged man said. Cam smiled and walked away, but a few minutes later he heard the man's footsteps behind him. "*Amigo*, I have a friend who reads. If you will sell me a little book, *por favor?*"

Cam handed over a Gospel and invited the Indian whose name was Tiburcio, to the believers' Sunday services. To his great joy, Tiburcio came and at the end of Cam's sermon declared himself a believer. Cam's morale jumped 1,000 percent, for this was the first person he had helped find salvation.

When he had finished selling in the twin towns, Cam wanted to visit other Indian communities around Antigua until it was time to meet Robby and return to the capital. Francisco Díaz, the first to greet him on his arrival in San Antonio, wanted to be his escort. "But I must harvest my corn and coffee first," he told Cam. They agreed to meet early in December in a town south of Guatemala City and go on a two-weeks' campaign.

For the next two weeks Cam had a variety of guides and interpreters. From them he learned many of the Indians' traditions. One named Lucas told why Indian women were treated as servants by their husbands. "When God removed the rib from the first man's side, a little dog snatched it up and started to run away. God broke off the dog's tail, but the dog got away with the rib. So he had to make woman from the dog's tail."

When they visited a mountain town just after All Saints' Day, Lucas explained that food, cigars, and liquor had been placed on altars to satisfy the spirits of the dead who were supposed to return on the holy day. Further on, he pointed to a cross on the trail and said, "Someone died at this spot. The cross is to keep his spirit from wandering here forever."

Lucas also talked about the various Indian tribes. "Your friend is working Quiche territory," he commented, referring to Robby. "They speak a different language than we Cakchiquels, but both our tribes and the Tzutuhil people are descended from the great Mayans. The Spaniards made slaves of our forefathers. Those who tried to run away were tracked down with bloodhounds or hung as examples to others who might think of escaping. They even tried to force their religion on our ancestors, but it didn't work. The Indians continued to secretly worship the old gods. They still do today."

Cam was learning strategy, too. In the high valley of Chimaltenango he and his escort were surrounded by a town mob. "*Evangelistas!*" they shouted. "Stop the accursed Protestants!" Before the crowd could do any damage, soldiers came and escorted the two visitors to the town hall for their own protection. While there, Cam made friends with the town officials and won their cooperation. This taught him a lesson. In the future, he decided, he would contact local officials before starting to work a town.

Then it was time to meet Robby in Santiago and set out on the hot, dusty trail to Guatemala City. Taking turns walking and riding Robby's horse, they compared experiences. Both were eager to read the mail they hoped would be waiting for them in the capital. They weren't disappointed. But one of Cam's letters mentioned that his college friend Carroll Byram had been killed in France. Saddened, he remarked to Robby, "He could have been a big help down here. But we can't second-guess the Lord."

They soaked up Bible study and fellowship during the week-long conference of C.A.M. missionaries that began the day after their arrival, and they enjoyed Thanksgiving dinner with one of the Presbyterian missionary families. Then they separated again; while Robby stayed to work in the capital, Cam headed south to join his Indian friend Francisco.

They met in the town of Escuintla, and Francisco told Cam that Tiburcio, his first convert, was following the Lord faithfully. "The owner of the *finca* [big ranch] where he works has noticed the change in him and has made him a foreman! He is paying off his debts."

Cam was overjoyed at the news.

As they trudged across lowland plantations, Cam wondered why there were so many Indians working other men's fields in the low-lands.

"It's the *mozo* servant system," Francisco explained. "A man bor-rows a little for drinking. Then he borrows more and must work to pay it back. As he keeps drinking, the debt grows larger and the wages smaller. Soon he must mortgage himself to the lender and work on his *finca*. If he tries to leave, he is usually caught and taught a lesson at the whipping post. And he can be sold to another *finca* owner. The *mozos* you see here were purchased from *fincas* elsewhere."

Cam was amazed. "My father farms the land of others," he told Francisco. "He owes a debt. But he never had to sell himself into slavery."

By December 23 Cam and Frisco, as he now called the Indian, had worked around to a railroad station. Frisco wanted to be home for Christmas and Cam was due in Guatemala City. They planned to meet the next month in the capital and take off on another Bible selling trip.

Cam enjoyed Christmas with Robby and missionary friends. The food and camaraderie were cheering, but his mind was on the bur-dens of the Indians. "The Word of God will set them free," was his conclusion to the telling of Tiburcio's story. "We've got to get it out."

Christmas night, Cam and Robby were sleeping soundly at the Presbyterian school when an earthquake shook the building. The two salesmen jumped into their clothes and rushed out to help nurses and patients pouring from the Presbyterian hospital across the street.

Later in the day Cam walked across the stricken city to the plaza, where city officials had set up temporary headquarters, and gave each official a New Testament. Then with boldness, surprising even to himself, he suggested that the mayor immediately close the saloons to keep liquor from being sold in the streets. The mayor looked startled, but turned to a general and ordered them closed.

Aftershocks continued for the next three weeks, and Cam was kept busy distributing tracts and Gospels and doing relief work with the missionaries. "The opportunity for the spread of the gospel is tremendous now," he wrote his family on January 22. "I have bought Testaments for each of the president's cabinet with the money [sent by a Christian Endeavor group]. In presenting them, we will have an opportunity to give them the gospel."

With the aftershock of January 24, half the city had been destroyed. So when Frisco arrived from San Antonio, Cam was hesitant to leave with him until Edward Bishop assured him that relief agencies were getting things in hand.

Once again Cam set out with his Indian friend. For the next eleven months he would traverse a "thousand trails" in Guatemala, El Salvador, Honduras, and Nicaragua. Incredible hardships would toughen him. Spiritual experiences would deepen his conviction that the Bible was the Indian and peasant's best liberator. Comradeship and conversation with Frisco would draw him toward service with the Indians.

They ate whatever they could buy or was given to them, usually beans and tortillas, often sweetened with honey. Once they had spareribs for breakfast which Cam felt certain came from a starved-to-death cur. For overnight accommodations, any sheltered place would do, if one could be found, because drenching tropical rainstorms could leave them cold and shivering. Cam had a hammock which had been given to him by an American who was returning home. Frisco, without complaining, slept on the ground.

Dust, sometimes blinding, plagued them during the dry season. The jungle was so thick in some places they had to stay close together to keep in sight of each other. Both were deathly ill with the flu in the fall of 1918. Along the way Cam was given a pack mule to carry their books and literature, and later he purchased a riding mule which he named "Peregrina," or Pilgrim.

Cam had kept a regular diary until the earthquake. Now he made only occasional entries, some of which he inserted into letters for home. He complained of only one thing: Bugs!

I don't mind the heat like I do the insects. I am covered with bites all over. . . . The hang of it is that a fellow can't sit down anywhere along the road to rest or read without running into a nest of ants, mosquitoes, or something else.

He was so tormented with fleas at one place that he described his sufferings in a humorous blend of poetic Spanish and English.

Hay pulgas en mis trousers,
Millones en mis shoes,
Habitando all mi underwear,
Bailando twos por twos.

Mi patria es California
Y amo aun sus fleas
Pero estas pesky pulgas
De todas take the cheese.

Still he would write, "Frisco and I are having a great trip. The darkness is simply awful."

He was learning to use diplomacy. Arriving in a new settlement, he followed a consistent pattern of asking the mayor, plantation owner, or military commander for permission to sell in the town before attempting to visit any homes.

Although he was at times dismayed and disgusted by the Christo-paganism that pervaded the lowlands, Cam felt that harsh judgments would only close minds further. Instead he used the limited biblical knowledge the people did have as openers for proclaiming the gospel. For example, on "Holy Thursday" he and Frisco met a crowd of men carrying a long pine tree. "We're going to hang Judas in the plaza," one explained.

They followed the men into the small town and watched them lift a stuffed effigy up the trunk of the tree. Then they barged in on a group at a saloon and began telling why Christ died. After awhile, one of the men stopped and invited them to "come and tell my wife and mother this message." He led them three miles to his mother's farm where his wife and children lived in extreme poverty because of his drunkenness. That day his life was changed through faith in Christ.

Cam was determined to pass no one by. Along dirty alleys and narrow footpaths that served for streets they trudged until they had visited all the houses in view. In one town they could find no more huts until Cam spotted a brood of chickens scratching at the top of a hill. They followed the chickens and found another family.

During the long weeks and months, Cam's admiration for his Indian companion grew. As he watched the Indian preach and converse, he thought: "He certainly isn't lazy or dull-witted as some of the *ladinos* say Indians are. He's eager, industrious, and skillful in missionary work. What the Lord could do with a hundred like him! They could evangelize their people in their own language."

Around many a campfire Frisco described for Cam the plight of his people. "There are three kinds of oppressors who keep the Indians down. The witch doctors teach superstitions, telling the Indians that the sun is their father and the moon their grandmother, and that every hill and volcano has its spirit-owner who demands worship and sacrifices.

"The clergy try to impose the Spanish religion upon us. They only come when there are children to baptize or someone to marry or bury. Even then they use a language the people do not understand. And for all these services they expect to be well paid.

"And the saloon keepers. They are almost always *ladinos*. They sell liquor for religious festivals, marriage feasts, baptisms, and wakes for the dead. They cooperate with the *finca* owners who let the Indians drink on credit enough to keep them in the forced labor systems. My people have little hope."

"Aren't there any Indian schools?" Cam asked.

"Ha," Frisco exclaimed bitterly. "Who would teach us, when the *ladinos* say it is a disgrace to even talk to an Indian?"

"What about the evangelical missionaries?"

"They go to the Spanish-speakers. Not one evangelizes the Indian in his own tongue. *Don Guillermo*, why don't you come and be our missionary?"

"But I don't know Spanish well, much less Cakchiquel," Cam protested.

"We'll teach you," Frisco promised.

In the silence that followed, Cam mulled over the challenge. If he learned Frisco's unwritten language, he could then translate the Bible into it. But with no special training, how could he ever do it? The task seemed monumental, even impossible.

Perhaps he could still do something. "You know, Frisco, that I only get thirty dollars a month salary, but I also can keep half of anything I sell over five dollars per month. I could give that half toward starting an Indian school in San Antonio."

"Would you, *don Guillermo*?" the Indian said excitedly. "All of us will help."

"Well, I'll pray and you pray. We'll see."

A few days later Cam wrote his parents that he wanted to stay on in Central America awhile longer. It was a hard letter to write because he knew how much they—especially his mother—wanted him to finish college and go on to seminary.

He was delighted to receive an understanding reply.

May God direct you, Son, in everything you do. When you do God's will, you do mine, for I don't want you to do anything but His. I want you to live for that end for which He created you—to honor and glorify God, and I am glad you are doing so. Here is a dollar. Papa.

They were in El Salvador on November 12 when Cam overheard an Indian woman say that the war was over. It was a time of sober reflection. Carroll was dead and he was alive. There had to be a purpose in that. And he had to fulfill that purpose.

The middle of the next month they reached the railroad town of Moran south of Guatemala City. From here Frisco would take the cart road to San Antonio and Cam would go to the capital to rest, for he was still weak from his bout with the flu and covered with red welts from insect bites.

"We'll be looking for you to come and start the Indian school," Frisco said in parting.

"I'll be there," Cam promised.

"Each language must have its own pattern."

5. A New Bride and a New Language

Robby was not there to welcome Cam back to Guatemala City. He had been called home for induction into the army shortly before the end of the war. The other missionaries welcomed Cam as a seasoned worker, but he found himself missing his friend.

One evening at dinner with the William Allisons, Presbyterian missionaries, Cam was seated by Elvira Malmstrom, a first-term missionary from Chicago. Though four years Cam's senior, she was younger than the other missionaries. She listened eagerly to stories about his travels and laughed at his jokes and amusing incidents. Cam decided she was much too vivacious to fit the old-maid missionary stereotype, and he felt strongly attracted to her. Adept in social graces, she spoke Spanish like a cultured Guatemalan.

She was excited about his plans to start a school for Cakchiquel Indian children. Though she taught a class of girls in the capital, she had made mission trips into the country and thought the Indians "charming," but in great need of the gospel.

Cam felt himself more and more drawn to her. He kept finding excuses to be with her during the Christmas holidays and confided to her his hope of learning the unwritten Cakchiquel language and translating the New Testament. To do that he would have to resign from the Bible House and work independently until affiliating with a mission. "I've saved $100 from sales commissions and contributions from my folks at home," he said confidently. "Mr. Bishop has promised a cow and calf to help get the school started. Other missionaries have pledged money. When I need more, the Lord will send it." Elvira smiled and made him feel that she shared his vision.

He would have enjoyed staying longer in Guatemala City, but duty came first and he rode off on his mule, Pilgrim, toward San

41

Antonio. He got only as far as Antigua, however, when he became
deathly ill with malaria. By February, however, he was eagerly awaiting a visit by a C.A.M. couple, Mr. and Mrs. A. B. Treichler along
with Elvira. When they arrived he proudly escorted them to San
Antonio and Santa Catarina, with Elvira riding Pilgrim along the
shady road. The sickness had not dulled his enthusiasm, and he
talked eagerly of the Bible and education as complementary keys
to the uplifting of the Cakchiquels.

"The Lord will help us break down the barriers, and the Cakchiquels will be examples to their Indian brothers in other tribes," he
predicted. "They'll become full citizens of the Republic."

The believers turned out in force to greet them. None was happier than Frisco. "When will you start the school, *don Guillermo?*"
he wanted to know. "I've told everybody."

"Just as soon as possible," Cam assured him.

Certain now that Elvira felt as he did about the Indians, he
proposed on Valentine's Day. She waited a few days, then just
before leaving said yes. Cam saw her acceptance as another indication of God's approval of his work with the Indians.

When the engagement was announced, the Presbyterians wanted
Cam and Elvira to join their mission. Although Elvira was not
officially a member, they felt that she, along with Cam, was fully
qualified. They would ask their board to accept them on the basis
of experience, since neither had the required education. However,
the Presbyterian area did not take in the Cakchiquels.

Cam wanted to keep an open mind, so he rode three days across
the mountains into Presbyterian territory where Quiche Indians
lived. "I felt as if I were in a foreign country," he reported back to
Elvira. "I feel stronger than ever that my place is with Frisco among
the Cakchiquels."

Back in Cakchiquel country, Cam wasted no time in starting
the school. Frisco helped him arrange housing for boarding students
from other villages. A chief loaned a room in his house for classes.
One of the few literate Cakchiquel believers who could teach in both
Spanish and Cakchiquel accepted employment as a teacher. Cam
felt he should be paid ten dollars a month, equal to plantation
wages for a free man.

Since the school was primarily for the children of believers, and
Cam knew their parents couldn't afford to pay tuition out of local
wages of five to thirty-five cents a day, outside support was neces-

sary. But Cam was becoming known in Antigua. The governor had him teach the Bible twice a week to his children. Then the straw boss on a plantation gave a sizable donation. After deliberation, Cam made a radical departure from usual mission policy and asked some of the merchants to contribute. "The whole area will benefit from Indian education," he told them. "They'll get better jobs, earn more money, and become better citizens."

And so in March 1919, Cameron Townsend opened what is believed to be the first local *Indian* mission school in Central America, and possibly in all of South America. The school had less than twenty-five students.

In inaugurating this milestone in Indian education, Cam was further ahead of his time than anyone realized. Educators in the Americas would long be (and many still are) shackled to the melting pot philosophy of offering schooling to minority linguistic groups in the language of the majority.

But schooling wasn't the whole answer. Convinced that the Cakchiquels must have Scripture in their own language, Cam began building a notebook of Cakchiquel expressions. The Indians responded with amazed delight, for he was the first outsider ever to attempt this task.

He took time out only for the wedding, set for July 9. Cam wanted to be married on his birthday as his father had on his. Having put all his money into the Cakchiquel school, he was grateful for the help of friends. A. B. Treichler of the C.A.M. gave him a $2.50 gold piece which a jeweler hollowed into a wedding band for Elvira. The visiting president of the C.A.M. board of directors, Luther Rees, paid for his wedding suit. Others provided an array of palms, ferns, and flowers to decorate the Presbyterian church. Elvira's white bridal gown was made by a Guatemalan Bible woman, one of the best dressmakers in the capital.

Paul Burgess, a Presbyterian missionary, officiated, and Elvira's brother Carl, who had come to represent their family, was Cam's best man. Elvira's Sunday school class of girls sang and a small reception followed.

The couple spent their wedding night in a missionary's home in the capital. The next morning Carl joined them on the bouncy stage for Antigua.

After a week of meetings in Antigua the three embarked on an eighty-five-mile evangelistic safari into the mountains. Elvira rode

Pilgrim, while Cam and Carl walked, and an Indian porter carried bedding and Elvira's portable organ. They stopped at villages to hold services and pass out Gospels and tracts. Such a "honeymoon" was not unusual for missionaries in those days, for their calling came before everything else. Also, Cam wanted to let his bride's minister brother have a taste of Indian work before he went home.

The Townsends had joined the Central American Mission a month before the wedding, even though the missionaries weren't enthusiastic about Cam's Cakchiquel language study, and Edward Bishop warned them they would have to look to God for funds. "Our mission has no central treasury for support," he said. "We all live by faith."

At first they lived in Antigua and traveled back and forth to San Antonio, but their financial situation was uncertain and erratic. And even with a buggy they found the ten-mile ride from San Antonio and back time-consuming. With $70 from Elvira's home church—Moody Church—in Chicago, they built a one-room cornstalk and log house next to the school in San Antonio, then added a kitchen with $25 given by a visiting American agriculturist.

Cam and Elvira were both hard workers. Besides writing dozens of letters to supporters each month, Elvira played the portable organ for all the services, and taught singing, organ, and sewing. She also called on sick people a good bit. In the housework she was assisted by Tomasa, the twelve-year-old Indian daughter of Cam's first convert.

Cam kept busy developing and encouraging Indian workers. He started a "school of the prophets" for Cakchiquel Christians that involved both classroom teaching and practical training. He believed that a strong cadre of Indian evangelists and pastors was essential for spiritual increase and growth. A missionary, he felt, could never do enough on his own, and the believers he won could easily become too dependent on him.

Frisco, Cam's old trail partner, was the star worker, and Cam was counting on him to become the spiritual leader of the Cakchiquels. Then he fell ill with malaria, and never recovered. His death was a serious blow to Cam. Not only had they been close, but in a unique way Frisco had been his teacher. He was more concerned than ever to train the Cakchiquel believers.

With Frisco gone, Cam had to do more counseling and exhorting. When one worker came to resign because of criticism, Cam's re-

In Antigua, Guatemala, Cam poses for a picture on his wedding day and 23rd birthday. The snapshot went to California with the inscription, *July 9, 1919. With untold love to father and mother. Cameron.*

By 1922–23 Cam and Elvira had built a home for needy Indian children in San Antonio where the children could live while attending the Indian school. Here the Townsends pose in Guatemalan Indian dress.

sponse was, "Very well, let's kneel in prayer and you can tell the Lord you wish to quit." The shamefaced Indian gulped. "No, I, I don't want to quit the Lord."

All this time Cam had kept building his word and phrase lists, and working on pronunciations. The differences of some words were almost impossible to detect. There were four different "k" sounds that were especially hard to distinguish. One was something like an English "k"; one sounded like a deep cough; one wasn't right unless it came out with a kind of pop; the hardest of all was sort of a choking sound. The last two were further differentiated by the way the Adam's apple moved—whether up or down!

There was one list of words that all had the same vowel "e" but that ended with one of the "k" sounds. He had to master these sounds if he was going to be able to hear and say the difference between "black," "flea," "red," "stingy," "their chicken," and "our chicken."

He further discovered that the Cakchiquels had their own numerical system. "One person" meant twenty, "two people" meant forty, and so on. When he learned that this was because one person has ten fingers and ten toes, it made sense. He always felt a surge of satisfaction upon finding new evidence of Indian smartness. The Cakchiquels weren't stupid. You just needed to understand them and their language.

Given enough time, he knew he could learn the words and their pronunciations. But the countless verb forms seemed to defy explanation.

One day in Antigua Cam met an American archaeologist who was looking for old manuscripts. Cam invited Dr. Gates home for the night and the two sat up late discussing the Cakchiquel language. "I'm trying to analyze the grammar, but this language doesn't work the way you'd expect. It puzzles me," Cam confessed.

The archaeologist smiled knowingly. "Young man, I suspect you've been trying to force Cakchiquel into the Latin mold. Dr. Sapir, the University of Chicago linguist, stresses the importance of a truly descriptive approach."

Cam pondered that statement. Then his frown slowly turned into a smile. "Of course," he said. "Each language must have its own pattern!"

"Exactly. Try to get the Cakchiquel viewpoint. You'll find a regular and logical development of the language."

This advice turned the would-be linguist in the right direction. He badgered language helpers with questions. He listened. They patiently repeated words and phrases over and over and over. He wrote and wrote. The pages of notes piled up. And slowly the pieces of the puzzle began fitting together.

It soon became clear that Cakchiquel was built by attaching prefixes and suffixes to word roots—just as a simple English word like "point" can become "disappointed." In time he discovered that one verb could be conjugated into a possible 100,000 forms in contrast to five possibilities with some English verbs, not counting compound forms. A single Cakchiquel verb could indicate time, number of subjects, number of objects, location of the doer(s), several aspects of action, and many other ideas.

As Cam became more fluent in Cakchiquel, he realized that in San Antonio the Indians had adopted many Spanish words. So he and Elvira began spending more time in the highland town of Patzun where purer Cakchiquel was spoken. Patzun had a strong evangelical congregation—thanks to Indian evangelists. But life was cheaper here among the unbelievers than in San Antonio. A dog sold for ten pesos, a cat for five, but a young girl could be bought from her father for four pesos (then about 12¼¢ U.S.). The Townsends were upset to find Indian girls of ten to fifteen often serving as common-law wives and looking old at twenty.

It was terribly hard not to start a campaign for eradicating social vices. They did what they could to help, but they felt only the gospel could work permanent changes. And for the gospel to take effect, Scripture must be translated into the Indian tongue.

With the help of an Indian from the neighboring town of Comalapa, Cam began translating the Gospel of Mark, using the Cakchiquel expressions he felt were closest to the Greek. He realized his grasp of the language was far from perfect after only a year of study, but he was sure that even this "temporary" Mark would be a blessing to the Cakchiquels.

After he had translated four chapters, Elvira typed them up, and Cam took the manuscript to a printer in Antigua. He found the printer in the office of the mayor. When the mayor discovered what the American wanted printed, he became quite upset. "We're trying to get rid of the Indian languages. We want everybody to speak Spanish!"

The printer nodded in agreement. "But you see, your honor,"

Cam suggested diplomatically, "we have the Indian language on one page and the Spanish on the other. This way they can learn to read first in their own language and then make an easy shift to Spanish."

The printer brightened. "Oh, well, I guess we could print that." The mayor agreed and the job was done cheaper than Cam had expected.

The first printing of Scripture in their own language created great excitement among the Cakchiquel Christians. "God talks our language," was their reaction. Copies of the translation sold rapidly. The Cakchiquel preachers carried it as a badge of status whether they could read or not. Adults began begging for a reading class.

In November of 1920 a historic diplomatic congress was held in Antigua to discuss the possible union of all Central American countries. After a special mass was announced in honor of the delegates, a Guatemalan lady asked the Townsends, "Why couldn't you hold a Protestant service in their honor?"

Cam thought this a great idea. He and Elvira sent written invitations to the delegates, mentioning that Indian believers would participate in the service.

That Friday afternoon the evangelical chapel was filled. A group of Indians from San Antonio sang special hymns and Cam concluded with a short gospel message. He was preparing to dismiss the group when a distinguished Guatemalan congressman asked for the floor. "It's marvelous what the Bible has done for these Indians, a people that the conquerors saw only as beasts of burden," he declared. Then the brother of the president of Honduras jumped up and voiced his delight, and the secretary of the Congress expressed his approval.

The enthusiasm of the delegates gave Cam a vision of what such quasi-official ceremonies could do in advancing the liberation of minority groups from spiritual darkness.

Shortly after the Congress, Robby returned from the States with his bride Genevieve. The two buddies were excited at being together again, so much so that the Robinsons decided to stay over for the Cakchiquel Bible Conference scheduled for January 1921.

The invited speaker, a former missionary to the Comanches in Oklahoma, had been highly recommended by a missionary friend of Cam and Elvira's. Leonard Livingston Legters was loud, colorfully outspoken, and sometimes given to exaggeration. But Cam saw that he was a go-getter. He would preach in English, Cam would translate into Spanish, and an Indian would translate from Spanish into Cakchiquel. (Cam later learned to do both Spanish and Indian himself.)

Legters delighted the Indians by acting out key points in his messages. "When you enter a new life," he would declare, "close the door behind you," and he would stride to the door of the chapel and slam it behind him. In speaking he was not at all like Cam who rarely raised his voice.

Cam and Robby were both pleased with the results of the conference. Sixty Indians, including an influential chief, surrendered their lives to the Lord's service. They agreed to make the conference an annual affair for the Cakchiquels. Then Robby and Genevieve left for the mission station they were to occupy at the Cakchiquel lake town of Panajachel.

Legters, however, wanted to preach to more Indians. So he, Cam and Elvira, and a Cakchiquel worker made a mule trip through the western mountains. Then he visited other Indian areas without the Townsends. However, all the translating so cramped Legter's style that he too became an advocate of translating the New Testament into the language of the local people.

Cam saw in Legters a valuable ally for promoting the Indian work in the United States, and invited him to return the next year. Back in the U.S., Legters demonstrated his enthusiasm. He became the first field representative for the newly founded Pioneer Mission Agency, created to forward funds to worthy missions, and he bombarded every audience that would listen with the spiritual need of the Cakchiquels. Some of his letters were printed in the widely read *Sunday School Times*. When copies reached Guatemala, a missionary pointed out to Cam exaggerations such as "I have seen the fires of a *thousand* villages." Cam smiled and said, "Forget the exaggerations. He has a marvelous vision."

6. Sorrow and Loss

While the Cakchiquel work was going very well, the same could not be said about Cam's home life. Cam discovered very early in his marriage that his wife had two personalities. One was sweet and charming, especially with visitors. The other Elvira would explode in uncontrollable bouts of temper, seemingly without provocation. She would scream and scold, completely losing control of herself. Then after the emotional tirade had run its course, her sensitive conscience would move her to confess her failings with great remorse.

One such outburst occurred when she was riding with Cam and Legters near San Antonio. She suddenly reined in her mule and began screaming, "Call the police! Call the police!" for no apparent reason. After helping Cam calm her, Legters was very sympathetic and understanding, yet definite in saying, "Elvira must have rest, Cam. She can't keep up this pace."

As a result, Cam felt Elvira should go to Chicago for some relaxation and spend time with her aging parents. Later he would join her in California at his parents' home. It would be his first visit home after four years on the field.

Cam wrote his parents about these plans. "Standing on her feet so much is awfully hard on her hernia and it is getting worse," he said. "She keeps up as bravely as can be and turns out more work than I do but we realize something must be done." He did not mention her emotional problems.

Robby agreed to oversee the school and a training conference for pastors in Cam's absence. After a long train trip across Mexico, during which he saw the Lord provide for him when he ran out of money, Cam arrived in California where Elvira was waiting for him at his parents' home.

The pleasant Elvira charmed the whole family. Then her other personality showed up. Cam's folks were very understanding. Always one to look on the positive side, Molly said, "Elvira has so many wonderful qualities. This is a sickness. Can't you get her to a psychiatrist?" They did and he advised her to get back to work among the Cakchiquels.

It was at this time that Cam moved his church membership to the independent Church of the Open Door in Los Angeles. It was a strong Bible-teaching church with an active interest in missions. And when the missionary committee invited him to tell about the Indians in Guatemala, he eagerly accepted.

In the audience were young Dr. Charles Ainslie and his wife. As Presbyterian mission volunteers, they had been trying to decide between going to Alaska or to Guatemala. After hearing Cam, they settled on Guatemala.

Cam's brother Paul and his new bride Laura also expressed interest in missionary work, and Cam encouraged them to come to Guatemala under the C.A.M. They made no promise, except to pray.

Cam took time to look up some old friends and teachers. Mrs. Louise Heim, a former Sunday school teacher, remembered him well. "When you were about four years old you used to lead my blind father around Santa Fe Springs," she reminded him. "And now you're leading Indians to Christ."

He shared with her his dreams for the Cakchiquels. "We want a new school, and children's home, a clinic, a light plant."

"But, Cameron," she said, "you aren't with a denomination. Who will pay for all that?"

"We believe the Lord will provide some way."

Before he left for Guatemala, Mrs. Heim gave him a check for $3,000. "That's for the new enterprises," she said. Cam was overwhelmed at this unexpected gift, the largest he had ever received. Later, his old Sunday school teacher followed up with $4,000 more.

He met Charles Fuller, the president of the Orange Growers Association and teacher of a large Bible class. The Fuller family pledged to support two Cakchiquel preachers. Through Charles Fuller's father, he met the Joe Woodsuns. They donated a manual multilith printing press for Cam to take back.

A letter came from Robby reporting that the four-week training conference had succeeded beyond all expectations. Robby wanted to start a permanent Indian Bible Institute at Panajachel.

All Cam could say was, "The Lord is so good. Look how He is honoring our faith."

In February 1922, the couple returned to Guatemala. With Robby now responsible for training the Indian preachers, Cam had more time to concentrate on mastering the Indian language and doing some translation work.

After spending nearly six months grinding away at that task, a welcome invitation came from Robby to come to Panajachel on beautiful Lake Atitlan. "Lady Genevieve is going to visit a plantation for a week or ten days," he wrote, "so how about spending that time with me in concentrated language, Bible study, prayer, and conference relating to the Lord's work in our fields?"

The two friends met at the village of Guatalon on Thursday, June 23. They evangelized villages along the way to the lake, arriving at the Robinsons' lakeside home about noon the next day. Robby told Cam about the dramatic recovery of a woman he had treated for gangrene poisoning. "The doctor had given her up, and the family had even prepared a crypt for her. But I stayed with her, soaking her swollen foot in warm water all night long, and God intervened."

The two ate dinner, took a nap and then Robby suggested a swim. Cavorting through the water Cam felt the cares of the world slipping off his shoulders. He was swimming on his back, headed back to shore, when he noticed Robby suddenly throw up his hands, shake his head, and slide under. Fearful, Cam started toward his friend. By the time he reached the spot, Robby was going under for the third time. Cam grabbed him, but Robby pulled him under about nine feet. As Cam struggled to the surface, Robby's arms suddenly went limp and he fell away. Cam swam to shore where he called for help.

Upon finally recovering the body, they tried artificial respiration for nearly two hours. A vacationing judge came to assist. He looked at Robby's purplish face and shook his head. "Cerebral hemorrhage," he said grimly. "There's no hope."

While the rest sat in stunned silence, Cam opened his Spanish Bible and read from the eleventh chapter of John. Then he sent telegrams to Genevieve and the Treichlers of the C.A.M.

It was Sunday morning before word reached Genevieve. The young widow rode eighteen miles on muleback to catch a boat across the lake.

The funeral was held Monday morning with a short service in the lakeshore home and a public service in the school. Robby was so well loved in the town that the mayor declared a day of mourning and the town orator gave a eulogy. Trinidad Bac, the Indian pastor, preached the sermon. "Robinson's coming marked a new day for Indians," he declared. "He gave us the Good News and helped us turn from superstition and fear to love and the true God." Then raising his voice, the Cakchiquel preacher shouted, "You say our friend Robinson is dead. That's not true! He is alive. He lives right now in heaven with God."

At the cemetery near the lakeshore, Cam saw his best friend placed in the crypt which had been prepared for the woman whose life he had saved a few days before. Then a stone was pushed in place behind the coffin with the inscription,

W. E. Robinson
Bearer of Good News

It was one of the saddest times of Cam's life. Frisco was dead, and now Robby. They had been his strongest allies in the Indian work.

"I believe in grace. God's grace."

7. Cam's Theology

"Panajachel is a splendid center for training Indian preachers," Cam wrote in the C.A.M. *Bulletin.* The town lay in the heart of Indian country, surrounded by Cakchiquel villages. It was near the main east-west road and on the lake, so it was accessible by land and water. He asked readers to pray that God would send someone to fulfill Robby's dream of a training school, since he had the translation to do.

The need for leadership at the San Antonio station was solved with the arrival of Paul and Laura Townsend. Cam's younger brother didn't have Cam's ear for language, but he had skilled hands. He became not only the preacher but also the carpenter, mechanic, plumber, electrician, and agriculturist.

By this time the boarding school at San Antonio had grown to an enrollment of around one hundred, and three single lady missionaries worked with the students. But Cam saw the need for further expansion. He wanted San Antonio to be a model for Indian work elsewhere: a strong group of believers, a well-equipped school, vocational training facilities, a clinic, an orphanage, and cooperative enterprises for building the Indian economy—all were needed. He felt the Indians had to gain self-sufficiency if they were ever to rise above the centuries of degradation and oppression.

Money given by Cam's former Sunday school teacher enabled Paul and a team of Indian carpenters to build a clinic. When the buildings were completed, the C.A.M. assigned a new missionary nurse to San Antonio. "Doc" Ainslie, whom Cam had recruited in Los Angeles, was now in charge of the Presbyterian Hospital in Guatemala City, and he began making trips into Indian country to treat the most serious ailments.

Cam next put Paul to work building a home for needy Indian children. The twenty or more children Cam and Elvira were helping in various Indian homes needed a dormitory. Two of these were very special to them. Elena Trejo was a Quiche Indian girl who had been brought to them by a missionary. Joe Chicol was a Cakchiquel from Comalapa. Although Cam and Elvira had considered it, they decided not to adopt these two formally. They wanted to be free to love and help all the Indian children. Also they still hoped to have children of their own.

Cam was very pleased when A. E. Forbes, a coffee manufacturer in St. Louis, read about the work in the *Christian Herald* and sent money for a turbine and coffee sheller. He helped the Indians form a coffee cooperative. By bringing their coffee to the sheller and shelling their own beans, they increased profits immensely. And the Forbes Company bought all they produced. The cooperative was another milestone for Cam and may have been the first of its type for Indians in Latin America.

Soon after the 1922–23 year-end conference, a new C.A.M. recruit appeared in San Antonio. Archer Anderson, a graduate of the Philadelphia School of the Bible, had read Cam's article in the C.A.M. *Bulletin* asking for help in establishing a Bible institute for Indians. "What's been done about it so far?" he asked.

Cam looked amazed. "Well, we've been praying about it. I guess God has sent you."

Cam took Anderson to Panajachel and the two of them started renovating the building Robby had purchased for the Bible school. Six weeks later the Robinson Bible Institute opened its first session with students from the three surrounding tribes. Elvira taught music. Cam gave chapel talks and some lessons and interpreted for Anderson, who was the Bible teacher. After classes Cam worked on his translation while Anderson and about fifteen students erected the first dormitory building from plans Robinson had sketched before his death.

Cam insisted on a balanced regimen of study and practical work. Each Saturday students and faculty took off on foot and by launch for villages in the area. By Monday noon they were back with stories of ministering to spiritual need.

Cam saw that every student was given some menial task to perform, besides his work on the building project. One fellow was assigned to feed the hogs they would later butcher for meat. When he didn't clean the pen thoroughly, Cam showed him how it should be done, all the while delivering a lesson about doing a task correctly.

Visiting missionaries were continually amazed at Cam's common-sense adeptness in dealing with difficult situations at the Panachel station and on itinerant trips. On one such trip Cam and a new Presbyterian worker met five *ladino* drunks, who insisted that the two Americans have a drink with them. "No thanks," said Cam.

A short while later the gang overtook them on the road and one of the drunks whirled his mount in front of Cam's and thrust a pistol into his face. A second slid off his horse and jabbed his machete against Cam's stomach while demanding Cam take a drink or else. "But aren't we friends?" Cam asked. "Yes," the pistol-wielder replied, "but you must prove your friendship by drinking with us."

"If you came to my house and I offered you something you didn't like, what would you do?" Cam asked.

The man rolled his eyes and finally said, "I'd pretend to take it, then when you weren't looking I'd throw it away."

"Well in that case, give me the flask," Cam said. He poured himself a palm-full, shouted jovially, "To your health!" and turned his hand over. The new missionary, who had not understood much of the conversation, followed suit and the appeased drunks rode away.

Cam could handle situations like this, but Elvira remained a problem. Since returning from California her health had improved, but not her emotional instability. She would have been content with a more conventional work among *ladinos*, but Cam was determined to stick with the Indians. His adaptation to the Indian culture irritated her. Things that were important to her didn't bother him in the least. Like the broken windowpane in their cornstalk house in San Antonio. She had begged him for weeks to take the frame into Antigua and have a new pane inserted. One day he finally got around to it, though the day seemed to him wasted on the trip. They were returning in Paul's Model T when Cam slowed to pick up an Indian. "Go on, Cam," Elvira urged, "we're in a hurry." Cam ignored her and stopped anyway. The Indian climbed into the back seat and sat down smack in the middle of the new glass.

She was happy when Cam decided to make Panajachel their new headquarters. The C.A.M. home the Robinsons had lived in was a larger, frame house, and faced the beautiful lake away from the main town. There was more room for entertaining official visitors and it was surrounded by a lawn and flowering trees and shrubs, providing an atmosphere that helped reduce her outbursts.

Still Cam never knew when she would fly into a rage. One day she suddenly turned on him and began kicking him—hard. To avoid more violence he went down the trail that led to the next town. Finally in a secluded spot he found a log and sat down.

While he was sitting there, feeling very sorry for himself, an Indian came along and noticed Cam's feet sticking into the trail. Cam forced a smile and mustered his Cakchiquel to greet him.

As they exchanged greetings, Cam's sense of duty wrestled with his despair. Finally he asked, "Have you heard God's Word?" The Indian had not. Cam began explaining the Good News, rather mechanically at first, then warming as he continued. After awhile he became so engrossed in giving the message that the pain inflicted by Elvira vanished. He returned home with joy in his heart.

Despite Elvira's outbursts, which continued throughout her lifetime, Cam loved his wife. He was very patient with her and always remembered her on every appropriate occasion with a bit of sentimental verse or doggerel, if not with a gift. On one anniversary he wrote her a three-verse poem of which this is the first verse:

> Nineteen, nineteen, on the ninth of July
> By the Jefe Politico we were married, you and I.
> You remember, I'm sure,
> How so love-sick we were.
> How our lives were united
> And our promises plighted
> On that glorious day
> Not so far, far away.
> Nineteen, nineteen, on the ninth of July.

The school work was encouraging, though, and Anderson was a gem. He quickly learned Spanish, freeing Cam from interpreting for him. Cam still had administrative and teaching chores and field trips, for the school was growing, and surrounding Indian congregations were increasing in size and number. He struggled to find time for translation.

It would have been easier had all of his fellow missionaries believed in what he was doing. Many of them felt the Indian work was divisive and would only drive a deeper wedge between *ladino* and Indian believers. Some were irritated by Cam's practice of socializing with the Indians and thought it unseemly to bring Indians into their homes. They saw no future in translating Scripture into the Indian languages. Cam, however, continued to believe that the Indian Christians must develop on their own with only limited financial help and guidance from missionaries and *ladino* leaders.

The displeasure of colleagues developed into formidable opposition. Cam was notified that the issue of translation would be debated at the next general council meeting in Chicago, so when Dr. Lewis Sperry Chafer, the executive secretary of the Central American Mission, arrived from the home office in Dallas, Cam was anxious to make his views understood. Despite a broken foot from a motorcycle accident, he drove Chafer around to various mission points.

As they jolted along the bumpy roads in the Model T, Cam explained his reasons for trying to reach the Indians within their own culture. "If the work was integrated," he told Chafer, "the *ladinos* would continue to dominate and discriminate against the Indians as they have always done. When the Indians attain education and economic freedom, then they can meet the *ladinos* as equals. But to do this they must have a training school and Scripture in their own language."

Chafer agreed that education was important and confided that he was starting a new seminary in Dallas that would counteract the liberalism in some denominational schools. "What's your theological background?" he asked Cam.

"Well, I didn't finish college and never went to Bible school," Cam admitted. "Maybe I'll finish my education sometime. But here I seldom see a book on theology or church history. I spend my devotional time studying the Bible and Scofield's notes. And I keep trying to find more time to translate the Bible into Cakchiquel."

Chafer was surprised that Cam was a missionary and hadn't had theological training. But he conceded that one could learn a lot from Scofield. He asked if Cam had met the famous Bible teacher, who had founded the C.A.M.

"Well, no," Cam replied. "But I have worn his pants! Got them from a missionary barrel. They were twice too big for me and didn't fit my needs. Not any more than the Spanish Scriptures fit the needs of the Indians."

Chafer chuckled at Cam's ability to keep getting back to the Indians and steered the conversation back to theology. Did Cam agree with Scofield that the Sermon on the Mount was meant for the dispensation of the Kingdom?

"Well, you'd know more about that than I," Cam replied. "I must confess that at times I do try to apply the principles Jesus taught there in my daily life. I remember one time I was selling Spanish New Testaments in San Juan Sacatepequez when a fanatical Indian pulled a Testament from my hand. The crowd began throwing sticks and stones and trying to club me, so I ran to ask the mayor for protection. After I told him what had happened he put the main troublemaker in jail.

"But I knew I hadn't acted in love, so I went back and begged the mayor to release him. After he had been freed I explained to the grateful Indian, the mayor, and the big crowd that had gathered that I only wanted to tell people about God's love.

"The Indian listened and then meekly admitted to the crowd he had been wrong to fight against us and advised them to listen. I then had an attentive audience as I delivered a gospel message."

"What are your views on election?" Chafer persisted.

"Oh, I believe in election all right," said Cam. "I also believe in my responsibility to tell the Good News to every person possible. One time two of the Cakchiquel preachers and I went to a Quiche community. Each time we would approach a group of huts where a clan lived, everybody would hide. But at one place a woman stayed out to tend the ants she was toasting in a big skillet over a campfire. I pulled out a coin and politely asked if she would sell me some.

"She called inside for a bowl which she filled with the Quiche delicacy. The Cakchiquels frowned. 'We've never eaten ants,' they told me. 'Well, I haven't either, but we're going to eat some now,' I said. 'It'll be worth it if it encourages them to listen to the gospel.'

"And you know, it worked. While we were munching on the ants the Indians began to emerge from their hiding places. They were so impressed at outsiders eating ants that they lost their fear and listened to the gospel as long as we kept eating. So one of us would preach while the other two ate. The people received a steady sermon as long as the ants lasted."

Chafer laughed and asked Cam if, indeed, he held any strong doctrinal positions.

"Well, I guess Mr. Bishop—he's sort of my 'missionary daddy'—influenced me to be strong on fundamentals and on grace. I believe in grace. God's grace. And I want to share it with the Indians."

The discussions went on day after day as they toured Guatemala and El Salvador. When the tour was completed, Chafer told Cam that he was convinced that the Indians needed Scripture in their own language. "When the question comes up for a vote at the council, I'll be on your side," he promised. Then before leaving he invited Cam to speak at the seminary he was planning to start.

During the weeks that followed, Cam was more convinced than ever that he should attend the 1925 council meeting in Chicago. "There's too much at stake for them to stop the translation now."

Cam and Elvira first went to California for a few weeks with his family, then went on to the council meeting at Moody Church in Chicago. There the C.A.M. directors received Cam cordially and asked to hear his side of the controversy. After he spoke, they had a short discussion and recessed for lunch.

Cam and R. D. Smith walked along North Avenue on their way to a restaurant. The man who had first sent him to Guatemala urged Cam to retract his stand on translation and serve as a general missionary. Cam, who rarely became ruffled, suddenly boiled in anger at the thought of having to leave translation work. "Whether you like it or not, Mr. Smith," he said sharply, "the Cakchiquel New Testament will be translated."

That afternoon they voted. Louis Sperry Chafer and Luther Drees, the man who had bought Cam's wedding suit, stood with the majority of six in Cam's favor. Smith and one other member remained in opposition to the Cakchiquel translation.

Cam and Elvira returned to Guatemala rejoicing over the victory. Paul and Laura were happy when they heard the outcome, but they had made a decision of their own to transfer to the Presbyterian Mission. Paul was now teaching at the Presbyterians' Industrial College in the capital.

Without his dependable brother around, Cam had to shoulder all the responsibilities at San Antonio, in addition to the work at the Robinson Institute. In the year following the council meeting, Cam managed to spend only two weeks on what he considered his main work—translation. Searching his soul, he recalled the sharp remark he had made to R. D. Smith back in Chicago. He felt convicted that he had spoken in the wrong attitude.

"Please forgive my anger," he wrote Smith. Then with all the pride drained from him he added, "I've found that unless the Lord undertakes, I will never finish the Cakchiquel translation."

8. The Lost Sheep

The next year language work started going better. The days seemed to hold more hours. "I've learned a lesson," Cam told Elvira. "It isn't *my* work, but the Lord's. I pray I'll never again be filled with false pride about what *I* am doing."

The first achievement was the Cakchiquel grammar. Only forty-nine pages, it was for 1926 a significant contribution to linguistics. Comparative linguistics, the study of the relation of languages to each other, had been developed over a century before in Germany. But descriptive linguistics, which describes the grammar of a language from its own point of view, was then in its infancy and there were very few reference works or texts available on the subject because of the paucity of field research. Though Cam was not a scholar, he had lived among the Indians and tenaciously applied what he had learned to the study of the language. His grammar was another demonstration that so-called primitive languages had developed their own complex patterns.

Cam mailed a copy of his grammar to Edward Sapir at the University of Chicago. Sapir called the work "an adequate analysis of the (Cakchiquel) grammatical system."

With Elvira typing and Cakchiquel language helpers checking, Cam began spending seven and eight hours a day on translation. "We feel like hurrying," he wrote home, "but then we realize that the work must be done well, and so we plod on."

The Cakchiquel preacher Trinidad Bac was Cam's most helpful critic. If a meaning wasn't clear to Bac, he didn't hesitate to say so or to suggest an alternative. He knew the colorful Cakchiquel idioms better than anyone Cam had found and would explain them in vivid detail. For example, he told Cam that the expression for "neighbor," when broken down, meant, "your companion in cootie cracking." A *good* neighbor, Bac explained, is one "who will pick your cooties without pulling your hair."

Cam found the work fascinating, but prefixes and suffixes didn't make for exciting reports to mail home. Supporters preferred thrilling stories of evangelizing on the trail. Then too, Cam and Elvira had influenced many of their backers to contribute to the varied ministries at San Antonio and the training of Indian preachers at Panajachel. So they weren't surprised when personal support took a down turn.

When Cam mentioned this in a letter home, Molly became disturbed. She felt "most Christians want to identify with some denomination. . . . How much you could accomplish if you had the Presbyterian Board back of you. There is nothing wrong with receiving guaranteed, regular support." Will disagreed. "Some of us . . . are depending more on money and wealthy organizations than we are on God. . . . Nothing is too hard for Him if we will only commit and trust all to Him."

Having been influenced earlier by pioneer missionary Hudson Taylor, Cam agreed with his father. He and Elvira saved by making fewer trips. When they did get to the capital, however, Cam refreshed his interest in the outside world by reading the Spanish newspapers. In the fall of '26 he was intrigued by an announcement that five U.S. Navy planes on a goodwill flight around South America were due to land in Guatemala City. Though Lindbergh would not make his famous solo flight until the next year, interest in aviation was rising. And Cam had been thinking about how airplanes might help missionaries reach tribes in remote areas.

Cam was at the airport when the navy planes landed and managed to meet the commander, Major Herbert Dargue, and tell him about the Cakchiquel work and his idea for using planes in Amazonia. "How much do you think an aviation program for a jungle area might cost?" he asked the flier.

Dargue liked Cam and what he was doing. "I really can't give you an intelligent answer," he said. "But I'll get together some facts and figures and mail you a report."

Cam pushed the idea of missionary aviation to the back of his mind and returned to translation. But the idea surfaced from time to time, especially some months later when Legters arrived for the annual Cakchiquel Bible conference, and told Cam about his second missionary trip into Amazonia with his seventeen-year-old son, David Brainerd. "Look at the map," he told Cam. "The Amazon basin covers two and a half million square miles. There must be Indian tribes all over the area."

"How many missionaries are in there?" Cam asked.

"Precious few," Legters replied. "Amazonia is a missionary graveyard. If disease doesn't get them, hostile Indians will. Arthur Tylee and his wife are trying to reach Indians in the Xingu area. He told me that twice he has felt cold steel at his throat. They're so far from civilization that they could be killed and the world not know about it for months. Why it once took Arthur three weeks to travel forty-two miles!"

"A plane could make that in three or four minutes," Cam responded, and told him about Major Dargue and the idea of a jungle aviation program.

"You have something here, Cam. Keep thinking while I'm home recruiting pioneers."

When Legters left, Cam pitched into the translation work with renewed vigor. As he worked he kept thinking of all the unknown tribes without even an alphabet. From what Legters had said, he guessed there must be about 500 in Latin America alone. He prayed Dargue wouldn't forget to send the report. Then he could make a presentation to C.A.M. leaders. But first the Cakchiquel translation had to be completed.

By June he was able to report in the C.A.M. *Bulletin* that the first draft of all the New Testament except Revelation was done. It was five years since the portions of Mark and three since John had been printed in Cakchiquel.

But then the bottom fell out. A generating plant was given to the San Antonio station, and with Paul gone Cam had to set it up. The rest of the year was one long series of complications. The big ditch from the turbine to the river seemed to cave in every day or so. Cam finally had to build a conduit of cement and stone to carry off the water. Everything was a crisis. Everything took time, precious time. And when he did get a day free for translation, his helpers would be off planting corn or harvesting coffee. Always something.

The frustrations continued on into the spring of 1928. Finally he reached the end of his patience and announced to Elvira one day, "We're leaving. We're going to California to get away from all the interruptions so we can finish the translation. We'll take a couple of language helpers along. If we stay here it will take years."

Arrangements were made for fifteen-year-old Joe Chicol and for Trinidad Bac to accompany them as language informants, and in the fall they arrived in southern California. Away from tribal distractions, Cam and Elvira, Joe and Trinidad translated and revised and typed —checked and double-checked, changed and improved. Cam wondered why they hadn't thought of this before. It was a must, he decided, for the translator at some point in his work to find an interruption-free haven away from the tribe to facilitate study and tedious labor.

By the spring of 1929 Trinidad felt he should return to his family, so Cam and Joe continued alone. Finally, on October 15, 1929, ten years from the time Cam began working on the language, Elvira typed all but the last two words in Revelation.

Before sending the manuscript off to the American Bible Society in New York, they held a dedication service in the First Presbyterian Church of Santa Ana. Cam phoned the news around, and a large crowd of friends, relatives, and supporters gathered for the event. Dr. P. W. Philpott, Cam's pastor at the Church of the Open Door, spoke and Robert McAuley, a Presbyterian minister and friend from college days, presided. Cam recalled the ten years of work in a short, emotion-filled address. Through the difficulties, God had been faithful. After acknowledging the help of the Cakchiquel informants, Cam said, "I'd like Daddy and Mother to come forward now and write in the last two words."

Molly nudged Will, who had not heard a word, and they stepped forward from their front pew. Beaming with pride, Molly wrote the Cakchiquel word for "you." Then Will took the pen and laboriously scrawled "Amen."

Cam then gave an impassioned plea. "Over one thousand years after the New Testament was written it was translated into English. Nearly two thousand years have elapsed until now it is given to the two hundred thousand Cakchiquels. How much time will you let go by before the other 500 or more languages in Latin America have the gospel?"

They mailed the manuscript the next morning. Then Cam rested —briefly. In the six months before the proofs would be ready to check he wanted to stir up interest in the airplane project.

Major Dargue had not forgotten his promise, and had sent an outline of what he felt was needed at a jungle outpost: three "flying boats" with pilots; mechanics, radio operators, and medical personnel; a hangar equipped with repair facilities, spare parts, and extra fuel; and insurance. He had estimated the first three years' operational cost at $134,000.

Cam talked the idea up around southern California. Most who heard him were pessimistic and some were incredulous that it could ever be done. With the stock market crash of October 29, 1929, the nation plunged into the Great Depression, and not enough money was being given to support missionaries on the fields. Something as experimental and extravagant as aviation seemed unlikely to attract support.

But as Cam talked and wrote letters, he had the satisfaction of receiving encouragement from a few far-sighted persons. Dr. Howard A. Kelly, the famous Baltimore surgeon, endorsed the proposed plan. "This," he predicted, "will open up a new era in missions." Harry Ironside, Elvira's pastor at the Moody Church, was convinced and declared, "Surely the unevangelized Indians should be reached in the shortest possible time." And, naturally, Legters added his voice. "If the wild jungle tribes of Latin America are to be reached for Christ in this generation," he wrote, "this is the only way it can be done. Why, I've recruited forty volunteers this past year, but they have all been siphoned off into Spanish or Portuguese missions. We need those planes!"

By this time Cam and Elvira were in Chicago where they had rented a small apartment while waiting for the proofs. Here a well-known missionary brought Cam down to earth with a lecture about his responsibilities to the Cakchiquels. "Now that you've finished the New Testament, your work is just beginning," he said. "You know their language and their ways. They believe in you. Go back and train more preachers."

Cam had hoped the Indian pastors would be able to assume full leadership when the New Testament was available to them. But how could he be sure? He did know the language better than any other outsider. Would he be deserting them by moving on to another tribe?

Wrestling over the direction to take, Cam finally did something very unusual for him. Shutting his eyes, he closed his Bible, then opened it and put a finger on a verse. It read: "What man amongst you, having a hundred sheep, if he lose one of them, doth not leave the ninety and nine in the wilderness and go after that which is lost, until he find it?" (Luke 15:4). "Well, Lord," Cam prayed, "that settles it. Unless you definitely lead me down a different path, by closing doors and putting obstacles in my way, then I'm going to the one percent."

Cam translated his vision into a poem he titled "Other Sheep." Elvira matched it to a tune and sang it at a missionary rally at Moody Church.

> Out where lost sheep are wandering,
> Far from the Shepherd's fold,
> Perishing there in dark despair,
> Since they have ne'er been told
> That there is One Who loved them
> So that He bore their sin,
> Out in the night won't you go with Him
> There some lost souls to win?
>
> Africa, Russia, Asia,
> Romanist lands as well,
> Latin America's Indian tribes
> Waiting for you to tell
> How the dear Lord would save them
> Who then will gladly go?
> Numberless thousands depend on you
> For the Good News you know.

A few days later Elvira spoke to the Missionary Union at the Moody Church about Cam's plans for Amazonia, and mentioned the plane project. Lynn Van Sickle, a recent graduate of the Moody Bible Institute, told her afterwards, "I must talk to your husband. I've felt planes were the answer for some time."

Cam and Van Sickle soon discovered they both had had the idea of using planes about the same time. "How much experience have you had?" Cam asked.

"I can get one up and down. That's about all."

"I think you should apply for membership with the C.A.M.," Cam advised him. "Then maybe we can get them to underwrite our project." Van Sickle agreed to do this.

By now the proofs had come and Cam and Elvira were laboriously checking them, always conscious that one misplaced letter could change the whole meaning of a sentence. Letter by letter, word by word, page by page they checked and rechecked day after day, week after week, month after weary month. The knowledge that no one else would be able to spot a mistake spurred them to strive for perfection.

They were almost finished when they received the news that Arthur Tylee, his baby daughter, a missionary nurse, and three friendly Indians had been killed by savage Indians in Brazil. Mrs. Tylee was left for dead, but was recovering in a hospital.

After a long silence in which he had to blink back the tears, Cam said, "Maybe now people will realize the need for airplanes in situations like that."

The news gave Cam a stronger urgency than ever. He felt they should go back to Guatemala and hold literacy campaigns while the book was being paged and bound, then prepare to pioneer again.

With $300 that had come in, the Townsends planned to buy a car to drive to Guatemala. Then they heard about Mr. and Mrs. Frank Bundy, recent Moody graduates who wanted to go to Guatemala under C.A.M. but had no funds to get there. Without hesitating, Cam and Elvira gave the Bundys the $300 for the trip. "The Lord will provide a car for us some other way," Cam said.

Then they took the last of their money and bought train tickets to Denver where Cam had speaking engagements. While there they heard from Legters, offering them a Whippett car that had been given to him by a Denver friend. Thankful again for this provision, the Townsends drove on across the Rockies for a few final days with his family.

Cam's nephew Ronald White was home from college when they arrived. Cam challenged him to take time off to help in the Cakchiquel literacy programs. "The Lord has given me a new system to teach reading," Cam said. "You'll have fun trying it out. I call it the psycho-phonemic method. The alphabet I've used is phonemic—each letter stands for only one sound. Then, instead of throwing the whole alphabet at them at once, I form words with just four or five letters. That way they can be reading a few words the first day. This really encourages them and gives them confidence that they can learn. Each day I add a few more letters, and make words using all that they have learned to that point. Adults can learn to read in a month or less."

Ronald was properly impressed and eager to go. When their visit was over Cam and Elvira, with Ronald, headed for Dallas where Cam was to link up with Van Sickle and present the airplane project to the C.A.M.

"The key to Indian education is the mother tongue."

9. Cakchiquel Triumph!

The C.A.M. leaders in Dallas remembered Cam well from the disagreement over Bible translation five years earlier. This time Cam spoke fervently about the unreached tribes in the Amazon basin and related some of Legters's adventures. Catholics were already utilizing airplanes in three missionary fields. "With an aviation base we can sustain Bible translators and keep them healthy and working."

Someone asked about the cost. When Cam mentioned the major's figure, there was a general look of horror. Their conclusion was that the mission had neither the people nor the money to go into Amazonia. "We are the *Central American* Mission," they said. "There are other groups working down there."

"But they aren't reaching many Indians," Cam protested.

When Cam saw that they would not change C.A.M. policy, he asked permission to try a plane project in northern Guatemala. "The jungles and rivers there are like Amazonia," he pointed out.

Though skeptical, the council gave the go ahead on the condition that Cam raise the money.

The optimistic Cam wrote his sister Ethel, "The council okayed the airplane crusade." Then he found a Christian broadcaster with an early morning program in Dallas who agreed to let him present the plane project to listeners. A single dollar bill was all that came in the mail. Undismayed, Cam told Van Sickle to "come on anyway. You've been accepted as a member and the Lord will work something out. We'll just have to keep praying."

Cam, Elvira, Van Sickle, and Cam's nephew, Ronald, arrived in Guatemala City on December 23, 1930, where they spent Christmas with Paul and Laura Townsend and other friends. Paul was still teaching at the Presbyterian Industrial College in the capital.

Leaving Van Sickle behind for orientation with other missionaries after Christmas, Cam, Elvira, and Ronald took the stage to San Antonio where serious problems were awaiting them.

The clinic and boarding school were still operating, but some of the Indians had broken with the C.A.M. The congregation had been agitated by anti-American propagandists and was making life uncomfortable for the missionary staff. They welcomed Cam, however, as a beloved brother. The old men poured out their grievances to him as they couldn't to the Spanish-speaking missionaries. He sympathized with them, but encouraged them to cooperate with the mission. "You can do better working with them than against them," he advised. Because of their great admiration for Cam they took his advice.

Another concern was the education of Elena Trejo, their beloved Quiche girl. The Townsends felt she should go to the States. They were grateful when Will and Molly gladly invited the young Indian girl to stay with them while she was learning English.

For the four months before they would receive the printed New Testaments, the Townsends planned literacy campaigns, all of which were very successful. At the same time Cam was at work on the plane project. He had heard stories about the wild Lacandon Indians that were supposed to live in the jungled Peten region of northern Guatemala. Thinking this might be a good place to start, he and Van Sickle took a commercial flight to an airport near the Peten jungle. It was Cam's first flight and it didn't exactly inspire great confidence in the future of aviation. The tri-motor plane lost one motor as it climbed over a steep ridge. When a second motor conked out they had to land in a cow pasture where the pilot made emergency repairs so they could return to Guatemala City.

Van Sickle and a Nazarene missionary then decided to explore the Peten territory by trail. Cam asked them to look for a training camp site for future Bible translators, who shouldn't be sent green into the jungle. He would have gone himself, but he felt he couldn't spare that much time away from the Cakchiquels. After crisscrossing the territory by horseback, dugout canoe, and on foot, the two explorers finally located one Spanish-speaking Indian who claimed to be Lacandon. While still in Peten territory, Van Sickle came down with malaria and dysentery and had to return to the States.

By this time the Cakchiquel New Testaments were overdue from the Bible Society. Cam drove into Guatemala City and persuaded a postal clerk to let him look in the archives. There were all eighteen copies of the advance shipment. He took one of the beautifully bound volumes and rubbed it to make sure it was real. He had special plans for these first copies—a dedication ceremony with the president of Guatemala.

The arrangements took some time to make, but at 4:30 P.M., May 19, 1931, President Jorge Ubico received them into his office. After exchanging greetings, Trinidad Bac, the Cakchiquel preacher, handed the president a leather-bound inscribed copy of the Book. Cam made a brief presentation speech about what the Bible had already done for Guatemala. Then after R. R. Gregory explained the part played by the Bible Society, Bac gave a personal testimony.

"I congratulate you and thank you, for this is a forward step for our country," the president answered. He then suggested that Cam translate the New Testament into another Guatemalan Indian language.

The formalities over, Cam asked the president to pose with the group for a picture. Although the president was known to be reticent about having his picture taken, he agreed. The photo was published with a front-page story about the Cakchiquel New Testament in the newspaper the following day.

From the capital, Cam and his friends went to Patzun for a dedication ceremony in Cakchiquel territory. When Mr. Gregory presented Trinidad with a copy, the Indians repeatedly shouted, "*Matiox chire Dios!*" (thanks to God). Various Cakchiquel preachers read from the new Book. Although a hard shower dampened the congregation in the leaky tent, they sang "Showers of Blessings" and continued on into the evening. The last Cakchiquel to speak declared, "This Book marks an epoch for us. Each year we should celebrate the twentieth of May as the day upon which we received God's Word in our own language!"

After the Patzun celebration, Cam and Gregory left for an eleven-day trip on mule back visiting sections of the Cakchiquel field. Cam talked earnestly about future goals. "There must be an intensive literacy campaign. The masses of Cakchiquels must be taught to read and write, with new literates teaching others. And the other tribes of Guatemala must receive the Scriptures in their native tongues. Freed from superstition, vice, and ignorance they can journey together to a new day of freedom and prosperity.

"God will send young men and women to the north and to the south with a burning desire to plant His Word in every language. I tell you, Gregory, the tribes of South America will have the Bible. And North America, Africa, and Asia also."

For the moment Cam seemed to have forgotten the airplane project, he was so occupied with the literacy campaigns. But his brother Paul hadn't. He wrote in the Presbyterian newsletter, "We want an airplane. We want a good plane. We're going to get it and you may be the one to help. There is surely some Christian oil man who would give us a plane."

Cam was still thinking of reaching Amazonia, though. One evening at Panajachel he theorized to Frank Bundy that a specially constructed steamboat could carry people and cargo up the Amazon. "It could be taken apart and carried over areas where portage was necessary."

Bundy chuckled and shook his head. "It would never work, Cam. It just isn't practical."

Cam was turning other ideas over in his mind, when one afternoon he noticed a stranger with a camera in Panajachel. When he introduced himself, the stranger said he was Moisés Sáenz. Cam had heard of the educator from Mexico and his statesman brother General Aarón Sáenz. Dr. Moisés Sáenz had studied the Indian problem extensively in his own country and had come to see what was happening in Guatemala.

They talked education for awhile and Cam told him about the work he was doing. "My parents were pillars in the Presbyterian church," Dr. Sáenz said. "We had missionaries in our home all the time."

Cam invited Dr. Sáenz to stay overnight and the next morning showed him around the Robinson Institute, which now had fifty-three students, and explained his *modus operandi*. "The key to Indian education is the mother tongue, the language of the soul. Help them learn to read their language and become proud of it and their heritage. Give them the Bible to set them free from vice and superstition. Have Indians teach Indians and allow them to stand on their own feet. Once they have dignity, spiritual freedom, and self-assurance, they can move into the Spanish-speaking world as equals with the *ladinos*."

The Mexican educator was impressed. "Why not transfer your

efforts to my country?" he suggested. "You would find a favorable climate of social reform. Our revolutionary leaders will help you."

Several weeks later Cam received a letter that repeated the invitation. He filed it away for future reference.

While at the lake Cam heard that his mother, who now had cancer, was growing weaker. His sisters, who were taking care of her, were also concerned about their father, who devotedly stayed by her side, cooked her breakfast each morning, read to her, and did what little he could to comfort her.

Cam wished he had the time and money to go home, but since he didn't he wrote her that he believed she would be healed. He also sent her a long poem that began:

> Mother dear:
> How I long that you were here;
> That I might look into your eyes
> And see
> The love that time defies,
> My mother's love
> For me.

Shortly before Christmas of 1931 a resolution came from the C.A.M. committee in Dallas that was disappointing to Cam. While expressing "deep appreciation of the monumental work done in translating the New Testament into the Cakchiquel language," and "recognizing" Cam's "gift and vision for pioneer work," the committee recommended that he "exercise this gift in occasional exploration into unoccupied fields, at the same time continuing his directive leadership in the Cakchiquel work . . . at least until adequate leadership is raised up to continue the work."

The committee cited as reasons: (1) Cam and Elvira were "the only missionaries with a working knowledge of Cakchiquel"; (2) as translators they were "best fitted for bringing adequate returns on the large investment of time and money made by themselves and the American Bible Society"; (3) the "abundant fruitage of their past labors" was evidence of "the divine blessing upon their ministry" [among the Cakchiquels].

Cam took "adequate leadership" to apply to missionaries. "What they mean is missionary bosses," was his reaction to Elvira. "They should let the Cakchiquels themselves take over. They have enough well-trained leaders, and more being turned out every year.

They have the New Testament. Why do they need American overseers?

"And they want me to do 'occasional exploration into unoccupied fields.' How can I do that, when five hundred tribes in Latin America await God's Word?"

In Patzun a few weeks later Cam received the news of his mother's death. He had believed that God was going to heal his mother—but no. He had taken her. The cloudy afternoon became dark, until suddenly he became aware of a golden glimmer. Looking up he saw that the setting sun had set the upper clouds aglow. The break in the darkness rekindled his spirit and enabled him to say, "Praise God, my wonderful mother's up there now—her pain and suffering are gone forever."

Despite the discouragement over the executive committee's resolution and the blow of his mother's death, Cam completed the month-long literacy campaign at Patzun with a big ceremony presided over by town officials. Then they drove to Guatemala City, where Dr. Ainslie diagnosed Cam's cough as T.B. and ordered him to go to the warm climate of the lowlands. "The rest will do you both good," he said.

After five months of recuperation Cam and Elvira returned to Guatemala City to pack up and leave for good. "Our ministry to the Cakchiquels is finished," he announced to their missionary friends. "We believe the Lord is leading us to pioneer again."

They were saying goodbye to friends when they heard an encouraging story. A Cakchiquel Indian was sent by his town to complain to the president about the Protestant workers bothering them about a new religion. The president asked him if he could read. "Yes," he answered, so he was handed a copy of the Cakchiquel New Testament. After reading a few lines, he looked up in amazement. "This is wonderful! God speaks our language! Where can I get a copy of this book?"

"From the people you were complaining about," the president replied. The spokesman returned home, bought the book in his own language, and became a believer. "Now he goes everywhere," Cam was told, "telling people that the president evangelized him."

"You're right. They [the Indians] have had too much religion. But they have never had the Bible in their own tongue . . ."

10. Chain of Providence

When Cam and Elvira had left California less than two years before, it had been with a feeling of triumph. The Cakchiquel New Testament was completed and they were going to present it to the tribe. Cam was full of ideas for evangelizing the jungles of Latin America by plane. Now, they were back home, tired, discouraged and sick.

Not only did Cam have T.B., though he didn't have to stay in a sanitarium, but Elvira was discovered to have a serious heart condition. The doctor ordered complete rest in bed for her—no housework or any other kind of work, and as little emotional stress as possible.

This meant Cam had to do all of the housework. He was so eager to get at the task of reaching Bibleless tribes, and instead he was up to his elbows in dishwater. One day, however, when he was reading Colossians 1, he came to the eleventh verse, and his frustration calmed. With the assurance that God would strengthen him "unto all patience and longsuffering with joyfulness," he could wait.

Meanwhile, he started a fifteen-minute weekday radio program on KVOE, Santa Ana. While the dreary pall of mid-depression hung over the land, Cam called for prayer and workers to reach the lost tribes.

The arrival of L. L. Legters and his new bride was a tonic to both Cam and Elvira in February 1933. Edna Legters was petite and demure, a very feminine complement to her boisterous husband. She had been a college professor before meeting Legters at a "Deeper Life" Keswick Conference in New Jersey.

Legters recalled a visit he had made to Mexico. "Why not start

closer by instead of South America?" he suggested to the Townsends. "There are at least fifty Mexican Indian tribes without the
Bible, and some are large. I'm told there are three hundred thousand Mayans in Yucatan alone. Tell you what; you go, and I'll help
raise support."

Cam was agreeable to Mexico, but he wanted a broader strategy.
"It isn't enough for Elvira and me to go to only one tribe. We
need to start a summer training school where young pioneers from
all missions can come and rough it and learn how to reduce a
language to writing and translate the Scriptures. Only three or four
universities in the country now offer much in the way of descriptive
linguistics and their courses are spread out over four years. That
makes it difficult for the average missionary candidate to take
them."

This seemed logical, so they decided to go to Mexico the following fall or winter and seek permission from the Mexican government to bring in translators. The next summer (1934) they would
start the training camp for recruits.

After the Legters left Cam began compiling notes for the training school. Under "methods of reaching Indians," he wrote:

*The methods used in the cities won't work. They don't serve the
needs of the Indians. Counting in a city is different from counting
in a village. . . .*
*We should utilize the experiences of the Indian. His information
isn't organized in his mind. Study the situation in which he lives.
Endorse the good traits. Exhort against the bad ones. Don't try to
teach things that are outside the realm of the Indian's daily living.
Develop your own system rather than follow others.*

Cam wrote old friend Karl D. Hummel, secretary of the C.A.M.
in Dallas, that they were "pulling up stakes for good" in Guatemala
and would be launching Bible translation in Mexico. Hummel replied that he "hoped they would not have to start another mission,"
adding that the "multiplicity of independent missions in recent
years is making it hard on all concerned."

In his next letter Cam forwarded money to the C.A.M. which
he and Elvira had received for Guatemala. He inquired about support for C.A.M. missionaries working in Cakchiquel territory, suggesting a replacement for himself. Neither Cam nor the C.A.M.
secretary mentioned resignation.

Meanwhile Legters was barnstorming across the country. The second week in August he arrived at the Keswick Bible Conference in New Jersey where he and missionary James Dale from Mexico were the main speakers. Dale gave a bleak report about conditions in Mexico. "Antiforeign and antireligious feelings remain high fifteen years after the Mexican Revolution that broke up the big plantations. Rebellion against the feudalistic Catholic hierarchy in Mexico has caused a backlash of feeling against all religion. All religious schools have been taken over by the government and all church properties have been placed under government control.

"New foreign missionaries are not being allowed in, and those already there are working under severe restrictions. Perhaps saddest of all is that it is very difficult to work among the Indians, who have the greatest need."

Dale then challenged the group to pray. The result was that Thursday, August 10, became a day of prayer. The Legters prayed all night in the auditorium, and after Director Addison Raws announced that the leaders would be fasting for the day, none of the group went to the dining hall for dinner. Even the waitresses spent the dinner hour in prayer.

So sure were the people at Keswick that God had heard their prayers that they felt Legters and Townsend should go immediately to Mexico and ask authorities for permission to send in Bible translators. (They did not then know that a group at the original Keswick conference in Keswick, England, had been praying for Mexico's Indians at about the same time!) A woman at the conference gave the Legters a car. Others gave money for gasoline and oil. Legters wrote to Cam suggesting they meet in Dallas early in November. Although Cam had no funds, he agreed to come, wondering as he did so how the Lord would work it out. For awhile it looked as though John Brown, the evangelist educator from Arkansas, would pay the Townsends' way to Texas to produce some Spanish programs for a broadcast to Mexico. But that fell through.

Cam still knew that God would take them to Texas. When the time came for them to leave California, they still had no money for train tickets. Nevertheless, they made the rounds of the relatives, saying goodbye. At Oney's house, Lula handed them a letter from a "friend" in San Diego. It contained $200. "Half for Cakchiquel work and half for 'pin money' for your trip"! The "pin money" bought their train tickets for Dallas.

In Dallas Cam found Karl Hummel preparing to leave for several days in the Wichita Falls area. "Come along with me," he invited Cam. Since the Legters had not yet arrived, Cam accepted.

In Wichita Falls a civic club invited Cam to speak on the Indians of Mexico. Just before the meeting an Episcopalian rector phoned Cam. "I saw the announcement in the papers that you are to speak. I can't come, but I've traveled in Mexico and am interested in the ancient Aztec religion. Could you come to my house?"

After Cam agreed, Hummel mildly reprimanded him. "Why didn't you make him come here, Cam?"

"I just thought it would be more courteous to go there."

At the rector's home Cam listened attentively to a long discourse on the Aztec religion. Then the rector scribbled on a card: "This will introduce you to the Episcopalian dean of Mexico City. He can put you in touch with some influential people."

Back in Dallas, Cam and Elvira discussed with Karl Hummel their future relationship to the C.A.M. Elvira was opposed to resigning, and Cam saw a possibility of returning later to the Cakchiquels for a year of literacy work. Hummel suggested they let matters stand until they returned from Mexico.

When the Legters arrived, it was agreed that Elvira, who still had a heart problem, should go on to Chicago to be with her family while the three others went on to Mexico. But when they reached the Rio Grande on Armistice Day, 1933, the Mexican immigration officials refused them entry. As they sat in the waiting room at the customs station through the noon hour, they wondered how God was going to break this roadblock. Over and over Legters hummed the chorus of his theme song:

> Faith, mighty faith the promise sees,
> And looks to God alone.
> Laughs at impossibilities
> And shouts, "It shall be done!"

With a sudden flash of memory, Cam began digging in his battered briefcase, finally extracting the letter written by Dr. Moisés Sáenz, the Mexican educator who had visited him in Guatemala. "Come to Mexico," Dr. Sáenz had written, "and do for our Indians what you have done in Guatemala."

The officials read the letter closely. They knew of Moisés Sáenz, the "father" of Mexico's high school system. His brother Aarón was Head (Mayor) of the Federal District (Mexico City) and an important political figure. Obviously the letter could not be ignored.

For instruction, the border officials called Mexico City. The director of immigration said that the foreigners could enter with the stipulation that if Legters should preach or Townsend try to study Indian languages they would be fined and expelled immediately.

That evening at a hotel in Monterrey, Cam and the Legters' turned to the Scriptures for encouragement. The outlook was not bright. The reading for November 11 in the devotional guide, *Daily Light*, changed their gloom to joy. It included, along with other reassuring verses, Exodus 23:20: "Behold, I send an Angel before thee, to keep thee in the way, and to bring thee into the place which I have prepared."

"Well, amen!" Legters shouted, slapping his knee. "Amen!"

"Praise the Lord!" was Cam's quiet but equally fervent response.

At Tamazunchale the next day, they met the James Dale family who had returned to Mexico before them. Their news was not good. Dale's son Johnny said he had spent hundreds of dollars and still couldn't get a resident visa for Mexico. "And I was born here!"

In Mexico City, the more missionaries they talked to, the darker their chances seemed. They waited days in government offices, trying to find someone high up who would listen to them. Cam's advocate, Dr. Sáenz, was lecturing at the University of Chicago. With him out of the country Cam had no official friend to help.

But Cam continued to feel confident. "The Lord has brought us this far and He will carry us on," he assured his companions. Legters, however, became impatient at spending so much time sitting around in anterooms, unable to preach. In desperation he announced, "You can stay here and sit it out, Cam. Edna and I are going back to the States next week to renew our Bible conference ministry."

Then Cam pulled out the card of introduction to the Episcopalian dean of Mexico City which he had been given back in Wichita Falls. Maybe this man could help.

After the service the next Sunday at the Episcopalian cathedral, he presented the card to the dean, who invited him to a dinner on Tuesday night. An English ethnologist Bernard Bevans, who had been studying Indians, would be there.

Cam accepted gratefully, and at the dinner managed to sit by

Bevans, who quickly became interested in what Cam wanted to do. "You simply must meet some of my friends who can help you," he said. "I know—I'll give a little luncheon at the Lady Baltimore Dining Room and invite these people. Especially Dr. Frank Tannenbaum. He's from Columbia University and is well liked by Mexican educators."

After he arrived at the luncheon, Cam learned that Tannenbaum had written a book on the economic effects of the Mexican Revolution. While the others were chatting, he discreetly dashed to a nearby bookstore, bought a copy of *Peace by Revolution*, and rushed back to the luncheon. In his disarming manner, he asked Tannenbaum to autograph the book. To Cam's delight Tannenbaum also scribbled an endorsement of Cam's work in Guatemala. "I'm giving you a note of introduction to the director of rural education, Rafael Ramírez," he said. "He can take care of your problems, but right now he's away in the north visiting schools."

"Where can I locate him?" Cam asked eagerly.

"He'll be in Monterrey on the 23rd."

Cam and the Legters were waiting when Ramírez arrived in Monterrey. The prominent educator frowned when they introduced themselves. "You're the men who want to translate the Bible for the Indians. We certainly can't have that. The Indians have too much religion as it is."

Cam smiled. "You're right. They *have* had too much religion. But they have never had the Bible in their own tongue to teach them morality and good citizenship."

Ramírez was momentarily flustered. "I don't know about that," he admitted. "But you can't bring in translators for the Indians. And if you did, we wouldn't allow the Bibles to be distributed."

Then he noticed the book under Cam's arm. "You have Tannenbaum's book I see. He's a good man. Understands our Revolution. Most people in the States don't."

When Cam showed him Tannenbaum's endorsement of the work among the Cakchiquels, his attitude changed. "Tannenbaum's word is good enough for me. I think I'll invite you to study our rural education system, but not the Indian languages. You can visit areas where Indians live and see what we are doing. Maybe you can write some articles."

Ramírez wrote out the authorization and the door to Mexico opened another inch.

Equipped with the permit, Cam set out on a six-week tour of rural government schools in Indian areas of the states of Chiapas, Campeche, and Yucatan. He interviewed teachers and students, making extensive notes, and also compiling word lists from several languages for comparative purposes. He observed that the breaking up of big estates, transferring all education to the government, and establishing of new schools in once neglected villages, had vastly improved rural society. He sensed a strong reaction to feudalistic Catholicism, especially in Campeche where there was an official propaganda attack against all religion.

His notebooks were filling fast when an urgent message caught up with him that Elvira was gravely ill and wasn't expected to live long. He immediately boarded a north-bound train.

11. Rolling Back the Waters

At the border Cam left the Mexican train and took a bus to Sulphur Springs in the northwest corner of Arkansas, where his brother Paul was the new director of the John Brown Academy. Then he borrowed Paul's car and with his nephew Fleet White at the wheel drove to Chicago.

He found Elvira improved, but the doctor gave her only a year to live. Feeling that the warmer climate would be better for her, Cam made a bed in the car, and drove back to Sulphur Springs. There he accepted Paul and Laura's invitation to stay with them. But when Elvira suffered another attack, Dr. George Bast, a naturopath, and his wife, requested that they move into their fourteen-room house. "I can keep a close eye on her here," Dr. Bast told Cam, "and you can be freed to do more work."

Cam reviewed his notes from the interrupted tour of Mexican rural schools and began writing to inform Americans of the progress in Mexico. He cited examples of how the Mexican Revolution had transformed rural education, and gave statistics showing that Federal rural schools had increased from 309 in 1922 to 7,504 in 1933.

The articles were printed in the *Dallas News* and *School and Society Magazine*. After receiving copies of the published articles from Cam, Rafael Ramírez wrote, "They were written with the deep sympathy which characterizes you."

Ramírez's response made Cam feel that the door to Mexico had opened a little further. He wrote their financial supporters of their intentions to serve Indian tribes of other lands, and requested that gifts be channeled to C.A.M.'s work in Guatemala rather than to them. "We will enter Mexico as linguists rather than as missionaries," he told them. "The Indian languages must be learned and the New Testament translated into them. It matters not to us whether

82

we be classified as missionaries or ditchdiggers if we be given a chance to labor toward that end."

He also shared plans with five Christian leaders. Four cheered him on: Lewis Sperry Chafer, president of the new Dallas Theological Seminary; Charles Fuller, director of the "Old-Fashioned Revival Hour" broadcast; Harry Ironside, pastor of Moody Church in Chicago; and Will Nyman, a retired businessman in California. The fifth, a prominent evangelical Bible teacher, replied, "I cannot back missionaries going into a country under another label."

Nyman was then head of the missionary committee at the Church of the Open Door where Cam held membership. "Have the church transfer our support to a regular missionary," Cam told him. "We are looking to the Lord to raise up individuals to back us. Then if officials ask how I get my living, I can refer them to individuals rather than to a church."

All along Cam had been thinking and planning for the first training camp, although the economic outlook in the spring of 1934 couldn't have been more discouraging. Some Christian schools had closed. Many congregations had lost their church buildings through mortgage foreclosures. He and Legters lacked a campus, a student body, and faculty. Their intended field had closed its doors to missionaries. Cam's wife was a semi-invalid. But they had a vision!

When Loren Jones, a revival song leader for John Brown, offered the barn on his farm near Sulphur Springs, they had a campus. And when Cam worked up a one-page outline of subjects with possible faculty, they had a catalog. The "Catalog" announced:

SUMMER TRAINING CAMP FOR PROSPECTIVE
BIBLE TRANSLATORS
June 7–September 7, 1934

PLACE: Happy Valley Farm, Sulphur Springs, Arkansas

TEACHERS AND SUBJECTS TO BE COVERED AS TIME PERMITS:

L. L. Legters	Indian Distribution and Tribal History
	Indian Customs and Psychology
	Indian Evangelization and Spiritual Development
	How to Get Guidance
	How to Work with Others
J. M. Chicol	Spanish

      Indian Orthography and Pronunciation
      Indian Superstitions, Vices and Religions

W. C. Townsend Economic and Cultural Status of the Indians
      Governmental Programs Regarding the Indians
      Indian Translation—Field Problems
      Indian Philology
      Why and How of Reading Campaigns

Paul Townsend The Indian Workers' Practical Living Problems

An added footnote mentioned that the school hoped also to secure Frank C. Pinkerton, M.D., for courses on "keeping well in the tropics," first aid, and Indian archaeology; and Dr. E. L. McCreery, a returned missionary from Africa and teacher at the Bible Institute of Los Angeles (BIOLA), for a short course in phonetics.

In search of students Cam sent an announcement to Dallas Seminary. Richmond McKinney promised to come.

Then he went to Columbia Bible College in South Carolina where Legters had recommended him to Dr. Robert McQuilkin, the president. Here he persuaded one student, Ed Sywulka, to drive back with him.

The week before the training camp was to begin, Cam was walking through the park in Sulphur Springs when he noticed a man fidgeting on a bench. In conversation he discovered that Amos Baker was a widower and was in town waiting for his children to finish classes at a local boarding school. "I work for an oil company," he told Cam. "What's your line?"

Cam was off and running. When he stopped talking about the training camp and the goal of Bible translation for all tribes, the oil man squinted into the sun and remarked sourly, "What a crazy thing to do."

Instead of replying defensively, Cam resumed talking as if his new acquaintance had just given him a pat on the back. Finally he said, "We need your help."

"I'm all tied up," Baker replied lamely.

"Oh, you can make time for the Lord. Come on out and see what we're doing."

"Well, you see, I'm not even a Christian."

Cam switched gears and began evangelizing the visitor, who remained unmoved. "Tell you what," Cam concluded, "I'm going to pray for you until you accept the Lord."

A few days after this encounter, a vacant farmhouse on nearby Breezy Point was offered for $5 a month. It wasn't much, but it beat using Jones's barn. When school opened, the faculty out-numbered the students. Besides Richmond McKinney and Ed Sywulka there was only Joe Chicol who had been studying at John Brown University. And since the Cakchiquel teacher merely sat in on classes he did not teach, Cam could count him only as a half student.

"What shall we name our new school?" Cam asked. Several names were suggested, but they chose Camp Wycliffe after John Wycliffe, the translator of the first English Bible.

Cam and Legters, who stayed only two weeks, both insisted that the students train by living like pioneers. They sat on nail kegs furnished by local hardware merchant Tom Haywood, and slept on hard lumber softened only by a spread of cut grass. They prepared their own meals from local farm products. Water came from a pump in the yard.

Finances were lean. A few dollars trickled in from Cam's relatives and the Nyman family in California. Moody Church continued sending a small allowance to Elvira. Students and faculty picked up small offerings by speaking at nearby churches. Despite grumbling stomachs, they prayed, studied, and hung on to the vision. Their theme song was Legter's favorite, "Faith, Mighty Faith."

As the three-months' school session drew to a close, Cam realized the boys needed more phonetics. Dr. McCreery had been unable to come from California to teach, so Cam sent the students to him. They stayed with the Will Nyman family in Glendale, a suburb of Los Angeles.

The year following the first session of Camp Wycliffe was spent battling illness and just waiting. A landslide kept them from getting to Mexico City and Elvira's heart condition forced them to return to Dallas. While they waited, Cam launched a new effort to ac-quaint Americans with the needs of Latin American Indians. He wrote a short pulpy novel about the spiritual and economic struggles of an impoverished Cakchiquel Indian. *Tolo, the Volcano's Son,* was more fact than fiction. With a few facts changed and names disguised, the people and events were straight from the Townsends' experiences. *Revelation* (now *Eternity*) magazine published it in serial form.

In the spring of 1935 the Townsends returned to the Ozarks

where the Bast family again welcomed them into their home. Cam wrote many letters promoting the second session of Camp Wycliffe, and prayed for patience. In his eagerness to get workers to the field, time seemed to crawl. Colossians 1:11 was again his verse for those days. Everything seemed to call for "patience," including Elvira's illness and emotional upsets.

Reports from Guatemala were discouraging. The New Testament he had toiled so long to translate was not being pushed. After missionaries wrote reminding him about the year he had promised to give to Cakchiquel literacy, he and Elvira began making plans to return to Guatemala after the second Camp Wycliffe.

A few days before camp began a shiny automobile stopped in front of the Basts' home. A long-legged man with a big smile emerged. "Amos Baker!" Cam exclaimed.

"I had to let you know your prayers were answered," Amos said. "I've accepted the Lord. Now I'm so glad to be a Christian I want to tell everybody about it. And I'm ready to help with your training camp in any way I can."

"Well, amen!" Cam responded. "This is the best news I've had in weeks."

The student body for the second camp session more than doubled. Besides Joe Chicol, who taught again, Richmond McKinney returned. Max Lathrop, Bill Sedat, Kenneth Pike, and Legters's son Brainerd were new recruits. Young Legters, Lathrop, and McKinney were seminary students. Bill Sedat was from the National Bible Institute in New York. Pike was a graduate of Gordon College. Brainy, but thin and nervous, he had been rejected twice on the grounds of potential health problems by the China Inland Mission.

The students were moved by Townsend's tremendous interest in their potential. Cam insisted that the students elect their own officers, manage their own affairs, make their own rules about day-to-day living. "When you're in a tribe and on your own, you won't have anybody to turn to except the Lord." This year also the group had to live frugally. Amos Baker sometimes got them donations of groceries from local churches. Will Townsend, Cam's father, was the camp cook.

Legters was there again for two weeks and lectured on anthropology, missionary policies, and the victorious life. And Dr. McCreery came for ten days to teach phonetics. Joe Chicol taught Indian customs. But Cam was the main teacher, showing how the

Cakchiquel language worked with a little chart in which he could slide different stems, prefixes, and suffixes to make up 100,000 possible forms for a single verb. The students also tried to analyze the dozen or so American Indian languages sketched in a handbook published by the Bureau of American Ethnology.

Amateur night was initiated as a regular event in the calendar of Camp Wycliffe. Cam was the lively master of ceremonies for hilarious games. On such social occasions, Cam would say, "If you don't have a sense of humor, you shouldn't be a missionary."

Everyone kept an ear tuned to Mexico, which remained closed to newly assigned religious workers. The new president, Lázaro Cárdenas, reportedly had several very antireligious officials in his cabinet.

Late in June Dr. McCreery called for a day of prayer that Mexico would welcome Bible translators at least. Students and faculty knelt around the nail kegs and implored God for a miracle. When they arose at noon, joints and muscles ached. But the discomfort was forgotten upon hearing through a radio news broadcast that President Cárdenas had dismissed his cabinet, including the fanatical atheists. "Praise the Lord," Cam exclaimed, for he felt that the reformist president would now have more liberty to utilize Christian linguists in his program of helping poor peasants.

Cam was anxious to go to Mexico immediately after the second session ended. But there was the promise of a year of literacy work in Guatemala. He had already secured the necessary visas when a letter came from Guatemala. Elvira's brother Carl wrote, not as a relative, but as a representative of the C.A.M. missionaries. "We want you Cam," he said, "but not Elvira. We feel she would be more of a hindrance than a help."

Cam was upset. "If you can't take Elvira, then I won't be coming either," he replied.

The way now seemed clear to stay in Mexico after escorting the first corps of workers there. To help care for Elvira, whose heart condition remained uncertain, Cam's niece Evelyn Griset had offered to spend a year with them.

Cam had already made arrangements by mail with Rafael Ramírez and other officials in Mexico City to bring some of his students into the country for linguistic research. Pike, Lathrop, Brainerd Legters, and McKinney planned on staying only three weeks and could get by with tourist visas. But Cam, Elvira, and Evelyn were under a different classification and were supposed to have $60 each for every month they planned to stay in the country. Not until they got to Dallas did they even have money to travel on. There they received a $90 check from Moody Church. On the strength of that they started toward the border in an old Buick pulling a cumbersome housetrailer. The students had preceded them in another old car.

At the border, while the chief inspector thumbed through the papers, Cam talked at full speed about his work and his plans. The official stamped the papers and waved them across the border without asking about money.

The Townsends and Evelyn caught up with the students near Monterrey, and the caravan made good time on the road to Mexico City except for a near catastrophe when the Buick nearly skidded over a precipice. A crane operator helped them pull the car back to the road and across the bad spot.

When they reached Villa de Guadalupe, on the northern edge of Mexico City, Cam stopped to check his trailer taillights before plunging in the madcap city traffic. Their destination was Coyoacan on the opposite side of the city. Suddenly two motorcycles roared to a stop behind him. Policemen! One smiled and said in excellent English, "Last year I visited Los Angeles, California, and was treated royally by the chief of police. Please allow us to escort you through the traffic."

With their sirens blaring, the motorcycles parted the traffic before them. "It's just like the Lord rolling back the waters of the Red Sea," Cam chuckled in delight. "I wish some of the skeptics could see us now!"

"Let's run our own affairs from the field."

12. The Summer Institute of Linguistics

When Cam read in the next morning's newspaper that the Seventh Inter-American Scientific Congress was about to convene in the Palace of Fine Arts, he hurried all the students down to the national theater. There he spotted Rafael Ramírez and embraced him heartily with a Mexican *abrazo*. Ramírez responded cordially and introduced him to three other influential Mexicans who were concerned about Indians: Genaro Vasquez, Secretary of Labor; Dr. Silva y Aceves, founder and director of the Mexican Institute of Linguistic Investigations; and Professor Javier Uranga, secretary of the Indian division of the Congress. Presenting the young Americans as "linguistic investigators," Cam led them to seats for the opening session.

During the days that followed, Cam mingled with delegates from many countries, mentioning at every turn the praiseworthy results of the Mexican Revolution he had seen on his survey trip the previous year. He patiently answered questions about what his group hoped to do in Mexico. "We want to help by carrying out a thorough investigation of the Indian languages. In doing this, we want to serve our fellow-man in any way possible. I disagree with scientists who use people as laboratory specimens in their research but do nothing for their welfare. We wish to have a small part in the great work of your government in bringing Indian peoples into the social and economic life of the nation."

Cam told some of the leaders of their intent to translate the Bible. "We will not propagate any sectarianism," he assured them, "but we will translate the Book of goodwill and brotherly love for the Indians."

The highlight of the Congress came when President Lázaro Cárdenas made an appearance. Even before the reformist leader was

89

introduced, Cam recognized him from newspaper pictures—a man with a short bushy mustache and dark hair curling slightly over a high receding forehead. Cam whispered to his companions, "They call him the 'Peasant's President.' He shocked Mexican aristocracy by moving from the presidential palace into a middle-class home."

When the students' three weeks were up, Brainerd Legters and Max Lathrop went home to get married, and Richmond McKinney returned to school. Ken Pike, however, arranged to stay on in Mexico and traveled south to the mountainous state of Oaxaca, where he began work in a Mixteco village. Cam, Elvira, and Evelyn set out with the Buick and trailer for the sixty-mile trip to Tetelcingo, the town which people had told them was the most backward Aztec settlement in the state of Morelos.

As Cam maneuvered the car and trailer along a cobblestoned street, dark eyes peered from every doorway. By the time they reached the dusty plaza, a mob of ragged Aztec children were warily circling around them. Cam stepped out onto the running board of the old car and asked for the mayor. A short swarthy Indian with a serious, square face came forward. He wore huaraches, the open peasant sandals, a baggy white muslin suit, and a black sarape bearing a red and orange Aztec design. He was one of the very few citizens of the town who spoke Spanish fluently.

Cam showed Mayor Martín Méndez his papers from the Ministry of Education and announced that he had come to learn the Aztec language and help the villagers in practical ways.

"How do you greet one another in your language?" Cam asked while Mayor Méndez was still trying to absorb what he had heard.

"Shimopanotli," he replied automatically.

"Shimopanotli," Cam echoed, writing the word in his notebook. A grin spread across the mayor's face. Cam asked him for more words, repeating each and writing it down. "Your language is very beautiful," Cam said with a disarming smile.

When the mayor welcomed them cordially and invited them to live in the town, Cam pulled the trailer into the shade of a tree beside the public fountain in the center of the plaza. Nearby was the village hall and the school. On the opposite side was a Catholic church with an old tower. Above the door of the church Cam noticed a painted cross, with a sun on its left and a moon on the right. The ancient symbols of Aztec worship had been syncretized with Catholicism.

With the first mail they received in Tetelcingo was a check from Moody Church for $70. Cam felt it was oddly providential since Moody Church had sent the same amount when they were building the cornstalk house in Guatemala. He used the money to buy rough timber and bamboo for building a shed around two sides of the trailer. The narrow L-shaped lean-to became kitchen, dining room, reception room, and Evelyn's bedroom. He covered the bamboo walls with cheesecloth to ward off the insects.

Cam's experience with Cakchiquel made learning Aztec easier, since both languages were agglutinative, having constant root stems but with numerous prefixes and suffixes forming the various verbal forms and nominal derivatives.

As he had with the Cakchiquels in Guatemala, Cam became thoroughly involved with the life of the Mexican Aztecs. He felt that to learn the language of the people and to gain their complete trust, he must as far as possible become one of them. He took advantage of every opportunity to make this desire known.

One morning, for example, he asked a peddler for a sample of her wares. She replied in Aztec, "Help yourself." He popped into his mouth worms which had been wrapped in cactus skin to keep them alive. The peddler smiled at his apparent enjoyment and asked if he wanted to buy a supply. He also ate tadpoles, fried or raw in a salad Aztec style. Elvira and Evelyn declined.

Elvira spent a great deal of time in bed, and did not become intimately involved with the people. But she kept their business affairs in order, wrote many letters to their friends at home, and was a charming hostess to the many visitors that stopped by. Cam was always inviting officials to Tetelcingo.

Cam and the mayor of Tetelcingo became fast friends. Don Martín had served in the Mexican army before becoming mayor of the one thousand citizens of Tetelcingo, and Cam soon learned that he had moral problems and carried a pistol because of his enemies.

As their friendship grew, the mayor asked to borrow the little Book Cam frequently read to him. He began reading the New Testament to hangers-on at the municipal building. Some days he read for three hours at a time.

A few weeks later he told Cam, "Professor, something has happened to me. I can't lie or get drunk as I used to. I've quit beating my woman. This Book stops me."

Shortly after this he asked to buy three New Testaments from

Cam. "I'm sending one to each of my chief enemies with a letter saying that this Book has helped me to forgive them and that I hope they will read it and forgive me too."

When he explained that he had put away his gun also, Cam exclaimed, "*Don* Martín, you have been spiritually reborn. Now you must help your fellow Aztecs find this same new birth."

Cam planted other seeds too. First he got villagers to carry manure, bat dung, and ash heaps to the plaza to replenish the soil that had been scraped off to make adobe. Then he had *don* Martín hold a citizens' meeting to find what the town needed. Cam took careful notes and then made a trip into Mexico City to see his government friends. He returned with vegetable seeds.

A few days later Cam went back to Mexico City where Professor Ramírez made a donation of fruit trees. With regular irrigation and the tropical climate, the plaza became a horticulturist's delight. Visitors could follow flower-scented paths around vegetable beds. There was a rich harvest of lettuce, radishes, celery, and beets. Beginning with the mayor, the cautious Aztecs broadened their diet beyond tortillas, chilies, and beans.

Evelyn and Elvira started sewing classes for the women while Cam set off again for Mexico City to report to the officials the results of the garden. He left a giant head of lettuce in some of the offices he visited, making it easy to tell what had happened. In each conversation he was careful to give due credit to the government policies which were raising the standards of village life. He told how the Indians now had land to till. The school had more teachers and a cooperative store started. The saloon had been closed. A basketball court had been built to provide recreation. Water had been piped from a spring to the plaza.

The officials were pleased and listened appreciatively as Cam presented a list of additional village needs: a doctor to make a medical survey and treat the poor free of charge; printing of a bilingual Aztec-Spanish primer which he was preparing for literacy classes; a loan to the cooperative store so its inventory could be increased; a swimming pool; 500 trees to plant along the streets, including orange trees; more school supplies; cows for a community dairy; lumber for outhouses, and pipes to extend the municipal water system. The officials became enthusiastic and agreed to help.

Genaro Vásquez donated an old truck which Cam taught the Indians to drive. Then they went to work on the street that connected the town with the highway. Each Indian was responsible for repairing a section of road, and Cam took his turn with the others.

When Professor Flores Zamora, the new director of rural education, visited Tetelcingo, Elvira served a delicious lunch and Cam showed him around and talked about future plans. The Indians were going to whitewash their homes inside and out, a pottery industry was in the works, and there was a campaign to eradicate hills of "sacred" cutter ants. Zamora was so impressed with these and other changes that he readily agreed to help as much as he could.

Early in December of 1935, Cam, Elvira, and Evelyn drove to Mexico City for a time of rest, and Cam had a chance to tell Ambassador Josephus Daniels about the work at Tetelcingo. Daniels suggested Cam write a report that he could take back to Washington, showing something favorable about the changes in Mexico.

Cam's four-page report explained his goals in Mexico and the developments at Tetelcingo. "Our contacts with Mexican officialdom have inspired us with confidence," he concluded. "I doubt if there is a country in the world where more interest would be shown in helping a backward town. . . . We consider it an unusual privilege to participate even in a small way in one of the greatest surges forward recorded by any people."

Because he wanted to be open and aboveboard with Mexican officials, Cam gave a copy of the report to his friend Genaro Vásquez, the secretary of labor. Vásquez had it translated into Spanish and took it to the president.

The Townsends hadn't been back in Tetelcingo long when on Saturday, January 21, 1936, a chorus of dogs began barking. Dressed in his working clothes, Cam peered around the trailer to see what was causing the commotion. Four or five men were walking away from two shiny black limousines toward the schoolhouse. He recognized the stride of the man in front—President Cárdenas!

Feeling he should not take time to change, Cam hurried through the crowd to where Cárdenas was talking with the teachers. When the president turned toward him, Cam followed the Latin American custom of the inferior extending his hand first.

"Buenos dias, Señor Presidente," Cam said respectfully.

"Buenos dias, Señor Townsend," replied the ruler who had rankled foreign businessmen with his socialistic efforts to elevate peasant life.

Cam was amazed that the president knew his name. But Cárdenas knew much more, having read the report.

"Señor Presidente," Cam continued, conscious of his soiled clothing, "I am glad you are a friend of peasants, for you have found me one today. Will you come to our trailer home and inspect the work we are trying to do?"

Cárdenas looked across at the trailer beside the green garden, and nodded. "After I finish my visit to the school and talk to the people. Wait for me."

By this time a large crowd had gathered in the school. Even the normally shy women were there in their blue costumes and long black braids. Cárdenas spoke to the crowd briefly, then asked, "Are there any special needs you wish to bring to my attention?" He listened to the Indians' petitions for half an hour. Then he accompanied Cam across the plaza toward the trailer.

He appreciated Cam's report to Ambassador Daniels, the president said, and the articles about the rural school system Cam had written. He was glad for the publication of the primers and for the reading classes Cam had started for both adults and children. The government intended to stop all restriction of religion and would not interfere again if the church stayed out of politics.

As they walked through the garden, Cam presented his hope of bringing young people to Mexico to translate the Bible into Indian languages. Cárdenas shaded his eyes against the hot sun and squinted at the rows of vegetables. "Will they help the Indians in the practical way you are doing?" he asked.

"Certainly, *Señor Presidente*," Cam declared. "We only want to follow the example of our Master who came not to be served, but to serve and to give His life for others."

"This is just what my country needs," was Cárdenas's response. "Bring all you can get."

Cam sent an enthusiastic report of Cárdenas's visit to Ken Pike who was struggling with the knotty Mixtec tonal language across the mountains. And when Max Lathrop returned to Mexico with his bride, they went to work with the Tarascans in President Cárdenas's beautiful home state of Michoacan. Cárdenas paid special attention to the Lathrops and sent commendations to Cam.

As June approached, Cam wondered how many new students would come to the third Camp Wycliffe. Two of Evelyn Griset's UCLA classmates, Eugene Nida and Florence Hansen, had written for information. Ken Pike's nurse sister Eunice had also inquired. Altogether, fourteen regular students and four part-timers turned up for the opening of camp in Sulphur Springs. The faculty was the same with one change. Cam invited Pike to teach phonetics. When Legters arrived and saw the boyish instructor before a class, he called Cam aside. "Don't you think he lacks maturity?"

Cam replied, "I believe he has exceptional possibilities. If he doesn't make it, we won't use him next year."

Legters conceded on Pike, but was very reluctant when Cam proudly announced that the two single girls, Florence Hansen and Eunice Pike, intended to work in a tribe. "Think of the criticism we'd get for sending two young girls into an Indian tribe where not even male missionaries have ever gone."

Cam pleaded their case until Legters said, "Oh, all right. Go ahead, Townsend, and do what you think best. But I don't like it."

When the training camp was over, Evelyn Griset returned to UCLA, and Ethel Mae Squires, another of Cam's nieces, came to be Elvira's nurse and helper for the coming year. Trailed by a second carload of linguistic investigators, including the brilliant Gene Nida, a Phi Beta Kappa graduate, and the two single girls, they headed for the border, again on the faith that God would supply the money.

In Mexico City a check caught up with them. A mining engineer and his wife in El Paso had heard Legters speak and sent $1,500. This would keep the entire group going for at least two months.

The group now needed an office larger than Cam's briefcase. H. T. Marroquin, the American Bible Society secretary, came to the rescue and offered to share his own small facilities for their growing correspondence and records.

Then a letter from Legters presented a new problem. He was having trouble with the Pioneer Mission Agency. "The board says we can't continue forwarding funds to workers on the fields who have no organization," he wrote. "You must organize a committee."

His disagreement with the Central American Mission over the Cakchiquel translation and the advance into other tribes had influenced Cam against forming a Stateside organization. He did not like the idea of placing the fledgling group under a board of home supporters who might not understand what they would be doing. The channeling of support through the Pioneer Mission Agency had left them free to develop their own policies, and he wanted this to continue. If Legters and the P.M.A. wanted a field committee, they could form the committee among themselves.

Cam called his group together. He pulled a few letterheads from his briefcase and passed them around. "When Bill Sedat went to

Guatemala after the second training camp, immigration required that he have a document from some academic institution sponsoring him. I had this printed up with the name Summer Institute of Linguistics. What do you think?"

There were differences of opinion. Some preferred International Institute of Linguistics, a name Legters had previously suggested. "The advantage of a name like Summer Institute is that it doesn't sound too pretentious," Cam explained. "A suspicious country wouldn't consider it a threat. And we do train during the summer. We could have a lawyer draw up a constitution here in Mexico and the Pioneer Mission Agency can continue forwarding money to us."

The seminary men argued that this was highly unusual. Missionary groups usually organized in the homeland and operated under a board of directors in the States. "Do we want well-meaning people at home who lack knowledge telling us what to do?" Cam asked. "Let's run our own affairs from the field under the Lord's leading."

When they finally agreed, Cam suggested that the group be democratic and meet annually for business conferences. Between times, an elected executive committee of three or four members would function. This committee would have authority over the director who would be elected periodically by the conference.

It was obvious that Cam would be elected director, but his proposal that he be under the executive committee surprised them. This was something new in the history of missions—a founder-director telling a crew of young green members, some unhappy with past decisions, to take charge. But Cam believed it was dangerous for one man to have control. It meant he would have to use persuasion and charisma in attempting to put across his policies.

Ken Pike, Brainerd Legters, Eugene Nida, and Max Lathrop formed the constitutional committee and worked with a lawyer in drawing up the document. When executed and signed in the fall of 1936, it marked the first time in history that an organization had been formed for the primary purpose of reducing languages to writing and translating the Bible for minority groups.

The third Camp Wycliffe almost tripled in size over the previous summer. *From l. to r., top row:* Joe Chicol, Gene Nida, Ken Pike, Walter Miller, Robert Smallwood, Jacob Johnson. *Middle:* Eunice Pike, Ethel Squire, Elvira, Cam, John Twentyman, Isabel Twentyman, Grace Armstrong, Florence Hansen. *Bottom:* Joe McCullough, Rowland Davis, Landis Christiansen, Wilfred Morris.

During the first years of Camp Wycliffe in Arkansas, equipment was scarce. One lack was solved by a gift of old nail kegs.

Above: Elvira, Evelyn Griset (later Pike), and Cam stand in front of the Buick and trailer which took them to Mexico and the town of Tetelcingo, Morelos, in 1935. *Below:* In 1937 Cam visited the place in Morelos where Zapata, one of the revolutionary leaders, was shot and killed in 1919. Zapata was an Indian and the Indians had responded to his leadership and agrarian program.

13. Cam's Social Service

"Who permitted your workers to enter Mexico?" a veteran missionary asked Cam.

"President Cárdenas. He is helping us because we're helping Mexico in practical service to the Indians."

"How are you listed on the immigration forms?"

"Linguistic investigators."

"You're in the country under false pretenses," the missionary complained.

"The government knows that we will translate the Bible."

"Perhaps so. But you're doing other things besides linguistic work. You're deceiving your home supporters."

Cam did not press the matter. A few weeks later the critic left for the States to warn churches about the "fakery" and "dishonesty" of Cameron Townsend.

A different criticism came from a Presbyterian missionary friend of Cam's. "Captain" Norman Taylor disapproved of Eunice Pike and Florence Hansen going to live in a Mazateco village. "I've been through there," he told Cam, "and heard there is a lot of killing. Please don't let them go."

Cam respected Taylor, but when he mentioned the warning to the girls, they looked at him in surprise. "Why, don't you believe God can take care of us?"

Set back, Cam replied, "If you put it that way, go ahead."

But before any of the translators could leave for their tribes, an official messenger came from the president saying he wished to welcome them back to Mexico with a banquet in Chapultepec Palace. The presidential limousine would call for them.

They assembled for the nine-course meal in the large chandeliered

99

salon where visiting heads of state were entertained. Cam and Elvira sat on either side of the president at his request. Two key officials sat nearby. As the hungry translators ate ravenously, Cam spoke of their motivation and aims to Cárdenas. "Each of us wants to follow Jesus Christ by serving the Indians in practical ways, assisting your government in its program of bettering the masses. We have found, too, that it helps to translate God's moral and spiritual revelation into the Indian language."

The president was attentive. "My government will help you in every way possible," he promised. "But have these young people enough money for living expenses?"

"Well, two have their support pledged by friends in the States."

"In that case," the president resolved, "I will assign rural schoolteachers' salaries to the other eight."

Cam was overwhelmed. Here was the man some thought to be anti-Christian offering government support for the needy translators. "Gracias, Señor Presidente, gracias. They will try to be worthy of your government's confidence."

The following day the Townsends and the young ladies went by invitation to visit Señora Cárdenas. When Elvira inquired about Amalia Cárdenas's young son, the First Lady said she would send him to the Townsends' apartment the next day.

Buoyed by the backing of President and Mrs. Cárdenas, the linguists scattered to their chosen tribes. Brainerd and Elva Legters went to the large Maya tribe of Yucatan. Richmond McKinney selected the needy Otomis in the dry Mesquital Valley north of Mexico City. Walter and Vera Miller took the large Mixe tribe in Oaxaca. The scholarly Gene Nida rode a bus to the cold Sierra Madre Mountains of the north where fleet-footed Tarahumaras lived in shanties and caves. Cam personally took Landis Christiansen into the rugged mountains of Puebla where Totonacs grew corn on land so steep they sometimes had to tie themselves to trees or boulders to keep from falling out of their fields. And Ken Pike escorted his sister Eunice and her partner Florence Hansen to their mountain Mazatec village in Oaxaca. Then after helping them rent an Indian house and learn their first Mazatec words, he walked to a country depot and caught a train into his Mixtec area.

As he waited at a remote stop for his luggage to arrive, Pike watched a line of Indians carrying big bags of grain to warehouses. Remembering Cam's emphasis on service, he walked over and shouldered a hundred-pound bag. He made it only to the railroad track where the steel cleats on his boots caused him to slip and break his leg. The Indians put him on the next train to a hospital.

He had vowed to "come back with four Gospels in Mixtec or bust." Now he was laid up for no telling how long. Suddenly he remembered the paper on phonetics Cam had suggested he write "to demonstrate that we are really linguists." While in traction he started on the manuscript.

When he was permitted to leave the hospital, Cam brought him to Tetelcingo where he finished the 125-page manuscript which Cam mailed to Dr. Edward Sapir. When a complimentary reply came from the distinguished linguist, Cam suggested that Pike go to the University of Michigan the following summer and take the special linguistic course. At Camp Wycliffe he had seen Pike's scholarly potential. He knew that the group had to have teachers to train future translators and set the scientific pace while also providing a witness to the academic world. Pike was his trusted lieutenant and it was hard to send him off. But future advance had to take precedence over present needs.

In Tetelcingo, President Cárdenas was fulfilling all the promises he had made to the villagers. In addition a new industrial school and an elaborate farm irrigation system were built. To some of his critics who disapproved of lavishing so much aid on little Tetelcingo, Cárdenas wrote:

When there are folks like this American couple living in a village with the know-how and enthusiasm to help personally in the improvement projects, that's where the government can put forth special effort with more assurance of adequate returns on its investment.

On one of his frequent trips into the capital, Cam suggested that the Summer Institute of Linguistics [SIL] and the Mexican Institute of Linguistics cooperate in a week's seminar on Indian languages in January 1937. Dr. Silva y Aceves liked the proposal and had Cam summon the translators from their tribes.

The Mexican scholars were pleased at what the American linguists had learned in so short a time. The minister of education awarded Cam the title "Honorary Rural School Teacher of Mexico." Silva y Aceves invited Cam to teach a class on linguistics at the

National University. Cam accepted and twice a week he commuted to the university to teach the class of three students until it was time to leave for the fourth Camp Wycliffe.

Before leaving for the 1937 session, Cam went to say goodbye to the president. He found Cárdenas deeply disturbed about the petroleum industry. "The oil workers are on strike," he told Cam, "but the companies are mainly owned by U.S., British, and Dutch interests, and they refuse to submit to our courts. Gasoline is hard to get. Mexico City's bus lines are partially paralyzed. I'm trying to get the workers back to work by promising a thorough government study of the foreign-owned oil business. But the greatest problem of Mexico, as elsewhere, is the human heart."

"Christ can change the heart," Cam declared.

Cárdenas raised his eyebrows. "What about your religious capitalists in the United States who exploit the poor?"

"We must distinguish between a hypocritical profession and a true faith that changes the heart," Cam pleaded. "Look at Christ as your example. He 'being rich, became poor that we through his poverty might be made rich.' "

Cárdenas seemed moved. "Perhaps my government can cooperate with the evangelical missionaries if they are willing to help people in practical ways as your group is doing."

Cam had been disappointed by the attitude of some missionaries, but he felt confident that the majority would help the government if they knew the president felt this way.

"When I return in the fall I will get them together," Cam promised. "I'm sure, *Señor Presidente*, they will join hands."

This summer classes were held at the wooded Baptist Assembly grounds near Siloam Springs. Two of the fifteen newcomers were Otis and Mary Leal, who had been recruited by L. L. Legters. Otis was a recent graduate of Westminster Theological Seminary.

The students were not sure how they should address Cam. *Doña*, the Spanish equivalent for "Madam," was used for Elvira. Legters was always "Mr." or "Reverend." But Cam was not ordained and looked too young to be called "Mr." When she was introduced to him, Mary Leal had asked, "Are you the son of the famous missionary?" When the question of address was put to Cam, he chuckled and said, "Well, my nieces Evelyn and Ethel Mae called me 'uncle' in Mexico." And so he became "Uncle Cam."

Gene Nida, who had had to return to the States because of

illness, had recovered sufficiently to teach morphology—the study of form and structure of a language. Pike taught phonetics part of the summer. He had spent time with Dr. Sapir to discuss the Mixtec puzzle of tone. The only difference in many words was a higher or lower pitch on a syllable. Sapir thought that pitch, or tone, in language was centered in "relationships, and that the pitch of each word should be compared with the pitch of others." This idea helped Pike develop a formula for analyzing tone languages that made linguistic history. Through Sapir, Pike met University of Michigan linguist Charles Fries, who arranged a scholarship for Pike's study the following summer.

Support was low for the group even with the small salaries coming from the Mexican government. Attacks by critics may have caused some prospective donors to close their purses. There were frequent editorials in U.S. newspapers lambasting the Mexican president for following a "socialistic" policy, and Cam found himself criticized when he tried to defend Cárdenas and his programs.

However, their friends from Sulphur Springs continued to help. The biggest boost came from newly married Amos Baker who stopped, learned of the need, and promised Cam, "I'll borrow money to keep your new kids from going hungry in Mexico."

Returning to Mexico City, the SIL linguists held their annual business conference, then dispersed to their tribes. Remembering the president's desire to work with the evangelical missionaries, Cam and Elvira stayed on in the capital to try to foster some co-operation. Cam drafted a letter which Cárdenas approved:

Missionaries of Mexico:
You missionaries will be surprised to receive this letter, because some of you do not even know me and I, in turn, am but poorly acquainted with the work you are doing. Nevertheless, I am not unacquainted with the religious, social, economic and even political problems of this great nation, for I have made a careful study of them during the past four years. I must confess that I have fallen in love with the country and her aspirations and am doing my bit to help in the crusade of reform headed up by President Cárdenas. . . .
It seems to me that the movement needs now more than anything else a spiritual force which can bring about a rapid regeneration of men. . . . Apart from the personal example of the President himself, which is indeed exercising a tremendous moralizing influence, there is little in the revolutionary movement which serves to develop

*in the people a spirit of self-sacrifice, absolute honesty, and an ability
for cooperating with one another in a democratic fashion. . . .*

*To this end I invite you to attend or to be represented at a meet-
ing for an exchange of impressions which will be held at . . . [the
Bible Society office], January 3rd, at 10 o'clock in the morning.*

*I should make it plain from the beginning that I shall not be able
to serve you in this matter further than to help get the project
started and to present it to the President, since my linguistic work
and writing would prevent it.*

*In these moments of such great importance in the history of
Mexico we evangelical believers should remember what the Bible
says: "Pure religion and undefiled before God and the Father is this,
to visit the fatherless and widows in their affliction, and to keep himself unspotted from the world."*

> *Affectionately your fellow believer,*
> *(signed)* W. C. *Townsend*

On a separate page Cam presented his *"Suggestions for an
Evangelical Project."* These included such things as a center to help
drug addicts, alcoholics, and prostitutes; bringing in experts in irrigation, reforestation, small industries, etc.; opening clinics and cen-
ters for Bible teaching; the sale of some mission buildings to the
government and the investment of at least half the sale price in
some social service; teaching peasants principles of practical morality
and citizenship, with help from the Bible.

Only a few of the missionaries then in Mexico turned up at the
meeting. The Presbyterians showed some interest, but most of the
independents saw little possibility of working with the government.

Not having been involved in issues that were then dividing U.S.
Protestants, Cam could not understand why so many missionaries
felt as they did. The Stateside controversy over the "social gospel"
had made some feel that spiritual work should not include social
service. The traditional separation of church and state in the U.S.
made others unwilling to cooperate with the government. A third
factor was separatism. Many felt that accepting help and/or cooperating with the Cárdenas regime would mean compromise and
dilution of the gospel.

By coming to the field as a green college student, Cam had missed
being influenced by the ecclesiastical and theological controversies
of the times. With a mindset shaped primarily by the Bible, he
had no qualms about stepping across social and political boundaries
to accomplish the goal of Bible translation.

*"I'm willing to go to Washington and New York
and plead Mexico's case."*

14. "Good Neighbor" Policies

Early in February 1938 President and Mrs. Cárdenas joined the Townsends for lunch in Tetelcingo. Elvira had fixed a simple but delicious meal and had served it in her gracious style. After the meal the men carried folding chairs to the shade behind the trailer and talked about Mexico's problems with the foreign oil companies.

"The companies are getting more belligerent each day and the workers who returned to their jobs at my request are getting restless," Cárdenas told Cam.

Cam nodded his sympathy. He recognized the workers' plight: low pay, rampant disease in some oil fields, and lack of safety precautions, while the oil companies kept extracting high profits from the nation's soil. He knew that the foreign companies had obtained most of their leases during the prerevolutionary Díaz regime, when outside interests were buying their way in through bribes.

"If I could only reach the stockholders of these companies," Cárdenas sighed, "instead of their high-salaried agents who refuse to concede the justice of our demands. But I can't. If the companies keep up their defiance, Mexico will have to meet the issue squarely."

After awhile Cam turned the conversation to the Bible. He tried to explain how prayer could help with burdens of life.

Cárdenas listened with interest. Then he promised to let the Bible and other books of high moral value come into the country free of duty.

He gave a fountain pen inscribed with his name in gold letters to Cam. "With this I have signed my documents and decrees for the past three-and-a-half years. More land has been given to peasants with it than any pen in Mexican history. I want you to have it."

Cam was deeply moved. "I will treasure it as a gift from a dear friend and a great man," he said.

105

After President and Mrs. Cárdenas left, Cam used the pen to write his friend a letter in which he reviewed "some of the qualities of the best Friend I have."

He also was a Ruler, but the most powerful one there could possibly be. He loved His subjects greatly but they, due to their rebelliousness, did not wish to take advantage of His love. Not finding any other way to release them from the dreadful situation into which their rebelliousness had dragged them, He disguised Himself and lived among them as a poor carpenter. He was so poor that He had not where to lay His head. . . . He gave assistance to as many people as asked for His aid. He never denied help to anyone. His patience was inexhaustible toward all types of people except the hypocritical religious leaders whom He called a "generation of vipers." . . .

In the long essay letter Cam movingly summarized the character and life of Christ, climaxing with His death, resurrection, and presence with believers. Then he added a short personal testimony:

Mr. President, is it any wonder that I have dedicated my life . . . to such a Friend? At least I can assure you in the most categorical way that in Him I have found everlasting joy and peace, because He has the faculty of imparting His own abundant and eternal life to His followers . . .*

Two weeks later the Mexican Supreme Court ruled in favor of the workers and against the oil companies. When the companies refused to obey the court, the workers pressed Cárdenas for action. He responded by expropriating seventeen companies, declaring that the nation's economy could not stand a strike. Cárdenas pledged to pay back the money invested, but the companies demanded 400 million dollars on the basis of expected future earnings.

The impasse deepened the crisis. The companies called for "gunboat diplomacy." Terribly concerned, Cam prayed to be shown how he might help improve relations. He wanted to show Cárdenas that there were Americans who cared for Mexico. An idea came: Why not a corps of American young people to help with Mexican social projects. They could both demonstrate fraternal friendship and take

---

* Ethel E. Wallis and Mary A. Bennett, *Two Thousand Tongues to Go* (New York: Harper & Bros., 1959) pp. 85–86. Used by permission.

back home a true picture of Mexico. It was similar to the idea that two senators would suggest to presidential candidate John F. Kennedy twenty-two years later which led to the Peace Corps. But there was one key difference. Cam's "Inter-American Brigade" would be paid small salaries by Mexico.

When he presented the proposal to Cárdenas, the president liked it. Cárdenas was also agreeable to a discussion with the oil companies on indemnification. Cam offered to go to Washington and New York and plead Mexico's case, and at the same time recruit some young people for the social projects.

Cárdenas expressed his appreciation, adding only one stipulation. "You must allow my government to buy you a new car. I don't want your sick wife riding in a bus."

Cam thanked the president and accepted a $1,000 check. Then he went to the American Embassy and discussed the trip with Josephus Daniels. The ambassador wrote a letter of introduction to President Roosevelt's appointment secretary, and Cam and Elvira left immediately for Arkansas where they purchased a new Chevrolet. Elvira remained with the Basts in Sulphur Springs, while Cam drove on to Washington.

Unable to see Roosevelt, he went to Standard Oil headquarters in New York. John D. Rockefeller, Jr., was too busy, but a company executive saw him and promised to discuss the "possibility" of a settlement with his superiors. Cam waited and the response was that the company intended to continue fighting to get the properties back.

Cam refused to quit. He presented Mexico's side of the controversy at clubs and to any group of educators and businessmen who would listen. He stressed that the Mexican government was willing to pay a reasonable price and that even poor people had donated jewelry, chickens, cabbages, and other sacrifices to a fund for payment. But he got nowhere.

Calls at the New York offices of two large Protestant mission societies were equally discouraging. After hearing Cam tell about Camp Wycliffe and the challenge of the tribes, both responded in effect: "We already have more than we can handle."

A record enrollment of thirty students at the 1938 Camp Wycliffe was heartening. Seven of the group were volunteers for the Inter-American Brigade. Elvira gave them special lessons in Spanish and Latin American culture. Her lectures were later printed in a helpful book called *Latin American Courtesy* and distributed to all members of the Summer Institute of Linguistics (SIL) before they went to Latin America.

Pike and Nida were mainstays on the faculty. Pike had already completed initial study for his doctorate at the University of Michigan and Nida was planning graduate work also. Near the close of the session, Pike and Evelyn Griset, Cam's niece, delighted everyone by announcing their engagement.

Cam had stayed tuned in to the continuing diplomatic tug-of-war between the U.S. and Mexico over payment of the oil claims. When the U.S. State Department pressed for payment of an old ten-million-dollar indebtedness while the oil companies pushed a boycott of Mexican petroleum products, Cam fired off a telegram of protest to Secretary of State Cordell Hull.

WHY PLAGUE MEXICO ABOUT A SMALL DEBT WHEN EUROPE OWES US SO MUCH? THE FRIENDSHIP OF LATIN AMERICA IS WORTH MORE THAN TEN MILLION DOLLARS. JAPAN, GERMANY, OR ITALY WOULD GIVE MORE THAN THAT FOR IT. FURTHERMORE THE AMERICAN PEOPLE ARE NOT SHYLOCKS TO EXACT THE LIFE BLOOD OF MEXICO'S UNDERNOURISHED MASSES. LET THEM PAY WHEN THEY GET THEIR BREAD AND BUTTER PROBLEMS SOLVED. I PROPOSE THAT A COMMITTEE OF CITIZENS BE ORGANIZED TO DISCUSS DIRECT WITH COMMITTEE OF MEXICAN CITIZENS ALL OUR PENDING PROBLEMS.

Secretary Hull merely acknowledged the message.

By the time camp ended Cam was tired and drained emotionally from his frustrating efforts to help Americans better understand Mexico. Those around him sensed that the big-stick diplomacy was driving him to closer identification with Mexico.

When they crossed the border back into Mexico his spirits seemed to lift. There were now thirty-two in the Mexico SIL group, plus the seven Brigaders Cam had recruited. The first linguist had been sent to the southernmost state of Chiapas which had an 80 percent Indian population.

The expansion was gratifying to Cam, but it meant more work for him as the director. He chose to delegate responsibilities. The experienced Max Lathrop helped the new linguists get outfitted for primitive living. Pike and Nida advised on linguistic problems.

Cam's expertise was in government relations. He usually took any linguist who happened to be in the capital with him on calls. This trained the linguist in the fine art of diplomacy, and gave Cam the opportunity to use the linguist as Exhibit A of the work. Cam usually carried along some practical result from the work: a primer, a vowel chart, or an article on some Indian language.

While feeling ran high against the foreign oil companies and their allies, SIL continued to be well received. The National University invited them to participate again in the annual "Linguistic Week," the highlight of which turned out to be a banquet given in honor of SIL.

All this took time away from tribal work. When some of the linguists grumbled, Cam reminded them that good relations with officials and educators was making it possible for them to translate the Bible. "If some of you are getting impatient over slow progress," he wrote in a circular letter, "remember Noah and his 120-year foolish task, or David's extra wait of seven-and-a-half years after the death of Saul."

Cam himself continued efforts to build understanding between the U.S. and Mexico. When he heard that Cárdenas was planning a trip to Baja, California, he suggested a "Good Neighbors" picnic near the border. Cárdenas thought this a grand idea and reserved an old hotel building near Tijuana for July 7, 1939.

Cam hurried to Santa Ana and presented invitations to friends and relatives around southern California. He asked Will Nyman to coordinate transportation from Los Angeles. About two hundred American guests came and everyone ate at long tables spread along the patio. As master of ceremonies Cam read 1 Corinthians 13, the "Love Chapter," and thanked President Cárdenas for help given to SIL. Then he asked parents who had sons or daughters serving among Mexico's Indian tribes to stand so the president might know who they were. All stood, except Cam's father who had not heard the request. Will was now very feeble, but had gotten out of his sick bed, eager not to miss the occasion. Cam asked his sisters to have him stand. Will stood as tall and straight as he possibly could. President Cárdenas took one look at the determined eighty-four-year-old man and stood to his feet in tribute, thanking "the man who has given his son to serve Mexican peasants."

Europe was heating up for a major conflagration when the 1939 Camp Wycliffe met at Siloam Springs. The Townsends, Nida,

Lathrop, and Legters served as faculty. Ken Pike arrived late from his study at the University of Michigan.

Acting on a suggestion from Brainerd Legters, Cam asked Dr. Eric North, General Secretary of the American Bible Society, if the A.B.S. wished to take over the training school as its "official center for training Bible translators. It has grown so and the prospects are for much more growth. Some of us wonder if a larger and more experienced organization shouldn't run it," he wrote. "There is no dissatisfaction with the Pioneer Mission Agency [which was continuing to channel support funds] whatever, but all concerned merely want the best plan possible to hasten the giving of the Word to all the tribes of the earth."

North declined, but sent a small gift from the Society for operating expense.

Legters ran on at full steam during his two weeks at camp. On the Camp Day of Prayer Cam asked, "Couldn't you give us more time next year, Mr. Legters?" The old warrior looked wistfully at him and replied, "I'd like to, Cameron, but the Lord hasn't given me liberty to take any appointments beyond next May. I don't know why. Maybe He's going to promote me to Glory by then."

After camp the Townsends went to stay with friends near Brownsville, Texas, while Cam completed a booklet on the oil controversy. The eighty-five-page *Truth About Mexico's Oil* was published the next year by an Inter-American Committee which Cam set up, and copies were sent to all members of Congress.

After emphasizing Mexico's willingness to pay a fair settlement, he asked, "When are we going to pay for that land grab (2/5ths of all Mexican territory) of 1848?" He wished that "American citizens *en masse* would serve notice on American companies abroad that henceforth and forever they will have to use their brains to get out of their difficulties and not expect a single gunboat . . . or diplomat to pull their chestnuts out of the fire." He pleaded for the legislators to resume silver purchases, cut off by Secretary of Treasury Morgenthau, and stop trying to "starve Mexico into submission." Then he proposed in a letter to President Roosevelt, included in the book, that a high level "Good Neighbors' Committee" be formed by U.S. and Mexican citizens to find friendly solutions to their problems.

On Christmas Eve Cam received a telegram from his sisters telling of his father's death from kidney failure. He didn't have the funds to attend the funeral so he wrote a eulogy praising his father for

His faithfulness in pointing me to God and His Word.

His habit of telling the truth at all costs.

His practice of resting on the Lord's Day.

His advice to do something until it becomes second nature.

His principle of delegating responsibility.

His courage in espousing the cause that he felt was right whether there was any chance for it to win or not.

I am truly grateful that Will Townsend was my father.

The following May the SIL group was having the annual business meeting in Mexico City when the news came of L. L. Legters's fatal heart attack. Less than two months later his wife Edna died. Cam had lost another pair of dependable helpers.

15. Wycliffe Bible Translators

It was Cam's idea to give a banquet in Mexico City to celebrate five years of service to Mexico's Indians in cooperation with the Ministry of Education and the National University. Among the guests were Ambassador Daniels, the ambassador from Guatemala, and two Mexican cabinet officers, but a poised young woman doctor stole the show.

Elena Trejo told of her struggles to get an education from the time she had been brought to the Townsends in San Antonio, Guatemala, as an illiterate Indian girl. "All that I am I owe to God and to my spiritual parents, Mr. and Mrs. Cameron Townsend."

After the banquet, Cam presented "Fifth Anniversary" Spanish New Testaments to various officials. With the name of each recipient stamped in gold, the Testaments were eagerly received in places where only a few years before employees had been under pressure to deny their religious faith.

The group was becoming well known and respected among Mexican educators for their work among the Indians. Cam made it a point to remember numerous Mexican friends at important milestones in their lives. He might attend a wedding or a funeral, or if someone was gravely ill hurry to his bedside.

For example, when he heard that Silva y Aceves was afflicted with cancer, he and Pike went and read Scripture with him. Later Cam returned to find him sinking fast and his nun sister at his bedside. She listened attentively as Cam quoted Scripture. Then after Cam led in prayer, the nun followed him outside the room where she threw her arms around his neck and sobbed her thanks for "giving us the Word of God."

He also kept trying to be of service to President Cárdenas. While the oil dispute simmered, he continued writing letters to help Americans "understand Mexico's side." When the conflict was finally settled by a joint Mexican–U.S. commission that awarded the companies payment for their investment only, both he and Cárdenas felt relations would improve between their respective countries.

On one visit with Cárdenas, Cam dreamed with the president about a united hemisphere. Deeply moved by the thought of what a closer relationship could mean, Cam took pen and wrote a "Hymn of the New America," which he dedicated to Cárdenas. A sampling of stanzas reads:

> We sing to one America,
>   United Hemisphere,
> Blest harmony of nations!
>   The world our song must hear.
>
> Nor Latin, now, nor Saxon,
>   We'll one another call;
> Henceforth we're one America,
>   With equal love for all!

In Guatemala and now in Mexico Cam had noticed that some missionaries identified constantly with the American community— too closely, he thought. Cam himself spent his energies cultivating Mexican friends, with the primary exception of Ambassador Daniels. The two genuinely liked each other and Daniels privately agreed with Cam on many policies.

While Cam was grateful for opportunities for friendships with the president and other high officials, criticism arose among his associates over "secular involvements." He was charged with "not doing Christian work." One translator even resigned from SIL and left Mexico so he could "evangelize."

Cam was further criticized for his policy toward church work. He had encouraged the linguists to attend evangelical churches when in the capital, but he cautioned against passing out "doctrinal" tracts. They should stick to translation, avoid sectarian involvements, and witness only on a personal level to friends.

When the criticism persisted, Cam spelled out his position in a crucial policy letter to all SIL members.

It seems to me there are three policies which might be followed by Christian workers in Mexico. The first is frank cooperation with and commendation of the government projects which we can heartily endorse while carefully abstaining from anything that could be considered as opposition. The second is strict neutrality concerning government policies, neither commending nor criticizing them. The third is opposition, either actively . . . or only verbally as is involved in open censorship. Those few of our number who cannot follow the first should . . . consistently follow the second to avoid getting us into trouble, and that is what I am now pleading with them to do—just to be consistently neutral. Let us realize that censorship may become deadly opposition and if we cannot commend, let us be careful not to oppose.

We are in Mexico to serve and not to dictate policies to the government. If it wants to teach the children of Mexico to share with one another as sincere socialists should, that is Mexico's lookout and not ours. We should be more anxious than ever to give the Word of God to the people, for it is the best preparation in the world for sharing. If you and I lived in Russia we would find that the life and love of God in our hearts would be ample preparation for living under that regime and it would be less exacting than the Sermon on the Mount. If they would let me teach the Bible in Russia, I would gladly abstain from censorship of their policies that I did not like. After all who called us to pass judgment upon rulers? Are we not commanded to obey and pray for them? Let us be consistent. If anyone feels obliged to hold himself aloof from government as regards cooperation, let him also hold himself aloof as regards criticism.

. . . There is too much at stake for this [criticism] to continue. Twenty million Indians in Latin America wait to see the spirit of the Gospel demonstrated in a way they can comprehend and to read the Word in a language they can understand. Our linguistic group must make both the demonstration and the translations. Is there any other way we can do it than by patiently following by faith the humble path of cooperation in which God has blessed us signally thus far?

He was more blunt in a second letter:

I don't blame you for getting a wrong slant on things, for you have more contact with the American colony, which is generally very alarmist in its views, than you do with the Mexican element that is responsible for the laws, and furthermore, many of you read the _____ [an antigovernment newspaper], and that is like trying to get a fair view of Martin Luther from reading histories compiled by Jesuit fathers.

However, I find it absolutely necessary to point out to the ones who went off half-cocked in their criticism . . . that it was very unbecoming of us who have received so many courtesies from the government of Mexico. . . . Will you not respond to this in the right spirit, recognize your mistake and look up with a new faith and trust in the One who is going to visit Mexico with a great spiritual awakening if we but continue faithful.

Most of the SILers went along with a minimum of grumbling. But Max Lathrop and Brainerd Legters argued loudly against the director's "nonsectarian policies." Cam convinced Lathrop, but young Legters finally resigned in favor of general missionary work.

With increased responsibilities as SIL director, Cam began spending less time in Tetelcingo. There were now thirty-seven translators (including five pairs of single girls) in eighteen tribes. He was particularly frustrated over spending so little time in translation himself. *Don* Martín, the former mayor of Tetelcingo, was now pastor of a congregation of sixty, and longed for the New Testament in Aztec. When Dick Pittman, a young teacher from Wheaton College, and his wife Kay offered to serve wherever needed, Cam gratefully assigned them to Tetelcingo. They moved into a little house near the orange grove and began language study.

With the Pittmans in Tetelcingo and Pike willing to help in "diplomatic emergencies," Cam and Elvira felt free to accompany Dr. Elena Trejo to Guatemala. They longed to revisit the beautiful land of their first missionary endeavors, and this seemed the ideal opportunity.

While in Guatemala Cam had the opportunity to talk with President Jorge Ubico who was still in power. The president expressed opposition to anything that would accentuate or perpetuate existing distinctions between Indian tribes and the rest of the population. Cam interpreted this to mean that he would be displeased with publications in the Indian languages which did not have parallel columns or pages in Spanish.

Cam returned from Guatemala with a renewed conviction of the need for a corps of workers large enough to handle the entire task of working on the Indian languages. The neglect of the Cakchiquel New Testament by other missionaries indicated to him that linguistic needs were being overlooked.

At the business conference of SIL in Mexico City in 1941, however, pesos were so slim that they voted on whether to have coffee in the morning or the afternoon. Financial support had always been borderline, but with the death of Legters, their number-one fund-raiser, some workers began suffering real hardship. Cam encouraged them to continue "in the same heroic spirit . . . remembering that Paul himself was not unacquainted with want." He suggested that "we all try to interest our own friends more vitally in Bible trans-lation by frequently writing them interesting details."

There were encouragements though. Will Nyman, the California businessman who had given hospitality to SIL's first students, came to Mexico and was overwhelmed. Although he had a heart con-dition, Nyman eagerly volunteered to take over the mailing of the circular letters to home supporters. And by time for Camp Wycliffe to begin, the rough draft of the Mazatec New Testament—a first in the history of Mexico's Indians—had been completed by Eunice Pike and Florence Hansen.

While the new recruits were settling in their tribes in the fall of 1941, Cam mulled over a request by an official to send workers to the Lacandons, a tribe of only two hundred in the rain forest of Chiapas who were considered the bottom of the cultural barrel. Another official had mentioned the Seris, a smaller band of Indians living along the Pacific coastline of Sonora.

Pike's Mixtecs numbered 200,000 and the various dialects of Aztecs included two or three times that many. But did tribes of 100 and 200 merit the life work of educated linguists? Cam thought again about Jesus' parable of the shepherd who sought out the one lost sheep. Yes, the small tribes also needed the Word, he decided. But would there be volunteers for them?

In October, Cam and Elvira were with the Lathrops on the shore of Lake Patzcuaro. Cam rose early for devotions and sat watching some Tarascans throwing their fish nets. The scene reminded him of Jesus watching other fishermen at Galilee and saying, "Follow me, and I will make you fishers of men." He took out pencil and paper and began writing to the now forty-four workers under his leadership: "Will each of you be responsible before the Lord for one new recruit for Bible translation? . . . I'm sure He would give us six extra for good measure."

Fifty new workers would more than double the force. But where would the training school be held to accommodate so many? Where would they get the supporting funds? Cam prayed long and hard.

Back in Tetelcingo he and Elvira met a new friend, A. M. Johnson. He had heard about the work and was curious. The Townsends welcomed "Uncle Al" into their home. Cam devoted the morning to telling him the history of their work and filling him in on future plans. They learned that Al Johnson was a widower who had retired from his post as president and board chairman of the National Life Insurance Company. "Guess the most interesting thing I ever did was to build a Moorish castle in Death Valley, California," he told them. "Built it for an old prospector friend of mine named Scotty who once saved my life when I was sick. But if you folks ever get up that way, I'd be pleased to have you stay there awhile. Or in my Hollywood home if that's more convenient."

When Uncle Al left it was with the promise, "You'll be hearing from me."

When the Pioneer Mission Agency in Philadelphia heard of Cam's call for fifty new recruits they wrote, "We can't handle double your number. You should organize your own office." The letter made it clear the decision was final, so Cam wrote three key friends about the possibility of opening an office for SIL.

All three quickly responded. Dr. Stephen Slocum, father of a Wycliffe member, estimated an office would cost $15,000 the first year—"money we don't have." Will Nyman said, "Sounds like a big assignment. If I can help, let me know." And Clarence Erickson, pastor of the Gospel Tabernacle in Chicago, asked, "What do you have in mind?" He invited Cam to speak at a missionary rally in his church and sent a $200 advance for expenses and honorarium. The money was a godsend, since the Townsends were almost penniless at the time.

Shortly after Pearl Harbor Cam and Elvira drove to California to discuss with Nyman a home organization. At the same time they decided to accept the invitation of the Board of Regents of the University of Oklahoma to hold their summer training sessions there, with full academic credit. The invitation had come through Della Brunstetter, a language teacher at the university, who had attended Camp Wycliffe to help her in her study of Cherokee. The university had long been a center of study for American Indian cultures. Definite plans for an office were left until next summer, to go over with Nida and Pike at Norman, Oklahoma.

After presenting a recruiting program at the Bible Institute of Los Angeles, Cam fulfilled the assignment to speak in Chicago, then went on to Philadelphia to arrange for the transfer of SIL records and files from the Pioneer Mission Agency office.

While in Philadelphia he received an invitation to visit a New York farmer who had read of the request for fifty new recruits. He took a bus to see the farmer and was given $250. This paid the first month's rent on an additional office in Mexico City, for they had long since outgrown the space shared with the American Bible Society secretary. Then he and Elvira started off again in "Don Lázaro," the '38 Chevrolet given by Cárdenas, with a load of linguists for Norman.

There, Nyman, Pike, Nida, and Cam met in a motel to chart the future. They took the 1936 Mexico SIL constitution as a guide. "We don't want a U.S. board telling the field workers what to do," Cam insisted. "Direction must come from the field."

All felt that the name Summer Institute of Linguistics would not carry a Bible translation image to Christians in the States. "Why not have two organizations, then?" Cam suggested. "SIL can handle our training and contracts with foreign governments and universities. The Bible translation organization can do what the Pioneer Mission Agency did—receive funds and publicize the field work." After considerable discussion they agreed on this plan. Adopting a suggestion from Eunice Pike, passed along by her brother, they called the new organization Wycliffe Bible Translators.

The twin organizations would have interlocking directorates, and in most cases the same officers. Cam was elected general director. Nyman, who agreed to manage the home office, was to be the first secretary-treasurer. Pike was given the responsibility for academic affairs, with Nida as his associate.

The constitution for Wycliffe Bible Translators (WBT) had one unique feature. All monies received would be allotted directly to members who would assign back a tenth for the administration of field and home offices. As under the old SIL constitution, the general director would be elected by the board every four years. He would be responsible for "maintenance and expansion into new fields" and opportunities for expansion, subject to limitation by the board. Board members' terms would be staggered with some being elected by the member-linguists in business conference each year.

They adopted intact the doctrinal statement of the China Inland Mission which Cam had long admired. It included belief in the divine inspiration of the Bible, the Trinity, the fall of man, the atonement of Christ, justification by faith, the resurrection of the body, eternal life of the saved and eternal punishment of the lost.

The purposes of Wycliffe Bible Translators should center on "putting the Word of God into all the tribal tongues of earth in which it does not yet exist." This included assisting evangelical missionaries to get special linguistic training and other aids in Bible translation.

With their ideas on paper and agreed upon, Nyman looked squarely at his colleagues. "My health isn't good, as you know. I don't know how many more years the Lord will allow me. But I believe the Lord is in this thing. We'll have trials, but we can weather them with His help and if we stick together. I propose that we four covenant to stick together a minimum of five years. Then if one of us wants out, he's free to go."

All agreed.

Nyman returned to California to have the legal documents filed for incorporation. Cam and Elvira stayed on for the training institute, now called Summer Institute of Linguistics as well as Camp Wycliffe. Cam watched with great satisfaction as Pike, Nida, and six other linguistic veterans kept the 130 students interested and learning. However, the founder himself presented the greatest challenge in his chapel messages. His quiet, folksy stories made the young listeners want to pioneer in Bibleless tribes at whatever cost or sacrifice it might require.

By the end of 1942 Cam had his fifty new volunteers for Bible translation, plus one more for good measure.

"If I have been devoted to my Lord's service in the past, by His grace my devotion shall be a passion from now on."

16. Tears Do Not a Vision Dim

SIL '42 was challenging and exciting, but the war news was grim. Axis forces were sweeping across North Africa. Around U.S. shores German submarines were torpedoing Allied ships. In the Pacific Japan had reached the Aleutians and New Guinea. But Cam was dreaming advance.

"Who will open Tibet, or claim the last acre of the Amazon, the hills of central India, the jungles of Borneo, the steppes of Siberia—the merchant or the missionary?" he asked the SILers. "When the war is over, let us take up the Sword of the Spirit and march."

But it was not enough to dream. There were mundane things to do. There was the Wycliffe office to be set up in the apartment over Nyman's garage. Nyman took no salary and donated the space. The only paid employee was a secretary, and since they bought a minimum of supplies, the cost of running the office was only $150 a month at the beginning.

While Cam and Elvira were there helping, Nyman mentioned that only $105 was lacking for the field workers to receive 100 percent allowance during the current month. Cam raised his eyebrows questioningly at Elvira. They had $105 set apart for a refrigerator. She nodded and Cam said, "We'll give what's lacking."

That same day the Townsends received three separate gifts totaling exactly $105. Later, on the way back to Mexico City, a motel owner in New Mexico presented them with a check for $200 instead of a bill.

Back in Mexico, Cam greeted Dawson Trotman, the founder of the Navigators, who had come down for the annual business conference. "Win a convert and train him to reproduce spiritually" was the motto of Trotman and his Navigators. Trotman was captivated by Cam's dream. "The burden of reaching whole tribes who had never had a single sentence from the Word of God translated into their own tongue gripped me," he wrote to his servicemen who were serving on over a hundred ships. Before leaving, he assured Cam that he would recommend Wycliffe to Navigators seeking further opportunities of service.

About this time a new problem arose among the WBT/SIL members. It dated back to the last summer's training school when Cam had stirred criticism from the independent fundamentalists by inviting a member of the Presbyterian (U.S.A.) Board to study, and had invited a woman with "Pentecostal leanings" to speak in chapel. The Pioneer Mission Agency, which had continued to funnel some funds to WBT/SIL, threatened to cut off support. Also, questions had been raised about students and some new translators who did not adhere to the doctrine of eternal security generally held by old members.

The founders of Wycliffe had discussed the question of admitting Pentecostals, and others who believed healing was provided in the atonement, to the summer school. Nida, Pike, and Nyman wanted to exclude those holding "doctrinal differences." Cam wanted them in, if, as he said, "the differences are in nonessential matters." They had tabled the issue, with the serious division of opinion remaining.

On February 23, 1943, Cam summed up his reasons to Nyman in a key letter. WBT/SIL was not dedicated to propagating any system of theology or to extending existing denominations, but to give the Bibles to tribes that did not have it. Members should be as careful about "matters of purity, love, mercy and humble service" as about nonbasic doctrines.

We can't take ourselves as a standard, nor the organizations from which we come. Let's stick to the Bible as our gauge—no broader and no narrower—as exclusive but with a love that is inclusive. What we know, or think we know, about that Book and the way we live it should not be the mold we pass on to the world, but rather the Book itself.

In the scientific world we are supposed to accept facts even though they go against our theories, but in spiritual things we tend to discount all the virtues a man has . . . if we hear that his connections are under ostracism. Four of our new workers came out under such a cloud last summer. All four have fitted in beautifully.

He then suggested that the accepting of candidates be left to the staff at the summer sessions, who would know the students from their studies at SIL, rather than being submitted to the directors.

He stressed again that they were doing something new and departing from old methods. Looking to the future he saw Wycliffe with a thousand members in all parts of the world "serving evangelical missionary organizations which have all kinds of doctrinal peculiarities. The more we can serve them, the more accurate and efficient their work will be. Let's not limit our sphere of service by officially condemning their pet theories."

In a follow-up letter, Cam suggested to Nyman the distribution of responsibilities in the Wycliffe work:

You should have complete charge of business matters, Nida of public relations in the States as regards Boards and schools, Pike as regards scientific connections, and I of advances on the field. We can each be like generals in our particular field, the Board will be like Congress and the missionaries like soldiers with voting power that gives them ultimate control.

. . . You need sub-councils in different parts of the country composed of men whose hearts God has touched to the point where they have already rolled up their sleeves and gone to work for us. When God, Himself, has chosen the men, we can trust them with jobs. We don't need to be afraid of their lack of reputation or even that they aren't accepted in the inner circle of certain doctrinal groups. . . . Here in Mexico we've seen God work through men we would have thought to be most unlikely. Let's never try to cramp the Lord by setting up our judgment as over against His.

Then Cam outlined the "distinctive features" of Wycliffe work as he saw them:

1. We specialize on giving the Scriptures to tribes without them.
2. We pioneer, going preferably to closed fields.
3. We cooperate with missions, governments, scientific organizations, philanthropic organizations, always cooperate and serve, never compete.
4. We follow the linguistic approach.
5. We dare to follow even when God leads along strange paths.
6. We are not sectarian or ecclesiastical, not even dogmatic. We don't try to force people into any type of denominational or anti-denominational mold.
7. We look to God to raise up the men and means and to open the doors.

8. We should use all the aids of science, including radio, air-planes, etc., when going to jungle tribes.
9. We expect to finish the task in this generation.

Throughout the war years, WBT/SIL kept expanding. A branch SIL summer school was started at Briercrest Bible School in Canada. An official bulletin-magazine called *Translation* was started with Max Lathrop as editor. Membership and finances steadily increased.

Cam wanted evangelical pastors to understand what they were doing and to get behind the work. At Muskogee, Oklahoma, Dr. W. A. Criswell, pastor of the First Baptist Church, invited Cam and some of the linguists to present a program. Afterwards Criswell commented, "I'm impressed. I'd like to help you."

Oswald Smith, the fiery pastor of the missionary-minded Peoples' Church in Toronto, Canada, was more encouraging. When he visited Mexico he told Cam, "You folks are on our wavelength. The world can't be evangelized until every tribe has the Bible in its own tongue. My church will be with you 100 percent." Peoples' Church was soon supporting almost a score of Wycliffe linguists.

With Cam's approval, Pike had joined the faculty part-time at the University of Michigan. He had also written a text on phonetics and had helped Dr. Charles Fries prepare textbooks for teaching English to foreign students at the university. Pike fretted at being away from his tribe, but Cam felt that in the long run he would be of more value "helping us get recognition in the linguistic world."

In 1943 Pike was in Mexico when the American Bible Society asked him to make a trip to Peru, Bolivia, and Ecuador to assist missionary translators with linguistic problems in the Quechua language. Cam was enthusiastic about the invitation. Pike wasn't so certain. "I don't know if we're ready for such an undertaking." Cam reminded him of the vision he had had of reaching the forgotten tribes of South America. Finally Pike agreed, saying, "I'm a little frightened at the magnitude of the project, but this could be the hand of God, so I am willing."

Upon reaching Lima, Pike called on the minister of education, Enrique de La Rosa, and gave him his book *Phonetics*. Impressed, La Rosa asked about SIL's work in Mexico. When Pike told him about the linguistic study, practical service projects and Bible translation, the high official said, "Why not do that for our Indians in the Amazon jungle?"

"We haven't been invited," Pike replied.

The minister talked briefly to an assistant, then said, "You're invited. Come back tomorrow and we'll have it official and in writing." When Pike returned he was pleasantly surprised to be "introduced" to one of his former students from the University of Michigan, now an official of the Peruvian government. Everyone seemed not only willing but anxious for SIL linguists to help the Indians of Peru.

Cam received Pike's report with elation. For twenty years he had been looking in this direction. Now it seemed to be the Lord's time for definite plans to be made to go. It also seemed to be the time to start the boot camp for translators going to the jungle that Cam had been dreaming of for so many years.

A site in the Chiapas rain forest near the Guatemalan border was recommended—as similar to Amazonia as it was possible to be in Mexico. And the Lacondon Indians there were just as primitive as some in Peru.

Cam went to Chiapas and bargained for a lease. The land owner agreed to build three huts for the first jungle camp set for the fall of 1945.

When he returned to Mexico City, several members told him something had to be done about more adequate housing. "We can't continue to live like gypsies in such overcrowded quarters." As a result, they rented an old downtown gray building called "Palacio Quetzalcoatl" that had once been a boardinghouse for tourists. Though twenty-five rooms at first seemed a lot, they were hardly enough for offices, printing facilities, and bedrooms. Furniture was sparse and many had to sleep on webbed rope beds while visitors were given cots. Still, "The Kettle"—as they affectionately called it —became a home for members who had to be in the capital.

With Mexico growing and Peru calling, Cam still found time to think of further advances. He and Elvira visited Mr. and Mrs. Turner Blount and Miss Faye Edgerton who were working on the Navajo reservation in Arizona. Although English-speaking missionaries had worked among the Navajos for years, they had had limited success, and there was little or no Scripture in Navajo. The trio had been working in the language for three years, and after attending SIL, wanted to join Wycliffe. On Cam's recommendation the board unanimously accepted the Blounts and Miss Edgerton into membership. Their acceptance was another milestone, for it marked the first work outside of Mexico.

Cam was eager to make a survey trip to Peru, but first he wanted to work on a biography of Cárdenas. Uncle Al Johnson invited him and Elvira to stay a few weeks at his Hollywood home where Cam would have solitude.

They had just gotten in bed on December 23, 1944, when Elvira started gasping, "There's no air! There's no air!" Crawling out of bed, she staggered to the window, took one deep breath and collapsed into Cam's arms. He got her back to bed and called Uncle Al to get help.

Through the night and on into the next day Cam sat by the bed, holding her hand and fearing that each breath was the last. He was only vaguely aware of relatives coming and going. After nearly twenty-four hours Elvira's breathing stopped altogether. But Cam still sat there until Uncle Al led him into another room.

At the funeral in Glendale, Dawson Trotman read a statement from Cam who was still too shattered to speak.

God gave Elvira as a love gift to the people of Latin America and to us. He used her by His power and now He has taken His handiwork to Himself. The task she served, however, remains; and we remain.

Face to face with that task, recalling our Loved One's devotion to it, recognizing the Power that works through weakness, and with greater longing than ever before to hasten the return of our Lord. "What manner of men ought we to be?"

My own answer to that question is as follows: If I have been devoted to my Lord's service in the past, by His grace my devotion shall be a passion from now on. . . . If I have permitted hardships, dangers, pleasures, and the powerful chords of human love to swerve me at times from full obedience, henceforth "none of these things shall move me," neither shall I count my life dear unto myself, so that I might finish my course with joy. . . .

This pledge is not taken lightly. It has been burned into my soul, and though the branding processes have not been easy, the pain now seems like nothing as I visualize the fruit and joy of a truly all-out effort for my Savior and the unevangelized tribes that need Him so.

The task of giving God's Word to all the peoples of the earth can be finished in this generation.

Cam had requested that, instead of flowers, Spanish New Testaments be given for distribution in Guatemala and Mexico. The Testaments were stacked around Elvira's grave. One of the few floral pieces was shaped as a large V in which were the words: "O grave, where is thy victory? Thanks be unto God which giveth us the victory through our Lord Jesus Christ."

Uncle Al paid all funeral and burial expenses and took Cam under his wing as a younger brother. Slowly Cam began to adjust and to accept the reality of his wife's passing. She had been his co-worker for a quarter of a century, handling their many social obligations with gracious hospitality in spite of her physical and emotional illness. He had seen her before at the apparent brink of death. Still, he missed her presence.

Cam was forty-eight years old. He had lost his parents and his three closest friends and supporters—the Cakchiquel Francisco, Robby Robinson, and L. L. Legters. Now his wife was gone.

Part II
WIDENING HORIZONS

"The job can be done . . . it must be done."

17. Amazonia—a New Frontier

As he had from previous heartbreaks, Cam quickly snapped back. The work was more important than his own feelings, and there was no time to feel self-pity.

He wrote Enrique de La Rosa, minister of education in Peru, accepting his invitation to work in his country. Describing the educational and social projects in Tetelcingo, he suggested that similar programs might be undertaken to help the Peruvian jungle Indians. The minister replied by return mail. "Cooperatives are of special interest to me. I will be happy to introduce you to scientific societies in Peru." But he added, "I will write you when I judge it the right time for your trip."

While he waited, Cam negotiated the purchase of the old hotel they had been renting in downtown Mexico City. And he made arrangements for leadership in Mexico, since he expected to head the advance into Peru.

Dick Pittman, Cam's successor in Tetelcingo, had functioned as director while Cam had been away during the past months. He seemed to have understood and followed Cam's policies, and had kept up contacts with the government officials. The soft-voiced, slow-speaking little American was also making good progress on the Aztec language, and this pleased the Indians as much as it impressed the Mexican officials. Cam felt that Pittman should continue to direct the Mexico corps.

John McIntosh, with the Huichol tribe, was another potential leader. He had listened to Cam on the radio in California back in the Thirties when he was still in high school. He had told Cam then that he wanted to be a translator, and Cam advised him to complete his education, then get in touch with him. He had. The

129

determined young man had kept his eye on the goal of Bible translation until he made it. Cam felt that anyone with that kind of
perseverence had possibilities, and he invited McIntosh to go with
him on some of his rounds of government offices.

The young translator was pleased to be asked, but got a little
fidgety waiting for Cam to get down to business. When they
entered a man's office, Cam would never just tell what it was he
wanted. First he would inquire about the man's family. Or he'd
remember a sick child, a son in the university, or a hobby. Then he
would ask McIntosh to say something in Huichol. Cam and the
Mexican would talk and talk while the young American fidgeted.
Finally when it seemed time to be going, Cam might say, "Oh, by
the way, I have some papers that need signatures." Then he would
hand them to the official. The man would do his best to cut bureau-
cratic red tape saying, "Happy to help you in your important service
to my country's minority language groups."

Then it might take some time for Cam to get out of the building.
He would stop and chat with minor officials, ask about their families,
or remember someone to them. "Don't overlook anybody," he told
McIntosh. "The man in charge who signed our papers was only a
clerk when I first met him."

Once in a while Cam would be stopped by a traffic policeman.
McIntosh noted that Cam would greet the officer as graciously as
if he were the chief of police. Then he would pull out his briefcase.
"Do you know we are working with Mexico's Indians?" he would
ask. "I have some pictures. Would you like to see them?" Without
waiting for an answer, Cam would pass a few photos of Indians and
linguists to the policeman. And if the officer happened to spot a
picture of Cam with some high official, it couldn't be helped. They
might talk for fifteen minutes and end with the policeman gladly
returning the license plate he had taken off. As they drove away from
one such incident Cam said, "Never offer a bribe, John. That
demeans them. Just tell them about our work."

Otis Leal was another translator Cam spent time with. When
Leal returned to his Zapateco village, he told his wife Mary about
the experience. "He just wouldn't accept closed doors," he recalled.
"He might say, 'Let's see how God is going to solve this.' But he
never doubted that God was going to work out a problem. He has
an utter conviction that God wants every language group in the
world reached—and that Wycliffe is His means of doing it."

The tall, good-looking Ben Elson, who had heard Cam and Gene Nida speak when he was a student in Los Angeles, also was taken around with Cam. So was George Cowan, one of the few seminary trained men, who had married Florence Hansen, one of the first two single girls. They had worked together in the Mazateco tribe. All of them found it so hard to keep Cam on a schedule that they had quit promising he would be in a certain place on a certain day. One suggested that he operated by a cloud in the morning and a pillar of fire at night.

Then in the spring of 1945 another letter came from the Peruvian minister of education. The time was "right" for Cam to come. Because of the restrictions placed on U.S. citizens during wartime, Cam had to apply to the State Department in Washington for a permit to go. While waiting for the permit, Cam heard that the globe-trotting literacy pioneer Frank Laubach was in Mexico City. In Laubach, ten years his senior, Cam found a kindred spirit. Laubach's "Each One Teach One" campaigns, using his alphabet and word picture charts had taught great numbers to read in many countries. Cam explained his psycho-phonemic method for teaching literacy and presented the challenge of the Bibleless tribes. Laubach was intrigued. Then Cam took him to meet the Mexican minister of education and arranged for a pilot project of the Laubach method.

Some time later Cam called on the commercial attaché at the U.S. Embassy, who had visited Tetelcingo. He was surprised to hear that Cam hadn't received his permit, since he had an official invitation from the Peruvian government. "Let me make a phone call," he said. When he hung up the receiver he told Cam, "Go see the Consul General. He might have good news for you."

The permission was waiting for Cam when he arrived at the Consul's office. The Consul made no explanation, but later Cam heard that an influential ultraconservative Catholic in the State Department had been sitting on his application.

Flying over the desert coastline of Peru between the Andes and the Pacific on his way to Lima, the capital of Peru, Cam thought back over the past two decades and his dreams of entering Amazonia. He remembered how he and Lynn Van Sickle had tried to persuade the Central American Mission to expand into Amazonia. When that failed he was still determined to go until Legters persuaded him that he should start in Mexico. But he had never lost the vision.

The very immensity of the area was staggering. The great

Amazon River drained an area almost as large as the continental United States, and covered large portions of six countries. Amazonia had been a graveyard for explorers and missionaries for four centuries. It would take recruits with some real gumption as well as special training and equipment to be willing to pioneer there.

Peru seemed the natural starting place. The network of rivers that veined the forests and timbered highlands could accommodate amphibious planes. From Peru they could gain invitations to neighboring countries until every tribe in Amazonia had Scripture in its own language.

Cam felt confident since Pike had been received so cordially in Peru two years before. And Moisés Sáenz, the Mexican educator, had served there as ambassador before his untimely death in 1941 and had recommended the SIL program to Peruvian educators. Yes, Peru would be the next frontier.

Cam's host, the minister of education, welcomed him as an honored guest and sent him around to local linguists, anthropologists, and educators. In his careful courteous manner, Cam asked questions, realizing that his hosts were eager to help the Indians.

Dr. José Jiménez Borja, a prominent professor at San Marcos University, and the director of Indian affairs, was assigned to orient Cam. On a large relief map in his office he pointed out various strategic locations. "Here, near the Brazilian border is our largest jungle city, Iquitos. The Amazon divides a short distance upstream into the Ucayali, fed by streams out of our southern mountains, and the Marañón, fed from streams in the north and south. Most of the jungle Indians live along these rivers and their tributaries."

He fingered an area on the upper Marañón. "The proud Aguarunas and other warlike tribes live here. Our frontier soldiers have a mutual agreement to be friends from a distance. The Campas and Piros are down here to the south. They are not so hostile."

After making his preliminary contacts with officials, Cam flew across the Andes as the guest of the Ministries of Education and Aeronautics. His plane landed on the main street of Pucallpa which served as the air strip of the booming riverfront town that lay beside the muddy Ucayali. The acting mayor of the town met the plane, introducing himself as Joe Hocking, a Plymouth Brethren missionary. Cam spent the afternoon with him discussing the possibilities of translating the Bible for the Indian tribes of Amazonia.

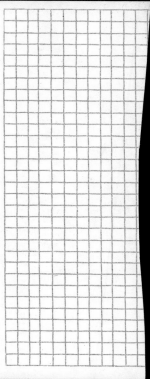

VMC

P. O. BOX 1431
528 S. 13th STREET   HARRISBURG, PA. 17105   (717) 232-6761
                                              (800) 932-0285

Then he boarded a steamer that was to take him seventeen hours downstream to a Shipibo village.

The rest of his time was spent traveling to various Indian tribes, by plane, river boat, and canoe. "The Indians are dear people though primitive," he wrote back to Mexico. "I heard of four savage tribes that kill intruders . . . but those I met were friendly and were glad to give me, through interpreters, words in their languages. I saw much more, but best of all, I saw that there is *hope*, that the job *can be done*, that it *must be done.*"

Cam was deeply impressed with the need of providing workers with medical assistance in time of emergency. One missionary told him of a harrowing twenty-five-day raft trip on a stretch he had just flown over in a few hours. "I see why missionary work has been so very difficult," he wrote in his notebook, after a severe bout with stomach pains. "A few have weathered the storms like rugged oaks, but it is evident that the average worker will need modern equipment, health aids, efficient backing and good linguistic training."

Back in Lima Cam met again with the minister of education to go over the proposed contract in which SIL would study the Indian languages and prepare primers, translate articles of law, sanitation procedures, farm manuals and some literature of high patriotic and moral value. The latter, Cam explained, would include parts of the Bible. The government, in turn, would provide entrance visas, travel discounts, office space, licenses for planes and pilots, land for a base and other facilities.

When the contract was drawn up and signed, Cam bid farewell to the officials. Then in the few hours before his plane was due to depart, he went sightseeing in the fascinating capital. As he was crossing the central plaza he noticed a crowd milling about and went over to investigate. A thin dignified man was chatting with people in the park near the entrance to the presidential palace. "Who is he?" he asked a street vendor.

"*Es el Presidente,*" the hawker replied.

Cam pushed through the crowd and bowed before President Manuel Prado y Ugarteche. "*Buenos dias, Señor Presidente,*" he said with a smile. The president extended his hand and returned the greeting. Then the crowd surged forward cutting off conversation. But it seemed to Cam providential that the last man he met on his trip was the chief administrator of the land.

"God is my heavenly joy and you are my earthly joy."

18. Elaine

In Mexico, the response to Cam's report was enthusiastic. Everyone was glad to have Cam back, and he was glad to see them all again too. But the one he wanted to see most was the tall blue-eyed young educator who had been teaching the Wycliffe children at Tetelcingo.

Immediately after Elvira's death Cam had felt that he would not remarry—certainly not for several years at least. He needed to be free for pioneering. How could he ask a wife to tolerate his long absences from home?

But unknown to him WBT/SIL members had been busy speculating on who would make the best director's wife among the more than a score of single girls in the group. At least five separate groups had concluded that the ideal one was Elaine Mielke.

The daughter of a Chicago printer, Elaine had been named at twenty Chicago's "Outstanding Young Protestant" by a newspaper and was awarded a trip around the world. Six years later she was the supervisor for special education in 300 Chicago schools. She had promised the Lord that she would support four missionaries from her salary, then discovered that full commitment required the giving of herself. This she had done, coming to SIL in '42 and going on to Mexico a year later to become the first "support" member of the linguistic group.

She was a godsend for translator parents who could not provide education for their children in the tribes. The children whom she taught in the makeshift classroom in Tetelcingo loved her.

Cam was quite attracted to Elaine and spent as much time with her as he could, after the Peru trip, before leaving for appointments in the United States. He asked her to write him at stopping off

134

points on this journey. Unsure but hopeful of his interest, she promised to do so.

While in Los Angeles Cam stopped by Dawson Trotman's office. The only one there was a businesslike young lady who introduced herself as Betty Greene, a member of a new organization called Missionary Aviation Fellowship. "The Lord has called us to provide flying service for missionaries in remote places," she explained. "We're just getting started, so the Navigators let us use their office."

"*You* are a pilot?" Cam asked in amazement.

"I was a WASP—a Women's Air-Force Service Pilot during the war."

Recovering quickly, Cam began telling of plans for Peru. "We're going to need a pilot and a plane to start. I know of a plane in Texas we can get for $2,500. Will you come and fly it for us?"

Surprised at the quick invitation, Betty Greene promised to "pray about it and talk to my associates."

Whereupon Cam quickly dashed off a letter to Pastor Clarence Erickson in Chicago. "I've got a pilot, but no plane. Do you think your church could raise $2,500 for this most needy project?"

Cam then left for Norman, Oklahoma, and SIL '45. He taught no classes that year, but talked up Peru in the daily chapel. One of his most interested listeners was Dr. Kenneth Altig, a tall angular physician from San Gabriel, California, who promised to pray about joining Wycliffe.

From Oklahoma, Cam moved on to the Canadian linguistic school at Briercrest to scout for more Peru recruits. While there he heard that Elaine's grandmother had died and that she had gone to Chicago for the funeral. His first thought was to phone her. Then he reasoned that he needed to see Pastor Erickson about the plane, so he would go on to Chicago.

He took the train to Minneapolis and there between trains called from the station. It was good to hear her voice. He was tempted to voice his love, but there wasn't much privacy in the station. He hesitated to use Spanish, since some passerby might understand, so he tried Aztec. "Temitztlasohtla meac."

"Pardon?" Elaine asked. She had picked up a smattering of the Indian language. Cam repeated the message. "Oh, thank you," she replied. She wasn't really sure what he had meant. But she thought she knew.

In Chicago Cam saw Clarence Erickson, who promised to give the money for the plane. There was also time for some sightseeing with Elaine. Then Cam asked to speak privately with her father. "I want to marry your daughter," he told the printer who was less than ten years his senior. "I've observed her for three years, and I feel that she would make me a wonderful wife. Would you consent? I haven't a thing materially to offer, but I promise to love and cherish her as long as the Lord gives me life."

Mr. Mielke was a natural tease and was greatly tempted to make Cam squirm. But when he saw Cam sitting nervously on the edge of his chair, so intense and serious, he thought better and for once played it straight. "If that's what Elaine wants, you have our consent and blessing," he replied.

On his way back to Mexico, Cam stopped again at Norman where SIL was still in session. He confided to Dawson Trotman about how God had "greatly blessed—providing us with a pilot, a plane, a doctor, and a wife for the director." Trotman was enthusiastic until Cam mentioned waiting three years before marrying Elaine. "Whatever for?" he demanded.

"That would give me time to get things going in Peru."

"Well, that just doesn't make sense. You need a wife. She could be of great assistance to you in Peru. Besides, it seems to me that anyone marrying a tremendous girl like Elaine would want to spend as many years of his life with her as he could."

After the biennial conference in Mexico City in October 1945, Cam and Elaine had a little time together before she left on a literacy campaign in the far south of Mexico. But they wrote every day. While she was away Cam followed Mexican custom and asked approval of two special friends: General Cárdenas and Hazael Marroquin, the Mexico representative of the American Bible Society. Both gave enthusiastic approval, feeling that Elaine had the necessary educational background and training along with the natural charm, gregariousness, and leadership ability Cam needed in a wife.

Their encouragement was all Cam needed to push up the date. "Will you marry me in March?" he wrote. Her answer came quickly:

For years I have wondered whether the Lord would ever bring across my life a companion I could love with all my heart; one whose interests were the same as mine. One who is thoughtful, understanding, loving, patient, loves children, generous, hospitable, self-sacrificing, dynamic personality, a leader, a pioneer in the Lord's work, one who practices what he preaches, a man of prayer. All of these qualities, I have found in you, Dear, so in answer to your question I can gladly say, "Yes!"

As far as a home is concerned, just to be near you will be enough. Although we probably won't be able to have a permanent home for many years, if ever, I think we shall enjoy making a temporary home wherever we are.

As far as being willing to undergo hardships, let me assure you that I came to the mission field expecting to endure hardships as a soldier of Jesus Christ and I shall still be happy to do so. It will be a happy day in March when the Preacher asks me, "Do you take W. Cameron Townsend to be your wedded husband?" and I can tell the whole world, "I Do!"

With all my love to the one I love dearly,

Elaine

In Elaine Cam had found a loving and competent partner who never questioned his leadership. She enjoyed people and was always doing things for others. She loved him and never failed to show her appreciation when he expressed his sentiment in pet names and bits of poetry. Since cherry pie was (and is) his favorite dessert, it was natural that Elaine became "My Cherry Pie." "Beloved Joy," he called her in one letter, "because you are the Joy of my life." On Valentine's Day before they were married he drew a big heart on an old napkin and wrote across it, "JOY IS MY VALENTINE." On the inside fold he penned:

> For you I pine, my Valentine,
> For you I sigh, my cherry pie.
> For you I dream, whose eyes so beam.
> For you I wait, my helpmate great.
> And now I write my angel bride,
> To say I love you, Precious Dove.

Jungle camp for the Peru recruits came before the wedding. The Waco biplane which Erickson's church had purchased for Missionary Aviation Fellowship was not yet fully equipped, so Uncle Al Johnson chartered a local bush pilot to fly the twenty-three Peru volunteers, including six single girls, into the remote jungle area. For the next three months they took survival hikes, swam, hunted, rode canoes through breathtaking rapids, learned first aid, prepared maps, built individual jungle huts without benefit

of hammer and nails and in general learned to survive and live off
the jungle. Cam stayed busy supervising and planning the activities,
which also included building palm-thatched buildings for the next
contingent of campers.

When the jungle camp ended in February 1946, Cam felt that
Elaine should continue with her literacy work in the hinterlands.
"But the wedding?" she protested. "Who'll make arrangements for
the wedding next month?"

"Well," replied Cam calmly, "after all the problems involved in
setting up jungle camp, making plans for a wedding shouldn't be
too much trouble. Please trust me to have everything tastefully
done."

"Of course," she replied. "If you plan it I know I'll be pleased
with it all."

Letters flew back and forth between Cam and Elaine, jammed
with details of their busy lives and plans for the coming ceremony,
all spiced with endearments. "Your delightful letter from Yochib
arrived today," Cam wrote on February 21. "You must bewitch those
Indians to get them to study so long at one sitting and you cover so
much ground! You'll beat Laubach's record. God bless you. You
bewitch me, too." Three days later he waxed eloquent with, "God
is my heavenly joy and you are my earthly joy. . . . Love, kisses and
hugs, bear hugs, honey kisses and eternal joyous love to the most
kissable, huggable and lovable person in the world."

General Cárdenas had already agreed to be best man, and his
wife Amalia matron of honor. They wanted the ceremony held in
their home on Lake Pátzcuaro, in the state of Michoacan, about ten
hours' drive from Mexico City. Because of space limitations they
asked that the guest list be limited to one hundred.

As the big day drew near Cam began to get a little apprehensive.
Besides the invitation list, which included many high government
officials, he had to make travel arrangements for guests from Chicago
and California to get to Lake Pátzcuaro.

"I just know I am going to forget something," he told Adele
Malmstrom, one of the twenty-three recruits for Peru who also happened to be his first wife's niece.

"What about the ring?" she asked.

"Uncle Al Johnson is bringing it," he replied. "He's also buying
my wedding suit."

"And Elaine's dress?"

"She is going to wear her sister Millie's dress. It has arrived already."

"The wedding cake?"

"The Cárdenases are having it made; it will be delivered the morning of the wedding."

"Well, I can't think of a thing you've forgotten, Uncle Cam. Don't worry now. It will all come off beautifully."

"I just hope Elaine is pleased with the arrangements I've made," he sighed. "I certainly will be glad when she gets back!"

A death in the family of General Cárdenas caused the wedding to be postponed one week, to April 4. The big day dawned bright and sunny. The Nymans had come from California, Uncle Al Johnson was there, and so were several Mielke relatives, Mexico's leading anthropologist Dr. Manuel Gamio, six generals, and other prominent Mexicans. The orchestra played. Amanda Marroquin sang "The Love of God" in Spanish. The local mayor presided.

As Elaine walked toward him, Cam thought, "She is wonderful!" The short ceremony was soon over and they were *Señor* and *Señora* William Cameron Townsend. The reception seemed a blur of picture-posing and hand-shaking. Finally it was over and the bridal couple started toward the door.

"Oh no!" Cam blurted out, consternation on his face. "I know what it was I forgot!"

"What was it?" everyone wanted to know.

"It doesn't matter, dear," Elaine commented. "Whatever it was I didn't even notice."

"But—but," Cam stammered, "I forgot to get a place for us to spend our wedding night!"

After some good-natured teasing, Uncle Al came to the rescue by offering his room at the nearby Don Vasco Hotel.

Then Cam and Elaine left, arm in arm, filled with anticipation of the new life they were beginning together.

"We'll donate the gas tanks to the Peruvian Air Force."

19. Faith on a Shoestring

Cam and Elaine enjoyed only two brief days of honeymoon before plunging into last-minute preparations for Peru. There were supplies to be packed, crated, and shipped. And last-minute diplomatic ruffles to be ironed out for twenty-three members of WBT/SIL who had been assigned to Peru. Not until Cam was assured that everything was in order did he and Elaine take off ahead of the others for a planned stopover in Venezuela.

In Caracas they talked with President Betancourt and a cabinet member about beginning work in their country with its twenty or more languages the following year. Both officials were encouraging.

Joining their colleagues in the new "promised land," Cam and Elaine set up headquarters for the group in the Hotel Maury in Lima. Living accommodations were fine and all seemed promising when an audit of group finances in Mexico City showed that instead of having funds for three months, they had less than one month's living expenses. Cam quickly transferred them into a large unfurnished house. He and Elaine added over $1,100 of wedding gifts to the group's bank account. A supplementary check came from the Church of the Open Door in Los Angeles for $500. The Christian & Missionary Alliance Bible Institute lent them some used mattresses which they scattered about on the floors for sleeping. Even so they were going to be on short rations.

Prayers and optimism kept them going. "God brought us this far and He will see us on," Cam assured. But the girls were nervous whenever Cam invited government officials in to eat, for they didn't have adequate table service. One official broke a pewter ware fork trying to cut the meat. After he and other guests had left, Cam laughed. "At least they know we aren't a rich bunch of Americans. They realize we need their help and cooperation."

140

April 4, 1946, Cam and Elaine Mielke were married at the home of General Cárdenas on Lake Patzcuaro. *Above:* Before the ceremony General Cárdenas takes a boutonniere for his lapel from the bride's bouquet. *Below:* Lázaro and Amalia Cárdenas were best man and matron of honor at the wedding.

Cam gives Billy, Elainadel, Joy, and Grace a piggyback ride with Elaine's help in Lima, Peru, 1953.

One way the Peruvians helped was by allowing the group to attend Spanish classes in government schools free of tuition and providing equipment and medicines. Cam was careful to inform them about everything the group was doing and planning. This kept him in government offices almost daily. The American ambassador to Peru, the Honorable Prentice Cooper, and his mother, became friends of the group. The Mexican ambassador to Peru, General Adalberto Tejeda, an old acquaintance who had traveled through Sonora with Cam and President Cárdenas, was very helpful.

Cam's main push was now toward finding a suitable base in Peru's eastern jungle for a center of operations and a jumping off point for tribal linguists. It would need to be near a large river or lake to accommodate amphibious planes which would ferry workers and supplies to other water landing sites near tribal locations.

Then friends told him about an abandoned government-owned hotel on a high bluff overlooking the Aguaytia River, which is a tributary of the Ucayali, north of Pucallpa. After getting a go-ahead from Peruvian officials, Cam made a quick trip to check it out. The location seemed ideal. It was on the main road so supplies could be trucked over the mountains from Lima. It was near the juncture of two rivers, and there were tribes in three directions. Although the unfinished building needed rewiring and carpentry repairs, Cam felt it was usable. Planes would have to land and take off under the longest suspension bridge in Peru, but that problem could be overcome, Cam felt. Perhaps an air strip could be built on an island down the river.

Returning to Lima, Cam got permission to use the abandoned building. He then sent Ralph Sandell and Sylvester Dirks to prepare the base for occupancy, while he worked on tribal assignments. He was glad to welcome Doc Altig and his wife Lucille who flew in after a stopover in Panama City to pick up a couple of old radio transmitters which Cam had arranged for. "One for the new jungle base and one for Lima," Cam said. "The Lord provides."

He took Altig downtown to the Ministry of Health that afternoon and obtained a medical license. The only stipulation was that the first Wycliffe medic must restrict his practice to the back country. "But first," Cam told the new doctor, "you're needed at the new base to do a little rewiring and patch up a generator. And while there, you can set up one of the radio transmitters."

Altig protested that his experience with wiring and motors was limited. "You can do it," Cam assured him. "Later on the Lord will give us some real electricians."

The linguists were anxious to get into tribes and begin work. Gloria Gray and Olive Shell were assigned to the Cashibos near Aguaytia, Esther Matteson and Irene McGinnis to the Piros in the south, Ellen Ross and Lulu Reber to the primitive Machiguengas, Titus and Florence Nickel to the fierce Aguarunas along the Marañón River in the north.

The Nazarene Mission had an outpost among the Aguarunas, but the language barrier limited their outreach. "Our pioneer, Roger Wynans, lost his wife out there," a Nazarene warned the Nickels. "It's a rugged two-week trip overland and by canoe." But the Nickels were not to be discouraged, even though they had funds for only four weeks' rations.

"We've got to get an amphibious plane," Cam told them. "But go ahead overland if you feel this is what the Lord wants you to do."

He was still hoping for a plane and pilot from Missionary Aviation Fellowship when a young Army Air Force lieutenant called at the house. Larry Montgomery, a pilot, had heard about the work, and he knew of an old surplus amphibious double-winged Grumman "Duck" plane. "The Navy is selling it for $3,500. It needs some repairs, but that's a fantastic price. I'd say it has a lot of life left."

"We're interested. Would you be interested in flying it for us?"

"W-w-well, I have a few months left in the service," Montgomery stammered. "But my wife and I will certainly pray about it."

Cam sent a letter to MAF describing the plane and how badly they needed it. The reply was disappointing. MAF doubted the wisdom of purchasing such a powerful plane. But Cam refused to close the door. "If the Lord wants us to have that plane, then He'll provide the funds for its purchase!"

With growing concern for the Nickels and others who had left for tribes, Cam talked to Ambassador Cooper. The diplomat offered to help negotiate the purchase of the plane.

Next Cam sent three cables to friends in Philadelphia, Chicago, and Santa Ana, California, saying, "Plane available for $3,500 if we act immediately." To the first two messages he added, "Please pray." On the third to Herbert Rankin, a merchant friend in Santa Ana who had encouraged his dream of missionary aviation nearly twenty years before, he left off the prayer request.

Responses were quick in coming. The first two promised prayer and nothing else. Rankin replied, "Your cable came as an answer to prayer for . . . I was having to decide how to distribute some contributions. I'll give $3,000."

The next day an invitation came for Cam and Elaine to attend a cocktail party honoring Minister of Education Luis Valcarcel. Elaine worried that their missionary friends might "misunderstand" their going. But Cam felt it was very important for them to be at the function. "We'll just politely decline alcoholic drinks."

At the party Cam sat next to the head of the antileprosy division of the Ministry of Health that maintained a leprosarium in the jungle. When the official heard about their plans and need for a plane, he said, "My department will help you. We'll give one-fourth of the cost of the plane."

Thrilled and grateful, Cam passed the good news on to Dr. Valcarcel. "Well, then," he responded, "the Ministry of Education will pay one-fourth also."

"Great," Cam declared in exuberance. "Now we'll all donate the gas tanks to the Peruvian Air Force. They're interested in the jungle Indians also."

Cam conveyed all this to the MAF people in California who now agreed that the Lord must want the linguists to have that plane. The president of MAF wrote that their pilot Betty Greene would be coming immediately.

Cam planned a program for the plane's christening which was set for Saturday, July 27, just two weeks after his fiftieth birthday. Lt. Montgomery flew the plane for a demonstration. Ambassador Cooper gave a speech delivering the plane to Peru. The Peruvian minister of health spoke eloquently about the help the U.S. had given through various service institutions and accepted the plane. The American ambassador's mother and the minister of education's daughter christened the plane. Then Cam spoke briefly about how the craft would be called the *Amauta*, an Inca word meaning "a wise man at the service of the people." He ended by quoting Jesus: "I have not come to be served, but to serve."

That afternoon the ceremony was front page news in Lima. Now it was urgent to get the repairs done, for there were eleven pioneers out in the jungle needing flight services. As yet there had been no word from the Nickels in Aguaruna land.

Meanwhile Elaine had been lecturing on literacy methods, especially the psycho-phonemic system, at San Marcos University in

Lima. She had been well received and the Peruvian-American Committee on Cultural Cooperation asked her to train literacy teachers at a seminar to be held close to Lake Titicaca near the Bolivian border. This would entail a trip to Puno, high in the Andes, but the opportunity couldn't be missed. She worked with a Peruvian professor to prepare a basic primer in the Aymara language. Although both she and Cam dreaded the separation, they both knew that her experience in Chicago's public schools, her literacy campaigns in Mexico and her knowledge of his psycho-phonemic method made her uniquely qualified to share her experience and knowledge with the fifty-six government teachers who were about to set up literacy campaigns among the Aymara and Quechua Indians. And they would write.

Before Elaine left Lima, they suspected she was pregnant and while she was gone Cam worried about how she was faring in the high altitudes. He had gone to Aguaytia to work with Dr. Altig on the campsite. Although he would have liked to be back in the capital before she arrived, duty held him there.

Doc Altig and the others were trying to convince him that Aguaytia was not the most desirable location. Cam felt they could "make do" with the situation as it was, even though the facilities were terribly crowded. But the most serious problem facing them was the river. A pilot might have difficulty landing and taking off under the suspension bridge. Then, too, the currents were quite strong, and the Indians told them the river sometimes flooded in rainy season.

"It would be nice if we could have a location that was nearer the center of the tribal areas," Cam agreed, "but we just can't afford to move elsewhere. Maybe we could build a landing strip on that island downstream. Let's get a canoe and paddle over."

Although Altig was far from enthusiastic about it, he went along. But on the way to the island, their canoe hit a submerged log and split open, dumping them into the water. They were only about fifty feet from shore, but the water was too dangerous for swimming through the swift current. Clinging to the sides of their disabled craft, they were swept rapidly downstream.

Fortunately two Indians saw them, paddled their dugout out, and rescued the two drenched men. When they finally stepped on dry land, Cam agreed that a new base site would be required. But it would take time.

"Well! I'm a father. And I wasn't there."

20. Dedication in an Embassy

Cam stayed on at the jungle base to work on the "Nestle Inn"—a hut he hoped would give him and Elaine the privacy they had lacked since their marriage. In his thinking, it would be four years at least before they could leave Aguaytia for another jungle base.

But one night Joe Hocking, whom Cam had met at the central river town of Pucallpa on his 1945 trip, stopped by. Hocking dreamed of recording the gospel in tribal languages so that Indians could hear the Good News in their own tongues even before the written Word became available to them. He, like Cam, was a visionary, and the two enjoyed swapping ideas for the future.

When Hocking learned of the disadvantages of Aguaytia, he suggested a site near Pucallpa. "There's some land you could get on high ground overlooking Lake Yarinacocha for a reasonable price."

"We don't have the funds," Cam responded, "but maybe I should go look at it when the plane is fixed. I should have the information just in case someone in the States wants to make a special investment for the Lord."

Cam worked a few days longer after Hocking left, then left the "Inn" still unfinished to hitchhike across the high mountains to Lima. There was a weekly lecture series he had promised the University of San Marcos. With Cam, duty—especially to foreign governments and educators—always took precedence over personal concerns.

It was so good to be with Elaine again. She had finished her literacy teaching and had gotten back to Lima before him. She was indeed pregnant and the baby was due in January. But there still had been no word from the Nickels who had been isolated in the jungle for almost five months. The *Amauta* Duck plane, unfortunately, was still not ready for a flight over the Andes.

When Cam went to the university to lecture on American Indian languages, he was welcomed by a dark-haired secretary with an unusual air of competence and authority. He thanked her courteously. Soon they were old friends. Rosita Corpancho had been born and raised in the jungle and had a lively interest in the welfare of the jungle tribes. In briefing her on WBT/SIL's plans for the future, Cam candidly admitted the group had a few problems. When she offered to help, he expressed his appreciation for "any bit of assistance you can give."

Not long afterwards Cam received a call from an important Lima businessman. "My friend Rosita Corpancho told me about your good work among the Indians," he said. "She gave such glowing reports I felt I had to call and offer my help."

"Rosita," muttered Cam, straining to place the name. "Rosita Corpancho. Oh yes! The secretary for the linguistic department at the university!"

The calls kept coming. From businessmen, newspapermen and politicians. They all said, "Rosita thinks we should help you."

Cam discovered that the unassuming secretary was a member of one of Lima's outstanding families, and her brother was an important member of Congress. Rosita's position in the social elite of the city gave her entree into important government and diplomatic circles. Thus began a friendship that was to prove extremely helpful to the Institute and the work among the Indians over the years.

At the time Cam needed encouragement. Repairs on the plane were subject to faith-testing delays. Betty Greene was frustrated at having come all the way to Peru and not being able to fly.

The plane was finally ready in December. Cam felt obligated to make a flight into the interior to allocate two teams. Although Elaine was eight months pregnant, the doctor assured him that he could get back before the baby's birth.

Cam, Betty, and translator Sylvester Dirks took off in the single engine *Amauta* on December 20, 1946, to fly across the high mountains. They climbed to a height of 17,000 feet and then dropped to the foothill town of San Ramón, gateway to Amazonia at that point. Here they were weathered in until Christmas Day when the clouds cleared, permitting them to fly to Pucallpa on the Ucayali where ships docked over 3,000 miles from the mouth of the Amazon.

Betty landed smoothly on the local air strip—the main street of the town. Joe Hocking pushed a wheelbarrow through the crowd for their luggage and took them to his house where his wife waited with refreshments. Without realizing it, they were celebrating an event of historic significance: Betty had been the first woman to pilot a plane across the Andes.

After greeting them, Joe handed Cam a rumpled note scrawled in crude Spanish by an Indian chief.

Dear Mr. Hocking: We have made a school house. We want to follow your commandments. Come and teach us. I will not go anyplace until you answer me. We await you. Come.

"I have too much to do here. I can't help him, but maybe your people can. And in his own language," Joe explained.

"That's why we're in Peru. We'll help him. Now let's go see that base site."

They struck out along a trail that led through timbered lowland past Indian huts. "Shipibo Indians," Joe said. "They're all around here. You could build a road along here from Pucallpa."

After about five miles they reached the high bank above Lake Yarina and looked out at the half-moon of water around an island. A long straight stretch of lake could handle float planes, and there was space to build a landing strip.

They tramped along the lakeshore, disturbing four- and five-foot iguana lizards that slithered off into the high weeds. Monkeys chattered in the trees above them. "Gators are in the lake," Joe casually said. "But they won't harm you, and there's an occasional boa."

Cam was impressed. "This may be what we need, though I would prefer not to be this close to civilization for the sake of the Indians whom our folks will be bringing in for language study. How many acres could we get here, Joe?"

"Well, there are several parcels. You could buy ten or fifteen acres on the lakefront now and later get more adjoining as the need arose."

"Good! Then we'd have enough room for individual homes, a clinic, a sawmill, a printing plant, a radio tower, and hangars at the air strip."

"You really like to plan big," Joe commented.

"Let's claim this land for God, and the Indians," Cam responded.

They knelt under a giant ceiba tree. "Lord, you know we don't have the money to buy this place," Cam prayed. "But You can provide it. We ask You to sanctify this land, that it might be set aside for Your glory."

The next day Betty landed the *Amauta* on the lake, then flew back to Pucallpa. Cam radioed Elaine from the Peruvian Air Force's station. "Everything's fine," she reported. "You'll be happy to know that Titus and Florence Nickel just arrived from Aguaruna land. Safe and sound and full of great stories. Took them twenty-one days of nearly impossible traveling to get out, but they did it."

"Well praise the Lord," Cam exclaimed. "I can hardly wait to hear their report."

Cam, Dirks, and Betty took off the following day for Atalaya, a small town at the junction of the Urubamba and Tambo Rivers where Dirks intended to start a survey among the Campa Indians. The first to welcome them on landing was a short, stocky, Franciscan missionary priest. Padre Pascual Alegre cordially invited them to tea.

Dirks gave the cheerful missionary monk a book of D. L. Moody's sermons in Spanish. "Thank you very much," the little Franciscan said. "I'll preach these." And he did.

When they returned to the military post on the 28th, the commanding officer met them grinning. "You've had a radio message, *Señor*," he told Cam. Cam looked around at the other soldiers whose smiles indicated they were also in on the secret.

"Congratulations, Mr. Townsend. You are a father," the C.O. announced ceremoniously. "Your daughter was born yesterday, December 27. Both she and your wife are doing fine."

"But—but—it isn't time," Cam stammered. "Well! I'm a father. And I wasn't there. A daughter! They're both fine, you say? I have to get back to Lima. Where's Betty? I have to go meet my daughter!"

Betty flew him back to Pucallpa where he caught a commercial flight across the Andes. In Lima, he went directly to the hospital to see his wife and daughter. When he marveled that she was so tiny, Elaine laughed. "Babies that are so impatient that they can't wait usually are small. She weighs only six-and-a-quarter pounds. But she's perfectly normal. As a matter of fact, I think she's just perfect."

They named her Grace Lillie—Grace for "God's unmerited favor" and for Grace Fuller of the Old Fashioned Revival Hour radio broadcast, and Lillie for her Grandmother Mielke. Cam thought she looked very much like his own mother.

Announcements went to friends at home and in Lima. Many of the Peruvians expected to be invited to a christening, always a big event in Lima. As five weeks passed and no ceremony was held, the Townsends started getting questions from their Peruvian friends.

"Oh, we'll wait until she is old enough to make her own decision," Cam told them. "When she accepts the Lord as her Savior, then she'll be baptized."

"But if she dies," a distraught official's wife worried, "she'll go to limbo. You should have a ceremony now."

When Cam and Elaine realized the problem, they began to think of having a dedication service. But they realized that their friends in officialdom would be reluctant to attend a service in a Protestant church. Cam was telling the Mexican ambassador and his wife about his problem one day. "Have the ceremony for your baby in our embassy," Ambassador Tejeda responded. Cam gratefully accepted the offer. Invitations were sent to about thirty people, including the Peruvian ministers of education and defense and their wives and the American ambassador and his mother.

The day before the ceremony, the first secretary from the Mexican embassy called Cam. "We've been discussing your ceremony," he said. "It's against Mexican law to have a religious service in one of our government buildings. You must not bring a clergyman."

Cam agreed. "But can I say a few words?" he asked, "And perhaps a friend who isn't a clergyman could read selections from the Bible?"

"Surely!" the diplomat replied. "Just so we don't have clergy."

At the last moment it was decided to include Bob and Lois Schneider's infant son, Jonathan, in the ceremony. John Twentyman, an unordained representative of the Bible Society, read carefully selected Bible verses. Cam told how proud the group was that Grace and Jonathan were Peruvians. They were links that bound the two countries together. He then talked about how the love of Christ motivated young pioneers to go to the jungle to teach the Indians to read and write and give them the Bible in their own language.

He looked at Ambassador Tejeda who had been listening intently. "Could we have a minute of silent prayer for little Grace and Jonathan and for our workers in the jungle?"

The Mexican dignitary nodded.

Everyone went away happy. Now no one would worry about the

babies going to limbo, and they were also now better informed about what the translators were trying to do.

Two days later on February 16, 1947, Cam and Elaine and baby Grace boarded a Panagra plane to begin the trip to Mexico. They would stop off at jungle camp in Chiapas, check on operations in Mexico, move on to the summer SIL campuses and attend the group's biennial conference. At the same time Cam would be recruiting, trying to raise interest in an aviation program for Peru, and if he "happened" to find someone willing to make a large investment for the Lord, he could tell them about the property at Lake Yarina.

He left Bob Schneider in charge of government relations in Lima, and Doc Altig in command at the jungle base at Aguaytia, where they were struggling along in spite of the many difficulties.

The week in jungle camp in Mexico was busy. Everyone was properly impressed with little Gracie. Cam and Elaine told Peru stories around the campfire each night, fanning interest among the campers.

When it was time to leave for Mexico City, Cam and Elaine climbed into the back seat of the tiny commercial Piper Super Cruiser in back of the bush pilot. Their scanty baggage was on a shelf behind. Gracie lay on a pile of fresh diapers in a long Mexican cane basket across Elaine and Cam's laps.

The jungle campers stood waving as the plane ran about two-thirds of the way down the 2,000-foot strip and then lifted off. They had started to turn away when the inexperienced pilot turned the plane downwind through a gap in the tree line, missing the treetops by inches. Suddenly—because it still didn't have sufficient speed— the plane lost altitude and crashed.

*"We are in aviation (by being in the jungle)
whether we like it or not."*

21. Jungle Aviation and Radio Service

The first to reach the crash scene was a Tzeltal Indian who had been working nearby. The plane had hit one side of a ravine, with the force of the impact causing it to bounce head-on against the other bank. Gasoline was streaming from the engine, drenching the passengers and baggage, but not a drop fell in the baby's eyes.

Although Cam's left leg was broken and blood was streaming from his left hip, he was clear-headed enough to hand the baby out to the Indian. "Take her away," he gasped in Spanish, fearing the plane might catch on fire. "Away, away from the plane." The Indian quickly moved the baby to safety.

Elaine's left ankle had been pulled out of its socket and was dangling by the flesh. Somehow, despite their injuries, they managed to crawl painfully out of the crumpled cabin. The pilot didn't move. His head was jammed against the instrument board, but he was still alive.

By this time the first jungle campers had reached the site. They started pulling out the unconscious pilot as Dr. Paul Culley, the camp medic, went to work on Elaine. He managed to stop the bleeding and placed her on a stretcher made from an old army blanket fastened over poles.

Cam was fully alert though in great pain. "Get your movie camera," he called to young Dale Kietzman, "and take pictures before they move us. People need to see how badly we need safe aviation for pioneering in the jungle." Kietzman got the pictures.

As soon as Cárdenas heard of the accident, he requested the governor of the state to fly in a doctor, an aide, and medical supplies. Harold Goodall made rustic crutches for Cam from two saplings. But it was twelve days before the doctor felt Cam and

Elaine could be flown out to a hospital in Mexico City where a metal plate was inserted in Cam's leg and Elaine's ankle was operated on. Both were fitted with casts. It was six months before Elaine could walk without crutches. During much of this time Grace was cared for by various Wycliffe members.

The confinement gave Cam time to think more about an aviation department, although he had no funds to count on and could only plan by faith. He was determined that the young translators must have the best pilots and equipment to provide transportation to and from tribes where there was no other way of going.

He was grateful for the fledgling MAF which had just begun services for missionaries in Mexico. But he questioned whether they could meet the special needs of WBT/SIL in Peru. Betty Greene, MAF's one pilot there, was as brave and capable as they came, but she could not handle the job alone. "We should have our own flying program," he told Elaine. "Larry Montgomery is finishing his tour of duty for Uncle Sam. We can start with him."

Cam was confident that God would have someone to spearhead the aviation program that was still only a dream in his mind. If not Larry, then there would be someone else. Only twelve years had passed since the first linguistic investigators entered Mexico in 1935, and the Lord had since provided key lieutenants for the other aspects of the ongoing program.

Heart patient Will Nyman, for instance, still going strong despite medical predictions, ran the home office efficiently, keeping administrative costs to less than five percent. Ken Pike, who now had his doctorate, was heading up the academic arm, SIL. Gene Nida was pushing ahead as Pike's associate. Dick Pittman had been elected Mexico branch director with George Cowan as assistant. Otis Leal, another of Cam's Mexico "Timothys" had been formally elected candidate secretary. Certainly there were disagreements— that was to be expected. But they worked together as a team.

Besides these, there were many others showing leadership potential. For many years Cam had prayed for each member by name every day. Now there were so many involved in the total program that Cam no longer knew everyone personally. He was aware, too, that the greater numbers had resulted in new demands: a residence home for the children whose parents were out with tribes; a translation center in Mexico where translators could come apart from village distractions and work intensively with informants; literacy campaigns to produce more readers for the translations; and no less essential, an enlarged jungle base in Peru and the aviation program which he considered essential. This would be only taking care of the current situation. With the hundreds of new recruits and the opening of new fields which he anticipated, other challenges would arise.

As if all this were not enough to occupy his mind, Cam felt that he owed it to the world to finish the biography of Lázaro Cárdenas, whom he considered one of the most remarkable men of the century.

Because he felt constrained to work on the book, and because Elaine was still having difficulty walking, Cam accepted an invitation from Uncle Al Johnson to stay at his castle in Death Valley.

Some members questioned the wisdom of taking time off to write the biography of a radical statesman at a time when demands from expansion were so great. Furthermore, they felt Cam might become involved in political matters, which was against WBT/SIL policy. Cam, however, felt it his duty to inform the American people about Mexico's remarkable friend of the common man. While drafting the biography, he sandwiched in a trilogy of articles for the then influential *Sunday School Times* (January 24, 31, Feb. 7, 1948). In them he pointed out how WBT/SIL was overcoming three barriers to reach Bibleless tribes:

1. The barrier of a closed door to evangelical missionaries. He cited Robert Morrison, who had translated the Bible into China's major dialect when Chinese law forbade foreigners even learning the language. He started as an interpreter for the East India Company and later for the English ambassador.

2. The barrier of learning unwritten languages. Wycliffe members, he noted, are trained linguistically at SIL to hear difficult sounds, and to find the logic and symmetry of complex languages.

3. The barrier of geographical inaccessibility. This, he said, could be overcome by aviation.

After making good headway in the writing projects, Cam took Elaine and Grace to Santa Ana. There an appendicitis attack put him in the hospital for immediate surgery. This meant more time recuperating, when Cam was anxious to get back to Peru. But if he couldn't leave the country for a few weeks, he could recruit.

Dawson Trotman put him in touch with one of his top Navigators, Don Burns, who told Cam of his desire to attend the University of San Marcos in Lima and live Christ before the students. Cam sold Burns and his wife Nadine on the idea of going to Peru as Wycliffe members with Don attending the university and both serving as houseparents for the group in Lima.

While visiting with Nyman in the Glendale office, Cam took a call from Ernie Rich in nearby Downey where Cam had lived as a boy. "I've had four years of college and three of Bible college," the inquirer said. "My mission board wants me to get three years of seminary before going to the field."

"What's your skill?" Cam asked.

"It isn't preaching. I've been a mechanic for Standard Oil. I like working with tools and my hands."

"The Lord must have wanted you to call," Cam said. "Can you come down here tomorrow?"

Rich could and did. Cam asked him a few quick questions, then suggested he get some training in aviation mechanics.

Encouraged, Rich said he could get a license in a year.

"Fine. When can you start? Oh, by the way, you and your wife will need a summer at one of our linguistic schools."

Rich reported back to his wife, "That Townsend is just like a vacuum cleaner. He sucks you right in."

About this time disturbing reports began coming from Peru. Some members were complaining about operating procedures, and funds were scarce. Rations were so short at the base at Aguaytia that they were almost counting out the peas on each plate. Then there had been two near tragedies with translators. Ralph Sandell and Harold Goodall had almost drowned in a river rapids. And Harriet and Dale Kietzman were taking a raft down a swift stream when they had slammed into a log and were dumped into the river with their baby. Other translators were having to wait for days and weeks for the one plane.

As soon as they could, the Townsends headed south. Cam left Elaine and Grace in Mexico since Elaine was expecting again and the trip to Peru would be too much for her.

From Lima he went directly to the base at Aguaytia. "We must move to a new base," Doc Altig and Larry Montgomery insisted. "We've tried, Uncle Cam. We've given it all we can. This is just an impossible situation."

Cam agreed and left immediately for Pucallpa. He and Joe Hocking went to see the man who owned the thirty-five-acre tract bordering Lake Yarina. Cam settled on thirteen acres for $375.

Cam then turned his attention back to the aviation challenge. Larry Montgomery was flying the old Duck four and five days in a row. That was too heavy a schedule even under ideal conditions, which they certainly didn't have in the tropical rain forest.

Betty Greene could only help part-time, since MAF asked her to fly their plane for other missions in Peru, too. Also, they did not agree with one of Cam's basic principles, flying for the Peruvian government. Cam felt that they should seek opportunities to serve the government. To him, serving was a privilege, since service was the major means by which political barriers were overcome.

Cam was now even more convinced that WBT/SIL must have its own aviation program with a fleet of planes, hangar facilities, and pilots and mechanics to ensure regular, dependable service.

Meeting in Santa Ana without Cam, however, the board didn't see it his way. They knew they were lacking in the know-how for running an aviation program, whereas MAF had technical experts. WBT/SIL was also walking a tightrope financially. There was no money whatsoever to buy even the first airplane.

When Cam learned the board had declined to act, he began writing letters to everyone he thought might help change their minds. In a letter to Evelyn Pike, he said:

We are in aviation (by being in the jungle) whether we like it or not. The thing to do is to look to God to enable us to handle it in the most efficient way possible. This means a department manned by the most capable and consecrated men possible and concentrating on our Amazonian problem rather than on a lot of other fields as well, as is the case of MAF's vision.

I believe God can and will raise up a technical aviation secretary for us who will be just as outstanding [in his department] as Ken [Pike] and Gene [Nida] are in theirs.

Between writing letters Cam tried to build the morale and strengthen the faith of his young colleagues now attempting the seemingly impossible. Living in primitive tribes, learning the languages and customs, some were even beginning to translate Bible passages. "I wish I could do what you're doing," he said sincerely. "But God has called me to be your leader. Please trust me as I try to follow Him."

He had been back in Peru for only a few weeks, but he needed to raise funds for the new base as well as more support for the

Peru pioneers who were living on a shoestring that kept breaking. More recruits were needed, and there was the Cárdenas biography to finish, and he had to convince the board that they must have an aviation program. So he flew back to Mexico and Elaine and Gracie.

In the Cárdenas's home on beautiful Lake Pátzcuaro where they had been married only two years before, he polished his book for publication.

In the concluding chapter, Cam revealed his concern for new U.S. initiatives toward its smaller Latin neighbors. He called for:

—A counterpart of the Marshall Plan for Latin America with Cárdenas as chairman.

—Appointment of athletic attachés at U.S. embassies in Latin America. "People in the habit of playing together are more apt to work together."

—Increasing cultural exchange.

—Tourist offices in U.S. embassies.

—A New America, Amerinova, "free from prejudice, exploitation, imperialism."

—Acceptance of the principle championed by Cárdenas of nonintervention in a neighbor's affairs.

Then in the final paragraph Cam called for Amerinova to "consider the record of this Mexican democrat":

He ruled without shedding blood. He made no political prisoners. He welcomed home all political exiles. He opened the doors of Mexico to political refugees from other lands. He gave liberty of expression to the press. He restored liberty of worship. He took the government to the people. He exalted the dignity of the common man. He combatted vice, ignorance, selfishness and prejudice. He sought the welfare of the Indians. He respected other nations and secured their respect for his own. He worked for peace and for a western hemisphere united as "one great spiritual fatherland." This he did and then retired to work, fight and work again in obscurity that Mexico might be democratic. *

With the manuscript in the mail to a publisher, Cam turned his mind to rethinking policies for future advances. Against the background of problems in Peru, he wrote to the Wycliffe workers:

---

* *Lázaro Cárdenas, Mexican Democrat* (Ann Arbor, Mich.: George Wahr Pub. Co., 1952), pp. 370 ff.

The first five years in a new field are very critical. In critical situations democracies are accustomed to give extraordinary authority to the leaders they have chosen. In the future we will have to give the man who leads a new advance full authority until his teammates are in a position to exercise their democratic privileges wisely. And of course if the leader makes bad mistakes, the board in California can step in and either correct or appoint a new man.

It will still be a team effort. Like a well-trained football team, the quarterback calls the signals, but the plays have to be carefully and enthusiastically carried out by the team if they are to be successful. Every team must have a quarterback. It's not that he's infallible, but simply that he does his best and everyone follows without a moment's hesitation.

The spelling out of Cam's "advance" policies was not premature. Pike was now making arrangements for a third SIL training school, this one in Australia where aboriginal tribes needed linguists. (Pike had turned down an invitation to teach linguistics at Yengching University in China because of his commitment to WBT/SIL.) Contact had been made with New Guinea where numerous languages awaited translation. Cam sensed that the vast Pacific area would soon be opening to Bible translation and he wanted WBT/SIL to be ready.

Their "Mexican" daughter was born May 5, 1948. Cam was pleased that she chose to arrive on a Mexican patriotic holiday. They named her Joy, Cam's pet name for Elaine and the name of their missionary recording friend Joy Ridderhof, and Amalia, in honor of Señora Cárdenas. They dedicated her as they had Grace with the ceremony observed at a hotel in Mexico with many Mexican friends present.

Coming after news that Uncle Al Johnson had died, the financial statement for June reported less than $10,000 total gifts for all 160 WBT/SIL members, with less than $2,000 for Peru. There was understandable questioning by some members of Cam's plans for an aviation program and advance into the Pacific.

Cam refused to be discouraged. He kept writing letters. He wrote to every evangelical leader he knew in the U.S. and some he knew only through third parties. He did not mention the low receipts nor did he solicit directly. He emphasized the "open doors," the biblical injunction to take the gospel to all nations, and the necessity of aviation and radio for reaching the remote tribes.

The replies were mixed. One said he had bought another Christian radio station and was under a "heavy load." Another thanked him for "acquainting me with the particular needs of Wycliffe" but "could not" make commitments.

J. D. Hall, an executive at Moody Bible Institute was the most encouraging. Hall had visited the first Camp Wycliffe and had been an "admirer" ever since. He persuaded the missionary committee of Moody Church to send a donation and talked to Henry Coleman Crowell, vice president of the Institute. Crowell, son of the founder of Quaker Oats, thought WBT/SIL might receive some surplus government equipment which Moody had secured.

At the board meeting in the States, five of the seven members present did not readily approve Cam's plea to begin "our own aviation and radio program in Peru." Cam, Nyman and Pittman voted in favor; Pike and Nida said no. Then Pike consented to go along *if* $40,000 came in by the next biennial conference in 1949. Cam was certain it would.

Traveling on to Chicago, Cam spoke to the students at Moody Bible Institute, interviewed young mission majors, and talked missionary strategy with President William Culbertson and a few faculty members.

J. D. Hall had already arranged for him to meet Henry Coleman Crowell. Crowell was enthralled with Cam's report and promised that any war surplus equipment the Institute couldn't use would be set aside for Peru. He also accepted Cam's invitation to accompany Paul Robinson, head of the Institute's missionary technical department, on a visit to Peru.

After holding a rally to arouse interest in the aviation program, Cam drove his family back to southern California where he kept speaking engagements and met with a JAARS (Jungle Aviation and Radio Service) committee that had been formed as a subsidiary of WBT/SIL. A member of the committee, San Diego grocer Earl Miller, donated a small plane. It was sold and the money put toward the purchase of a four-passenger amphibious Aeronca to be delivered in the spring.

Jim Price, one of the men who had volunteered to help fly the Aeronca to Peru, mentioned to Cam that he was also a carpenter. Cam invited him to stay awhile in Peru. "You can help us build the new base."

"Well, my wife and I aren't members yet," Price noted, "but we plan to attend SIL next summer."

"Good. Then you're planning on joining."

"We hope to. If your group will accept members of the Assemblies of God."

Cam was quite aware that WBT/SIL had no Assemblies members at the time. Still he did not hesitate in promising, "We are nonsectarian, so of course, we'll accept you. If you can accept us and our doctrinal statement."

"How can we deny tribes the Bible while we debate minor issues."

22. Compatible vs. Incompatible

Confident that the additional pilot was on the way, Cam and his family returned to Peru after almost a year's absence. In Lima they were pleased to see Don and Nadine Burns. They were house-parents at the Lima group house, and Don was already enrolled in San Marcos University.

The short wave radio transmitters and receivers had been set up while the Townsends were away. To Cam it was confirmation of his vision to be able to talk to translators, and to hear Doc Altig prescribe for a patient three hundred miles away.

Cam was pleased that Acting Director Bob Schneider had kept up government contacts. He took Cam around to see various officials. The Air Force promised more gasoline, the Ministry of Health free medicines. Cam was in rare spirits. "They're helping us because we're helping the Indians," he exulted.

In the spring of 1949, Crowell and Robinson came from Moody. Cam met them at the Lima airport and they flew with Larry in the Duck first to the new base site at Yarinacocha, and then to a Piro village where Esther Matteson, a graduate of Moody, and two other girls were living in a thatched hut.

After Cam saw the visitors off in Lima, he commented to Don Burns and Bob Schneider, "This is the way to give people a vision of the need. Get them here to see for themselves. We're going to hear more from Crowell and Robinson."

Funds were trickling in for the new base now and an all-purpose building was going up. Cam was there building a shelter for his family which was due to increase in December. For its walls and roof Elaine sewed together mosquito cloth and canvas from five tentlike jungle hammocks to hang over a wooden frame. Doc Altig shook his head. "You'll either suffocate or the mosquitoes will eat you alive," he warned. Cam shrugged and remarked it would have to do until they could build a better house.

When it was finished, Elaine and the children came to the new base. It was the first home of their own, but just as Doc predicted it was hot and was a haven for jungle critters. Still it was better than trying to crowd into the all-purpose building where four families were already living.

Candidate secretary Otis Leal wrote that new recruits weren't coming fast enough. Cam replied that he could not understand this. Might they be rejecting some borderline candidates who with a little help might make the grade? "It's been four years now since the president of Venezuela asked us to come to his country. Without an adequate number of recruits I'm sad to confess that we might have to further postpone that advance."

It was with this concern that further advance not be slowed that Cam went to the biennial business conference in Oklahoma in September 1949. The good news was Nyman's report of a quarter-million-dollar net income for the past year, which included $41,000 designated for the aviation work, JAARS. This seemed to convince everyone that the Lord wanted them to do their own flying. And Ken and Evelyn Pike would soon be going to Australia to help missionary leaders there set up an SIL school.

The bad news for Cam was that the question of accepting Pentecostals had become a touchy subject. The subject had been discussed six or seven years before, but had been tabled. This time the issue brought an extended floor debate. The application of Jim and Anita Price which had initially provoked the controversy was forgotten as opponents talked mostly about members as "compatible" versus those who were "incompatible." Suppose they mixed people from the Assemblies of God in among Baptists, Methodists, Presbyterians. Wouldn't that cause dissension? There must be harmony among the WBT/SIL workers.

Cam countered that to reject the Prices and other applicants from the Assemblies of God would be violating the group's nonsectarian policy. "How can I go on telling governments that we're nonsectarian when we won't even accept true believers who disagree on nonessentials?"

He also argued that in rejecting candidates, the conference was keeping the tribes of Peru from receiving the Bible. Money couldn't do the job alone, nor airplanes. The tribes had to have dedicated, Bible-believing workers, and the Prices certainly were all of that.

He acknowledged that Assembly people didn't believe exactly as those at the conference did, but the differences were really minor. Certainly, he went on, Wycliffe shouldn't delay giving the Bible to people who had never heard while its members sat and debated minor issues.

Cam continued to argue and plead, even threatening to resign if the Prices were not accepted, while his colleagues sat distressed. Then the highly respected Nyman said that what really bothered the objectors was that some Pentecostals believed no one has the Holy Spirit unless he has spoken in tongues. But then he emphasized that not all Pentecostals believed that. "Why don't we define 'incompatible' as someone who believes speaking in tongues is essential for the indwelling of the Holy Spirit?" he proposed. "Then we can continue our policy of accepting candidates on the basis of compatibility versus incompatibility."

The members voted their agreement and Cam had his pilot and construction worker, with his capable wife. Then he hurried out and sent a telegram to the Prices in California.

REGRET HARDSHIPS CAUSED YOU. IF YOU CAN FORGIVE US, WE WOULD WELCOME YOU FOR PERUVIAN ASSIGNMENT. LOVINGLY, UNCLE CAM.

One other item of controversy on the agenda was the timing of a translator's New Testament. Gene Nida felt the linguist should strive first to win tribesmen to Christ and not complete his New Testament until the latter part of his missionary career. Cam, Pike, and some others disagreed. Finally Pike presented a motion calling for a completed New Testament within ten to fifteen years after the work began. This passed.

From Oklahoma Cam went on to Chicago where he was a guest at the Crowell estate on Lake Michigan. In talking to the Moody executive about equipment for new recruits and the base at Yarinacocha, he proposed a stateside organization be formed to facilitate the equipping of missionaries. It would certainly save a lot of time and trouble and money to those on the field. Crowell thought this a great idea. Eventually he got a committee together which started

Missionary Equipment Service. It has served thousands of missionaries overseas.

After speaking to the Moody students several times, Cam moved on to Dallas for recruiting at Lewis Sperry Chafer's seminary. Then it was Glendale, California, for the board meeting. There Cam jolted everyone with his announcement, "We ought to make a film. A real top-notch, professional-type movie that will demonstrate to audiences across America just what we are doing and why. It will be the next best thing to visiting the base."

"What would such a project cost?" asked Treasurer Nyman. "And do we have anyone who is qualified?"

"Mr. Crowell has recommended Irwin Moon who has done the Moody Science films," Cam said. Most of the group had seen at least one of those films, and were enthusiastic about his abilities.

"And the cost?" Nyman persisted.

"About $5,000 expense money. Moon has offered to donate his time for the two or three months it will take him to shoot the footage in Mexico and Peru if Moody would get first use of the footage."

"When could he go?"

"Right away."

There was a long silence. Five thousand dollars seemed like a fortune.

"We've never spent much for promotion," one of the board members conceded. "We could scrape up the money somehow," another agreed. "If you think we should do it, Cam, I'll go along," Nyman said. "I make the motion . . ." The motion carried.

After a brief visit with friends and relatives, Cam flew to Lima and over the Andes to Yarinacocha and home. As he walked around the base with Elaine he saw that more homes were up. With their palm-thatch roofs, the base now looked like a semi-modern Indian village. Quite a difference from the first time he had seen the patch of solid jungle with Joe Hocking, and claimed it for the Lord.

Irwin Moon arrived shortly and shot film around the base and nearby villages. Larry flew him to Aguaruna country far to the north for pictures of tribal life, and then he left for Mexico to film among the Tzeltals.

Elaine and Cam's third child who was supposed to be "Junior," but turned out to be a girl, was born December 28. They named her Elainadel (for her mother and Adele Malmstrom). Their friend Padre Alegre (or "Happy Pappy," as the WBT/SILers sometimes translated it) was a proud witness for the official registration of her birth in Pucallpa.

Cam was brimming over with happiness. Not only was he a father again, but a gift of $10,000 had come from Crowell. Three-fourths of the amount was marked for a clinic at the base, with the remaining $2,500 to be spent for a "decent dwelling" for the Townsends. Crowell had seen pictures of the tenthouse and wanted Elaine and the children out of it.

Cam was eagerly awaiting announcement of a date when Moon's film would be premiered when a letter came from Nyman saying there was no money to pay for professionals to edit and narrate the film. What did the general director want to do with the raw film?

Cam read the letter thoughtfully, then turned to Elaine. "Well, Sweetheart, it looks as if you and I are going to have to enter the motion picture business."

"We have purposefully restricted ourselves to translating the Bible."

23. Advancing Through Service

Cam and Elaine packed up their three "stairsteps" and flew to California. For the next five tedious months they worked on the film at the Moody Institute of Science Studios near Los Angeles. Moon and his associates advised as their time permitted, but the final responsibility fell on Cam.

Cam was encouraged to keep at the laborious task by reports from Ken Pike that the first SIL in Australia had enrolled thirty-nine students from eight denominations and sixteen mission boards. Pike had also visited New Guinea. "There are at least three hundred languages there waiting for Scripture," he told Cam, never dreaming there were actually over twice that many.

One day when Moon was with Cam, the scientist mentioned a Catalina "flying boat" at a nearby airport, which some executive was using for fishing expeditions.

As soon as Cam could get away he headed for the airport, taking along Crowell's son John, who was then working with the Institute of Science. The squat, two-story, twin-engine amphibian had room enough to carry two tons of freight plus passengers. Cam thought it ideal for Amazonia. He and young Crowell stood under a wing and prayed that God would give JAARS a Catalina.

The film "O, For a Thousand Tongues" was finally completed in July 1950. Radio preacher Charles Fuller recorded an introduction and Cam did the narration. Fuller premiered it at the Long Beach Auditorium for his Sunday afternoon audience. Many said it was the best missionary film produced up to that time.

Cam later showed the film to the SIL students at the University of Oklahoma, then went on to Chicago where he left Elaine and the girls with the Mielkes while he and Amos Baker went for showings in the East and Canada. Elaine premiered the film at Moody Church the same night Cam gave the first showing in Boston. Cam even had the privilege of showing the film in the main auditorium of the Department of the Interior in Washington before a distinguished group of officials from the Bureau of Indian Affairs.

He hadn't forgotten about that Catalina. At his request Larry Montgomery, home on a short furlough, located a used one in Newark, New Jersey, that he felt was a good bargain.

Armed with information about the plane Cam headed for Mexico to see his good friend, Dr. Ramón Beteta, the tennis champion who was still serving as Mexico's minister of finance. Cam wondered if Mexico might not give the plane to Peru in memory of the late educator Moisés Sáenz. "He first invited me into Mexico," Cam recalled. "Here is an opportunity for Mexico to promote international friendship and to help us help the Indians of Peru."

Beteta had been close to Moisés Sáenz and liked the idea. "Go see his brother, Aarón," he suggested. "The family and friends will want to participate. Then I'll call a meeting of key people."

Aarón Sáenz had retired from leadership in politics but was still an outstanding civic leader and industrialist. He promised his family's help. Beteta then called a meeting of Minister of Education Gual Vidal; Head of the Inter-American Indian Institute Dr. Manuel Gamio; Head of the National Indian Institute Dr. Alfonso Caso; Peruvian Ambassador to Mexico Dr. Oscar Vasquez Benevides, and Aarón Sáenz to discuss the project with Cam.

They all agreed that the work of the Summer Institute of Linguistics in Mexico was so meritorious that a grant toward an airplane for its work in Peru was highly justified. Then Beteta spoke to President Alemán about the government's participation. The president endorsed a substantial grant. This, plus the gifts from the private citizens, was enough to buy the plane.

Now only $5,000 was needed to put the plane in first-class flying shape. Then it could be ferried to Mexico for dedicatory ceremonies, and from there on to Peru. Crowell gave the amount, telling Cam, "Even if it shouldn't be of much service to you, the diplomatic good will is worth all the money."

On April 5, 1951, an impressive entourage of officials and diplomats assembled at the Mexico City Airport for dedication ceremonies. Besides President Miguel Alemán and three Mexican cabinet members, there were five ambassadors. The widow of Moisés Sáenz, stately and gracious *doña* Herlinda, christened the plane, and Aarón Sáenz thanked everyone for the honor paid his brother. The ambassador from Peru spoke in appreciation of the gift from Mexico.

All three major newspapers of Mexico City gave the ceremony front-page coverage, and there was also a television special. The Mexicans were pleased and freely talked about Cam's latest accomplishment for international good will.

Then the plane was flown to Lima for another ceremony with President Manuel Odría and other Peruvian officials.

The final lap took the "Cat," with a load of textbooks and school equipment for Spanish language schools in jungle towns, to Yarinacocha for maintenance and equipping for tribal flights. There it sat in the lake for a while because some of the members thought it too big and too expensive. Someone even dubbed it "Uncle Cam's Folly." However, Cam and Larry Montgomery finally convinced the objectors that the plane should be put into service.

There were other planes in use in Peru. One had come from Texas, a six-passenger amphibious Norseman. An Aeronca had been given by Crowell and another by missionary students at the Bible Institute of Los Angeles. There was still a need for another plane, Cam felt, one that could take off and land on extremely short runways. At the time he didn't know such a plane was available.

With four planes, the aviation program moved into high gear and the pilots had all the flying they could handle. But some months gifts for aviation totaled less than $100. Fortunately, the policy of serving everyone which Cam had continued to insist upon turned out to be the fiscal lifesaver. The gifts were supplemented with modest revenues from flying government officials, businessmen, missionaries, anthropologists, and other jungle travelers. Protestant and Catholic missionaries received a discount and WBT/SIL members flew at subsidized rates of 4½¢ a passenger mile.

Cam continued to keep the WBT/SIL family on both a Christian and nonsectarian course. When he spoke to the Peru group in the new assembly room that was used for base meetings, Sunday services, and a schoolroom, he cautioned members about "stepping out of bounds. We have purposefully restricted ourselves to translating the Bible," he said. "If we pass out tracts, hold meetings, and do other things regular missionaries do, the door could be closed in our faces. I'm all for witnessing in their mother tongue as friend to friend. But let's do it by inviting neighbors into our homes, visiting them, and building friendships."

The philosophy was easier to follow at the base than in Lima where the members attended local evangelical churches. One weekend when Cam was in the capital he attended worship services at a nearby church, where he found that Don Burns led the singing. Afterward Cam pointed out to Burns that only one Peruvian was on the platform in the church service. "Perhaps you should step down permanently," he suggested. "The Lord will give you enough to do without your taking a church job that a Peruvian should fill."

Cam also felt the evangelical churches in Lima were patterned too closely after their counterparts in the States. When the gospel singer Anton Marco, a former opera star, came to Lima, Cam suggested to Peruvian friends that they sponsor a benefit concert for the Indians in the Municipal Theatre. Over 2,000 Peruvians came, most of whom would never have entered a Protestant church. They heard Marco present a selection of classical songs, then listened attentively when he sang a hymn and told how he had become a Christian. "It just goes to show," Cam told Burns afterward, "that you can reach many people outside of church buildings on neutral ground."

Every few weeks Cam flew over the mountains from Yarinacocha on group business and to help Bob Schneider with public relations. But his trips became less frequent as he saw how well Schneider was building friendships and keeping up contacts with officials and educators.

Back at the base Cam now had a full-time secretary whom he kept busy with his prodigious correspondence. Cal Hibbard had been recruited during a previous trip to Chicago. Having a male secretary was customary for Latin American officials.

When time came for the 1951 biennial conference that followed the SIL training schools in the U.S. and Canada, Cam felt that the work in Peru was running smoothly enough for him to be away for awhile.

With total Wycliffe membership nudging three hundred, the conference voted to switch to a delegate system. Peru was voted in as a chartered branch. Cam was unanimously reelected to another five-year term as general director.

Dick Pittman had recently returned from a visit to the Philippines and reported that the country had been saved from near civil war by the new Secretary of Defense, Ramón Magsaysay. He hadn't been able to see Magsaysay, but he felt an invitation would soon be coming to begin work in the scores of languages spoken on the islands.

In his report Cam expressed disappointment that the door to Venezuela had closed "for the moment." A new government had rescinded President Betancourt's invitation. "Keep praying," he requested.

Buoyed by Dick Pittman's prognosis on the Philippines, Cam called for one hundred new recruits. He also asked for an agriculturist to come to Peru. "My garden in Tetelcingo drew the attention of President Cárdenas. He liked my idea of serving the Indians with practical projects. We need a man who will help us raise food for the base and also train Indians in scientific agriculture." Afterward a muscular recruit came up to Cam. "I'm Herb Fuqua. Just got my degree in agriculture. My wife and I are ready to go."

There was some criticism of the methods Cam had used to raise funds to buy the Catalina. Had he departed from the original principle of complete trust in God with no solicitation? "No," he replied, "I've never asked anyone to contribute to personal support. But when the Lord leads me, I'm willing to ask one government to help another. Or for a wealthy man to help buy an airplane for the people of another country."

Another matter concerned twenty acres of valuable land on the edge of Santa Ana, donated to WBT/SIL by a ranch combine. A majority of the delegates wanted to return the land and concentrate on developing a main center in Sulphur Springs, Arkansas. Cam didn't agree. "The Lord had something in mind when He led them to give us that land." But they still voted for the land to be given back.

An amendments committee proposed that the doctrinal statement calling for belief in the "divine inspiration of the Bible" be amplified to make it stronger. Cam stood to object. "I've only had three years of college and don't understand a lot of these big theological words," he said with a Will Rogers grin. "I believe we should keep it simple. If we add things, people will start quibbling. No one believes any stronger in God's Word than I do. Just to say it's inspired, as the China Inland Mission doctrinal statement has it, is good enough for me."

Nevertheless the members voted the change.

The next report was about the Bible Society. "They've declined to publish the Mixteco New Testament," Cam explained. "They say there aren't enough believers. But we want the Word not only for the believers but for the whole tribe! God has put it on the hearts of some Christian farmers in Canada to back publication. We want to continue working with the Bible Society, but when they won't publish, we'll have to go elsewhere."

After the conference the Townsends stayed on in the States to read proof on the Cárdenas biography. They spent the Christmas holidays with Elaine's family in Chicago, and kept busy speaking and showing "O, For a Thousand Tongues" in area churches. Soon after New Year's Cam received copies of *Lázaro Cárdenas: Mexican Diplomat*. He sent Pittman a copy for mailing to Ramón Magsaysay, the Philippine minister of defense, and sent review copies to magazines and newspapers. The *New York Times* called the book "significant." The *Washington Post* and the *Chicago Tribune* also praised the book. *The Saturday Review* termed it a "friend's-eye biography."

In February Cam spoke at a meeting sponsored by the Latin American Council. The main speaker was Dr. Alberto Lleras Camargo, former president of Colombia and the current head of the Organization of American States. Cam gave him a Cárdenas book, and he appeared interested in SIL's methods and goals. They agreed to keep in touch.

Driving back to the Mielkes, Cam told Elaine, "I have a feeling we'll see him again. Maybe he will get us an invitation to work among the tribes in Colombia."

Cam was glad to get back on the "firing line" at the Yarinacocha jungle base early in 1952. Here he could keep his finger on the pulse of advance in Peru. He felt that to be more important than to be close to the home office. Nyman faithfully sent him minutes of all board meetings so he could keep up. He studied them carefully and responded when he felt his opinion should be heard.

A discussion in 1952 on non-Caucasian members roused his interest. Cam immediately wrote to the board that he had been praying for years for Negro members. He recalled that a Negro doctor had once asked for information about attending SIL and had been steered to the school in Canada. The doctor had never filled out the application, possibly because of age. Now, Cam noted, the

University of Oklahoma was open to admitting Negro students.
"Our organization has never suffered from race prejudice," he
continued. "Our constitution has nothing that savors of discrimination. You won't find it in the New Testament either. Please send
along all the non-Caucasian workers you can, if they make out good
in courses."

Meanwhile Dick Pittman had finished his doctorate at the University of Pennsylvania and was in Philadelphia when a hard-to-
understand phone call came from the Philippines. He caught only
"thank you," "book," and "important for my people." When the
caller had hung up, he asked the operator who had called. "It was a
Mr. M-A-G-S-A-Y-S-A-Y," she spelled.

Pittman realized the caller had been the Philippine secretary of
defense. He quickly wrote Magsaysay thanking him for his expression of appreciation for the Cárdenas biography, and telling him
more about the work of WBT/SIL. That summer Pittman led the
newest SIL held at the University of North Dakota, where he
offered a course in Tagalog, a major Philippine language, and an
orientation to the Pacific area and Filipino culture. After the session
he and his wife Kay took a ship to the Philippines. When the boat
docked, Secretary Magsaysay's personal aide was there to meet them,
and told them that Magsaysay had just been nominated as a coalition
candidate for president.

Pittman and Magsaysay became good friends, and a contract to
bring in a translation team was soon signed. One day after the
election, President Magsaysay told Pittman, "Townsend's biography
of Cárdenas has given me a pattern for national reform."

This same year, 1952, Cam sent Don Burns to Guatemala. The
little country with over half its population composed of Indians had
been on Cam's heart since he had left twenty-two years before. He
knew there were at least a dozen tribes still without the New Testament.

Cam felt the Guatemala program was in good hands with Burns.
Since he had pulled the outgoing Scot off the church platform in
Lima, Burns had buckled down to become Cam's kind of man. He
had almost completed his doctoral degree in linguistics at San
Marcos University and some said he spoke the best Spanish of any-
one in the group.

Then an Ecuadorian diplomat in the U.S. who had heard about
the work in Peru wrote the University of Oklahoma an invitation for

SIL to "work with us." Cam wanted to go himself, but pressures in Peru were mounting. He sent Bob Schneider with careful instructions to keep the linguistic work in the foreground, and not give the impression of being ecclesiastics.

"Explain that we are anxious to find ways of serving in each country we work. That's where literacy and medical help come in. While we are evangelical in faith, we are not fighting anybody, not even the witchdoctors. If people are in need we will serve them, be they Catholic, Protestant or pagan. They in turn will serve us. All we want is an opportunity to give the Word of God to the Indians."

Schneider followed Cam's suggestions and soon obtained the contract. He found that Radio HCJB and Missionary Aviation Fellowship also worked under contracts with the government. They proposed that the Wycliffe base be located near Shell Mera where other missions were established. Cam felt this location would tie the group too closely with ecclesiastical groups. But the minister of education thought it a good idea, so Schneider and the new workers who had arrived began operations on a river a few miles from Shell Mera.

With so many new fields of service opening, new tribes being entered, and the number of recruits rising, Cam looked forward to the future with great anticipation.

"It's like Pharaoh's daughter paying Moses' mother to nurse her own baby."

24. Bilingual Schools

Evangelical educators in the U.S. were now recognizing that Cam had cut new niches in Christian service abroad. Successively, Seattle Pacific College, Wheaton College, and Biola College offered him honorary doctorates. Cam had high regard for each school, but he declined the honors. He was proud of Wycliffe members who had earned Ph.D.s but he feared that some potential recruits might believe a degree was necessary to translate the Bible. By holding no degree of any type, Cam could help refute that notion.

In Peru Wycliffe was experiencing growing pains. Translators equipped with two-way radios were now in fifteen tribes and being served by five planes, including the big Catalina which had been overhauled and modified at the Air Force arsenal in Lima. It was used to fly out supplies to central points from which the small planes ferried them to smaller rivers near the translators' stations. When costs were compared, Peru treasurer Watters found that although the Cat cost more per flying hour, its larger payload made it cheaper than any of the smaller planes. Cam's vision had been vindicated!

Esther Matteson's Piro New Testament was moving along ahead of schedule. Other workers were publishing primers and Gospels. But what good were they without readers? Cam maintained his optimistic outlook. He knew the Indians would learn to read, if they only had a chance in their own language. He invited General Juan Mendoza, the new minister of education, to dinner with the group in Lima to discuss the need.

"We've never been able to have a school system for the jungle Indians," Mendoza observed. "Most are too remote and in a few places where we've tried, the Spanish teachers don't understand their language. This language barrier is a real concern to us."

175

"An Indian understands his own language best," Cam mused. "What you need are Indian teachers. But they'd have to be trained."

General Mendoza smiled. "Townsend, the solution is bilingual government schools! Your linguists could pick out sharp young men in their villages, bring them to the base, and we could give them a training course. They could go back and teach what they learned, then come back for another course."

"That's right, General," Cam responded enthusiastically. "If you establish a training course, our linguists will help your educators train the selected tribesmen to teach. Indians will teach Indians, first in their own languages, then in Spanish. That would be a natural bridge into the national culture."

"Catholic doctrine would have to be taught," General Mendoza observed. "That's a requirement in all public schools."

"Well, we're nonsectarian Christians," Cam noted, "but we would be happy for Indian teachers to give lessons from Scripture in the tribal languages."

The General liked that idea. The proposal went through channels with gratifying speed. Afterward, President Odría invited Cam for an interview and praised the work of SIL.

With help from Rosita Corpancho, Cam lined up a *patronato* committee of important Peruvians interested in the welfare of Indians to serve as unofficial "sponsors" of SIL. One of the *patronatos'* first projects was the sponsoring of a program in the Golden Hall of Lima's Municipal Palace. With many high officials in attendance, Cam showed pictures of a trip across the jungle in the Catalina. Tribal dances and customs were demonstrated. *Patronato* members gave speeches expressing appreciation of SIL. The next day the Lima newspapers ran laudatory articles.

The minister of education appointed Dr. Martha Hildebrandt, a brilliant Peruvian of German descent and the youngest faculty member of the University of San Marcos, to direct the Indian teacher training course at Yarinacocha. Linguists in the tribes recruited prospective teachers and sent them to Yarinacocha by raft, boat and plane for the first teacher training course. Cam radioed his old friend Padre Alegre to send a Piro student from his Franciscan mission. Padre Alegre wrote Cam:

My highly esteemed friend,
You and I do not belong to the same religion, but nevertheless

*we ought to be united by the common purpose of every Christian,
which is to "love our brethren as Christ has loved us." Oh, how can
this union in love become a reality; love toward that Lord who gave
His life for all of us . . . For my part, you can be sure that whatever
I can do for others I will always do without laying down conditions,
for this is my obligation as an unworthy disciple of the one and true
Master.*

About twenty trainees were flown in for the first class. Some
didn't know how to hold a pencil. Many had never seen the
Peruvian flag. After singing the national anthem, and saluting the
flag, the school day would begin. They studied primers in their own
languages prepared by SIL linguists, Spanish, the three Rs, and
principles of teaching. At night the linguists helped the Indians with
their homework in their own tongues. The miracle of it was that
young tribesmen, whose fathers had been sworn enemies, ate, studied,
and played together.

Naturally there were questions from skeptical members. Wasn't
this going a bit too far? Wouldn't literacy classes in the tribes do
just as well? "No," Cam declared emphatically. "It's the government's responsibility to provide education for the jungle Indians
as well as its other citizens. I am very gratified that Peru recognizes
this obligation, when very few other countries of the world are doing
it for their minority language groups. We ourselves haven't the
means to provide such training. And we have a biblical precedent.
It's like Pharaoh's daughter paying Moses' mother to nurse her own
baby."

January 20, 1953, was an epochal day at Yarinacocha, because that
was the day the Townsends had a son. William (for Will Nyman)
Crowell (for Henry Coleman Crowell) Townsend weighed in at
nine and a half pounds, and his proud father was overjoyed.

The Peru branch had elected Harold Goodall director, but Cam
still carried the main responsibility for JAARS. Besides keeping on
top of maintenance and repair problems, Cam had to indoctrinate
new pilots in his policies.

The biggest hurdle for some newcomers was doing favors for
Catholic missionaries. Cam wanted mail and newspapers picked up
in Pucallpa and dropped off at Catholic mission stations. He also
sent special delicacies which Elaine made for the padres and nuns.
Some of the pilots thought this unnecessary trouble at best, and
helping the "enemy" at worst.

Merrill Piper of Park Ridge, Illinois, was one who said no. He had been told to drop off something for Padre Alegre. "Go talk to Uncle Cam about it," Larry Montgomery said when faced with the refusal. "It's his order."

Cam listened until Piper had wound down, then quoted some love passages from the Bible. When Piper still wasn't convinced, Cam said forcefully, "The newspapers and pickles must be delivered!"

Grudgingly, Piper landed at Padre Alegre's station. When he stepped ashore he looked up into a smiling face. "How about some cold lemonade?" the padre said, extending a glass.

Piper couldn't stay long, but the next time through the padre persuaded him to spend the night. After supper, they moved to the cool veranda. Curious villagers had gathered outside to see the newcomers. Padre Alegre pointed to a short-wave radio. "Like to hear something from the outside world?"

Piper dialed HCJB, the evangelical station in Ecuador. He turned up the volume and for the next hour the padre and a hundred villagers listened to a gospel message. When he returned to the base, Piper told Cam, "I've learned my lesson. If I hadn't done the favor, those people would not have heard that message."

With advances pushing ahead in three new fields, Cam kept his secretary, Cal Hibbard, busy with correspondence. Dick Pittman, heading up the advance in the Philippines, wrote that he needed travel money which hadn't been budgeted. Cam asked Nyman to take it from the "director's fund." This fund, provided mainly by the foundation established by the A. M. Johnson estate, was solely for Cam's use and discretion in financing special projects. The advance in Ecuador was also moving along, but Cam anticipated problems because of the base location. And Don Burns wrote from Guatemala that he needed Cam's help in diplomacy.

Cam responded to Burns's appeal by flying to Guatemala City, where he conferred with two cabinet members on four separate occasions. One, the minister of education, had been a student leader at Antigua during Cam's days with the Cakchiquels. Residence visas for the Wycliffe workers were cleared, and the minister promised to pay for the reprinting of Cam's old Cakchiquel primers. Cam left feeling the signals were all green, and returned to Lima where the government had loaned SIL half a block of choice residential property for a group house. The Air Force pledged 16,000 more gallons of aviation fuel.

Then news came that some Christian leaders in England had invited Ken Pike and George Cowan to conduct a linguistic training course in London. Cam's spirits leaped higher and higher. In his "Director's Letter" to the membership, he declared:

The movement to the small neglected tribes is gathering momentum every day. . . . Tribes-people are getting the opportunity to read God's Word in their own language. Seven thousand translators and supporting personnel (aviation, radio, literacy and supply) will be needed to complete the task of reaching all the tribes . . . including those behind the iron curtain. Faith knows no barriers!

Then came the storm that threatened to wipe out the entire SIL operation in Peru.

The first indication that trouble was brewing came during a teacher training course. Alarmed at Protestant growth in Peru, the Catholic hierarchy objected to what they considered "ecclesiastical activities" carried on by the linguists. Officials showed the complaints to Cam.

"These are not our members," he said. "Some are Adventists, and one is a former member who left Wycliffe and later came back to represent his church in Peru. We have no authority over what they do." The officials seemed satisfied.

A few days later the leading newspaper in Lima published an article by a jungle missionary priest saying that the linguists were Protestant missionaries in disguise. Orders went out from the hierarchy to the jungle priests and nuns to decline any lifts from the "Protestant pilots." The order sparked a wave of grumbling as Catholic missionaries returned to slow boat travel that required a week of sweat and mosquito bites instead of an hour or two in a JAARS plane.

More anti-SIL articles appeared in the newspapers. Privately, officials passed word to Cam that behind-the-scene pressures were being applied to "get rid of your organization. We know you're nonsectarian," they said, "but we'll need proof."

Cam came up with a new twist on the aviation program. He proposed that JAARS become, in effect, an adjunct of the government airline. The planes would carry commercial passengers, baggage, and mail, and would charge commercial rates, but planes and pilots would primarily serve to carry out the cultural and educational agreement between SIL and the Ministry of Education. All operations would be controlled by the Ministry of Aeronautics. The generals liked the idea and the papers were signed which solved the flight controversy.

Forced to change strategy, the attackers now charged that SIL was endangering the unity that existed between the government and the Catholic church. One critical bishop insisted that the summer school in Oklahoma was not affiliated with the university, but was in reality a Baptist institution. The university president, Dr. George Cross, quickly replied that SIL was affiliated with the university, and nonsectarian linguistic courses were being taught. A Catholic faculty member backed him up.

Cam took a week off to prepare his "one reply" to the opponents. His four-thousand-word letter to the editor of Lima's leading newspaper *El Comercio* must stand as a classic in Christian diplomacy.

He quoted endorsements and praises of SIL from numerous officials, educators, and Catholic clergy. He traced the history of SIL in Peru, with "each successive government enlarging our original agreement." He noted that SIL was cooperating with four departments of the state: education, aeronautics, health, and the army. "Our planes and radio stations are at the service of Peru," he said. "All our operations are controlled by competent government authorities from whom we have at no time tried to hide anything."

He described the faith and practice of SIL members in several incisive paragraphs, pointing out that all were true believers in Jesus Christ, but none could be an ordained minister. All had dedicated their lives to serve primitive Indian tribes.

I, your servant, do not belong to any denomination. I respect them all, however, and try to be a good neighbor to all. The Summer Institute of Linguistics, founded and directed by me, does not protest against anything and does not attack any. On the contrary, endeavoring to promote a spirit of love and brotherhood, we try to serve all. We don't call ourselves Protestants, but simply believers in Christ. . . .

Our nonsectarian attitude does not mean that we do not recognize and accept the Christian's duty of making Christianity known to the primitive peoples whose languages and customs we study. The great majority of the Indians live in fear of the witch doctors, and continue in their worship of the spirits of the forest, the whirlpools, and even in some cases, the boa constrictor. Many Indians suffer and even die because of witchcraft and their primitive beliefs, and a true believer who speaks their language cannot, and should not, show indifference to such situations. On the contrary, it is his duty to explain that God is love and that He desires to make us His children, and therefore, brethren, through faith in Jesus Christ. We do not go beyond the teachings of the Catholic Bible nor do we propagate any ritual or ecclesiastic system. . . .

If some of them [the Indians] meekly desist from accepting all the ritual and discipline of the State Church, it is expected that they will accept at least a basic Christian faith and this is the most difficult step. Because of our nonsectarian nature, we are not responsible for the teaching of rituals and ecclesiastical systems of any nature. The missionaries, whether Catholic or Protestant, are the ones to care for such. . . .

We love Peru. When we shall have completed our linguistic investigation, then we shall go, taking with us very pleasant memories and leaving behind our Base at Yarinacocha with all of its buildings, for a center of Indian education as we have said from the beginning. We shall also leave behind for the archives of the Peruvian Ministry of Education . . . and for the National Library, dictionaries, grammars, primers and articles concerning the languages of the jungle. I expect that in time these works shall come to be nothing more than souvenirs of the past because all tribes that now speak those languages will have been incorporated linguistically, and in every other sense, into the national life of this delightful land which we love as our adopted fatherland.

The conflict came to a head in early September 1953 when President Odría convened a special session of his cabinet. They voted to continue backing SIL and increase financial aid. A short time later President Odría had Cam decorated for "distinguished service" to the country.

Afterwards, a *Time* reporter who had been covering the controversy cornered Cam and asked him pointedly, "Are you people missionaries or linguists?"

Cam smiled and replied, "What would you get if you crossed a grapefruit and an orange?"

"[SIL] . . . is familiarizing the Amazon Indians with the rudiments of modern civilization and, as a result, is preparing them for gradual incorporation into the national life of the country."
—Arnold Toynbee

25. Family Fun and Practical Service

The gift from Henry Crowell to the Townsends had made possible a new residence at Yarinacocha. Elaine designed the plans and Cam hired Peruvian workmen, scrounged materials and fixtures, and planted mangos, avocados, and Brazil nut trees in the yard. Some of the WBT/SIL members living on the base helped as time and talents permitted.

When the two-and-a-half-story house was finally finished, it was large enough to accommodate the steady stream of distinguished overnight visitors who were coming to the base. Elaine welcomed government officials, military officers, anthropologists, missionaries (both Catholic and Protestant), professors, writers, and various home supporters who came to see the work. One night when they had seventeen guests, Cam and little Joy slept in a closet.

It was Cam's custom to ask a guest to read Scripture at the breakfast table, regardless of his religious affiliation or belief.

One night a week they invited members in for refreshments and socializing. The evening usually ended with Cam challenging them to keep advancing. "The greatest missionary is the Bible in the mother tongue," he would often remind them. "It never needs a furlough, is never considered a foreigner, and makes all other missionaries unnecessary."

While the Indian teacher training school was going on, the Townsends invited students and faculty in for fun and fellowship on Friday nights. Elaine served warm Kool-Aid (cold drinks hurt the Indians' poor teeth) and salty delights like popcorn. The Indians loved skill games such as darts and dropping peanuts in the bottle. They proved to have better memories than the linguists, and usually won when playing games such as "Going to Jerusalem."

Doc Altig became concerned. "Your family is liable to catch germs from the Indians," he warned Cam. "Maybe so," Cam admitted, "but we have to be with the tribespeople. That's the very purpose of our being here."

Doc grinned. "I knew you'd say that. But please be careful."

Cam had his own ideas about health and medicine. When visiting tribes he neglected to swallow the amoeba pills which Doc insisted visitors take. His cure-all for whatever ailed the children was hot lemonade with salt. For himself he prescribed raw egg in coffee for a quick boost of energy.

He frequently asked the base medic what he thought about certain Indian remedies. Doc was usually patient with him, but one day he snapped, "Uncle Cam, you believe in Indian medicine more than mine!"

The Piros gave Cam the name "Yawuro," meaning "stork." One evening an old Piro, José Domingo, told Esther Matteson a story.

"One day I stood near the house of Yawuro, your chief. I watched him receive the governor. He took him into the house, seated him in the best chair, and gave him a drink of lemonade. Then he sat down and talked with him. Yawuro was not in a hurry. He had all the time the governor wanted.

"A few days later, I asked to visit Yawuro. He came outside the house to meet me. He took me in and seated me in the best chair and brought me lemonade. Then he sat down and we talked together. He was not in a hurry. He had all the time I wanted.

"Yawuro, your chief, is a great man. He is my friend."

Because Cam had to be away so much, Elaine made the domestic decisions and handled most of the discipline, but Cam deeply enjoyed the time he did get to spend with his family. When he was home he usually cooked breakfast—almost always oatmeal—as his father had done. They read a chapter from the Bible and recited memory verses, followed by prayer. Evenings, he would romp on the floor with the children. When "Billy Boy" and "Dell-Dell" grew sleepy, he would sing them a lullaby.

When in Lima they would visit the children's zoo or go swimming in the ocean. Cam always brought little presents when he returned from trips—things like licorice, candy, and can-can slips for the girls.

Cam lamented his frequent absences from home, and so did Elaine and the children. Once seven-year-old Grace greeted him on his return by saying, "Daddy, you're never home. Please stay longer this time." Another time he found a big sign on the door made by the children: "WELCOME HOME, DADDY, BOY." But the separations were bridged with loving letters full of homespun details. Cam was always lavish with praise and expressions of love for his children:

Precious Gracie:
It was good to hear your voice over the radio today. Thanks so much for the promise to make a cherry pie for my return home next Saturday. I'm so glad that you know how to make good pies. I'm very happy, too, over the good progress you are making in music. Do you remember that I gave you your first piano lesson? It was "Peter, Peter, Pumpkin Eater."
Well, my darling daughter, it's getting late so I'll close. Kisses and hugs from your Daddy.

Darling Joy Girl:
You gave me a wonderful thrill over the air today. I'm still walking on air. When you and Mommy gave me the news that you were first on the honor roll, my heart filled with gratitude to God for enabling you to do it.
Good night, now, precious girlie of mine. . . . Hugs and kisses from your Daddy.

The separations were also eased because the whole family was encouraged by the common goal of Bible translation in which they were caught up. Unlike many modern families where children are not close to their father's work, the Townsend youngsters were surrounded during their formative years by evidences of their parents' accomplishments.

Cam needed the all-too-brief times of refreshment with his family, for his responsibilities were now heavier than ever.

After the Catholic criticism quieted in Lima, he was confronted with news that Gene Nida had declined to run for reelection to the board. He was heavily involved in his work for the American Bible Society, and he continued in disagreement with certain WBT/SIL policies. He was, however, willing to "continue serving [the group] . . . for I appreciate the excellent work which many are doing, but not as a board member."

Cam had always considered the American Bible Society an or-

Cam taught Bill to read Spanglish—English written phonetically using the
Spanish alphabet. Cam proposed in his book *They Found a Common Language* that English be changed to some form of phonemic spelling—as
Spanglish—or failing that, that a system of bilingual education be established in the U.S. to enable the many minority language groups to learn to
read and write effectively.

The 1960
family
picture.

Grace 13, Billy 7, Joy 12 Elainadel 10

Loving Greetings from Cameron and Elaine Townsend, June 1960.

In September 1973 the family gathered for a reunion: *L. to r., back row:*
Robert and Elainadel Garippa, David and Joy Tuggy, Bill Townsend, Grace
and Tom Goreth. *Seated:* Elaine, Christopher Tuggy, Cam.

ganizational brother in the work of giving the Bible to all tribes, but he felt that Nida was too valuable a man to lose from the board. He tried in a series of letters to reconcile some of their policy differences, but they were both strong men and neither moved the other. Still, they continued to admire and respect each other personally, with Cam praising Nida's contributions to Bible translation and assuring him, "All of us love you greatly."

The slackening of the clerical criticism from Lima caused Cam to feel he could go to the States for the group's business conference. Returning, he stopped in Mexico, Guatemala, and Ecuador for various appointments.

In Mexico he found a publisher for the Spanish edition of his Cárdenas biography, saw and shared his faith with the former president four times, and handled a diplomatic chore for the Mexico branch's new director, John McIntosh. The Mexico branch seemed to always have some matter for Cam to handle with officials. And Cam enjoyed helping out, for he was the nostalgic type who tried to keep old friendships alive.

In Guatemala Cam joined over a thousand Cakchiquels in celebrating the thirtieth anniversary of the Robinson Bible Institute. His address to the large assembly was in the tribal language, even though the others had spoken in Spanish. Afterwards the Indian pastors came around and said, "Nobody speaks our language as properly as you, don Guillermo." It was the highest praise they could give a linguist.

From Guatemala he flew to Ecuador to make a few official calls with Bob Schneider. One appointment took them and translator Rachel Saint to see President Velasco Ibarra. "She wants to go translate the Bible for the Auca tribe," he informed the Ecuadorian leader.

Velasco admired such dedication. But he warned that the Aucas were "very dangerous. I once flew over them and they threw spears at the plane."

Cam and Schneider also called on the Colombian ambassador to Ecuador and explained the SIL program to him. "When will you help us with our Indians?" the ambassador asked.

"We would like to immediately," Cam replied. "But we'd need a base and some planes."

After a few months at home in Yarinacocha, Cam flew south to La Paz, Bolivia, the highest capital in the world, for the Third Inter-

American Indian Congress. Francisco Arellano Belloc from Mexico was in Bolivia on an errand for the United Nations and took Cam to see the president of Bolivia. They talked about SIL serving the jungle tribes of his country. President Paz Estensorro showed keen interest in his country's Indians. He knew about Cam's biography of Cárdenas and was following some of Cárdenas's ideas. He put his stamp of approval on the SIL contract with only minor changes. When Cam talked to the head of the Brazilian delegation to the Indian Congress, Dr. José de Gama said he knew of the missionary group. "Too bad you aren't scientists. We could use you in Brazil."

Cam replied by acknowledging their concern to translate the New Testament, but went on to list the group's scientific and scholarly accomplishments, and expressed his desire to serve the Brazilian government.

Dr. de Gama gave no invitation, but when Cam returned to Yarinacocha he sent Esther Matteson to attend the Congress of Americanists in Brazil to demonstrate her linguistic accomplishments with the Piros. When she returned, she told the group that an invitation was in the offing, and Cam asked Dale Kietzman, one of the early Peru translators, to begin to gather a task force for that advance. The new workers in Guatemala were mainly from Mexico, but Ecuador had drawn largely from Peru and Cam anticipated that Bolivia and Brazil would use Peru workers also.

There were problems to be faced, though. Cam felt that the ratio of support personnel to translators should be about two to one. A steady supply of new linguists was coming from the States, but pilots and mechanics were in very short supply. The best source was the aviation training course of the Moody Bible Institute. Cam wrote Henry Crowell, whom he now addressed as "Kilo Kid," a joking reference to his friend's expanding girth. "Send me three mechanics and I'll give you a dispensation to eat all the oatmeal you want without gaining more weight."

Ecuador required a plane badly. Planes were also needed in the Philippines and for the Bolivian advance. But one month the total contributions for JAARS was only $21.67. Only the income from paying passengers and cargo kept the planes flying in Peru. There was nothing for new parts and planes. "We need $100,000 right now," Cam wrote Nyman.

The mail brought only a flow of criticism from those who objected to the group's "helping" Catholics. Day after day Cam dictated letters to Cal Hibbard, courteously giving the same answers he had spelled out to previous critics. He always tried to include a spiritual story about a tribesman, a government official, or even a priest. In his folksy way, he was plain, but never vindictive.

The news from the tribes was good, though. One morning he was called to the radio tower for an important message. Lorrie Anderson and Doris Cox from the Shapra tribe were on with the exciting word that Chief Tariri had received the gospel! "He's stopped warring against his enemies and no longer prays to the boas. He's a new man."

Cam was thrilled. News of the head-hunter chief's conversion spread across the jungle and over the mountains to Lima. Cam flew out to Shapra land to meet Tariri, who greeted his visitor as a fellow chief. Lorrie and Doris interpreted as the chief described how he had stopped killing and sent peace offers to all his enemies.

Dramatic stories were also coming in from other tribes. Hundreds of Piros, Aguarunas, Campas, Machiguengas, and other once superstitious jungle Indians who had lived in fear of the elements and witch doctors were turning to Christianity as they heard Scripture in their own languages. The news from Mexico was just as gratifying. Marianna Slocum and Florence Gerdel reported over five thousand new believers in the Tzeltal tribe.

The teacher-training course for Indian teachers was still being held each year, and a planeful of dignitaries came to the base for the 1955 graduation ceremonies. After the graduation Cam flew to Lima at the request of the Peruvian president to report on the work. In Lima, he gave a luncheon attended by many officials and a highly esteemed Catholic bishop. Members of Congress praised SIL in speeches before their colleagues. Afterward the vice president was reminded, "Don't you know they're Protestants?"

He replied, "Don't talk to me about Protestants and Catholics. The truth is that if Christ came to Peru today as He did to Palestine, He would choose Townsend for one of His apostles."

Historian Arnold Toynbee, visiting Yarinacocha in Cam's absence, gave a testimonial to the newspapers. SIL "enjoys the favor of the Peruvian government," he said, "because it is familiarizing the Amazon Indians with the rudiments of modern civilization and, as a result, is preparing them for gradual incorporation into the national life of the country."

Cam was grateful for the verbal bouquets, but he told the minister of education quite frankly that the very transformation of the Indians was causing other problems.

"They want a higher standard of living. The old hunting and fishing economy is not enough. They need cattle, chickens, fruit trees, new crops and land titles. This will require an agricultural course.

"In some areas they need justice. A few big landowners abuse the Indians, keeping them in virtual serfdom. Couldn't some Indians from each region be trained as local authorities?"

The minister promised to do all he could. "Will the Institute help us provide an agricultural course?" he asked.

"With God's help, we'll do all we can to serve," Cam pledged, sticking his neck out again.

To encourage the group at the base he mentioned his little garden in Tetelcingo until some grew weary of hearing about "Uncle Cam's cabbage patch." He would quote James 2:15, 16 quite often, adding that "we prove our love by service to the Indians in practical ways." He hinted to the new agriculturist Herb Fuqua that "we may be needing you for something more than growing vegetables for the base kitchen."

While Cam was laying the groundwork for the agricultural project, the invitation came to enter Brazil. Esther Matteson's visit, plus subsequent visits by Pike and Rosita Corpancho, had convinced the Brazilian Indian service that SIL could make a scientific contribution.

Dale Kietzman, as Cam had requested, led the advance team. About the same time Dick Pittman reported feelers from New Guinea and Vietnam. But the work in Guatemala, the Philippines, Ecuador, and Bolivia was still in the infancy stage. There were so many needs, especially a plane for Bolivia. From where would the money and personnel come to open these and other new fields?

Cam didn't know. "Our policy thus far," he explained to Harold Key, another promising young leader, "has been to advance without waiting for much more than a one-way ticket. Because of that policy, we've had some trying moments in Mexico and Peru. But I don't think anyone wishes we had delayed."

Key listened, agreed, and led a group to Bolivia under the same conditions. Another advance had begun. *Adelante! Siempre adelante!*

"I recommend that we ask for these planes, not for ourselves, but for the governments whom we serve."

26. International Goodwill Planes

One spring day in 1955 Cam was driving back to Sulphur Springs, Arkansas, from a visit to Tulsa. This was a furlough year for the Townsends, but Cam seldom rested even on furlough. He had been to Tulsa to try to interest Oklahoma citizens in providing a plane for Bolivia.

Suddenly he was jolted out of the future into the present. In front of him he saw a single-engine plane—not a helicopter—hovering overhead, almost at a standstill!

Hurrying to the nearby airport, Cam found and questioned the manager. The new Helio-Courier, he was told, could slow to 40 miles an hour without stalling, and could land at 30. It could get airborne in 50 feet. Yet cruising speed was 150 mph.

"This is just what we need for short land strips in the jungle," Cam exclaimed. "Where is it manufactured?"

"In Pittsburgh, Kansas," was the reply.

But before he could head for Kansas, there was the business conference to attend in Sulphur Springs. There an Australian missionary's report on New Guinea made the plane seem even more of a necessity. In calling for WBT/SIL to enter New Guinea, Robert J. Story passed around mimeographed tabulations of tribal groups on the island. "We now believe there are 1,300 different languages there and in the other islands of the South Pacific. Most have not a single verse of Scripture."

Cam sat agape. He had been talking about 1,000 languages to be reduced to writing. There must be over 2,000, he realized. And New Guinea was reported to have rougher terrain than Amazonia. Planes like the Helio would surely be needed.

With the conference over and the children enrolled in school in

191

Sulphur Springs, Cam took Larry Montgomery, Don Burns, and Lawrence Routh, a contractor from North Carolina, to the Helio-Courier factory in Kansas. Larry tested a model of the little four-passenger plane and pronounced it "a beaut. This is *the* plane, Uncle Cam."

Dr. Lynn Bolinger, president of the corporation and chief developer of the revolutionary new plane, smiled appreciatively. "How many can you use?" he asked.

"We could get by with six for now—four for South America and two for the Philippines," Cam said, with hardly more than lunch money in his pocket.

They went into Bolinger's office to talk. "We're not a business organization," Cam began. "We're helping poor Indian tribes," and he went on to describe the work, showing newspaper clippings, telling about interviews with presidents. "Once they see them in use, I'm sure some of the governments and other businesses will want Helios. I'm sure we could help sell some."

Bolinger's interest was caught. "Considering the work you do and that you'll help us with other buyers, we could sell the planes to you at our cost—$25,000 each. We could deliver one a month."

"That'll be fine," Cam replied.

Back in the car, Burns said, "Uncle Cam, I marvel at your faith. But where will we get the money?"

"Hasn't the Lord always provided, Don? He's given me a new idea which I'm going to present to the board."

Writing to the board about the Helio-Courier, Cam suggested that the latest Crowell gift apply toward a Helio for Ecuador. His new idea was about raising money for the six planes. He would like to use the planes as international goodwill symbols, and do that by raising money both in and outside the evangelical community (through commercial firms and possibly foundations)—the method they had used in South America which had proved successful there in fostering understanding and goodwill.

Cam envisioned christening ceremonies with speeches by the mayor of each city whose citizens had raised the money for the plane, and by the ambassador of the receiving country, along with demonstrations of the plane's capabilities. The publicity would promote good international relations. Further, he proposed naming the fleet of planes "Flotilla de Amistad Inter-Americana" (Inter-

American Friendship Fleet), with each plane named for the city, state, or company that helped buy it.

The first ceremony was already planned for Chicago.

The board found Cam's latest recommendations breathtaking, but voted approval. "Uncle Cam has always been a step ahead of us," Pike said. "He may be again."

December 17, 1955, was a cold, blustery day in the Windy City, but an impressive group of dignitaries was on hand for the first goodwill plane ceremony. Mayor Daley welcomed Ecuador's Ambassador Chiriboga, who in turn praised Inter-American friendship and SIL, "expressing the sincere admiration my country feels for all members of the Institute." After Don Burns conveyed a message of thanks for the plane from Ecuador's President Velasco Ibarra, the crowd went outside and watched Larry Montgomery put the Helio through its paces. Then the plane was flown to Ecuador and received by the president at an airport ceremony.

Back in Sulphur Springs, Cam was planning more International Goodwill plane projects when news came in January 1956 that five young missionaries had been killed by Auca Indians in Ecuador.

Cam knew one of the men, Missionary Aviation Fellowship pilot Nate Saint. His sister Rachel, a member of Wycliffe, was already working on the unwritten Auca language with a woman named Dayuma who had come out of the tribe to live on an Ecuadorian ranch. Profoundly moved, he wrote Rachel, "When I heard of the report, I prayed that the time would come when you would be able to introduce your brother's killer to the president of Ecuador as a transformed man who through faith had become your brother in Christ."

The account of the slayings in *Life* stirred the world. Some church leaders deplored the "needless sacrifice" of the five young men. However, many young people volunteered to go in their place.

Cam was anxious that the challenge of the tribes be continued while the event was still fresh on the minds of Americans. He wrote Rachel asking her to come for speaking appearances, but she felt she should wait, in deference to the widows. "We might be intruding on something that doesn't belong to us," she said.

So Cam returned to his plane project. He and Amos Baker went to Tulsa where they showed businessmen a notebook of clippings and photos of the Chicago plane ceremony. Although Cam talked enthusiastically about the need in Bolivia and the goodwill an Oklahoma Helio project would generate between countries, the businessmen made only limited commitments.

Feeling nothing could be gained by pressing for more pledges, Cam went on to start a plane project in California that seemed more promising. In Santa Ana, he got his nephew Lorin Griset working on the "Friendship of Orange County." Lorin, now a prominent insurance man, had high political contacts and thought Vice President Nixon might speak at the christening ceremonies, since he was from Orange County.

Assured that the Orange County project was in capable hands, Cam left for more speaking engagements, first in Denver and then in Kansas City. Kansas City Mayor Roe Bartle, to whom Cam spoke, thought a women's international friendship group would get behind a plane project in his city. He would arrange for former President Truman to speak at the ceremony.

Boosted by Mayor Bartle's optimism, Cam went on to Washington, D.C., where he called at the Soviet embassy. He had heard that there were numerous minority languages spoken in the Soviet Union, although he realized that the Cold War plus the group's limited funds and personnel made entry into the U.S.S.R. seem like an impossible dream. Nevertheless, Cam's faith thrived on impossibilities, and he felt there was no better time than the present to acquaint Soviet officials with the group's services.

Lawrence Routh, his contractor friend from Greensboro, North Carolina, accompanied Cam on his visit. The Soviet counsellor welcomed them cordially. He liked Cam's idea of cultural exchange: Soviet linguists coming to lecture at SIL and SIL people going to the U.S.S.R. "Could you go to Moscow and talk with our Academy of Science?" the diplomat asked. Much as he wanted to, Cam couldn't see his way clear to go just then. There were too many loose strings dangling. One worry was the stymied plane project in Tulsa.

Back at the hotel Cam handed Routh his worn Scofield Bible. "Read the story of Joshua marching around Jericho."

When Routh finished, Cam said, "You know why the Lord asked Joshua to march? I think it was to teach him obedience. To see if he would carry out the Lord's command. He's commanded me to march around Tulsa. I'm going back there and march until the Lord tells me to stop!"

He went to Tulsa and "marched"—patiently explaining Wycliffe's methods and purpose. And the wall came down.

The second Helio was christened at the University of Oklahoma. President Cross of the university presented the keys to Bolivian Ambassador Victor Andrade, who accepted the gift in behalf of his country and immediately turned over the keys to Ken Pike, who was representing SIL. A naval colorguard gave a nineteen-gun ambassadorial salute and Mrs. Cross christened the plane "Friendship of Oklahoma."

Funds for the "Friendship of Orange County" came much more quickly. Vice President Nixon had agreed to speak, and the Peruvian ambassador, Fernando Berkemeyer, was coming from Washington, along with other dignitaries. Then a few days before the ceremony, Nixon's father died, and an aide called to cancel the appearance.

The manager of the Santa Ana Chamber of Commerce was upset at the cancellation. "If the vice president doesn't show up, we won't have a crowd," he told Cam. "We've already spent hundreds of dollars."

"We'll pray," Cam replied.

The day before the ceremony, Nixon sent word he would be coming after all. The Chamber of Commerce man was so impressed by the answer to prayer that he later committed his life to Christ.

The plane presentation went beautifully. Cam gave a tribute to Peru and a pledge of service. Nixon spoke and the ambassador received the plane. The charming wife of the consul general of Peru in Los Angeles, Señora de la Fuente, christened it. Charles Fuller prayed. Then Pike intrigued the crowd by demonstrating with an American Indian how to begin to learn a language using gestures.

The Townsend's furlough year was up in the summer of 1956. Seeds had been planted, faith rewarded, and the campaign to reach all the tribes had increased in momentum. Cam was anxious to get back to Latin America.

*"We can't control what they [journalists] write,
but generally they are fair. And they tell the
world what we are doing."*

27. Tell the World

The years 1957–1960 were full and busy for Cam and for WBT/
SIL. The work of Wycliffe increased and became more widely
known, culminating in the 25th anniversary celebrations starting in
1959.

Two more goodwill planes were christened in 1958. The "Spirit
of Kansas City" was dedicated for work in Ecuador on January 19,
1958, with former President Truman and the former president of
Ecuador, Galo Plaza, speaking. The "Spirit of Seattle" was dedicated
in Washington, D.C., in June 1958 as a gift to the Philippines; the
mayor of Seattle and President Garcia of the Philippines participated
in the ceremonies. A second Catalina went to the Amazonia countries where SIL worked from Orlando, Florida, in 1959, and another plane was sent to the Philippines from Pontiac, Michigan, in
1960. Cam was at each of these ceremonies, and had done a good
bit of the legwork to raise the money.

Early in 1957 the first couple went to Vietnam, through the
recommendation of President Magsaysay of the Philippines. "A
further result of your Cárdenas book," Dick Pittman wrote Cam.
Translation teams were in Alaska and had set up an Arctic training
camp. Africa was beginning to call for translators. Cowan and Pike,
just back from a visit to Germany, felt Europe was a potential gold
mine for new recruits. And Cam was hoping to get contracts with
Colombia and Venezuela.

In Peru things were going well. Enrollment in the bilingual Indian schools kept increasing, blessed by the special presidential
decree calling for Indian Bible translations to be taught every day
to the students. Agriculturist Herb Fuqua was teaching classes in
scientific agriculture for the Indian teachers. That pleased Cam.

"We need cattle projects, too, and classes in carpentry and mechanics," he told Fuqua.

Herb threw up his hands in mock despair. "Give us time, Uncle Cam!"

When news came from Ecuador that Rachel Saint and Dayuma, the first Auca translation helper, would be flying to the States to be honored by Ralph Edwards on his television program "This Is Your Life," Cam had an idea. Rachel Saint had worked among the head-hunting Shapras before going to the Aucas. Shapra Chief Tariri could also appear on the program. He could tell about Rachel's living in his tribe and about his leaving his headhunting ways to serve the true God. Rachel and Dayuma were going from California to New York for an appearance at the Billy Graham Crusade in Madison Square Garden, and Cam was sure Billy Graham would welcome the chief to his platform also.

When Cam broached the idea to Lorrie Anderson and Doris Cox, the translators with the Shapras, they were opposed at first. Cam assured them that the intelligent, observant tribal leader would be a strong demonstration of what Bible translation could accomplish. The girls finally agreed to accompany Tariri, his wife and baby, to interpret for them and to protect them from civilization.

Attired in full tribal regalia of feathered headdress, beads and exotic beetle-wing earrings, Tariri was a great success in the Hollywood TV studios. After the program, the chief, his family, and Doris and Lorrie flew to New York for the appearance with Billy Graham. Then Lorrie brought the Shapras back to Peru.

"I talked to your countrymen," Tariri told Cam on his return. "I said, 'Let your ears listen to me. I used to think only of killing and cutting off many heads, but I quit that custom. Now I love Jesus and live well. Let's all stop killing and live well.' "

In sending Tariri to the States, Cam aroused a great deal of publicity, though there was some criticism for "exploiting raw savages," and some for giving a distorted idea of the citizens of Peru. Cam, however, was pleased, especially when the *Reader's Digest* wrote saying they wanted to do a story and would send senior editor Clarence Hall down. Harper & Brothers was interested in a book. On both projects Cam offered full cooperation. When Clarence Hall actually arrived, Cam was on his way to the States, but he mapped out a jungle itinerary for the journalist.

Hall was not the only journalist to come to Yarinacocha in those days. To each writer who visited the base, Cam always showed personal interest. He welcomed their questions and invited them to look around and talk to anyone. "We do everything in the open," he stressed. He realized this policy of press relations entailed risks of inaccuracies, and reminded supporters, "We can't control what they write, but generally they are fair. And they tell the world what we are doing." And that was always worth a great deal.

The *Reader's Digest* article appeared in August 1958. Cam flew to New York at the magazine's expense to check the article before publication, and was very excited at what Hall had done. In fact, he hoped that Hall would do the book that Harper wanted. However, Hall's feeling was that Wycliffe was too complicated for an outsider to do them justice; a Wycliffe member should do the book. Cam accepted Hall's explanation. He had a member in mind who just might do as the author, and she was in the States.

Ethel Wallis was an experienced Mexico translator who had already shown writing ability. Cam talked with her in San Francisco—after stops in Washington, D.C., Kansas City, and Seattle to work on fund-raising and ceremonies for goodwill planes. Ethel was somewhat taken aback by the request to write a history of WBT/SIL—it would be a tremendous task.

"How long would I have?" she asked.

"Harper's wouldn't need the manuscript until September."

"September? But it's already May, Uncle Cam. I'd have to do so much research." But Cam's expectancy broke down her objections. "I'll try," she said. "And I have a librarian friend, Mary Bennett, who might help. She's a good researcher."

Cam suggested they go on down to the Glendale office immediately, because a lot of the information was there. But when he phoned for reservations, everything was full. "Let's go to the airport, anyway," he suggested.

The ticket agent sold them open tickets—the planes were full for the day. Tickets in hand, Cam and Ethel started toward the gates. "But Uncle Cam," Ethel protested, "the man said there were no seats!"

Cam never slackened his pace. "Ethel, the Lord has taught me never to take no as a negative."

At the gate two passengers failed to show up and Cam and Ethel were seated in their places.

While in Glendale, Cam attended the 1958 board meeting, and

challenged the group to pray and work for 200 new recruits for their 25th anniversary year starting in 1959.

As Cam knew she could, Ethel Wallis with Mary Bennett did get the research and the writing of Wycliffe's history done. *Two Thousand Tongues to Go* was published in 1959, coinciding with the beginning of the 25th anniversary.

The impact of the *Reader's Digest* article continued to make itself felt throughout 1959. Over a thousand letters and about $15,000 in gifts came as a result, making 1959 the best financial year on record. Contributing to the increase in giving was the traveling of the 25th anniversary speaking teams, including Cam, Pike, Cowan, Burns, and others, who fanned out across the country holding round-tables and rallies in churches and auditoriums. And membership went over 1,000, including the first second-generation member—Dick and Kay Pittman's daughter Marilou.

For the first time, member "quotas"—minimal allowances estimated necessary for comfortable subsistence—didn't drop under 80 percent a single month. And this was the year the board reluctantly decided to resign membership in the Interdenominational Foreign Missionary Association. The reasons for this step had been building up for several years.

"If I were condemned to hang, I'd ask God to enable me to love my hangman."

28. The Language of Love

The same years that brought mounting recognition and publicity for Wycliffe also brought increased criticism both at home and abroad. The main area of attack was Wycliffe's relationship to Catholic missionaries. Abroad, the problem was primarily in Peru. In the States, the criticism centered in the Interdenominational Foreign Missions Association (IFMA), although questions were raised and judgments leveled from other quarters also.

Wycliffe had joined the IFMA at the suggestion of Oswald Smith, pastor of the People's Church in Toronto, who felt it would aid the young organization in being accepted by the Christian public. But when Cam returned to Yarinacocha, Peru, in July 1958 after his visit to the States for the *Reader's Digest* article and the Harper book, he found a number of problem letters waiting for him.

The one from Clyde Taylor, head of the Evangelical Foreign Missionary Association,* asked questions in a fraternal spirit. He wanted to know, "So you consider Catholics to be true Christians? And what about giving translations to Catholics?"

Cam replied:

You might also ask if I equate membership in a Methodist, Presbyterian or some other denominational organization with truly knowing Christ. I've known people in all those organizations who seem to be trusting the Lord . . . but, I've known many other members who did not impress me as being true believers in Christ. It's possible to know Christ as Lord and Savior and to continue in the Roman Church. . . .

* The EFMA, as part of the National Association of Evangelicals, allowed individual churches to be members, as well as denominations. The IFMA is an association of evangelical mission societies only—both denominational and interdenominational groups.

*We shall be happy indeed if the translations are used by anyone
and everyone. God's Word will not return unto Him void. We stake
everything on its power in the lives of those who feed upon it.*

*Just yesterday morning at the breakfast table I handed it to a high
government official to read. He read part of John 21 and then I read
from Isaiah 53. The hearts of all present were touched. My advice to
missionaries in these lands is to proclaim the Word more and argue
about it less.*

The letter from the director of a U.S. mission which had missionaries in Ecuador was more critical and judgmental. "I beg your
missionaries to change their attitudes toward priests," Cam pleaded
in reply. "The language of love is service. If I were condemned to
hang, I'd ask God to enable me to love my hangman."

It was Dr. Ralph Davis's letter, however, that caused the greatest
concern. Davis was president of the IFMA, and he cited charges
from "anonymous" persons that the primary purpose of Wycliffe's
work was scientific and cultural, not spiritual. And they used their
airplanes to help the Catholic church.

Cal Hibbard, Cam's secretary, expressed his concern. "This could
really mean trouble, Uncle Cam. A lot of folks support our work
because we're in the IFMA."

"I know," Cam agreed. "I just wish some of these critics would
come out in the open. But since they won't we'll just have to
answer Dr. Davis point by point and invite him to come see the
work."

Cam spent most of the next six months in his second-floor office
overlooking the lake. The correspondence was tedious, but he tried
to apply a reconciling touch in replying to each critic's complaints.
And having an uncanny memory for little personal incidents that
happened decades before, he might add a note in his tiny round-
lettered script to a dictated letter.

Much of the heavy correspondence during the late months of
1958 related to the IFMA controversy. Cam kept suggesting to
the WBT/SIL board that the best solution was for Wycliffe to resign from the IFMA. Nyman and company in California urged
him to be patient. The keeper of the Wycliffe purse knew how
precarious the financial support of the large growing membership
was, with some existing on less than $100 a month. Resignation,
or negative IFMA action, Nyman felt, could tighten the purse
strings of many supporters in conservative churches.

Even the usually positive Crowell had a question. His concern was the use of the two names, SIL and WBT. "Why not declare yourselves as missionaries?" he asked.

Cam pointed to great missionaries of the past who had plied a trade.

Paul made tents. Carey cobbled. Morrison was a bookkeeper. The first missionary to Guatemala taught English. We enter countries as linguists, even though everyone knows we are missionaries at heart.

The classical missionary approach will not get the job done in this generation nor in ten. It almost seems that some people are so tied to the hitching post of custom in missionary activities that they would let the job go undone rather than adopt a different approach. . . .

That seemed to satisfy the practical Crowell.

Pike, who had differed with Cam in the past but had always loyally stood by, hoped Cam would see the seriousness of the criticism from their conservative brethren. In December 1958 he wrote Cam an explanatory note.

We are in for objection and criticism for a long, long time. You have been a very great innovator. Wycliffe, following you, is similarly a great innovator. But every innovator has to expect resistance from the people following the normal course of events. . . . Anybody with any sense of historical development knows that innovators cannot be replaced by law, committees, or by appointment. We need you horribly. Yet, please bear with us if once in a blue moon we act like normal human beings with normal conservative tendencies trying to preserve our normal useful social order!

But the IFMA leaders remained unconvinced that the group's innovations were proper, and decided to send an investigator to Peru. Cam replied that the IFMA representative would be cordially welcomed at the base, but asked: "How can he possibly see everything in eight days?"

A week before the IFMA man was due to arrive, a new problem arose in Peru that might have confirmed the IFMA's suspicions. The new Peruvian director of the upcoming Indian teachers' course told Cam, "I have orders to permit a priest to teach a class in Catholic religion for the Indian teachers."

Cam had thought that the Catholic criticism had been taken

care of. At the beginning of 1958 he had landed in Lima, after several months' absence, to be handed a collection of antagonistic press clippings from the Lima paper. "The SIL people are not really linguists, but Protestant missionaries in disguise. The Indians speak Spanish. They are Catholics and don't need help in their own languages. By being allowed to meddle with the Indians with government support, SIL is dividing the country."

Cam had discovered that some conservative prelates had been joined by a few plantation owners whose exploitation of the Indians had been hindered by the bilingual schools and the new agricultural projects. "You wouldn't believe some of the stories they are spreading," an SIL member told Cam. "All over the jungle, they're saying we take Indians to the base, kill them, and render them into oil to use in our planes!"

"How could anyone believe something like that?"

"Well, someone found a skull in the garbage—it had been taken from an old Inca mound—and took it to the authorities as proof we were killing Indians!"

"There really isn't much we can do about that kind of yarn," Cam had said. "Just ignore it, and try to love everybody. I'll try to talk to the prelates though."

He had gone directly to the papal nuncio, the Vatican's diplomatic representative to the Peruvian government. The nuncio received him cordially and listened courteously. "Your Excellency, we're bringing the country closer together instead of dividing it," Cam explained. "We're also trying to be of service to all the missionaries, Catholic and Protestant, and others who serve the Indians. Our goal is to put sacred Scripture into every language on earth."

The nuncio was new in Peru, and had not heard SIL's side. "Could you give me a written report on your services to Catholic missionaries?" he asked.

"Certainly," Cam smiled. "Now, your Excellency, would you kindly ask God's blessings on our brave young people who are translating the Bible in the jungle?"

The nuncio promised he would.

Cam's report had cited many examples of service performed by SIL to the Catholic missionaries, and also detailed how Catholic missionaries had often helped SIL linguists. "The gracious friendly things they do for us," he concluded, "do credit to the Lord who said: 'By this shall all men know ye are my disciples if ye have love one to another.' I believe they love us and I know we love them."

About the same time the director of the National Catholic Information Service in Washington had inquired about relationships between SIL and Catholics. Cam again had replied in typical style:

. . . *Since we are nonsectarian and nonecclesiastical, we get help from Catholics, Protestants, Jews, Moslems, Buddhists and even atheists.*

Our big problem is that we are a new type of crusader whereas people try to put us in categories with which they are familiar. Missionary-minded people think we are just a bunch of scientists and should look to scientific institutions for support rather than to Christian donors. Protestant zealots find we transport Catholic missionaries in our airplanes and . . . cut off contributions, saying we're helping promote Catholic missions. Catholic prelates who don't know us personally object because we aren't Catholics and don't tell the tribesmen, whom we help spiritually through the Bible, that they should join the Catholic Church when they give up worshiping the sun, the boa constrictor or the spirits of the forest.

You might think that so much misunderstanding would make it impossible for us to forge ahead, but when people find we are reaching primitive tribes, who, due to language barriers, have existed for centuries outside the pale of modern civilization, they help us. People like for the primitive underdogs to get a chance even though it comes through a rather off-color branch of missionary-scientists who believe in Christ and the Apostles' Creed, but aren't sectarian about it and try to love and serve everybody.

After receiving Cam's letter and checking to find that priests had been attending SIL summer schools, the Catholic press service had given a favorable report.

Cam had then invited several newspaper writers to come to Yarinacocha to cover the festivities at the graduation of the Indian teachers. He had felt the resulting stories would help clear up the misunderstandings, and to a large extent they had. Glowing articles had appeared in Lima's major newspapers.

But now it seemed the criticisms had risen again. So he went to see the local bishop, Monsignor Gustavo Prevost.

"What can I do for you, Uncle Cam?" the red-headed French Canadian asked. The SIL group had given Monsignor Prevost a reception when he had been assigned to the area, and he and Cam had visited back and forth.

"Someone in Lima has ordered a religion class in the next Indian teacher's course."

Prevost smiled. "Yes, I just got a request to send a priest over to teach twelve hours of religion a week. I did think it strange. We don't teach that much religion in the Pucallpa public schools."

"We just can't allow that at our facilities. We're nonsectarian," explained Cam. "I hope you aren't offended."

"No, no. Not at all. My priests have too much to do already."

"We could allow a priest to teach if attendance was voluntary," Cam suggested.

"If it were voluntary no one would come."

"I would," Cam declared. "Or perhaps you would be willing to come and give our workers some lectures. We're all plain laymen. Maybe we could return the favor by teaching one of your priests the Shipibo language."

Monsignor Prevost seemed impressed. "Perhaps I could come and speak. But I don't think I could spare a priest to work with the Shipibos. Our territory is so big and the priests so few that we can't adequately handle our Spanish responsibilities."

"Well, whenever you can come, let me know. And, before I forget, my wife wants you over for a home-cooked meal."

The bishop came and by the time they were to the cherry pie, their friendship was stronger than ever. "Come again," Cam invited. "If the rain bogs up the road, you can spend the night in our 'prophet's chamber.'"

Cam then went to report to the minister of education in Lima about the order. "This violates our nonsectarian policy," he told the educator. "How can we serve all groups if we cater to one?"

When the minister had heard Cam out, he said, "I'll cancel the religion class, but you must help me reassure the Catholics."

Cam promised he would.

The IFMA investigator arrived just after January 1, 1959. He walked around the base, looked at the hangar, visited a tribe, spoke at the Sunday services. He was cordial, affable and gave Cam an *abrazo* when time came to leave. "It's easy to criticize from eight thousand miles," he said. But he politely declined to tell Cam the identity of the complainers. Still Cam was encouraged and thought this storm would soon be over.

But in mid-1959 he received a disturbing letter from Ken Watters in California who had been helping Nyman handle correspondence. "The IFMA matter isn't dead by a long shot," Watters wrote. "Their president claims numerous people have complained about us."

Cam wrote IFMA headquarters: "Name one critic. . . . I doubt if many of them are working in an Indian language. . . . We feel very strongly that the way our critics want us to treat the monks and nuns is unscriptural. . . . We simply can't do it."

But the IFMA leaders still would not name the complainers. Instead they requested that the Wycliffe board present an official answer to the anonymous charges. Cam felt this would be wasted effort, but he agreed that George Cowan could draft a defense.

Nothing, however, could change the mind of the IFMA leaders. And so the decision to resign was made. Cam commented on it, "We can best serve everybody if we don't belong to anybody."

Cowan mailed copies of the formal resignation statement to missions which were members of the organization, adding, "We hope to serve you at home and abroad as in the past, and to experience the same cordial fellowship in the Lord's work." The result was that only a few Wycliffites lost support.

And back in Peru, Monsignor Prevost from Pucallpa occasionally went to Yarinacocha to the Townsends' home for tea or a meal. He and his priests began distributing Scriptures in the public schools in 1963. "Pope John is bringing us into a new era," he told Cam and Elaine. "He talks about love among all Christians."

The new decade had begun.

". . . it is important to make every effort possible to identify our work with the national interests of the countries where we work."

29. Patience and Fortitude

In Mexico the work was growing and relations with the government were on an even keel. But the increased number of workers put an added strain on the already overcrowded Kettle in Mexico City. Everytime Cam stopped in the Mexican capital on his way to or from Peru—which was quite often at the end of the 50s—Ben Elson, the director of the Mexico work, would remind him of the need for a new headquarters. But there was no money to buy land.

Cam had been to see President Ruiz Cortines in the summer of 1956 on his way back from furlough. But the answer to his question about a gift of land from the government had been "Not yet." In the fall of 1957 he was there again on an extended stay while he waited for plans to be finalized on the Kansas City plane ceremony When the land question came up again, Cam told Ben, "I'll pray more about it." The next morning he read from Ezra how the Lord stirred up the spirit of Cyrus to rebuild Jerusalem. "Lord, stir up some Cyrus here in our behalf," he prayed. Then, like the evangelist D. L. Moody, who believed in a prayer that "had feet and walked," Cam began calling on government officials. But again the answer was "Not yet."

Still, he challenged the group to believe and pray. One morning he spoke to them from Acts 11:1-2. "The early Christians prayed without ceasing for Peter while he was in prison. That's the way we should pray. With definite goals in mind. Suppose the Lord should suddenly appear and say, 'I'll give you all you ask for during the next ten minutes,' what would you ask? Well, the Lord's here right now, just waiting to hear our requests. Let's tell Him what's on our hearts."

Early in 1959 Ben Elson wrote asking Cam to try again. The new president, Adolfo López Mateos, was now in office. Cam flew in late in February and immediately started making the usual diplomatic rounds, calling on his friends in government circles.

He had been met at the airport when he landed with a cable to radio Elaine, but had not been able to get a good connection, so he could just barely make out that someone might be having surgery for appendicitis in Lima. Billy had been having stomach pains before Cam left—but not being able to communicate with Elaine was almost unbearable. "If weeping would do any good, I'd weep," he wrote her after trying to reach her again.

Cam was never one to sit and bemoan circumstances, however. In addition to making the rounds of the Mexican officials, he made an appointment to meet with the second secretary at the Russian Embassy. He couldn't get away from the idea of getting into Russia.

The Russian diplomat was impressed by the stack of grammars, dictionaries, and primers which the group had translated into Mexican-Indian languages. "How are you supported?" he asked Cam. When Cam explained, "We look to God to move individuals who believe in our work," the Russian murmured, "Incredible!"

Cam also enjoyed a warm reunion with Lázaro Cárdenas, who had just returned from a trip to Russia, China, and the U.S.A.

And he kept trying to see the president. When he finally got in, López Mateos poured lavish tribute on Cam and the SIL group. He also said he would see what could be done about a land grant for the headquarters.

And about the same time, Cam received an ungarbled message from Elaine. The emergency was over. Billy had had surgery and was recovering nicely. By the time Cam could fly back to Lima in April, Elaine and Billy had returned to Yarinacocha, where Cam joined them for almost a whole month before he had to leave again.

This time he was going to Guatemala to the Inter-American Indian Congress. Dr. Efrain Morote Best, a former director of the bilingual teacher training course, was going too—both were members of the Peruvian delegation to the Congress. Dr. Morote Best shared Cam's vision for the Indians. He had promoted the bilingual schools and also wanted Indians to receive more training in scientific agriculture, commerce, and technical and political skills.

In Guatemala, Cam spent a weekend revisiting familiar sites, including San Antonio, accompanied by Morote Best. But he spent more time in the present, planning for the future. He had several conversations with the head of the Colombian delegation to the Congress, Dr. Hernández de Alba. "We would welcome the scientific contributions SIL could make to our country," the anthropologist told Cam, "but the concordat we have with the Vatican would likely rule out translating the Bible."

Cam replied with something Monsignor Prevost had once told him: " 'Better the Indians be Protestants than continue pagan.' We promote Christian faith," he added, "and no special brand of it."

"I don't think you could get past the concordat," de Alba concluded reluctantly.

Just before the Congress closed, Cam and John Beekman, SIL's director for Central America, were given an audience with Guatemala's President Ydigoras. Beekman had been one of the translators of the New Testament into the Chol language in Mexico while afflicted with a constricted heart valve. Surgery had corrected the problem with one of the first artificial valves which contained a plastic ball that rose and fell in rhythm with the beat. Beekman literally ticked like a clock. Cam used the novelty to break the ice with the president, then went on to tell about his old work with the Cakchiquels and SIL's present program.

Ydigoras smiled. "You don't have to convince me. This work should be supported by everyone. How can we help you?"

"Well," Cam said, "we do need a little land here in the capital for a headquarters. We will put up a building, keep it up, and turn it back to the government when the work is done in your tribes."

The president turned and telephoned his minister of education. "I'm sending Townsend and his assistant over. They need land."

Cam and Beekman went straight to the minister's office, and in a short time the grant was made and signed. The Guatemalan headquarters had been provided for.

Later, at the rented group house, Beekman talked to Cam about his future. "You know Ben Elson wants me to head up a translation consultation program in Mexico," he said. "When can you get someone to take my place here?"

"I'll work on it," Cam promised. "What we need is a Center. I remember how much it helped me to get away to a quiet place with Joe Chicol and Trinidad Bac when I was finishing the Cakchiquel translation. I've long dreamed of such a center in Mexico where translators could take their Indian assistants for a few months and work with trained consultants."

After the Congress was over, Cam waited on in Guatemala City hoping that he would receive favorable word from Colombia for SIL's beginning work there. Finally, however, he decided that Colombia was not yet ready. He flew to Orlando, Florida, to participate in a plane ceremony, and then came back with the new plane to Yarinacocha and his family.

During the Townsend's year in the States (1959–60), another call came for help from Mexico. The headquarters problem there was far from resolved. Cam and Elaine and the two older girls flew in for a few days' visit, and Cam went immediately to work.

He and Ben Elson first went to see the new minister of education. Jaime Torres Bodet, Mexico's poet-statesman who had been head of UNESCO, gave Cam a warm welcome. "Next year will be our twenty-fifth anniversary," Cam told him, "and the place we began was Mexico. We would like to have a celebration and a conference of educators and officials from sister countries who are interested in the welfare of Indians. They'd like to see the great advances you've made here."

"How is your headquarters project coming?" the minister asked.

When Cam replied that SIL had no land for it yet, Torres Bodet phoned the controller of public properties, who agreed at once to see them.

In the elevator, Elson said, "I can hardly believe it. He said he'd get on it right away, and I'm sure he will! Praise the Lord! It's a real miracle."

The five acres which the government gave was in the Mexico City Tlalpan district and worth then an estimated $300,000. The agreement specified that SIL would construct suitable buildings to facilitate its program of linguistic research and Indian advancement. Land and buildings would be returned to the government in thirty years.

Before returning to California, Cam and Elaine had a lingering visit with Lázaro Cárdenas. The ex-president was worried over the start of a nuclear war between the great powers. He asked what Cam thought were the prospects of lasting peace.

"The Bible tells us the Prince of Peace will return to earth and end all injustices," Cam replied. "He will give everlasting peace."

Then, as he had many times before, Cam shared the inner peace Christ had brought to his heart. Cárdenas listened attentively. When the Townsends were leaving, he embraced Cam and said,

"Thank you my friend for your good words. You're the only one who talks to me about my soul."

The Townsends' return to the States plunged them again into the hectic pace of cross-country speaking engagements. At the same time Cam was helping raise money for the building program in Mexico City. He also had another headquarters problem on his mind. JAARS needed a central location and a headquarters building.

Lawrence Routh, the Carolina contractor, had suggested the Charlotte, North Carolina area. Cam had also met mercantile executive Henderson Belk, who lived in Charlotte and was keen on helping Wycliffe. Belk offered a nice tract of wooded and pasture land near the town of Waxhaw, about thirty miles south of Charlotte, for the new aviation center. Cam flew in to inspect. The tract was large enough for a landing strip, shops, hangars, and housing. There was even an old white-columned antebellum house that could be repaired and used until more adequate buildings were completed.

While in the Charlotte area, Cam met Melvin Graham, a farmer and Billy Graham's brother. Mel was an elder and teacher in the independent Calvary Presbyterian Church. The rugged outdoor type, Mel liked a tractor better than a platform. The idea of a world missionary aviation center near Charlotte excited him. When Cam asked him to be the chairman of a JAARS committee in Charlotte to work with Lawrence Routh, who would oversee the building program, he agreed willingly.

Then Cam put in a call to Jack Kendall in California. The retired telephone company engineer had already installed telephone systems at the Peru base. Kendall agreed to come to Charlotte and help with the engineering.

By this time the Townsends' year at home was up, and they returned to Peru, though Cam didn't stay at home long. In January 1961 a telegram came saying Will Nyman was dead. Cam flew immediately to California for the funeral. Though Nyman's death had not been unexpected, Cam felt as though a part of himself was gone. Nyman had been a faithful, loyal supporter for the twenty-five years of Wycliffe's existence, and even before that. Ken Watters and Phil Grossman, who had been carrying much of Nyman's load, would take care of things, but Cam would miss his old friend and his loyal support.

From Los Angeles Cam flew directly to Mexico City where Elaine met him for the 25th anniversary celebration of the work in

Mexico. Guests came from three countries to help celebrate. At a gala banquet presided over by Minister of Education Torres Bodet, Cam was presented with a handsome 694-page volume of 58 articles on Indian life and language from fourteen hemispheric groups prepared in his honor.

The Mexican scholar who spoke at the banquet characterized Cam in terms that could also describe the work he headed: "One of those mystics in whom two tendencies meet; one seeks the salvation of the soul, the other applies the positive good in our civilization so that not only souls but bodies may be freed from the horrors of sorrow, sickness, poverty, exploitation and premature death."

Cam on a visit to Jungle Camp in southern Mexico in the early 60's.

Cam at SIL Board meeting in Mexico City, at the "Kettle."

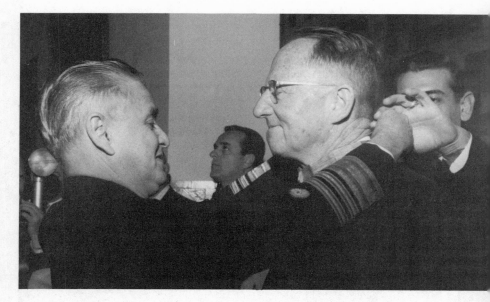

Above: In 1963 Cam and Elaine were awarded the Order of Distinguished Service of Peru. Here the Peruvian minister of foreign affairs presents the Order to Cam. *Below:* At Jungle Camp, Cam embraces Tzeltal Indian chief Marcos Ensin.

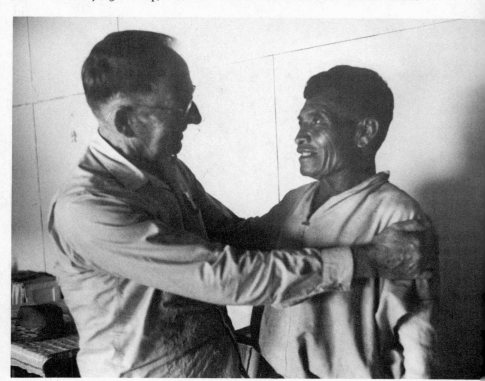

Above: Cam embraces General Mendosa, Peru, 1963. *Below*: Cam with U.S. Senator Fred Harris of Oklahoma, on Bible Translation Day, September 30, 1966, in Washington D.C.

Above: In 1962 Cam and SIL leaders presented the printed Tzeltal New Testament to the Mexican minister of education. *Below:* Cam gives Testaments to the Tzeltal Indians at Jungle Camp.

On a 1961 visit
back to
Tetelcingo,
Cam's former
village in
Mexico,
he greets two
old friends:
José Catonga
a believer,
and (above)
Josefina, a
former neighbor.

Cam parks his Texas hat, given him by his friend Bob Fenn, and his Mexican brief-case, given him by the Mexico SIL Branch, while he works.

"Don't apply unless you are willing to go an extra mile. . . ."

30. Colombia

In the two years since he had talked to Hernández de Alba about SIL's coming to Colombia, Cam hadn't stopped hoping and praying for an entrance. Actually, it had been nine years since he had met Lleras Camargo in Chicago, who was then head of the Organization of American States; now he was president of Colombia.

Cam knew the time would come when Wycliffe would be able to enter Colombia. In the meantime there was plenty to keep him occupied. When he left Mexico after the anniversary festivities early in 1961, he flew to Charlotte to look over the plans for the JAARS headquarters—hangars, shops, administration building, and a communications nerve center with radio contact to several Wycliffe fields.

Then there were plane projects in Greensboro, North Carolina, Philadelphia, and a speaking engagement on Long Island. There a ham radio operator conveyed a message to Cam from Bob Schneider in Ecuador: "President Velasco Ibarra is going to visit the base tomorrow to meet the Auca believers. Please come."

The message took Cam back five years to the killing of the five missionaries by Auca warriors. He had told Rachel Saint, whose brother was one of the five, that he would pray and believe that someday Rachel would have the privilege of introducing Nate's killers to the president of Ecuador.

Cam caught a flight immediately for Miami, where, in spite of being told he couldn't be cleared for Ecuador, he bought a through ticket, and caught the next plane, landing in Quito in time to join the presidential party at Shell Mera.

At the SIL base Rachel Saint introduced President Velasco Ibarra to Kimo, one of the Auca killers, who muttered something in Auca,

221

and reached out to touch the presidential pate. "I don't think he's ever seen a bald head before, Mr. President," Cam explained.

The president laughed heartily. "How were you able to teach such abstract conceptions as God and Jesus Christ to such savages?" he asked Rachel.

"May I suggest you ask Kimo, Mr. President?"

"Kimo, who is Jesus Christ?"

Rachel repeated the question in Auca. Kimo's face brightened as he replied, "Jesus Christ is the One who came from heaven and died for my sins. He made me stop killing and live happily with my brothers."

"Amazing!" the president exclaimed.

That night at a dinner banquet given by the SIL staff, Velasco Ibarra was still talking about the amazing transformation. "Mr. President," Cam assured him, "the same thing happens over and over again when primitive tribesmen hear the Word of God in their own language. Perhaps you see now why we are so eager to help the Indians."

"I think I do. Where will you be going next?"

"Back to Peru for the graduation exercises of the Indian teachers' course. Then to visit our work in Brazil."

"Ah, Brazil. Jânio Quadros, the new president, is a friend of mine. I will have my ambassador set up an appointment for you."

"Thank you, Mr. President."

"By the way, I've been hearing a lot about this preacher named Billy Graham. Would he come to Quito?"

"Dr. Graham is a good friend. He endorses our work. I'll ask him for you."

"Good. Good. I thank you. And I thank you for coming. My government will continue to back your work. Imagine, an Auca that has stopped killing and teaches the Bible. Amazing! I never would have believed it."

President Velasco Ibarra was true to his word. When Cam got to Brazilia in May of 1961, Jim Wilson, the new director of Wycliffe's work there, took him to see the Ecuadorian ambassador. The ambassador escorted them to the presidential palace where President Quadros courteously invited Cam and Wilson to his office for an audience. As a former teacher who had lived near the *campo grande* section of Brazil, Quadros was immensely interested in the Terena language primers which Wilson had brought with him.

"I know the Terena tribe," the president told them. "I lived near them as a boy. This is just what they need."

Cam and Wilson explained the work of SIL and the advantages of bilingual education. "It's a new day for the Indians, Mr. President, when they learn to read and write, first in their own language, then in Portuguese." Cam went on to describe how the Bible was changing the Aucas.

"How many tribes are you helping in Brazil?" Quadros asked.

"We have teams in nineteen tribes, Mr. President," Cam answered. "Some are single girls."

"Will you make primers like these for each tribe?"

"Yes. That is part of our agreement with your government."

"And there are young single women living among our Indians? They must be very brave."

"Yes, Mr. President, both brave and dedicated."

"How can I help?"

Wilson presented him a memorandum listing four requests. The president read them aloud, then said in a firm tone, "I will do it." He scribbled some notes across the top of the document, stamped it *URGENTE*, and handed it to an aide.

Cam flew back to Peru elated over the enthusiastic support promised by the Brazilian president, but his face dropped when he read his mail. Larry Montgomery wanted a leave of absence to work for the Helio corporation. His support had been dropping.

"I don't blame him for asking for a leave," Cam wrote Crowell, "but it's a hard blow when a partner, on whom you've depended for years, leaves you. I feel sort of lost without Will Nyman at home. Now I seem to have lost Larry's broad shoulders too."

Larry had been the dependable expert in aviation. Now Cam turned to Harold Goodall, Les Bancroft, a veteran mechanic, and Merrill Piper, an experienced pilot, who went to North Carolina to work on the JAARS project.

That summer—1961—Lima officials and educators gave a festive fifteenth anniversary banquet in Cam's honor. After the celebration, Cam and Elaine flew to Quito for a dinner with President Velasco Ibarra. From the high Ecuadorian capital, he wrote the membership a "Dear Gang" letter, reflecting on his sixty-fifth birthday.

My heart overflows with gratitude to God, to Elaine, to you and to our wonderful friends in Latin America, the U.S. and elsewhere.

Financially, I have almost nothing to show for my 44 years of labor on behalf of the Indians. We own an automobile that you folks gave us two years ago, a home in the jungles of Peru, five hundred dollars in savings for the education of our children and that's all. In the wealth of friendship, however, we are millionaires.

You live by faith the same as we. On faith accompanied by works, our organization has grown in 26 years to over 1,100. We get nothing (no personal support) from any government, nothing from the denominational organizations and very little from foundations or really wealthy people, but God has people send us enough food and clothing. It is the hand of God that feeds us as the mother bird feeds her fledglings. Our concerns therefore are even scantier than our savings. This is one of the reasons why we are such a happy group. True happiness comes through sacrifice for others.

It was biennial conference time again, and Cam took off for Sulphur Springs. The 1961 keynote continued to be advance. Otis Leal reported the acceptance of over one hundred new members. Ken Pike described linguistic workshops he had held in various fields. John Beekman felt that Pike's workshops, the Translation Center in Mexico, and technical aids would eventually cut in half the time required for translators to produce a New Testament.

John Bendor-Samuel, the Oxford-trained English linguist, was ready to start work in Africa. "Our supporters in England are expecting a visit from you, Uncle Cam," he told the general director. "You *must* come."

"I've been thinking of coming," Cam told him. "But lately the Lord has been speaking to me about Colombia. I want to be on stand-by when the opportunity comes there." This time it wasn't long in coming.

Cam was in Mexico City when Goodall phoned from North Carolina about routine JAARS business. "By the way," Goodall ended, "the Colombian ambassador is to be in Charlotte over the weekend to be guest of honor at the state fair, and will be staying with Henderson and Ann Belk." The statement electrified Cam. "I'll be on the next flight out," he declared. "Tell the Belks and pray!"

The weekend with the Belks was Cam's opportunity to orient Ambassador and Señora Sanz de Santamaria on the service of SIL. When they flew back to Washington, Cam was on the same flight, and they invited him to lunch at their home the next day. There, the ambassador gave Cam important letters of introduction. With the letters in his briefcase, Cam flew to Bogotá and looked up Director of Indian Affairs Dr. Hernández de Alba, whom he had met two years before at the Indian Congress in Guatemala City. Hernández de Alba gladly accompanied him as he delivered the letters.

The first was to President Lleras Camargo, who remembered Cam and his biography of Cárdenas from their meeting in Chicago nine years before. "We'll be glad to give you a contract," he said assuringly.

After they delivered the other letters, they visited Bishop Marceliano Canyes. He got to talking about his late brother, who had been both a priest and linguist. "I remember in 1937 your brother and I both had articles in the same linguistic magazine in Mexico," Cam said. "He was well known in linguistic circles."

"Yes, he always wanted to help the Indians. I have his manuscripts and books in my residence, but they've never been put in order."

Cam filed that piece of information in his memory, then outlined SIL's intentions. "In Peru we base our translations upon the Spanish *Nácar y Colunga* translation. We make them available to anyone who wishes to use them, evangelical or Catholic."

Bishop Canyes frowned. "This is a Catholic state, although Protestant missionaries are allowed in the Spanish-speaking areas. But the Church has an agreement with the government forbidding the Protestants to propagate their sects in the Indian territories."

"We should have no problem working with Catholic missionaries here," Cam said. "In other countries where we have government contracts, they help us and we help them when we can do each other favors. Our planes will be at your disposal at a moderate price just as they are to everybody else."

"Well, perhaps we can work together," the prelate concluded.

Cam left copies of SIL's constitution and contracts with other governments with Dr. Hernández de Alba. "I'll take it from here," the anthropologist promised. Cam went home to Yarinacocha and wrote the membership:

We need to be ready to start work in Colombia within six months. But how can we do it when we all have our hands full now? This morning we read Philippians 2 with our guests at the breakfast table and the 13th verse assured me: "For it is God which worketh in you

*both to will and to do.". . . . He will enable us. . . . Don't apply un-
less you are willing to go an extra mile in serving the monks and
nuns. Colombia's tribes will be reached only by loving service and
patient faith. Above all, pray. I'll let you know when the contract is
signed.*

Then while Cam awaited the execution of the contract, Goodall
returned to Peru to work on Peru branch business which had been
left hanging while he had been in North Carolina, and to start
closing up his house.

In January 1962, a letter came from Henderson Belk. "Either you
or Goodall," he wrote to Cam, "must come to Charlotte and super-
vise the JAARS construction." Fearing that the committee of businessmen might become discouraged, Cam decided to take charge
himself until Goodall could get away from Peru, which would be
about June. The Belks offered the use of their furnished river-front
summer home a few miles from Charlotte, so Cam moved the
whole family, enrolling the children in Charlotte schools at mid-
semester. Grace was a high school freshman, and the others were
in grade school and junior high. Elaine was glad to be closer to her
family in Chicago. Her crippled sister Shirley had died the preceding
fall and her father now had incurable cancer.

While they were living in North Carolina, the call from Colombia
came. Cam flew immediately to Bogotá where a smiling Dr. Hernández de Alba, greeted him with the news "The president and his
cabinet have approved the contract." Cam remained long enough
to work out final details for entry of the first SIL workers headed by
Bob Schneider. Then he flew back to Charlotte to assist in the
JAARS project.

When Harold Goodall arrived in Charlotte in the summer of 1962
to take over the leadership of JAARS, Cam felt he should go to
Colombia to help the Schneiders. Elaine and the three younger
children would return to Yarinacocha, Peru, where he would join
them later. This meant leaving Grace behind to attend high school
at Ben Lippen Academy, a Christian boarding school in the Great
Smokies just outside of Asheville. The parting was especially hard
for Elaine.

Cam was in and out of Colombia in the next few months. Bob
Schneider's first report was very encouraging. He had had good
cooperation from the Colombian government and from Catholic

missionaries. "We've put some teams in Catholic mission communities where they are enjoying beautiful hospitality. The Division of Indian Affairs has given us a fully equipped office in Bogotá."

In February 1963, however, Schneider made an emergency phone call to Cam, with the news that some of the bishops were beginning to have doubts about SIL. When Cam arrived Schneider showed him a newly published booklet that claimed to be a report of SIL activities in the country.

Cam's immediate reaction was "We must get this cleared up as soon as possible." First they called on Bishop Canyes, who greeted them with some reserve. Cam quickly asked permission to read aloud some of the charges in the booklet. Then he paused and said, "Bishop Canyes, the University of Oklahoma isn't a Southern Baptist school. The university might be very offended at this. And we certainly aren't translating a Baptist catechism. We translate only the Holy Scriptures and never even add doctrinal notes."

Bishop Canyes looked unsettled. "Evidently I have been misinformed," he admitted. "I'll take the little book off the bookstands."

"We'd be most pleased if you would," Cam said. I'm sure you want only the truth told. We need to know each other better. Perhaps you would tell us about your work in the jungle."

After a pleasant exchange, Bishop Canyes had an idea. "Why don't you speak to the Catholic missionary bishops who are meeting here in a few days. If you could tell them what you've just told me, I think they would understand."

Cam was only too happy to accept the invitation. After he and Schneider had been introduced and Cam had explained the work of SIL, a bearded Spanish bishop stood and said pointedly, "It's all right for Catholics and Protestants to be together in Bogotá with a Catholic church on this corner and a Protestant church on that corner. But out in the jungle it won't work. The Indians will just be puzzled at seeing two ways of worshipping God."

All eyes turned to Cam as he rose to reply.

"When I was in Brazil," he began slowly, "I heard how the Franciscans paddled a canoe for five days to take two of our linguists to a tribe. In Bolivia the good sisters nursed one of our radio men back to health. In Peru the monks and nuns have helped us more times than I can count. And of course we serve them too, when we have the opportunity, with our planes and other facilities. On the basis of our common love for God, we enjoy cordial relations.

"I'll admit we've never worked in a country where there were eighteen mission bishops as here. Doubtless we have much to learn in Colombia. But wherever we have worked thus far, the people see this loving cooperation, and say, 'That's true Christianity. That's the way it should be.' Furthermore, it seems to me this is what Pope John XXIII has been striving for."

"Yes, that's right," several bishops agreed.

"When we translate the Bible into the Indian tongues, we'll gladly provide copies for you," Cam continued.

"Would you include our footnotes?" one of the bishops asked.

"No, we couldn't do that. We're strictly nonsectarian. We can't prefer one group over another."

The meeting concluded amiably and the bishops seemed satisfied.

Anxious to keep their goodwill, Cam requested that SIL members in Colombia who were guests at Catholic mission stations attend mass "occasionally." When some members and supporters objected, he cited Paul's habit of attending synagogues as his precedent, adding, "I'm willing to attend any kind of worship, even a witch doctor's séance, if it opens the way to share the Word. We must not let old prejudices block the giving of the gospel to the tribes."

The next day Cam visited Bishop Canyes in his residence. Remembering the library of books and manuscripts the Bishop's brother had left him, Cam asked to see them. They were still in crates.

"Such books and manuscripts as these should be on shelves," Cam said. "Would you like to have one of our linguists catalogue them for you?"

The bishop was overwhelmed by the offer. "That would be marvelous!"

That afternoon Cam wrote Dr. Viola Waterhouse in Mexico, requesting her help in the special project.

After dinner Cam and Schneider talked a long while about the future of Colombia. "There are twice as many tribes here as in Peru," Schneider said. "We'll need lots of new personnel. Our rapid growth may bother the bishops."

"Well, if we follow the same policies that have worked in other countries, they'll see that we're here to serve, not to fight."

"Yes, Uncle Cam, but Colombia is different. We need you and Elaine. Peru is a chartered branch now; they could get along without you."

"Yarinacocha has been our home for seventeen years," Cam replied. "We love Peru."

"But we're just getting started here. Having the general director in Bogotá would encourage the group. Lois and I would stay on awhile and I'd work under you as we did in Lima."

"I'll pray about it," was as much as Cam would promise.

He wrote Elaine about moving to Colombia, and when he got to Lima he radioed her at the jungle base. "I've talked it over with the kids," Elaine told him. "They dearly love our home at Yarina. But if Colombia is what the Lord wants, then we'll move."

And so the decision was made. They would move, perhaps the hardest move they would make. At Yarinacocha they had had their first real home, the big house overlooking the lake where the children had spent their formative years. The fruit trees were just beginning to bear, and the hibiscus and bougainvillaea were never more beautiful.

Hardest of all was leaving friends. SIL members gave parties for them. Then Bishop Prevost and officials from Pucallpa came for a farewell tea. That was when it finally came home to ten-year-old Billy that he was really moving away, and he burst into tears.

Then there were farewell ceremonies in Lima planned by their Peruvian friends. Dr. Morote Best, who had directed the Indian teacher training course and was now rector of the University of Huamanga, granted Cam the title of Honorary Professor, and said of him, "You have given everything to Peru and taken nothing away."

There was a visit to President Fernando Belaunde Terry. And then a big banquet where the minister of education presented both Cam and Elaine Las Palmas Magisteriales awards, the highest honor Peruvian teachers can receive. The minister of foreign affairs pinned on them both Order of Distinguished Service awards.

The Lima newspapers published editorials about Cam. *The Expresso* called him "a truly extraordinary person," and went on to say:

He leaves the warm land of the Peruvian Amazon and his friends the Cashibos, Campas, Machiguengas, Piros, Culinas, and Amahuacas whom he taught to . . . know the existence of God and of Peru. . . . He came to give us his best. He takes with him the gratitude of thousands of dark-skinned men . . . and the heartfelt remembrance of Peruvian teachers who saw his work and had the privilege of working in the jungle at the side of a man of love and truth.

Even *Time* (the Latin American edition) took notice in its September 27, 1963, issue.

One day recently, Indians in the jungles of eastern Peru drummed a message on hollowed tree trunks: "Don Guillermo is leaving." Townsend was leaving Peru for Colombia, but 200 trained linguists and other personnel will carry on. His work had earned him Peru's Order of Merit, a warm farewell abrazo from President Fernando Belaunde Terry, and the affectionate title "Apostle of the Alphabet."

Close friends came to see them off on the steamer that would move them to Colombia. There was an emotional presenting of gifts and exchange of farewell *abrazos*. As the ship pulled away from the dock, Cam and Elaine stood at the rail waving until everyone was out of sight. As they turned to go to their cabin, Elaine saw tears streaming down Cam's face. She had never seen him so moved.

"God is calling us to take another step of faith."

31. The Pavilion of 2,000 Tribes

While the Townsends were living in Charlotte during 1962, Cam was introduced one day to a public relations man. After hearing a few stories about Wycliffe's work in Latin America, he said to Cam, "Your people ought to have a pavilion at the New York World's Fair. Even though it's a couple of years off, now is the time to start planning. And I have a friend on a Fair committee."

The idea stirred Cam's imagination. The publicity value of an exhibit there would be enormous. Not only would it bring Bible translation to the attention of the American public, but it would also introduce the work to foreign visitors.

"Yes, we might be interested," he responded. "Have your friend send me information and we'll consider it."

A few days later a packet came in the mail. Cam whistled as he realized a pavilion would cost at least a quarter of a million dollars. At the moment he had less than $250. It took so much to keep Wycliffe going. Still he felt there could have been something providential in bumping into the PR man. He would wait and see what else might develop.

He spent the rest of the summer on JAARS business, promoting the new headquarters in Mexico. He gave stories of the work to *Time*'s Jerry Hannifin in Washington, newspaper columnist George Grimm in Minneapolis, and world-famed photographer Cornell Capa in New York.

Cornell Capa had become interested in WBT/SIL after reporting the 1956 Auca killings for *Life*. He had visited Yarinacocha and seen the work in Peru first-hand. At the encouragement of Cam's friend Sam Milbank, Capa had teamed with anthropologist Matthew Huxley to produce a book on Peru's jungle Indians confronted by twentieth-century technology and civilization. In *Farewell to Eden*, published by Harper & Row, Capa and Huxley showed the challenge and responsibilities of the dominant culture and its "agents of change." They found that WBT/SIL alone possessed the philosophy and attitude most understanding of Indians' needs and most useful in preparing the jungle tribesmen for the inevitable confrontation with approaching civilization.

Capa was so impressed by the work of the SIL linguists that he volunteered to give his pictures and edit a book describing the work. Cam gratefully accepted the offer and the result was *Who Brought the Word*, a pictorial presentation of Bible translation.

At the board meeting in February 1963, held in Mexico City, Cam raised the subject of a pavilion at the World's Fair, but there was little response to his enthusiasm, and he dropped the subject. There was plenty of work to keep them all busy, and with membership at 1,500 and over, more funds were needed to support each worker and keep the growing number of planes in top shape.

At the biennial conference later that year news was both good and bad. Teams were now in Ghana and Nigeria. Translation workshops were proving so satisfactory that John Beekman and Ken Pike were predicting that many translators would be able to do two Testaments in a lifetime. Computer experts Drs. Joe Grimes and Ivan Lowe described how computers in Mexico City were greatly reducing the time it took to convert manuscripts into books. Literacy expert Dr. Sarah Gudchinsky felt the literacy workshops she was developing and holding would result in thousands of new readers for published Scriptures.

The bad news was from Vietnam. There had been an attack on Wycliffe personnel. The guerrilla grapevine said the linguists had been mistaken for government people. Gaspar Makil, a Filipino member, his infant daughter, and Elwood Jacobsen were dead. Calling them "Wycliffe's first martyrs," Cam challenged the membership: "The assassins did not know that Gaspar and Elwood were messengers of God's love sent to serve the tribesmen unselfishly, giving them Light and Life. We must forgive; we do forgive. But we cannot forget the two tribes that have been cheated nor the 2,000 more for whom no workers have ever been assigned.

"Bullets cannot thwart God's plan. We believe that a host of new recruits will pick up the task that fell from the hands of our martyred colleagues. . . . Wycliffe needs 200 more recruits this year. . . . By God's grace and with your help we plan to keep on until every tribe has heard the Good News."

Just before the Townsends moved to Colombia in August 1963, a Mrs. Myra Magnuson came to Yarinacocha from New York to see a private hospital near Pucallpa. She asked to stay at the SIL base for a few days. Cam and Elaine welcomed her, and took time to visit with her and tell her about the work.

"Everyone should know about this work," was Mrs. Magnuson's response. "You should have a pavilion at the World's Fair. The world must know what you are doing for the Indians. Listen, I know Bob Moses, the Fair manager. He'll give you a lot free, I'm sure. Then you'd just have to put up a pavilion. Call me next time you're in New York and I'll set up a meeting."

Later as Cam and Elaine talked, he said, "She's the second person who's talked to me about the Fair. Maybe God is trying to tell us something."

After the family had settled into their small apartment on the third floor of the rented group house in Bogotá, Cam took Grace back to school in North Carolina, and then flew on to New York. There he met with Cornell Capa to put the finishing touches on the book *Who Brought the Word*. He also called Myra Magnuson, who set up an appointment for him with the assistant manager of the World's Fair. He was impressed with Cam's idea of imitating a jungle hut and furnishing it with artifacts from primitive tribes.

"There'll be nothing else like it at the Fair," he said. "We'll give you a lot at the corner of the Avenues of America and Europe. It's a great location. But you must have money for the pavilion in three or four weeks and a guarantee that it would be open by next April." Cam was excited at the possibility.

When Cam left the next day for California, Mrs. Magnuson saw him off. "You must have that pavilion," she declared, and pressed a $1,000 check in his hand.

The night after arriving, Cam spoke at a church in Santa Ana and told about the offer of a free lot at the Fair and Mrs. Magnuson's contribution. Afterward, a retired missionary said, "My wife and I will give a thousand dollars."

The next day at lunch two relatives promised five thousand dollars. When the board convened, Cam recited what had happened. "God is calling us to take another step of faith. Think how many people will go through the pavilion during the two summers of the Fair!"

The more conservative board members were worried. "Uncle Cam, we love you," they said "but we've got too many other obligations to consider this."

"But we can sell books, charge an entrance fee. People will give donations," Cam pleaded.

"It's against our policy to go into debt beyond our resources," Pike protested.

"We could sell this building if we had to," Cam said. "The tremendous benefits of a pavilion would be worth it."

Most of the board members still were unconvinced. "All right," Cam declared, "suppose I found individuals who would underwrite a hundred thousand dollars. If we made enough money, they wouldn't be out a cent. I've got seven thousand dollars already."

They debated this proposal awhile, and finally decided Cam could proceed after he had the $100,000 underwritten.

Cam flew back to Charlotte and at noon began calling friends. At ten that evening he reached the mark when a farmer in Illinois said, "Put me down for five."

Lawrence Routh accompanied him to New York the next day to meet with contractor Ralph Howell and the Fair committee. The committee accepted the contractor's guarantee that he would complete the pavilion on schedule, and Cam signed the contract.

Through the fall and winter Cam kept boosting the World's Fair project. He felt that the planned Pavilion of 2,000 Tribes should not only contain rare tribal artifacts, large photographs and charts but should also portray graphically the power of Scripture in the lives of primitive tribesmen. What could be better, he decided, than the story of Chief Tariri painted as a mural. Former President Truman had told him it was the greatest story he had ever heard.

Charlotte restaurateur Frank Sherrill recommended Canadian muralist Doug Riseborough. He went to Peru and first photographed a reenactment of a tribal battle in the jungle. From this and other scenes on film, he painted a dramatic mural one hundred feet long and ten feet high depicting the transformation of Chief Tariri.

Cam also assigned Ethel Wallis to prepare Tariri's autobiography for Harper & Row, to be sold at the Fair. Then having secured $152,000 in cash, gifts, loans, and underwritings, with $18,000 more promised, he left in January 1964 to return to Colombia. There he joined Clarence Church, the new director, and pilot Ralph Borthwick in the search for a base site in eastern Colombia. They located "another Yarinacocha" beside a lake about 150 miles east of Bogotá. When Cam and Church explained their intended use to the Colombian Air Force Officer who owned the land, he donated the 250 acres to the government, which assigned it to SIL for the term of years needed.

Cam left his family again in April 1964 for the dedication of the Mexico Branch's Publication Building in Mexico City. It was named for Moisés Sáenz. President López Mateos himself presided over the inauguration ceremony. The minister of government of Colombia, Camacha Rueda, honored the linguists by attending.

Before leaving Mexico, Cam and Ben Elson talked about the need for an administrator in the California home office. "George Cowan has written that I should move to Santa Ana and be in charge, or else appoint someone," Cam told Elson. "Personally, I feel that my call is to stay pretty close to the firing line, so I'm thinking of asking the board to make you administrative head of all our work. I would just make suggestions and help on special projects."

"I don't know, Uncle Cam. That sounds like quite a job."

"You could do it," Cam said confidently. "Please pray about it. You and Adelle have done a bang-up job leading our oldest and largest branch. And you've worked in a tribe. It may well be, Ben, that you're God's man to lead us."

Shortly after the opening of the World's Fair in 1964, Cam went to New York. As he had predicted, the rustic, aboriginal hut was an interest-getter and stood in sharp contrast to the scientific exhibits, architectural marvels, and other displays of modern progress.

Thousands went through the pavilion, but by the end of the first month it was obvious that gifts and the sale of books would pay only the operating expenses. Cam sent out an appeal calling for 2,000 churches to buy a $100 share each to cover the construction costs. By September the board objectors were really disturbed. They called for an emergency session of the board to determine the future of the project.

Cam had been overoptimistic about the income from the pavilion, but he pointed out that closing it before the second summer would not pay the contractor or the debt to the underwriters. Feeling that it would be best not to attend the board meeting, he flew back to Colombia. A few days later he received a telegram telling him the board had voted to keep the pavilion open.

Relieved, Cam moved his family from Bogotá to the new base at

Loma Linda. They lived by the lake in one of two trailers donated by the Humble Oil Company, while a carpenter added three rooms. The two oldest girls, Grace and Joy, were going to school in Chicago, staying with Elaine's brother. Elainadel was taking her sophomore year by correspondence. Billy, a gangly sixth grader, attended the base school.

Cam was still as romantic as ever. For Elaine's birthday, he penned a jingle:

> She's forty-eight, my precious mate!
>   She's mighty fine, this wife of mine!
> She's young and gay, works every day,
>   To give me joy, she's sweet and coy,
> And smart! She's keen—the best I've seen!
>   And overall, she's heard God's call
> To serve the Lord at any cost.
> We pioneer and never fear.
> We'll e'er have fun till life is done.

Christmas passed and then Cam had his annual New Year's letter to Spanish friends to write. He always tried to include a spiritual message, then would add a personal greeting at the top. The list had grown longer each year.

When Elaine's father died at the end of 1964, Elaine brought her mother back with her to Loma Linda after the funeral. "Grandma" Mielke organized a much needed nursery school for the flock of preschoolers on the base, and her warm, loving smile soon endeared her to all the children.

Meanwhile Cam was out making friends in the adjoining town of Puerto Lleras. He won the friendship of the mayor and the local priest, whom he invited to attend Bible study at the base. The JAARS center in North Carolina was progressing nicely under Goodall's leadership. Lawrence Routh was devoting six months to promote JAARS, the Fair pavilion, and other special projects at banquets.

Ben Elson had been approved for executive director, and he and his wife Adelle were to leave Mexico for Santa Ana on February 1. With the Elsons at the international headquarters, Cam thought that Wycliffe would have good, persuasive leadership.

Despite the internal disagreement over the Fair project, 202 new members had been received in 1964—the highest number to that time. By the spring of 1965 membership was pushing 1,600. It looked as if total donations might exceed three million dollars. This included $100,000 from the International Lutheran Women's Missionary League, the first denominational group to help. They were backing a translation center in Nigeria where both Wycliffe linguists and Lutheran missionaries worked.

The Fair debt was still a worry, even though support was picking up. Lawrence Routh's banquets for "Operation 2000" were arousing interest. And Chief Tariri had been invited to be a special guest of the Fair at the end of July. Don Burns would bring him up from Peru. The Harper & Row biography of Tariri would be out then, and the publisher had some important appearances lined up. July 28, Peru's Independence Day, would be Peru Day at the Fair, with appropriate ceremonies. Dr. Alberto Escobar, one of Peru's top educators, was also coming to show Peru's appreciation of SIL's service.

Cam, Elaine, and the children came up from Colombia ahead of the Peruvian party. In New York they found crowds streaming through the Pavilion of 2,000 Tongues. Attendance was up over the previous year, but receipts from gifts and books still only paid operating expenses.

On July 26 Chief Tariri and Don Burns arrived in New York, with Dr. Escobar representing President Belaunde Terry, and Doris Cox and Lorrie Anderson as interpreters. Tariri was interviewed by reporters, news services, radio stations and programs, including the Today show on the 28th. One interview was given from the gondola of the Goodyear blimp, a story that won a two-page spread in the *Journal-American Sunday Magazine.*

On Peru's Independence Day, July 28, Tariri spent the day at the Fair. At the news conference that morning he told reporters, "My heart used to be bad, but since Jesus came into my heart, I've stopped thinking bad things. Look at all God has given you! Why don't you think of Him?" Later in the day the conference was featured on the Huntley-Brinkley newscast.

In the afternoon there was a ceremony on the rear lawn of the pavilion, with Dr. Escobar, *Señorita* Rosa Corpancho, representing the Peruvian Ministry of Education, and other dignitaries. When Tariri spoke, with Lorrie Anderson interpreting, his regal bearing and forceful speech kept the crowd transfixed.

At 9:15 P.M. a big audience gathered around Dr. Escobar and Tariri at the Fair's Tower of Light. Educator and converted savage placed their hands on the switch in the center of the pagoda. At the given moment they pushed the switch. The mighty beacon pierced the night for a distance of 250 miles.

Cam closed with an eloquent dedication.

As Chief Tariri's hand, guided by the hand of the personal representative of the president of his country, has turned on the most powerful light in the world, even so the Wycliffe Bible Translators and the Summer Institute of Linguistics in coordination with the ministries of education and the various countries where they labor, as well as the universities and their institutions of learning and research, are bringing the torch of enlightenment to once-forgotten tribes through bilingual education and giving them, in their own exotic tongues, the greatest spiritual light in the world—The Bible.

We further dedicate this act that has taken place on the 144th anniversary of the Independence of Peru to the cause of freedom, reminding ourselves that all men were indeed created free and equal and that they have an equal right to the Light—the Word and the Life abundant.

The Tariri party, including Cam, went on tour the next day, stopping in Philadelphia, Charlotte, Oklahoma City, and finally Dallas, where Tariri preached three times at the First Baptist Church to packed out audiences.

The debt that remained after the Fair closed was a concern to everyone. Most of the underwriters paid their pledges as donations. Two who had underwritten five thousand gave twice that much. Hundreds of Wycliffe members sacrificed from their meager allowances.

Cam felt the results had been worth all the sweat, strain, and struggle. Over a million visitors had seen the exhibit, with some 632,000 taking time to listen to the narration of Tariri's conversion while viewing the great mural. Articles had been published in over 100 newspapers and magazines with a circulation of seventy million. Fifty thousand copies of the Tariri book had been sold. (At Cam's suggestion a portion of royalties had gone to the chief.) People from scores of nations had learned for the first time of the over 2,000 Bibleless tribes and many had decided to help the Summer Institute of Linguistics and Wycliffe do something about it.

"I just wish some of our brethren would wake up to the changes taking place in the Catholic Church."

32. Winds of Change

Colombia was doing well under Director Clarence Church, so Cam felt the family should live in Charlotte during the winter of 1965–66. Here he was near the growing JAARS center and available for public relations work.

As the need arose he traveled—Washington, New York, Philadelphia, California for board meetings, back to Charlotte. Then to Chicago for the funeral of his dear friend Henry Crowell. The loss of such a partner made him feel as he had when Nyman went.

He and Elaine continually marveled at the Lord's provision through friends. They resided again at the riverfront home of Henderson and Ann Belk. Cam wore a broad-brimmed white Texas Stetson, a gift from a friend in Dallas, a topcoat that had been his cousin's, and traveled with second-hand suitcases. When the coat was stolen out of his car, he went to Goodwill Industries and bought another for fifty cents.

December was a busy month with family festivities and Cam's letter to Latin American friends which he sent out at New Year every year. Then there were the plans for Grace's coming marriage in Chicago to a young Christian engineer, Tom Goreth, in February 1966.

Cam could never let an opportunity go by of presenting the need of Bibleless tribes, and at the wedding supper, attended by 250 guests, he gave a rousing challenge for Bible translation. "Remember the story in Luke about the great man's supper?" he asked. "The first people he invited made excuses not to come, so the man sent his servant into the streets to invite the poor, the maimed, the halt and the blind. When they came there was yet room so he told the servant, 'Go out into the highways and hedges, and compel them

239

to come in, that my house may be filled.' Out there in the jungles and distant mountains of the world are *two thousand tribes* who have never heard. Who here will hear the call to take the Word of God to those who have never heard?"

After the wedding, life settled down to the normal hectic routine for the Townsends. On one trip to Washington, Cam talked to Oklahoma's Senator Fred Harris, a friend for several years, about an idea he had.

"September 30 is St. Jerome's Day. He's the first translator of the whole Bible. I thought maybe we could get the House and Senate to pass a resolution calling for the president to proclaim September 30 as Bible Translation Day. The Apache chief Geronimo, who was probably named for Jerome, must have been born on September 30. And the American Bible Society just published our Apache New Testament."

"And you want me to introduce the resolution in the Senate?" Harris asked.

"I was hoping you would. It would be a natural since you're from Oklahoma and our main linguistic course is there at the university. We'd need a Congressman to do the same in the House. Maybe you could get me an appointment at the White House?"

"All right, Uncle Cam. I'll take your materials for reference in preparing the resolution, but I don't know about the White House. I'll try."

Even though Cam was nearing 70, he wasn't slowing down much. After resting briefly at home, he flew first to Mexico City to help the Mexican Branch's new director, Dr. Frank Robbins, with some government contacts, then on to Bogotá for more of the same with Colombia Director Clarence Church.

While in Bogotá he discussed with Clarence Church a book he liked. "I wish all our evangelical brethren could read Father Grassi's *A World to Win*. It sounds as if someone from Dallas or Fuller Seminary who had strong indoctrination on Wycliffe methods wrote it, instead of a professor from a school that trains Catholic missionaries. Father Grassi did take our course at the University of Oklahoma years ago, you know.

"I just wish some of our brethren would wake up to the changes taking place in the Catholic Church. One of these days we'll have a Catholic applicant for membership. That's when our nonsectarian policy will really be tested."

From Bogotá Cam went on to Lima, where Elaine, Mrs. Mielke, and Mrs. Will Nyman joined him for the twentieth anniversary celebration of SIL in Peru.

Before the celebration got underway President Fernando Belaunde Terry invited Cam to lunch. Belaunde had recently visited Yarinacocha. "Your people are doing a great work for our Indians," he said. "But what really impressed me at the base was hearing your school children sing our national Peruvian anthem."

Cam grinned. "We've tried to teach them to be good citizens of your country."

Next came a ceremony at the University of San Marcos where Cam was awarded an honorary doctorate. Although he had declined three such degrees from schools in the States, he felt this honor from his beloved Peru could not be refused.

There followed a big banquet given by Minister of Education Dr. Cueto Fernandini. The minister introduced dignitaries present, using a long list of impressive titles—Minister, Senator, Ambassador, etc. When he came to Cam, he said, "And—Uncle Cam—as he is to all of us who know and love him."

Then Dr. and Mrs. Cueto Fernandini and a planeload of officials flew with the SIL party to the base for more festivities. Bishop Prevost and the military commander from Pucallpa joined them there to celebrate Cam's seventieth birthday. Bishop Prevost told Cam that his home Bible study groups were going very well.

Cam was pleased with the report of Director Gene Loos: 21 Peruvian tribes with one or more books of the Bible, 211 Indian teachers in government employ from 18 tribes at the last training course, and about 5,000 children enrolled in the government's bilingual schools. "Some of the Amueshas have organized their own churches and have applied for membership in the Peruvian Evangelical Union, and they have their own Bible school. There are several thousand Aguaruna believers. Revenge killing is on the way out. There are new groups of believers in other tribes, too."

The report was the best birthday present Cam received.

After three weeks in Peru, Elaine and her mother returned to the States and Cam went on to Brazil where he helped Director Jim Wilson on some aviation matters. Because of the vastness of the country, the group had five regional bases. Besides Brazilia, Cam visited two others and conferred with translators.

In the state of Matto Grosso he was especially thrilled at the report of Ivan Lowe and Menno Kroeker serving the Nambiquara tribe. "We were the first outsiders ever to spend a night in a Nambiquara village. Now there are new Christians reading Scripture in their own language and writing their own hymns. The Nambiquaras attacked the first missionaries trying to reach them about forty years ago—and killed two of them and a baby."

As Cam listened his memory was stirred and suddenly he felt the hair rise on the back of his neck. The Nambiquaras! Yes, that was the tribe that killed Arthur Tylee! Thirty-six years ago he had heard about the massacre while he and Elvira were checking proofs on the Cakchiquel New Testament in Chicago.

Cam returned to Charlotte for a few days with his family. He played Billy a few games of Ping-Pong at the Belk riverside home. "Either you're getting better or I'm getting older, Son," Cam commented. "I can only beat you two games out of three now."

At seventy he could feel himself slowing down, but only slightly. He napped a half hour or more after lunch now and tried to be in bed by 9:30 or 10. But by 6:30 he was usually up, reading the Bible, praying around the world, planning, figuring.

September came and he was in Washington attending to last-minute details for the September 30th Bible Translation Day celebration. Wycliffe, the Lutheran Bible Translators, and the Catholic Biblical Association were sponsoring the event. The Bible translation resolution had passed the Senate, but not the House, so there was no presidential proclamation as Cam had hoped.

On the 30th Senator Harris welcomed about a hundred guests, representatives of the Bureau of Indian Affairs, church leaders, missionaries, press, and others to the observance. Mrs. Britton Goode, an Apache Indian from Arizona, cut the red ribbon that encircled the Senate proclamation. Morris Watkins, head of the new Lutheran Bible Translation Society, Dr. Louis Hartman, a Bible scholar at Catholic University, and Cam gave short challenges for a speed-up in Bible translation. Britton Goode, in his colorful Apache costume, solemnly presented Apache New Testaments to Senator Harris and Congressman Ben Reifel, a Sioux Indian from South Dakota. Then he thanked translators Faye Edgerton and Faith Hill who had worked twenty-five years to complete the Apache Testament.

A few minutes later the program leaders met in a presidential office and Britton Goode presented a New Testament to President

Johnson's representative, aide Mike Manakos. Cam had hoped to see the president in person, but was pleased with what he felt was one more opportunity to alert the world to the call of the Bibleless tribes. "Next year we'll do it again," he said, "and keep reminding people of the challenge."

When he arrived back in Charlotte, there was a report, not unexpected, that a young Catholic scholar had applied for membership. Scores of priests and nuns had taken SIL training, but until Paul Witte, none had asked to join Wycliffe.

Young Witte seemed to meet the qualifications—educational background, linguistic training, personal character, emotional stability, consent to the Wycliffe doctrinal statement, etc. He gave a strong evangelical testimony that he knew Christ as Savior. He was engaged to a Salvation Army girl who had already been accepted for membership, pending the meeting of certain academic requirements.

Witte said he wanted to be a Bible translator. He did not hold to some traditional Catholic doctrines which are generally objectionable to evangelicals. The hitch was his statement, "I wish to remain a member in good standing of the Catholic Church."

Cam saw no reason why Witte shouldn't be taken in, "if we are true to our stated policy of being nonsectarian. We must not depart from our nonsectarian policy one iota if we are to keep entering countries closed to traditional missionary organizations," he said in a letter to the membership.

Cam was both praised and criticized by Wycliffe members for his stand. Most of the critics said they were not opposed to Witte personally, but feared the reaction of some members and supporters. Some frankly admitted a pragmatic concern: loss of support.

Cam was unbending. He wrote one dissenter:

I object to being forced to take a sectarian attitude that would rob us of many opportunities for Bible translation work. My one goal is that the Word of God be given at long last to 2,000 tribes. Somebody must look ahead and see what is needed to get the Word to the tribes that live in Moslem or Communist lands or behind doors that are closed otherwise. For this type of work the nonsectarian core of SIL and WBT must be preserved. If we are misjudged for this by some, so that support is cut off for some of our workers, God will supply from other sources. He has thus far and He will.

John Beekman expressed the sentiments of many members when he said, "Uncle Cam is probably right. He may be ten years ahead of the rest of us, as usual."

The discussion was long and spirited. The issue was, as it had been in the 1949 debate over the admittance of Pentecostals, "compatibility versus incompatibility." The simple question was: Would a Catholic be compatible within the membership? When the vote was finally tallied, the delegates said no by a two to one margin.

Cam confessed his disappointment over this major defeat, but added, "What the majority of you did here will not stop God. Nor will it stop Elaine and me from loving you and from going on in faith."

From Mexico the Townsends flew to Bogotá for the fifth anniversary of work in Colombia. After the big banquet, Cam told Bishop Canyes about Witte's being turned down.

"Our folks were just too narrow," he confessed. "Too afraid to risk offending some supporters. What do you think of Witte working with your Capuchin missionaries? He could go to our jungle camp and later receive technical help from our group here. What matters is that he and his wife give the Bible to a tribe."

Bishop Canyes appreciated Cam's forthrightness. "Yes, I think we could take them," he said. "But we don't have the funds to pay a full salary."

"Elaine and I will help," Cam volunteered. "And Father Louis Hartman might get some money from the Catholic Biblical Association."

"Tell them to come on then," the bishop declared.

Back in the U.S., Cam and Elaine saw Joy and Elainadel enrolled in Columbia Bible College and Billy entered as a high school student at Ben Lippen. Then they went to Memphis to get acquainted with and encourage Paul and Ginny Witte.

"I marvel at your patience, Paul," Cam told his young Catholic friend. "But the Lord is with us. Everything is all set with Bishop Canyes for you to go to Colombia. Besides translating God's Word for a tribe, you'll be a valuable bridge down there between our group and the bishops. However, you should first go to jungle camp. We've let a few nonmembers take the training," Cam assured him. "Go on and apply."

Then it was on to Dallas where Cam met with a civic committee about moving the Wycliffe home office there. The old building in

Santa Ana had been inadequate for years, and additional space was being rented several blocks away. The 1967 conference had decided to move to the Dallas area if certain conditions were met.

The president of the Dallas Chamber of Commerce was at the airport to award Cam the key to the city "in honor of the fiftieth anniversary of your beginning work in Guatemala." Cam blinked in surprise that the Dallas people were aware of the dates.

Cam looked at two sites, then flew to Washington to help Dale Kietzman, now the director of extension for Wycliffe, with the last-minute preparations for the second annual Bible translation cere-mony. Elaine continued on with speaking engagements. Senator Carl Curtis presided at the ceremony and Senator Mark Hatfield was one of the speakers. Translator Wayne Snell introduced two Machiguenga Indians as products of Bible translation.

Three days later in Guatemala, educators and officials from four Latin American countries joined in celebrating the fiftieth an-niversary of Cam's arrival there.

Cam and Elaine were received by the president of the republic and the archbishop of Guatemala. The mayor of Guatemala City made him an "honorary citizen" of the capital and the minister of foreign affairs awarded him the Order of the Quetzal, by disposition of the president of the republic. The vice president of Ecuador, who had come for the occasion, spoke at a special program in the munici-pal palace.

After several tributes from visiting dignitaries for SIL's work in their lands, Cam rose to respond, recalling how the Cakchiquel Indian Francisco Diaz had opened his eyes to the need of giving people the Word in their own tongues.

Then accompanied by Elaine and Mrs. Mielke, Cam motored over the green mountains to San Antonio, following the path he had taken by coach and on muleback a half century before. The San Antonio school was still going. Cam was delighted to find that the principal was an alumnus of the school. That night hundreds of Cakchiquels jammed one of the evangelical churches to hear their beloved *don Guillermo* speak in their own language.

From San Antonio the party moved on west, stopping in Indian towns along the way. In one town there had been one congregation when Cam left thirty-five years before. Now there were ten. In another large town the Indians said almost half the population were believers. The Cakchiquel tribe had grown to 250,000 of whom

50,000 or more were believers. At Tecpan they attended a wedding. The bride was the granddaughter of old friends.

At Patzun Cam met more old-timers. Five hundred believers gathered in one of the churches to hear him speak. Some Indians brought fading copies of the Cakchiquel New Testament. "When will some new ones be printed, *don Guillermo?*" they asked. He promised to see about that.

The sentimental journey climaxed in restful Panajachel by the beautiful lake. Pointing to a huge Chinese litchi that spread its umbrellalike shade beside the old mission home near the lakeshore, Cam told Elaine with awe and satisfaction, "I planted that when it was a little sapling forty years ago. Look at its enormous size now!"

Below: Cam preaches to his old congregation in Tetelcingo while Martín Méndez, Aztec preacher and former mayor of the town, listens. *Above:* Méndez preaches while Cam looks on.

Tzeltal Indian chief Marcos Encin
shares a hymnbook with Cam.

Part III
NEW BEGINNINGS

"We will assist in any way we can to promote peace and goodwill between our countries."

33. To the Soviet Union

As Cam looked back on the fifty years since he'd gone to Guatemala and the thirty-five years of SIL and Wycliffe, the old litchi tree at Panajachel seemed somehow symbolic of the tremendous growth of the work God had led him into.

But trees keep growing. And Cam never looked back for long. His eyes were again on the future. "Elaine and I want to invest our next years where they will count the most," he wrote the membership. "We'll have to learn a new language, adjust to a new way of life. . . . Pray for us as we make plans to go to the U.S.S.R."

Russia had beckoned Cam for many years, especially since he had learned of the more than 100 languages spoken in the Caucasus and the successful work of the U.S.S.R. in teaching these many language groups to read not only their own language but Russian. The success was achieved through bilingual education—something Cam had been advocating for almost fifty years.

Being relatively free of family responsibilities—one daughter married, two in college, and Billy in boarding school—Cam and Elaine decided to make Mexico City their base for awhile. In the fall of 1967, after their nostalgic time in Guatemala, they moved into an apartment at the SIL headquarters. Elaine's mother decided to remain for a few months and help with the housework.

They went daily to the home of a Russian woman for classes, and Elaine spent four and five hours a day studying. But Cam kept getting sidetracked with business, although he kept his vocabulary cards with him. At dinner one evening he tried out a sentence he had memorized in Russian on their guests from the Russian embassy. "If I didn't believe God would help me, I'd give up studying this difficult language!" Their guests laughed appreciatively.

251

Cam followed the same approach with the Soviet diplomats he had pursued with Latin Americans for fifty years: personal interest, openness and friendship. His friendship with and esteem for Cárdenas was a natural entrée with many of the Russians who also admired the Mexican reformer. He never disguised his desire to translate the Bible into some of the minority languages of the U.S.S.R., and he stressed the benefits of scientific collaboration and friendship.

At the same time he kept busy with WBT/SIL affairs. He continued to feel a keen responsibility for the expansion of the membership. To over one hundred presidents of Christian colleges, seminaries, and Bible institutes, he wrote letters asking for their interest and help in having workers in "two thousand more languages by 1985."

Cam also urged the board to reconsider their requirement that applicants from non-English-speaking countries learn English. "A linguistic organization like ours should be able to train leaders who speak other languages so they could integrate other nationalities into our program," he insisted. But despite Cam's protests, the board continued to hold speaking English a necessity for "compatibility." However, they did begin accepting non-English speakers with the provision they learn English during orientation.

He also wanted headquarters personnel to do more to recruit black members. At the time the only black member was a widow serving in the Philippines.

Racial discrimination in the United States had long bothered him, although it took the assasination of Martin Luther King to rouse his deepest concern. The day before the civil rights leader's funeral, he wrote a letter to the membership that was part a confession and part a plea for members to become more involved with blacks.

Americans everywhere must be searching their hearts. I am mine. What have I done to help my fellow citizens whose complexion is darker than my own? Oh, when we lived in North Carolina I attended Negro churches eight or nine times, but I didn't visit in their homes or invite them to spend a social evening in mine. I maintained that I loved them, but where was the practical demonstration of that love? I lied. You call on people you love.

Let's put ourselves in other people's shoes—people who differ from us in color, in religion, in social status, educationally or politically. We say that we love them all, but do we? Do we not act

toward them in a discriminatory way or at least ignore them? Dear
fellow workers, we need to search our souls. Are we living a lie?

As regards the Negroes, we have invited them to special gatherings
at our JAARS center in North Carolina. A few have attended but we
haven't really shown them love and Christian fellowship as far as I
know. Worse, we have gone along with certain prevalent attitudes
even though they were obnoxious to us. Another question: Are we
doing all we can to get Negro members? Shouldn't we assign someone to visit their colleges with the challenge of Bible translation
work and assure them that we would welcome more Negro members? . . .

When will prejudice, discrimination and hatred cease? When
Christ takes complete possession of our lives and of the world. For
the latter, His Word in every tongue is a vital factor—possibly a pre-
requisite.

Forward then, in the spirit of Him who died for all men regardless
of race, and who wants us all to be brothers and children of God
through faith in Him. Yours in memory of Martin Luther King.

Early in the summer of 1968, Cam wrote to the Soviet Academy
of Science in Moscow, requesting an invitation to visit the Soviet
Union for six months. He noted that several years before, the
Soviet Ambassador in Washington had recommended a trip to
Moscow for contacts with linguists. "We were too deeply involved
in South America then," he told the Academy. "My wife and I can
come now."

The first response was, "An invitation will not be extended this
year, but maybe next." Cam immediately wrote the Academy,
"When you're past seventy, as I am, it is hard to wait another year.
We are willing to be responsible for our own expenses if you will
invite us now."

At the time they did not have the money for one-way transporta-
tion to Russia, and they would need living expenses for six months.
But their faith was boosted by an unexpected gift of $1,000 from
Elaine's mother.

And then in September the invitation came. Elaine was in the
States seeing the children off to school, and Cam phoned her from
Mexico City. "Can you be ready to leave in ten days? I've booked
seats on a flight leaving New York on Wednesday, October 2. I want
to get to the U.S.S.R. on the third, the 51st anniversary of my
arrival in Guatemala."

The next day Elaine called eighty-two people to tell them they were going and asked them to pray. One was Pastor Charles Blair at the Calvary Temple in Denver. "We'll pray around the clock," he promised, and then sent $1,000. Smaller gifts came from other friends—enough for the trip. Elaine also wrote a prayer letter and sent it to over 1,000 friends. She was packed and ready to go when Cam arrived from Mexico.

From almost their first day in Moscow, the Mexican and Colombian diplomats were the Townsends' warm friends and boosters. They introduced them to Russians interested in Latin America who joined the Latins in taking them sightseeing, to a ballet and concert, and to favorite restaurants. The best opportunities to explain the work of WBT/SIL came later when Cam and Elaine showed films at institutes and universities. The films provoked questions that made it easy for Cam to tell about Tariri, Manuel Arenas, and other Indians who had been changed through the Bible.

Cam and Elaine had the gift of seeing the best in everything. The banners calling for "Peace" and "International Goodwill" impressed them more than the tanks and missiles which they viewed from their hotel window on the fifty-first anniversary of the Russian Revolution. However, plain-clothes police spotted Elaine holding a microphone out of a window to record the music and speeches and came to investigate.

Rather than being insulted, Cam commented, "In view of what happened from a window in Dallas, we understand your concern."

As he had done in Mexico, Cam wrote articles for the Soviet Press and dispatches on Soviet life for U.S. newspapers which pleased his hosts. For example, he reported for a North Carolina newspaper:

Friendship is the offspring of respect. We found many things in the USSR that merited respect and admiration. Everyone works and there are jobs for all. I am old-fashioned enough to admire hard-working men, but I found it difficult to get accustomed to seeing women driving tractors, running hotels and banks and operating radio stations.

They stayed in the National Hotel overlooking Red Square. Language study and writing took five and six hours of each day. For breaks they took short walks across the great Square, bundled in heavy coats.

As Christmas approached the children seemed even further away. This would be the first time none of the children would be with them for the holidays. Cam wrote a long letter recounting memories of Christmases past, mailing a copy to each. Elaine bought a tiny artificial fir tree and balanced it on a towel-covered suitcase. When the floor supervisor saw the tree, the Christmas cards, the family photographs and Indian weavings scattered around, she smiled and said, "This isn't a hotel room, this is a home."

Ethel Wallis joined them after Christmas for travel into the Caucasus areas where many minority group languages are spoken. Their itinerary was arranged by their official hosts. It was supposed to be warmer in the fabled region between the Black and Caspian Seas, but their plane landed at Baku in a snowstorm. The warm greeting of the head of the foreign language department at the local university, however, more than compensated for the cold.

Every day of the first week they visited an educational institution, conferred with educators, showed films, recorded exotic languages, examined bilingual texts, visited museums (some of which were former mosques), attended the opera, and enjoyed meals in the homes of hospitable linguists and educators.

They followed this pattern for seven weeks, moving from town to town by train or plane, marveling at the unity that had been wrought in the mosaic of cultures in this part of the Caucasus. Educators showed them how illiteracy had practically been erased and proudly displayed bilingual texts. Lenin himself, they said, had insisted that each minority group be taught to read first in its own language, then in the national Russian language. In some areas this had involved the use of three different alphabets! The linguistic groups had been encouraged to develop their individual cultures and languages with newspapers, magazines, and even radio stations and theaters. Cam, Elaine and Ethel saw ample evidence that all this was so.

An intriguing legend about the origin of the languages in the Caucasus was told them. "The story is that an angel flew over the land distributing languages. He flew too close to a cliff and ripped his bag on a sharp crag. Several dozen of the languages fell out."

At Mahachkala, a "linguist's paradise," they saw bearded oldsters walking firm of foot toward markets. When local hosts boasted that some of the residents had celebrated 100th wedding anniversaries, Cam responded smiling, "If I could be sure I'd be rewarded with a hundred years with my Elaine, I'd surely move here."

At Sochi, the popular resort beside the Black Sea, local scholars took the three Americans to a "Friendship" citrus tree on which 130 grafts had been made. The agronomist in charge handed Cam a tiny knife and a limb. Cam made his graft, remarking, "We need a tree like this in Peru. Someone from each of the jungle tribes could make a graft."

The director of the Armenian Linguistic Institute showed them a petrified Bible. Cam wondered if the archaic translation could be read by the people. "Only priests and scholars can now read the ancient Bible language," he was told. "The ordinary people cannot understand it when they hear it."

Later another Armenian mentioned the infamous religious massacre of 1915, in which a million-and-a-half of his people were killed, as "proof that God couldn't possibly exist."

"That only proves there is a devil," Cam replied.

In discussions with educators, Cam suggested that SIL linguists could help in the Caucasus by comparing languages and lecturing on linguistic theories. They also would like to translate portions of the Bible. One linguist appeared surprised. "We are atheists. We could never allow that." Then he seemed to have second thoughts. "Well, we do record the ancient legends of the people. The Bible could fall into that category."

Cam and Elaine were tremendously impressed with the educational wonders achieved through bilingual education. Having seen what had also been accomplished in Latin American countries, Cam was anxious to push the benefits of this approach in other countries, including the U.S.

Before returning to Moscow in late February, Cam wrote the president of the Academy of Science about a contractual agreement. The Russian scholar replied that exchanges of linguists could be made on the basis of an existing arrangement with the American Council of Learned Societies.

In Moscow a farewell dinner was given in their honor by the Academy. Afterwards Cam told the director of the Foreign Department of the Academy, "I'm going to talk to an American publisher about the great strides you've made in bilingual education. The world should know about this. We will assist in any way we can to promote peace and goodwill between our countries."

In 1969 at Sochi on the Black Sea in the U.S.S.R., Cam and Elaine each put a graft on the International Friendship Tree which bears several kinds of citrus fruit.
Above: Cam points to the signatures in the guest book being held by the agronomist in charge of the experimental farm where the tree is.
Left: Cam and Elaine with Russian dignitaries walk to the International Friendship Tree.

Cam and Elaine spent the winter of 1969 in the U.S.S.R. Here they stand in front of the Kremlin in Moscow.

*"Instead of two hundred new members a year
. . . we must have four hundred if we're to have
translators in every tribe by 1985."*

34. The Legendary "Uncle Cam"

The trip to the U.S.S.R. was over and Cam and Elaine were home.
Their most immediate need now was a permanent home for the
Townsends. After considering several possibilities, they decided on
a wooded lot in the Waxhaw area, to be near the JAARS center.

The responsibility for planning and building the house fell on
Elaine, and she sketched a rough plan for a multipurpose house.
There would be a lower basement level with a recreation room large
enough for group meetings for the JAARS people, and arranged so
it could be used as an apartment for Wycliffe members needing
temporary housing near the JAARS center. The main level would
have an office for Elaine near the kitchen to save as many steps as
possible. She still had problems stemming from the 1947 plane
accident. A large combination living room-dining room would be
on the same level as well as the bedrooms, bathrooms and laundry
room. Upstairs, Cam's office would have a rear balcony shaded by
a huge beech tree. There would also be an efficiency apartment
with separate entrance for use by JAARS trainees, visiting Wycliffe
members and friends.

While Cam was away in Mexico for the dedication of the branch
headquarters building, Elaine interrupted the house-building to
launch a whirlwind thirty-day coast-to-coast speaking tour about their
trip to the U.S.S.R. After one speech, a long-time financial supporter
lectured her sternly for being "taken in by the communists."

Reduced to tears by the tongue-lashing, she finally managed to
say, "We didn't go to the U.S.S.R. to find fault. We went to see
how we could serve and pave the way for the Bible to be translated
into more languages."

Upon completing the exhausting forty-eight-stop circuit, Elaine

259

returned to Charlotte to oversee the building of the house. She
started with about $10,000 from the earmarked donations and the
sale of their two South American houses, paying bills as they were
received.

Meanwhile, Cam was busy in Mexico City. The latest building
at the Mexican headquarters contained administrative and business
offices, computer equipment to speed translation work, a museum
for tribal artifacts, a library, and an auditorium. It was named for
the recently deceased former president, López Mateos, who had
helped them get the land. The auditorium in the building was
named for long-time friend Aarón Sáenz and the library for long-
time benefactor Ramón Beteta, who had also recently died. From
the giant sandstone mosaic portraying an Indian carrying a torch
on the façade over the entrance to the portraits of distinguished
Latin Americans looking down on the corridors, everything was
distinctly Mexican. With these facilities the Mexican Branch could
host the biennial conference of delegates from the fields that now
practically spanned the globe.

Because it was nearing conference time, Cam decided to stay on
in Mexico. During the short interim he made a quick trip in early
May 1969 to Colombia. Here he talked with various officials about
the Colombia Branch's participating in the hoped-for agreement
with the Soviet Union.

Returning to Mexico City, he reported to the biennial conference
that officials in Colombia would favor an exchange agreement between the Colombian WBT/SIL branch and the Soviet Academy
of Science in Moscow. The conference authorized Cam to proceed
with the agreement as outlined.

While the delegates marveled at this further extension of Cam's
audacious faith, some were not happy with his handling of the Paul
Wittes' support. After the 1967 biennial had voted that a Catholic
member would be "incompatible," Cam had recommended that the
Colombia branch engage Witte as an employee and pay him a small
wage. This, when added to the allowance from Bishop Canyes's
mission, Cam felt, would be enough to support the Wittes in tribal
work. Cam pointed out that Catholic nationals were employed for
various duties on bases and in group offices, and that hiring Witte
as a "consultant" would be no different.

Hearing that the Colombia branch had taken this action, the

Mexican branch had discussed the matter at their regular conference. The consensus was that their sister branch had violated the 1967 resolution, and they had voted to ask the WBT/SIL board to take action, requesting their Colombia colleagues to end Witte's employment status. The board had done so, though some members disagreed.

At the 1969 biennial of the whole organization, there was some feeling that Cam had violated the will of the 1967 delegates. There were also strong hints that he was getting too old for the job of general director.

But the issue was not brought to the floor. Cam's example in past service overrode any opposition that might have arisen. Many delegates were thinking not just of his achievements, but of acts of menial service they had seen him perform. One recalled in a corridor conversation, "He was at my house when my wife and I were called to attend an important meeting. 'Go on,' he said. 'I'll finish washing the dishes.' He insisted that we—his hosts—allow him—the general director—to do this menial task. Although I find myself disagreeing with some of his ideas, it's hard to speak against him."

So the opposition did not show itself and Cam moved ahead with his challenge for the future. "Instead of two hundred members a year, which is wonderful," he said, "we must have four hundred if we're to have translators in every tribe by 1985."

One evening after a session Dick Pittman cornered Cam about his future travel plans. "I'm going to write a book on bilingual education in the Caucasus," he told the deputy director for Asia. "That requires that we go back to Russia in the fall to do more research. On the way home we thought we might visit the Wycliffe fields in Asia and the Pacific."

"They won't believe it until they see you," Dick said. "We've been trying for years to get you to fields outside this hemisphere."

Cam sighed. "I know, Dick. But I've always been skittish about leaving my area of experience. Besides you've done such a great job leading advances, I felt I wasn't needed."

Pittman grinned. "Your coming will certainly make the branches happy, Uncle Cam. I hope you can do it."

Early in the fall Cam was in Washington, D.C., arranging for visas from the Russian embassy. Ben Elson and Morris Watkins, director of the Lutheran Bible Translators, joined him there for a conference. Watkins reported a half dozen members already serving jointly with his organization and Wycliffe, with forty more ready for training.

"Think what could be done by ten denominational groups like yours, Morrie," Cam sighed. "Add them to Wycliffe and every tribe would really be reached by 1985."

Elson had been visiting Wycliffe fields in the Pacific and Asia. "The Wycliffe members are all looking forward to you and Elaine coming," he told Cam. "You can't disappoint them now."

Cam pulled a paper from his pocket. "Here's our itinerary. We leave for Russia next week, spend a month in the Caucasus getting more information and pictures for the book. Then starting in November we go to India, Nepal, the Philippines, New Guinea, Australia and New Zealand before getting home in January. We've decided to take Bill with us."

"That's a pretty gruelling schedule. Shouldn't you take more time?"

"I wish we could, but Bill has to get back to school and other obligations are pressing."

"You know we'll be praying for you," Ben said looking down at the older man. "And Uncle Cam, I hope you know all of us love you. You've been like a father to me and the other old timers. The Lord has used you to make us what we are and to make Wycliffe what it is today."

Cam took Elson's hand and gripped it tightly. "Thank you, Ben. I appreciate your love and patience. Despite all my complaining about bureaucracy, I know we must have administration and order. I am just concerned about our basic policies that the Lord has used to open doors and keep us in places that otherwise might be closed.

"We've got to reach every tribe. Follow the Lord's command. Wake people up in the homeland to see that souls are dying without a glimmer of light. Read us a chapter, Ben, and then we'll pray."

The next week Cam, Elaine and Billy flew to Moscow. The Academy of Science people recognized the value of the book that Cam would be doing. They helped arrange their trip to the Caucasus and assigned a photographer for the project.

For the next month the Townsends visited schools and interviewed educators in four different republics between the Caspian and the Black Seas. Except for Billy's being detained once for inadvertently taking pictures in an unauthorized area, all ran smoothly.

In November they landed in New Delhi, India, where they were greeted by the Pittmans and called on educators. Then they went on to the high Himalayan kingdom of Nepal where Wycliffe members were studying twelve languages in cooperation with the national university. The Wycliffites hailed from six nations and were expecting to be joined by a Japanese member married to a German. The group had become truly international.

Cam called on the vice chancellor of the university of Nepal, inviting him to participate in a brief dedication of a new "goodwill" plane for service in his country. Several other important university people and government officials were present.

Moving on across Asia, the Townsends spent twelve days in the Philippines where 156 members were serving 42 language groups.

In Manila, Director Tom Lyman took Cam to see General Carlos Romulo, the minister of foreign affairs, whom Cam knew and admired greatly. Romulo expressed his appreciation for SIL work, and offered help in getting a government land grant for a group headquarters in the capital.

Next came two weeks in New Guinea where over three hundred members were involved in eighty-seven tribes. The big base with its JAARS planes and other facilities reminded them of Yarinacocha. But they were most impressed by the progress that had been made in training New Guinea tribesmen to run such technical operations as the sawmill and print shop.

When Director Al Pence remarked that the branch had over 500 more languages to reach, Cam did some quick mathematical calculations. "You should pray for at least fifty new workers for New Guinea this year and larger numbers each year in the future, if you intend to enter them all by 1985."

He saw needs all over the base and kept Pence busy writing them down. Perhaps it was because Billy was along that he showed special concern that the base teens have manual arts training. He dipped into his general director's fund and gave money to start a building for this project.

In an assembly he presented to the New Guinea members his impressions of needs in the U.S.S.R., India, and Nepal. "The group has only one pilot in Nepal." he said. "Would you give one of your pilots to help them out?" They would and Cam paid for the move from his general director's fund.

In New Guinea a radio report on the house caught up with them.

The construction account was $5,000 in the red. Although concerned, they kept on with the trip trusting that the Lord would supply. Their next stop was Brisbane, Australia, where they were interviewed and photographed by the local press as they arrived. With over a hundred and fifty members serving in Wycliffe, Australia was second only to the United States in Wycliffe membership.

Businessman Alfred Coombe, the chairman of the Australian home council, and his wife Sabina were their hosts. The day after their arrival, Coombe flew with the Townsends eighteen hundred miles to the base in Darwin where the Wycliffe members were gathered. The vast distances over which the translators were spread staggered Cam. Some had come over 1,000 miles across the hot dusty outback to the meeting and to see the general director and his wife. As at the other stations, everyone wanted to hear from the legendary "Uncle Cam." Then Director David Glasgow took Cam and Coombe by plane to four aboriginal tribes and to visit government educators.

Although it was after midnight when they returned to Brisbane from Darwin, Cam spoke the next afternoon at a big rally. During the next three days he challenged students at the Australian SIL. Then on Christmas Eve they enplaned for Melbourne, a thousand miles to the south for a planned ten days of rest. But when they arrived, they learned that a Bible conference was in session with over two thousand people present. The leaders insisted that the "distinguished Dr. Townsend must speak."

By this time, even Billy, soon to be seventeen, was beginning to run down. Elaine could tell Cam needed rest. A month's constant travel through changing time zones had sapped much of his energy. When he began experiencing shortness of breath between Christmas and New Year's she wanted him to see a doctor. "No," he insisted. "I'll try to take it easier from here on and get a checkup when we get home. It won't be much longer. I'll make it, Honey. You go on and get Bill back in school. Don't worry about me."

Shortly before Elaine left, a cable came from California saying they would receive an inheritance of over $3,000. With that good news, Billy and Elaine left for California, and Cam and Coombe flew to Canberra, the capital of Australia. Here they called on the minister of aboriginal affairs, who took them to see the minister of the interior.

Coombe listened in admiration as Cam established quick rapport.

"It's wonderful that your country wants to have all its languages analyzed, Mr. Minister. Our linguists are here to help you accomplish that purpose. We're ready to serve in any capacity."

"We're very happy about the language study your people are doing," the minister responded sincerely. "Is there any way my office can help, Dr. Townsend?"

"Well, yes, we are short of housing. Some mobile living quarters for our linguists out in the field would make their work more efficient and life more pleasant."

"I'm sorry, but we can only provide six," was the apologetic response. But Cam was jubilant; he knew how his colleagues had been living without proper housing.

By mid-January, when Cam landed in Auckland, New Zealand, he was feeling better. The Wycliffe council there gave him a royal welcome and the round of speeches, interviews and dinners started all over again. Then notification came of the death of his sister, Oney. "We'll see you when you get to California," sister Ethel telegraphed. "Don't try to come for the funeral."

About the same time a letter came from Elaine. The inheritance was from the Woodsun estate—the Woodsuns had helped Cam in Guatemala, a half-century before—and it was five thousand dollars instead of three. "Just what we owe on the house. It is manna from heaven!"

Now he had only a plane change in Hawaii before touchdown in California. But even in Honolulu there were friends and admirers to greet him. One young member of the Vietnam branch was on leave to complete his doctorate.

"I've always wanted to meet you, Uncle Cam," he said almost in awe. "When I heard you would be changing planes here, I had to come even if I could be with you only five minutes."

"I believe God is going to help us reach them all."

35. "Faith, Mighty Faith"

It seemed fitting somehow that the new decade of the 70s should begin on a double note of the new and the old. The new year had found Cam half-way around the world on his first visit outside the Western hemisphere, seeing the farflung results of what he had started in such a small way and presenting graphically the opportunities that lay ahead.

The old was very much in his mind as he visited his sisters Lulu and Ethel, who were eighty-two and eighty-four respectively. Oney was eighty when she died. His brother Paul had returned to Oklahoma where he was living in semiretirement and pastoring a small Presbyterian church. Cam recalled his family heritage and the help and loyalty of his sisters and Paul that enabled him first to go to school and then to leave for Guatemala at such a seemingly inauspicious time.

While he was in Santa Ana, Cam saw in the paper that literacy pioneer Dr. Frank Laubach was to be honored at a church in nearby Anaheim. He and Ben Elson drove over for the affair, and Laubach recognized Cam from the platform. He plugged Wycliffe's work and asked Elson to dismiss in prayer. Then the two old soldiers of the faith greeted one another. "I've had my eightieth birthday," the white-haired apostle of literacy said. "I don't have many more years left. But I predict that within five years you'll be in mainland China."

Back in North Carolina, Elaine reminded Cam of the checkup he had promised to get. "Oh, I'm feeling fine now," he assured her. "I'm going to Chicago in a few days to see about getting help for a second plane for Nepal. And I'm invited to speak afterwards at the

University of North Dakota. And then I must get to writing the book on bilingual education in the Caucasus."

"Honey, I love you," she sighed, "but you must slow down."

"I will when I get back," he promised.

Soon after Cam returned, they moved into their house. Their first overnight guest was Father Boni Wittenbrink, a dynamic priest who had helped Cam set up past Bible Translation Day programs. Wittenbrink asked how the Wittes were doing.

"We keep in touch," Cam said. "They're in Colombia, but aren't getting enough financial help. You should start a Catholic translation society, Boni. Since our round-the-world trip, I've been doing a lot of thinking and praying. At the rate Wycliffe is growing we're not going to reach every tribe by 1985. Perhaps we could get together a council or a board of leaders that would help other groups start their own translation societies. There could be a Catholic, a Baptist, a Presbyterian society and so on. Just as the Lutherans have done."

Wittenbrink laughed. "Uncle Cam, I wish I had your faith."

There was still a lot of fixing to do around the house. Cam enjoyed working in the yard in spare moments. Elaine was commuting every day to Queens College in Charlotte for Russian study. She redeemed the time behind the wheel by listening to Russian tapes.

When Cam's shortness of breath recurred and he started having chest pains, Elaine insisted he get an appointment with a heart specialist. An electrocardiogram showed an irregular heartbeat. "I'm going to put you on digitalis," the doctor said. "And you must slow down or you'll never make it back to Russia. Stay home awhile."

After so many years of constant on-the-go, Cam found it hard to obey doctor's orders. But there was his book on Soviet bilingual education in the Caucasus to write. And lately he had been thinking about the racial situation in the area.

They had been driving into Charlotte to attend church, but one Sunday morning Cam suggested they visit one of the black churches nearby. When they walked in the Methodist pastor was already into his sermon. He stopped and looked at them incredulously while the congregation stared. "You're the first white folks ever to enter this church!" the pastor exclaimed.

The next Sunday they visited the tiny black Shiloh Presbyterian Church located in back of the railroad track in Waxhaw. Cam and Elaine enjoyed the services. Elaine was asked to play the piano, and both were given an opportunity to share the work of JAARS. They kept attending this church and finally decided to join as associate members. The congregation welcomed its first white members joyfully.

Their first black dinner guests were ill at ease when they arrived. But Cam and Elaine quickly made them feel at home. Others followed. Billy became close friends with a black athlete at the consolidated high school both attended, and brought him home for meals and to spend the night. When racial trouble erupted at the school, Billy climbed on the bus and rode home with the black kids, though most of the white students took other transportation.

Cam was gently prodding the JAARS folks to develop friendships with blacks. "Let's have them in our homes for social occasions," he suggested. "Let's visit their churches and not just ask them to come to ours. Why if every white Christian in North Carolina would visit a black church only once a month, wonderful changes would occur."

He wasn't making much progress with the book these days, though, because of interruptions at the house. People were constantly coming and going. The phone rang incessantly. "I've got to get away," he told Elaine. When Arthur and Irene Morris invited him to use their Florida beachside apartment for a while, he gladly accepted. He got more work done there and rested up for the upcoming board meeting he planned to attend in Santa Ana.

The big item on the agenda was new buildings. The board voted to build the new administrative headquarters on a site near Santa Ana, and a linguistic training center and museum in the Dallas area.

Returning home Cam was just in time to see Joy and her fiancé David Tuggy, son of missionaries to Venezuela, graduate from Columbia Bible College. Their wedding followed on June 6 at the Calvary Presbyterian Church in Charlotte. At the reception Cam delivered his challenge for the tribes as he had after Grace's wedding. He was delighted to add the news that the newlyweds planned to attend SIL, then go to Mexico to finish the translation of the Aztec New Testament which he had started in Tetelcingo.

Meanwhile, Bible translation enthusiasts in Washington were promoting a Congressional resolution calling for the president to declare 1971 as the "Year of Minority Language Groups." Cam flew up and talked to Senator Curtis. "We think this will get through both the Senate and House," Curtis said.

The Nebraska legislator also wrote a letter to President Nixon, asking for an interview. Cam's nephew, Lorin Griset, now mayor of Santa Ana, knew Robert Finch, the presidential counselor. Ed Boyer, a high official in Health, Education and Welfare, talked to his contacts. Several other Congressional leaders, in addition to Curtis, pushed the resolution as well as a presidential meeting.

This time the resolution passed both the House and Senate. The president signed the proclamation and aides looked for a spot in his appointment schedule.

In October a tremendous jolt came when Cam's old friend Cárdenas died in Mexico. Cam left the same day he received the telegram to extend his sympathy to the family and attend the funeral of the man who had done so much for the group's linguistic research and service to long-forgotten tribes.

On December 2, 1970, President Nixon welcomed Cam, Senator Curtis, Ben Elson, Dan Piatt and James Hefley into the Oval Office.

After introductions, Cam showed the president a picture of the plane he had dedicated in California for Peru when he was vice president. Nixon recalled the ceremony which had taken place shortly after his father's death.

"How is your work going now?" the president asked.

"Mr. President, we've just entered our 500th language," Cam replied.

"What an achievement! You're doing two things. Giving them the Bible and teaching them to read. What can I do to help?"

"Mr. President, there are still over two thousand language groups without Scripture, or even an alphabet. We need eighty-five hundred new recruits, both translators and support personnel such as pilots and printers. Would you write a letter that we can use in challenging young people to volunteer?"

The president promised he would and handed Cam an autographed Bible.

During the spring of 1971, Cam and Elaine's twenty-fifth wedding anniversary neared, they became aware of secretive whisperings and sly glances. When the Henderson Belks invited them to dinner, they decided that a dinner party had been planned.

Arriving at the Belks' home, they went to the back door, as had always been their custom, but the maid refused to let them in. They looked at each other and grinned. "Well, it looks like we're to be treated like 'company' tonight," Cam said, as they entered the mansion through the front door. They suspected something, but were totally unprepared for the crowd waiting to call out "surprise." Grace and Tom were there from Chicago, as well as over a hundred others, some of whom had also come great distances. Joy and David were in jungle camp and couldn't make it, but had sent a message of love and best wishes. Elainadel had come from Columbia Bible College with her fiancé, Robert Garippa. They too were planning on missionary service. Billy and Mrs. Mielke arrived from the JAARS Center in *"Don Lázaro,"* the vintage blue Chevrolet Cárdenas had given Cam in 1938.

There was a basketful of telegrams, cards and letters, as well as many silver pieces for their silver anniversary, and a luscious buffet dinner. All the love and good wishes were a little overwhelming, but what thrilled them most was that their "kids," especially Grace, had gotten together with Juanita Goodall and Ann Belk and planned the whole celebration.

The next "anniversary" was the fortieth year since the publication of Cam's Cakchiquel New Testament. Friends Jack and Pat Morris of Charlotte and Scripture Unlimited financed a new edition of 2,700 copies to mark the occasion.

Cam mailed complimentary copies to mayors and other key leaders in Cakchiquel towns, then sent Fr. Boni Wittenbrink and evangelical missionary Larry Jordan to Guatemala to sell the rest. With the blessing of the local Roman Catholic bishops, the interfaith team sold every Testament in eight days.

The Caucasus book was almost completed in rough draft when time came for the 1971 May biennial in Mexico City. It would be a climactic milestone for Cam, for he had decided to resign as general director.

Perhaps it was that decision that made the statistics reported by Executive Director Ben Elson seem so dramatic to him. Membership had grown to 2,504. Annual income had leaped to $7.9 million. Wycliffe was now serving in 510 language groups in 23 countries. It had been a long uphill climb—and there was much yet to do.

Elson continued his report:

The world has changed since WBT was formed. Conditions today are not the same as they were in 1935 or in 1942. Uncle Cam set forth in those days revolutionary ideas about missionary service, about specialization, about internal organization, about relations with governments and those who oppose us. People could not quite make us out. We did not fit into neat categories. But those ideas were right and a lot of them have become standard practice with many other groups. We don't receive the same criticisms we received in the 50s since many of our brethren quietly acknowledge that Uncle Cam's ideas and methods were right after all, but were far ahead of their time.

. . . Are we ready for the new challenges that we will face in this revolutionary decade? Does God have more for us to do? I believe He does.

Then in a dramatic moment, Cam asked that he be relieved of the office of general director:

God has been good to us. He led us into our unusual policies. Let's be true to them. Let's forge ahead till every tribe has heard in its own tongue the Word of God. This involves a close adherence to our basic five points: The linguistic approach; the Bible first, last and all the time on a nonsectarian basis; pioneering; service to all; and a faith that takes God at His Word and forges ahead wherever there are Bibleless tribes regardless of barriers.

Leaving the conference, Cam returned to North Carolina as a Wycliffe board member, but no longer the roving "chief" of the organization he had founded. His future would be devoted to the Caucasus. He was polishing the book on bilingual education * when his seventy-fifth birthday rolled around.

On July 9, 1971, about a hundred friends gathered in a wooded grove across from the JAARS hangars—members of the Wycliffe family, friends from Charlotte and Shiloh Church, and Cam's family. The children and Elaine recited poems Cam had written years before. Harold Goodall presented Cam a bound, freshly typed copy of A Thousand Trails, Cam's own account of early adventures in Central America. Then before cutting the cake, everyone's "Uncle Cam" was asked if he had a word to say.

He stood erect on the portable platform. Typically, he thanked everybody effusively. Then waving his arms in a half circle, he cried, "Out there are two thousand tribes who still don't have the Bible! I believe God is going to help us reach them all. Don't you?"

---

* They Found a Common Language: Community Through Bilingual Education (New York: Harper & Row, 1972).

Suddenly he shouted, "I'm happy about what He's going to do. Aren't you? If you are, and if you believe, let's sing Legters's chorus that we've marched to all these years."

And so they sang with Cam's confident voice leading out:

> *Faith, mighty faith the promise sees,*
> *And looks to God alone.*
> *Laughs at impossibilities*
> *And shouts, "It shall be done!"*